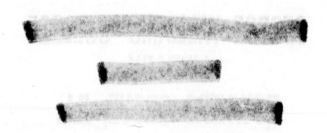

OPERATIONAL RESEARCH
AND THE SOCIAL SCIENCES

Operational Research and the Social Sciences

Edited by J. R. LAWRENCE

Tavistock Publications

LONDON · NEW YORK · SYDNEY · TORONTO · WELLINGTON

First published in Great Britain in 1966
by Tavistock Publications Limited
11 New Fetter Lane, London E.C.4
Printed in Great Britain
in 10 point Monotype Times, two point leaded
by Richard Clay (The Chaucer Press), Ltd., Bungay, Suffolk

SBN 422 70170 X
First published as a Social Science Paperback in 1971
SBN 422 75200 2

© *The Operational Research Society Limited 1966*

Based on the proceedings of the International
Conference on Operational Research and the Social
Sciences, organized at Cambridge in September 1964
by the Operational Research Society

Distributed in the U.S.A. by
Barnes & Noble, Inc.

Contents

Editor's Note

Since the material on which this book is based is extensive and complex, this note is provided to explain the structure of the work so that the reader may more easily find his way about its contents.

The book is divided into seven Parts: the first, Introductory, includes the editor's preface, a note of the background of the conference, and a chapter by Sir Charles Goodeve based on his opening remarks to the delegates. Each of the five Parts that follow corresponds to a session of the conference. Part VII, Conclusion, comprises G. Kreweras's closing remarks, a Combined Bibliography, and the Index.

Following this note, on pages xiii–xxxiv, is a synopsis of the whole book, indicating for each Part the sponsors responsible for the session of the conference from which that Part derives, a short paragraph outlining the purpose of the session/Part, and abstracts of all the papers that now constitute chapters of this volume. The affiliations of the contributors as at the time of the conference are set out after their names.

In each chapter references to the literature are indicated as they appear by superior figures in parenthesis. These figures relate to a list at the end of the chapter concerned, where the references are given in an abbreviated form (author and date) that permits the works to be identified in the Combined Bibliography on pages 641–59. Within this general scheme, minor variations reflect the preferred styles of presentation of individual contributors.

In the Combined Bibliography, the usual bibliographical details are set out in full, alphabetically by author. Although no attempt has been made to supplement the works cited in order to provide a completely comprehensive bibliography of the subjects covered, a very extensive source of relevant reading matter is provided by the collection together of all the contributors' references.

An Index of names of individuals and institutions completes the volume and enables the reader to locate in the text the names of specific authors and the relevant reference numbers. A subject index is not included, since the Synopsis, taken in conjunction with the analytical tables of contents appearing at the beginning of each Part, constitutes a more appropriate form of signposting for a volume of this nature.

J. R. L.

Acknowledgements

Thanks are due to the following owners of copyright for permission to quote excerpts from the works listed below: Harper & Row, Publishers in respect of *Dynamic Administration: the Collected Papers of Mary Parker Follett* by H. C. Metcalf and L. Urwick; Richard D. Irwin, Inc. (The Dorsey Press) and Tavistock Publications in respect of *Interpersonal Competence and Organizational Effectiveness* by Chris Argyris (copyright 1962 by Richard D. Irwin, Inc., Homewood, Illinois); the Oxford Area Nurse Training Committee in respect of *From Student to Nurse: the Induction Period* by Gillian M. MacGuire; Prentice-Hall, Inc. in respect of *A Behavioral Theory of the Firm* by Richard M. Cyert and James G. March (copyright 1963 by permission of Prentice-Hall, Inc., Englewood Cliffs, New Jersey, U.S.A.); Princeton University Press in respect of *The Governing of Men* by A. H. Leighton; Professor H. A. Simon in respect of his paper 'On the Concept of Organizational Goal', *Administrative Sciences Quarterly*, Volume 9, 1964.

Synopsis

SPONSORS: S. L. COOK, *Richard Thomas and Baldwins Limited*,
and W. N. JESSOP, *Institute for Operational Research, London*

This section considers attempts to determine performance criteria for all the main variables of systems – technical, economic, and human – and efforts to design new systems or redesign existing ones, in accordance with them. The session of the conference on which this section is based set out to review work of this kind by operational research and the social sciences, and to illustrate it by examples. The interaction between empirical studies and applications of the developed theory is examined in order to see how and to what extent now or in the future increased collaboration between operational research and the social sciences may be profitable.

The search for organizational effectiveness involves more and more managers, specialists, and scientists. Social science and operational research aim to help organizations to achieve their objectives, whether in terms of tangible variables, such as productivity, or of less tangible variables, such as morale, or both.
Operational research groups work within many of the larger industrial organizations. Applied social scientists have worked in organizations on a consulting basis, and some leading firms in the United States have

established internal groups. Basic research studies have been conducted by social science groups attached to universities.

The interdisciplinary nature of most internal operational research groups nowadays does not extend to the social sciences, and this situation needs to be corrected. Social scientists and operational research men generally need to know much more about each other's work in organizations. Collaboration is needed to design good systems and to implement change itself, especially as management moves towards more advanced techniques, control systems, and computer applications.

The paper by Bennis surveys the main activities of applied social scientists in organizations and is essential reading for operational research men. That by Churchman and Emery was written as a general introduction to the discussion and stresses the common interests of operational research and applied social science in organizations.

What we have all witnessed and participated in over the past two or three decades has been called the 'Rise of the Rational Spirit', or the belief that science can help to better the human condition. This paper will describe one indication of this trend, the attempts by behavioural scientists to apply their knowledge (primarily sociological and psychological) towards the improvement of human organizations.

Three assumptions underlie this paper: (*a*) that the proportion of contemporary change that is either planned or issues from deliberate innovations is much higher than in former times; (*b*) that Man's wisdom and mundane behaviour are somewhat short of perfection in so far as they regulate the fate and selective adaptation of human organizations; (*c*) that in view of the complexity and uncertainty of managing these social systems, behavioural scientists in increasing numbers are called upon to influence their functioning and effectiveness.

This paper, then, deals with the entire range of strategic, methodological, and conceptual issues brought about by this new development in the application of the behavioural sciences.

The authors present a set of assertions or theses. Together these theses argue that: (*a*) applied social science and operational research have a common interest in better understanding how to relate their scientific concerns to the practical affairs of organized men; (*b*) the dual character of human organizations itself demands the joint deployment of the two research strategies to which applied social science and operational research are respectively committed.

7 Connective introducing Chapters 8–19   85
s. l. cook, *Richard Thomas and Baldwins Limited*

These twelve papers were invited to provide examples to illustrate current work and thinking by social scientists, operational researchers, or both in the organization field. They are reviewed under four headings:

1 Observation of organizational behaviour (Chapters 8–10)
2 Theoretical models of organization and control (Chapters 11–14)
3 Specific applications of operational research or social science to organizational design (Chapters 15–17)
4 Factors affecting implementation of operational research studies (Chapters 18 and 19)

8 A Field Study of Management Control in Manufacturing Industry   95
joan woodward and samuel eilon, *Imperial College of Science & Technology, London*

The increasing rationalization and complexity of production processes puts additional emphasis on the planning and control activities in the industrial enterprise, and separates them from the execution of the manufacturing task. The people concerned with the execution at all levels may well operate within the framework of a control system that is independent of either the human system or the productive system containing the machinery and equipment. This can have a curious two-dimensional effect on industrial behaviour and attitudes. Those employed in a manufacturing firm can have an attitude towards, and an involvement with, their work situation as determined by the control system that is distinct from, and sometimes in conflict with, their attitude towards, and their involvement with, the firm itself.

The objective of the research undertaken by the authors is to find out more about the control processes and their effects. A number of cases in several firms were studied using the 'tracer' method, i.e. isolating a task and observing the way in which people and decisions become involved in it throughout its progress.

The paper reports some of the interim results, and attention is drawn to the way in which independent control systems emerge and their relation to informal controls, to the setting up of standards of performance by which the effectiveness of the organization is judged, and to an analogy of management control with control engineering procedures.

NEIL CHURCHILL and WILLIAM W. COOPER,
Carnegie Institute of Technology

This paper reports on one of a series of studies directed towards control (as distinguished from planning) in management. As part of a series devoted to investigating auditing as a vehicle for influencing the activities of managers, a field study was made to ascertain some of the perceptions which people who had had contact with the audit process held with respect to the audit and the auditors.

The study was exploratory in design and scope. Sixty-six interviews were conducted in eight industrial and business firms in and around the Pittsburgh area. The people interviewed were at various levels of the organizations; had had different intensities of audit contact; and were drawn both from accounting and non-accounting functions.

The interview data pertaining to the respondents' perceptions of internal auditing were categorized and subjected to content analysis. The results indicated that the intensity of audit contact, the position of the respondent in his organization, and the presence or absence of a review of the audit report with the respondent were significant in determining the respondent's attitude. It was anticipated that these attitudes would not always be expressed in a direct manner. Hence provision was made for securing indirect measures in the form of such things as education which respondents would see as desirable for auditors; the usefulness of the auditor's disclosure function relative to his recommendation function; the perception of the purpose of the audit; the effects and significance of audit activities, reports, etc.

The findings are discussed and indications given of further directions that such research might take.

MICHAEL RADNOR, *Northwestern University, Illinois*

This paper reports on a study of the control behaviour of top managers of very large industrial companies as related to their research and development activities.

Interview and documentary data were obtained from a sample of forty-eight of the very largest industrial companies in the United States. The findings were used to test a number of assumptions concerning top managerial perceptions of their research and development control environment. A theory relating the form of top managerial control responses to their perceptions of the control situation was proposed and partially tested. The utilization and prevalence of various control mechanisms, out of the repertoire of available control responses, was noted.

The interrelationship between the goals of an organization (in the Cyert–March–Simon sense) and those of its sub-units is discussed with particular emphasis on constructing the latter in such a way as to enhance the attainment of the former. An attempt is made to show, in part with reference to the authors' earlier work, that the goals of the sub-units need not, and probably cannot, be the same goals as, or smaller-scale replicates of, the organization goals. Rather, the goals of the sub-unit and the rewards structure accompanying goal attainment should be so constructed that by working towards its own aspirations the sub-unit will unavoidably work towards organizational goal attainment as well. This argument departs from certain kinds of utility and transfer pricing treatments in that it admits limits on both cognitive capacity and rationality.

Working communities contain, and consist of, a variety of social systems. One of these is the working ('formal') organization. Others relate to internal politics, careerism, professionalism, and age grades. Each 'system' exists as a logically coherent class of acts, relationships, and norms, and as a system of means and ends. It is argued that 'rationality models' of organizations, in ignoring the systematic nature of goals, acts, and motivation other than those which lie within the model of the organization and within the specification of organizational goals and organizational roles, both oversimplify and over-complicate the tasks of social scientists, consultants, and administrators in trying to understand, change, or control organizations. It is also suggested that the attempt to subsume all systems under a single comprehensive system of individual behaviours and of social action, although empirically an assumption of most people's lives, and theoretically alluring, belongs to meta-sociology and can only provide propositions which are either empty or tautological.

In this paper the decision-making process underlying the determination of the size and structure of the U.S. Military Air Transport Service fleet is analysed. The object of the exercise is to suggest how internal pricing techniques may make some aspects of this decision-making more effective. A decision-structure that exploits the informational efficiency inherent in decentralized decision-making is described. Decisions between air transport and its alternatives are taken by planners responsible for determining ways of coping, at given levels of effectiveness, with emergencies of various kinds. An internal pricing scheme is developed that equates cost minimization by each planner with the desired objective, minimization of the Defense Department's costs. Two aspects of the prices are rather novel. One is that prices are placed on the end-uses planners desire rather than on aircraft. The second is that, owing to the uncertainty regarding the occurrence of emergencies, the prices are annual charges for claims to the right to have needs filled by air transport in the event that an emergency occurs. In the course of determining prices, a linear programme with an interesting, and perhaps novel, economic interpretation is employed. Technological and strategic changes in the future are accommodated by the introduction of resale markets that also serve to determine the economic life of aircraft. Finally, some possible limitations to the use of the internal pricing device are discussed.

The paper views an organization and organizing as a way of systematizing decisions concerning certain activities and their actual execution. The paper has as its purpose to present one abstract model of how this may be carried out.
The motivation for this paper comes from observing one phase of the decision-making process at two large decentralized corporations in the United States. They had attempted to set up a systematic way by which the various divisions could co-ordinate their decisions. The main emphasis was on transfer prices as the main device for such co-ordination. However, little clear understanding was found of how the transfer prices were to be generated or used. Thus, for example, transfer prices for one group of products or services were based on outside market prices if such prices were available. When such prices

were used there would be considerable dispute among the divisions as to whether the outside products or services were identical and the effect of the supposed non-identity on the transfer price. As one would expect, the division producing an item for another division would claim that its products were of a higher quality. One can proliferate such arguments. Another type of pricing used, when comparable market prices were not available, was a mark-up on costs. This, of course, raised many disputes because of its arbitrary nature. Another type of phenomenon found was the attempt to use transfer pricing as a budgeting device. Transfer prices were used to put pressure on divisions to improve their performance. The sanctity of the transfer-pricing profit-centre system was sufficiently strong to make managers react in a 'desirable' manner.

The above comments suggest, on the one hand, that the transfer-price decentralized profit-centre approach is not purely of academic interest. However, it is clear that systematic study is needed to determine exactly the way such systems should operate, at least at the theoretical level.

The model the paper is based on contains several sectors representing divisions of a large organization, inter-sector constraints, and a general criterion function. We may have, as an example, a large motor company consisting of two divisions, each producing a different type of car. Each division operates independently with its own production and marketing, but finance and other general policy questions are controlled by a central group. Furthermore, each division may produce certain parts or services for the other divisions, thus causing further interconnexions. This type of physical exchange of goods and services suggests the use of some transfer pricing scheme.

The process discussed in the paper is a sequential adjustment procedure which leads finally to an optimal solution. Initially transfer prices are announced to the divisional managers. These managers take into account the transfer prices, outside prices, and their own technology and make a tentative proposal which they feel is best in terms of their criterion function. The proposal in the case considered would be in terms of various production and sales figures, amount of goods and services exchanged between divisions, etc. These proposals are co-ordinated by central management and new prices are announced. The paper concentrates on the precise way that the prices should be generated. The process is repeated until the divisional managers are not able to announce proposals for which they show a net profit.

Thus the paper attempts to discuss in some detail the workings of these types of system. It is hoped that by developing more realistic but systematic models in this area this will throw light on how firms should employ these tools.

This paper describes the history and uses of the Logistics Systems Laboratory at the Rand Corporation. The laboratory was created as the U.S. Air Force, and Rand made serious efforts to implement earlier-developed research findings that had been obtained using more traditional methods, including computer-simulation. The need to specify the organizational and data system aspects of a logistics system change was felt to be an important part of a proposed implementation. This led to the application of man–machine simulation as one way of representing explicitly these important aspects in studying improvements in the logistics system. This paper describes the four experiments which have been held in the Logistics Systems Laboratory, and relates the experience with them to the variety of systems that have been simulated and studied.

This paper attempts to formulate the area of decision-making in a complex university. In doing so it is hoped that a case is made for the need of this job and its importance as far as the social implications are concerned. Sub-systems are identified and decision points are located. The utility of this for analysis is pointed out both horizontally within sub-systems and vertically (functionally) among sub-systems. Finally further contemplated efforts are discussed.

The worker has three functions in a manufacturing process: to monitor, to make ready, and to operate. All three require him to receive and process information from the environment, the workpiece, and the tool. Mechanization is the removal of the need for the worker, by the removal of information from the process; automation is the transfer, from the worker to a machine, of the information-handling component of the work.
We distinguish four types of human ability: (*a*) to be an energy source; (*b*) to learn to make, and to repeat, stereotyped motions; (*c*) to respond bodily to environmental information; and (*d*) to exercise judgement and to innovate. The first two can be displaced by mechanization. The third involves information processing, and can be displaced directly only by automation (indirectly, the functional requirement may be

reduced to class (*a*) or (*b*) and then mechanized). The last is unlikely to be automated.

A high information content arises from variability in the raw material or in the environment, from lack of understanding of the process, or from variety of product and shortness of run-length. Processes with these characteristics require human skills, and are resistant to automation.

18 Experimental Studies of Implementation   **251**
PHILBURN RATOOSH, *University of California*

The failure of models of organizational processes to account for organizational behaviour is nowhere seen more clearly than in examples of technically successful operational research studies that are never put to use. Operational research workers have devoted almost no effort to the investigation of conditions for maximizing acceptance of research results.

This paper describes some experimental studies of implementation. A business organization is created in the laboratory. Subjects are instructed to maximize their firm's net profits. After several periods of operation the solution to all problems of the company's operations is presented in one of various ways. We investigate the resistance to the solution and consider ways of presenting the solution that will increase the likelihood of its being accepted.

19 The Evaluation of the Effectiveness of Systems of Command Support **263**
JOSEPH H. LEWIS, *Institute for Defense Analyses*

This paper concentrates on operational research in the area of command, as opposed to control. Command, for purposes of this discussion, means management. The paper proceeds from that definition to examine the matter of operational research in systems effectiveness evaluation in that context.

The purpose of command or management is to be right. There are not quantifiable criteria for requirements or measures of performance that permit valid, overall cost-effectiveness determinations of means for being right.

The improvement of command or management capabilities can be approached usefully only on a step-by-step, function-by-function, evolutionary basis, employing the criteria, largely qualitative, of relevance, utility, and convenience – all as seen through the eyes of the user.

The evolutionary approach is difficult. It makes continual living together of operators and technicians essential – acting on each other, performing the dual information-extraction process. It means that operational research in systems effectiveness evaluation is a *continuous* process which is related to organic growth.

Collaboration between operational research and social science could be valuable in basic and applied research areas, especially in the area of interaction between basic and applied research. In the applied area it could help in dealing with misunderstanding, conflict, and communications; in general problem-solving and the improvement of existing management and control; and in the design and installation of new management systems.

Obstacles to collaboration, which can be overcome if the optimism and goodwill generated at the conference can be maintained, include a tendency for the two groups to look at one another in terms of stereotypes; some basic differences in aims, philosophy, and methods compounded by insufficient knowledge of each other's activities; difficulties in interpreting the 'mixed team' concept in operational research; a shortage of 'social engineers' to develop applied social science; and difficulties in sponsoring and financing applied research studies in this field.

Recommendations are made on ways in which the two professions, the universities, the research foundations, and the managers of organizations can encourage greater joint activity by social science and operational research, aimed at better organization and control.

Any course of action leads to a ramifying chain of results. This is true both for the individual's pattern of behaviour and for the social decision on policy. A conceptual framework which has been used to interpret and clarify the situation among both sociological and operational research workers is the cost–benefit approach. This section explores both the theoretical basis and the practical potentials of this framework.

The commonest social welfare or decision function used in cost–benefit analysis attempts to take into account all benefits and costs to whomsoever they accrue, and gives every pound of benefit or cost the same weight (the Pigovian social welfare function). Nevertheless, it is well known that other social welfare functions could be used to achieve a different income distribution from the Pigovian. Political scientists have analysed two such: Vote Maximization, Majority Rule. But they have two principal defects. They do not allow for individuals' strength of preference or the opportunity costs of decision-making.

In the first section of this paper the concept of income distribution in cost–benefit analysis and different methods of allowing for it in decision-making are reviewed. In the second, the social welfare function content of Vote Maximization and Majority Rule are considered in the context of the application of cost–benefit analysis. A new decision function is put forward in the third section: the democratic strength of preference function. It combines the virtues of the political decision functions, in that it can be made operationally meaningful within the context of cost–benefit analysis. This particular decision function is chosen for explication (*a*) as representative of a whole family of such functions which may be used to make cost–benefit analysis reflect more subtle political value judgements than is usual at present, and (*b*) because it is interesting and possibly socially acceptable in its own right in certain circumstances.

Cost–benefit analysis attempts to determine the relative desirability of alternative courses of action in systems whose outcomes are described in various units of measurement, such as monetary units, time units, various measures of social welfare, ratios, and so on; such systems are often referred to as multi-goal systems. The usual procedure in such analysis is first to transform all measures of performance into equivalent units of one of the measures, usually into monetary units, and then to determine the relative values of the expected transformed costs and benefits resulting from the alternatives being considered. If we are willing to accept the notion that the goal of cost–benefit analysis should be to maximize the utility of the decision-maker, then such analysis is theoretically appropriate only if certain well-defined conditions are satisfied. This paper presents a series of theorems stating these conditions. The theory so developed is then illustrated via an application to a highway investment decision. The paper closes with a discussion of the practical applications of the theory.

The intent of the paper is to highlight the deviations from theoretical perfection which can be expected when cost–benefit analysis is used, rather than to criticize the methodology. It is only through awareness of such deviations that we can expect to improve this valuable aid to decision-making.

Cost–benefit analysis is the term popularly given to economic analysis applied to aid decisions on investment in the public sector. It can, in the writer's view, be adapted for use in town and regional planning. The justification for this view is given, stemming from the proposition that a town or regional plan is a supra-investment framework for private and public investment decisions, and therefore susceptible to cost–benefit analysis. Three case studies made to evolve methodology are briefly described in illustration.

But there are many problems to be solved. First, six are mentioned which relate to the analysis generally; and then a further five which apply to the field of town and regional planning in particular. There is thus some distance to go before the analysis can be used in everyday practice in planning. But some would doubt its usefulness even then. Three typical arguments are given with critical comment: that analysis which is economic in character is too limited; that economics is a positive and not a normative science and therefore cannot help; and that public decision-makers in any case would not use aids to rational choice.

The paper describes an attempt to allocate investments between individual and mass transport in a hypothetical linear city. It involves the comparison of different transport plans.

The theoretical basis for such a comparison has been provided by Lesourne. As applied here, it entails a number of simplifying hypotheses:

(i) The city is in a static stage, i.e. the population is constant in size and spatial distribution; so is the number of workers, whose places of employment are also assumed to be concentrated at one point.

(ii) The only trips are from home to work.

(iii) The transport system may include a railway line connecting the linear stretch of dwellings to the centre of work, and a motorway close to the railway line. Unlimited parking is provided at each railway station, and near the centre there is restricted parking under varying conditions regarding the number of spaces, the charging system, and price. The building of these facilities requires no time.

(iv) Minor additional assumptions further simplify the model.

The model has been devised in a way to allow several parameters to vary, namely the capacity and related characteristics of the various transport facilities. A first application deals with changes in the amount of parking spaces available near the centre. Construction and operating costs being given, the model aims at determining the distribution of commuters by mode of travel and subsequently at evaluating the balance of costs and benefits for any given set of two transport systems. The working schedule of commuters is known, so is the assignment curve between individual and mass transport which is based upon cost differentials to users, taking into account monetary costs and time loss.

A difficulty arises, however, in determining the traffic pattern on the motorway since the number of users and operating costs are interdependent variables. It has been solved by assuming a simplified traffic model in which cars cannot pass each other and travel in independent clusters. The chronological sequence of traffic flow at the exit nearest to the centre is first given. Working back to the far end of the road, the traffic flow at each entrance can be computed. It should be zero at the outskirts of the town. An iterative process is set up until traffic flows at each exit meet this condition.

Adopted data approximately describe a sector of Paris suburbs. The value of time losses has been derived from empirical studies pertaining to the choice of travel mode made by train commuters on their way from the station to their workplace in Paris.

26 Long-term Planning and Timing the Implementation of Transport Investments   357
INGE THYGESEN, *Technical University of Denmark*

One critical assumption usually made in applications of cost–benefit analysis is that the net benefits of implementing one particular project are unaffected by decisions taken with respect to other projects under consideration. In the case of transport investments, the services of which extend over a long period, such a partial analysis may yield seriously misleading results. The interdependencies between projects make it desirable to apply a total analysis, and for this purpose the concept of a project must be broadened even beyond that of planning an entire urban transport system; only a comprehensive plan for the city (or region) can be satisfactory in this respect. A total cost–benefit analysis is sketched stressing the analogy to the traditional operational research approach. As such a long-term plan is incomplete and subject to considerable uncertainty it is necessary to adapt it as new information becomes available. A simple method of dealing with one important aspect in this process of adaption, viz. timing the implementation of transport investments, is discussed.

PART IV: Conflict Resolution and Control   365

SPONSOR: ERIC L. TRIST, *Tavistock Institute of Human Relations*

This field of study has arisen from the belief that at the present time a general theory of social conflict may best be built up by systematically comparing its manifestations at all levels and in all forms of behaviour. The section, however, focuses on conflict regulation and reduction in and between social groups, rather than between or within individuals.

A simple non-zero-sum game with two strategies available to each player is used as a tool in laboratory studies aimed at uncovering some features of interactions between two players whose interests are partially coincident and partially in conflict. Specifically, both players can win if they co-operate, and both must lose if they do not. But in the absence of an opportunity for an explicit agreement, which is denied to the subjects, co-operation can be achieved only on the basis of implicit mutual trust.

In the experiments described, randomly paired subjects play the non-zero-sum game 300 times in succession. The sequence of the paired responses, of which there are four possible ones, forms the protocol of each experimental session. The variables examined are statistics derived from such protocols, such as probabilities, conditional and marginal, of the types of responses, correlations between the responses, the time courses, etc. Mathematical models are suggested, of which the various statistics are mathematical consequences to be compared with the data. The parameters of these models, as well as the statistical variables themselves, can be naturally interpreted in psychological terms, and these interpretations provide the basic concepts of a psychological theory assumed to underlie the dynamics of interaction in 'mixed-motive' conflicts of this sort.

The application of formal processes of decision under uncertainty requires, in addition to estimates of probabilities surrounding possible outcomes in the situation under consideration, estimates of the costs or values of outcomes in the light of possible actions. In the field of medicine and public health, research and the growth of data-processing systems are yielding useful probability data relating symptoms and diseases for diagnosis; however, the choice of therapeutic action must involve value considerations as well as probabilities. Therefore to exploit and develop formal statistical decision procedures – which in form lend themselves well to medical decisions – it is necessary to be able to handle the value or utility aspects of the problem.

An experimental procedure is described for measuring physicians' or administrators' utilities for medical resources and for the choice of appropriate or inappropriate therapy. The problem is expressed in game-theory terms – a game against Nature in which the decision-maker identifies some threshold of sensitivity of diagnosis below which, for a given prevalence of the suspected disease, he would, in effect, ignore a negative indication and treat as though the disease were present. From this threshold one may determine utilities held by the decision-maker at the time of the threshold determination.

When, for a given level of diagnostic sensitivity, two decision-makers choose different strategies, a conflict is said to exist. The format of the utility estimation procedure gives a quantitative representation of resolution of the conflict by dominance, compromise, or integration. It is argued that the experimental situation, since it permits examination of the subjective and ephemeral utilities which are the basis of conflict, provides a setting for resolutions of the conflict.

This paper presents a theoretical framework for analysing lateral relations. The point of departure is the manager's orientation to a joint decision-making situation; i.e. the degree to which his orientation is strictly one of optimizing the particular sub-function of the organization for which he has direct task responsibility. The theory postulates the effect of a sub-optimizing orientation on certain organizational variables, such as information exchange, interaction patterns, decision rule framework, and attitudes between interdependent departments. These organizational correlates of a sub-optimizing orientation and their implications are often ignored by operational researchers. ₁The paper is also a review of the behavioural sciences findings about conflict that are pertinent to the organizational processes included in the theory. The theory has led to an empirical study of lateral relations in six plants, to be reported elsewhere.

31 Structural Conflicts within Organizations   427
RUSSELL L. ACKOFF, *University of Pennsylvania*

Operational definitions and measures of *conflict*, *co-operation*, and *exploitation* are formulated. *Competition* is then defined as a type of human interaction which involves both conflict and co-operation. A classification of ways of affecting conflict is then derived from the definition of conflict and is related to Rapoport's corresponding modes of conflict: fights, games, and debates. A type of conflict is considered which results from the way an organization is structured. Mathematical methods of analysing and manipulating such intra-organizational conflict are considered, particularly from the point of view of an approach in which operational research and the behavioural sciences collaborate. Finally, some general observations are made on some essential conditions for such collaboration.

32 Industrial Conflict and 'Industrial Democracy'   439
EINAR THORSRUD, *Technical University of Norway*, and
F. E. EMERY, *Tavistock Institute of Human Relations*

In the particular conditions of Norwegian society labour and management have sought to restrict the traditional area of industrial conflict. At their instigation social scientific research has been carried out to test the efficacy of formal means of representing labour interests and to explore ways of limiting the area of conflict by expanding employee control at the primary point of contact – the job. This paper is confined to analysis of the formal mechanisms of conflict resolution.

33 Activating National Plans   449
BERTRAM M. GROSS, *Syracuse University, New York*

Conflict and conflict resolution are here discussed at the extremely high level of complexity found in the efforts of central governments to guide social and economic change. Many of these efforts produce attractive plans but disappointing results. Many failures in implementation are the result of inevitable obstacles . . . both the obstacles presented by nature itself and those presented by human resistance and opposition.

Many national planners display a disinclination to recognize or analyse the social conflict aspects of national planning. Mature rationality in national planning requires concentrated attention to the processes of mobilizing influence (as a way of building the 'activation base'), using an 'activation mix' of the various instruments of influence, coping with conflicts by working towards a variety of conflict 'outcomes' (victory–defeat, compromise, integration, deadlock, and avoidance) and linking these together in a flexible campaign strategy that capitalizes upon crisis, makes an appropriate use of timing, allows the maintenance of a positive stance, and brings improbable events into the sphere of the probable.

PART V: The Systems Concept as a Common Frame of Reference   499

SPONSOR: S. LANER, *University of California*

The systems concept implies a strong orientation towards the ultimate criterion of the performance or output of a whole set of resources or components assembled to serve a given purpose or variety of purposes. As the systems viewpoint is being increasingly used, both in operational research and in the social sciences, the time seems ripe for a joint examination of the claim that it constitutes a suitable framework for future common endeavour.

Increases in the size, cost, and complexity of man–machine systems result in problems in their design and operation. In this situation, systems theory is needed to predict the operational consequences of design trade-off decisions. Such theory may be developed either from a normative (economic) or a descriptive (behaviouristic) frame of reference. Because of the large number of variables which must be related in a systems model, and the difficulty of assigning utilities to these variables in dynamic situations, a descriptive feedback model is being developed, based on cybernetic concepts of regulation and control. This model comprises related design and operational sub-models. The design model is to be used to predict the expected performance consequences of design trade-off decisions. The operational model is to be used to predict the performance consequences of the tactical employment of system man and machine components in time. These models are presented in their qualitative form, and the procedures which are being developed to determine functional relations between the variables from submarine exercise data are outlined.

37 Conceptualization of a System as a Mathematical Model   **515**
ANATOL RAPOPORT, *University of Michigan*

General systems theory is a theoretical approach pursued both in technology and in natural science. The problems posed by this approach are different in each case.

In technology the systems studied are, for the most part, man made. Therefore, the identification of the elements of the system and of the relations among them presents no conceptual problem. The problems of a general systems theory in technology revolve around evaluating the overall behavioural characteristics of a system or of a class of systems whose structure is given or postulated, or around the task of constructing a system with prescribed behavioural characteristics. These are essentially synthetic problems.

In natural science, on the other hand, it is the gross characteristics of a system which are observed. The problem is to identify the important elements of the system and the interrelations among them which presumably determine the grossly observed features. These are problems of analysis.

Three approaches to a general systems theory in natural science have been proposed. One of them involves essentially a generalization of the types of system studied in thermodynamics to include open as well as closed systems and irreversible as well as reversible processes, with a view to deriving some features of life processes from physico-chemical phenomena taking place in systems possessing some measure of structural organization. Another approach stresses the study of the structure, the short-term responses, and the long-range development or evolution of living systems at various levels of organization. The third approach, the main topic of this paper, stresses the notion of mathematical homology as the conceptually unifying principle in the study of systems. Several examples are given of how the method of mathematical homology can be used in constructing a general systems theory.

The psychological demands made upon an individual in social interaction with other people are in many ways the same as, or analogous
to, those made upon a person working with inanimate objects such as
machine tools. In both cases data must be perceived, interpreted, and
used as a basis for action, often with constraints as regards timing. In
both, external stresses may be important and there may be opportunity
of learning techniques which will minimize them. In both, consideration must be given to the parts played by feedback of information
from one part of the system to another, and to the seemingly spontaneous tendency by individuals to adapt their techniques of work so
as to optimize the use of their capacities in meeting demands.

The relevant 'dimensions' of human capacity are much better known
for work with machines than they are for social situations. The aim of
this paper is to consider some of the ways in which knowledge of the
former could be used to develop theory and guide research in the
latter. By way of example, the interaction between instructor and
trainee in a teaching situation is compared with that of an operator
controlling a process plant in terms of:

1 Information transmission,
2 Short-term retention,
3 Sequences and routines,
4 Feedback, and
5 Under- and over-loading.

The same terms are then applied in whole or in part to communication
systems in industry, problems of leadership and size of group, incentives and responsibility in industrial work, behaviour of crowds, race
relations, and the function of social norms and customs.

The approach outline does not provide a simple, unified theory of
social behaviour or an easy means of obtaining significant data about
social phenomena. It does, however, bring the study of social processes into closer touch than has hitherto been customary with the
study of individual capacity, and suggest a means of bridging the
present gap between experimental psychology and sociology.

PART VI: Models, Decisions, and Operational Research 555

The paper opens with a brief discussion of normative and contemplative–explicatory versus operational forms of the social sciences, and of the general decision model. This discussion serves as a platform for the ensuing considerations on the theoretical possibilities of applying the general decision model in the social sciences. Thereafter, only operational applications are considered. In order to form an idea of how appropriate the general decision model is for operational applications in the social sciences, obstacles to application are discussed one by one: mathematical requirements, which raise but negligible difficulties, and pre-decisions, which, it is true, pose serious problems which are, however, not incapable of practical solution. Lack of knowledge about the distribution law over the states of Nature turns out to be the chief obstacle to application. Possible ways to overcome this chief obstacle are discussed: *a priori* procedures, *a posteriori* procedures, subjective probabilities, the use of normative judgements as a substitute for lack of knowledge. A further obstacle to application is the instability of the decision situation. Process interval and stability interval are discussed and compared with each other; this is followed by an enumeration of likely limitations of the stability interval. The conclusions summarize the most important results of the paper. These are mostly negative rather than positive. In closing, possible reasons for the low degree of suitability of the general decision model for operational applications in the social sciences are indicated.

A committee faced with the choice among several possible courses of action may adopt a wide variety of procedures for reaching a decision. By the application of the operational research techniques of game theory and set theory, it is shown to be possible to represent these procedures, and to calculate their consequences

(a) on the assumption that all voters vote 'sincerely', or directly in accordance with their preference-scales;

(b) if voting is not sincere, but rather 'strategic', as in the theory of games of strategy.

A procedure may be called 'straightforward' if no voter has any incentive for departing from sincere voting. An example is given of a procedure which is straightforward for the preference-scales considered.

The methods set out can be considerably extended to cover more complex procedures, and the question of coalitions.

A non-probabilistic method of multivariate analysis is distinguished under the name 'classification'. A sociological application with possible relevance to operational research problems is described. A necessary condition for a classification to be optimal reveals properties of an optimal classification which show how the subject is related to the analysis of variance, principal component analysis, and discriminatory analysis. A computer programme which obtains a locally optimal, and would seem usually to obtain a good, classification is described.

This paper outlines the methodology of choosing the size of hospitals and gives some research results.

The cost of hospital care has been shown to be independent of hospital size for any given branch of medicine in general hospitals.

So far only hospital treatment has been costed, and there are variations from one hospital to another. The effectiveness of hospitals has not been considered and would present serious problems of measurement. As an alternative, it is proposed to study the whole cost of illness. It is suggested that the choice of hospital size should be based on the effect on the total cost of illness and should also take into account all the hospital facilities in a region.

This paper summarizes and discusses the results obtained from a study of fifteen acute general hospitals with regard to five observables: (i)

B

sisters' opinions of senior staff; (ii) sisters' attitudes towards student nurses; (iii) stability of qualified nursing staff on wards; (iv) mean length of patient stay for general medical cases; and (v) the same for general surgical cases. The results showed a concordance in these hospital characteristics. The situation is discussed in terms of the social relationships and communication between the different types and levels of professional staff. The effect of an authoritarian and hierarchical organization of communication is considered. The paper then discusses a strategy for further research into hospital communication and how hospital communication might, in practice, be improved.

This paper presents the findings of an exploratory study of face-to-face and telephone communications between thirty-four executives in an industrial organization.

The interactions reported by the executives over a two-week period were checked against each other as to their participants and type of interaction. The amount of consensus as to the occurrence of the interactions was established as was also the number of interactions in which communications were transmitted in the spirit in which they were intended.

The measurements make it possible to describe the organizational structure in the form of a Communicogram, showing 'breaks' in communication, pointing to leadership qualities existing and required in key communication positions, and revealing various other aspects of the organization.

The study brought to light the surprising fact that only 12 per cent of the interactions reported by the executives conformed with the spirit in which they were intended.

PART VII: Conclusion   635

Part I
Introductory

1

1 · Editor's Preface

J. R. LAWRENCE

In 1962 the Operational Research Society set out to plan its first international conference, which was to take the place of the normal national conference due to be held in the autumn of 1964. The conference was to have a single theme of topical importance in many countries; of the possible topics 'Operational Research and the Social Sciences' was eventually selected.

Operational research and the social sciences were, and still are, rapidly expanding activities both very much concerned with using their abilities to effect improvement in organized human activity – in business, in government, in industry, and so on. They both wish to achieve their objectives through the use of scientific knowledge and the scientific method, and, while some scientists can validly pursue knowledge for its own sake, both operational researchers and social scientists must want to see their results being used and being shown to be effective; this must be so because their hypotheses can be tested and their models validated only in the arena of human activity.

While having, to a considerable extent, then, common purposes and objectives and a common scientific base, each discipline has been too engrossed in developing its own methodologies, techniques, and fields of experience to have much inclination to explore the other's field. This should not have been so, because operational research, to most practitioners, is in essence an interdisciplinary activity having within itself practitioners from the appropriate scientific disciplines, and because social science is science and hence interested in measurement and the development of models to explain phenomena. But unfortunate as the lack of mutual contact has been, it is to a very large extent undeniable. The longer this separation has continued, the greater has been the task that has been building up of integration – with its difficulties of language and of assimilating the other's history and case law.

We should perhaps interject here that there have certainly been one or two objections that the whole concept of separation is a chimaera, and, for

3

example, that social scientists have co-operated with other disciplines within operational research teams. That this has sometimes happened one would not deny, but, as we shall stress later, it is not sufficiently widespread to have led to a single paper for this conference.

Some operational researchers and social scientists were concerned at this state of affairs, and in addition other forces were necessitating greater contact. For example, separate operational research and social science groups operating in organizations found themselves tackling overlapping problems with little shared methodological understanding; several universities were attempting to bring the two together in the academic environment. And, again, the rapid development of computer systems was forcing attention on the interaction of human behaviour and logical decision-making. These, then, were the reasons for the selection of 'Operational Research and the Social Sciences' as the title for the international conference in 1964.

The broad technique adopted for the conference was to bring together leading world figures from both sides, theorists and practitioners, to discuss their similarities and differences of approach in certain areas, to explore the possibilities for greater collaboration in the development and application of theory or in general problem-solving and, indeed, to get one side talking to the other about what each was doing, and to try to establish that useful communication was possible and that the languages and jargons that had developed did not raise impenetrable barriers.

The areas chosen as topics were organization and control, the measurement of the social effects of policies, and conflict. It was also decided to explore the possibility that systems theory might provide a common language and approach.

By planning the conference in this way, it was hoped to achieve a number of broad but practical ends. A greater mutual awareness of basic knowledge and methods would lead to greater contact and communication for the future. Specific problems might be identified in one field or the other, which might be helped by collaboration, and a clearer idea could then be sought of how best to organize such collaborative work. More generally, ideas for further research could be discussed, and these might lead to more integrated approaches.

The papers were to be of two types, broad reviews as a basis for discussion of principles and a larger number of papers giving examples of work by operational researchers and social scientists, separately or in collaboration.

These were the lines of thought that led to this particular form of conference. Were they valid? Did they make sense to a randomly selected (the words average and typical cannot be used) operational research worker or social scientist? The questions in the minds of at least some operational research people, in approaching the conference, were on the following lines:

(*a*) Operational researchers who are deeply involved in the design and improvement of complex management control systems, based on logical and quantitative analysis, are often aware of their inadequate ability to understand and measure human behaviour and take it into account in their systems design.

(*b*) They are puzzled about how to deal with human reaction to change, when they come to try to implement change.

(*c*) They have read of descriptive research by social scientists such as Rensis Likert, March and Simon, Elliott Jaques, and many others. They are sympathetic towards this work but concerned about the lack of validated models and measurement in much of it. They wonder how it is viewed by the social science fraternity and how it can be applied in solving real organizational problems.

(*d*) They see organizational problems within their organizations, and they see many of the methods used for solving these as 'punditry' rather than the result of rigorous reasoning. Management changes achieved in this way can undermine the basis, and hence the value, of operational research studies that have been carried out. Perhaps an approach based on co-operation between operational research and behavioural science could lead to a more convincing and definitive methodology.

(*e*) They have heard of occasions when social scientists have been invited to study and improve organizations. They wonder how this kind of study compares with a broad operational research study with the same purpose – is it in effect the same kind of study under a different name, based primarily on a blend of scientific method and common sense, or is it quite different? If the latter, can the two be regarded as complementary, or is there a risk that the two could come to contradictory conclusions? If the latter again, then how valid have their models been?

(*f*) They have the impression that in some social science thinking the link between organizational effectiveness for productivity and measures of morale and good human relations is assumed without proof; if there is in fact a conflict of objectives, how is it to be resolved?

Just as the operational researchers had questions arising from both self-criticism and scepticism towards social science for its seeming failure to be rigorous and quantitative, so perhaps did some social scientists have a series of analogous questions.

(*a*) They have wondered about their relationship to this broad, interdisciplinary, problem-solving activity that is so rapidly expanding in modern industry under the name of operational research.

(*b*) They have heard that it is highly mathematical and wonder how the problems of human behaviour are handled. They are perhaps concerned lest, in practice, operational researchers may assume the behavioural variables out of their problems and that they sometimes act as though

rational economic man were a reality. They nevertheless want to see
what can be done to develop and handle quantitative, analytical models in
their own fields of study.

In many ways, even the papers themselves serve to underline the need for
collaboration that we have described. The number of papers, either from the
behavioural side carrying conviction as operational research studies, or from
operational research convincingly modelling human behaviour, was small,
perhaps nil. But there were many hopeful indications of things to come. It is
invidious to select; rather as examples, then, we would quote Geisler's paper
on the Rand simulations of management systems, and also the papers by
Ratoosh and Rapoport which attempt to quantify human behaviour, albeit
under artificial conditions; the papers by Churchill and Cooper, Weinshall,
and Woodward and Eilon describe studies of human behaviour in real situations, although the models are as yet still oversimplified or incomplete;
papers such as those by Flagle and Brink describe further models of human
behaviour, although they have yet to be tested and quantified; the discussion
of functions for cost–benefit analysis by Foster is fascinating and shows up
the crudity of what we have seen so far in examples of studies by this method.
And so one can go on cataloguing the exciting ideas, but drawing out the
scope still for producing convincing studies where the two approaches have
been successfully integrated and applied and the models tested in real situations. Not that such studies were not sought; several sponsors looked very
hard indeed for them.

One might have looked specially for this sort of work from the industry-
based operational research groups and social scientists, but there was not a
single paper from an industry-based author. (In fact, the list of forty-one
authors is dominated by thirty-four academics.) But whatever the reason for
the lack of good joint operational-research/social-science studies, the fact
makes it difficult to draw general conclusions about appropriate methods of
solution from examples of particular problem situations.

Having given some statistics, we might go on, parenthetically, to note that
the list of authors indicates how much more work in this whole broad area
seems to be being done in the United States (twenty-five out of the forty-one
authors).

Most of the participants came to the conference in an enthusiastic and
constructive frame of mind, and it was a resounding success in terms of the
stimulation it created and the better understanding that was gained of what
was being done. As one senior operational research man put it, both arro-
gance and ignorance were reduced. For example, the organization and control
session seemed to lead to a greater realization of the triangular relationship
between operational research, social science, and management research (as
exemplified by the work from the Industrial Administration Department of
the Carnegie Institute of Technology). One can contrast the advances in the

use of science to study *ad hoc* management problems with the lack of advance in attempts to use it to study the process of management itself. It may now be the turn of management research to make advances, possibly in collaboration with operational research inside organizations; indeed, there is already evidence of this sort of thing happening with increasing frequency. Such work will perhaps be the bridge between operational research and social science in their approaches to organization.

An analogous triangular relationship between social science, operational research, and community planning research was apparent in the session on the measurement of the social effects of policies. Decision-making in the public sector, besides taking into account straightforward cash effects, must be more closely related to the human consequences; and to study these in relation to any major decisions is likely to involve the manipulation of complex quantitative models.

One could quote many such points; but the real extent of the value of these discussions, often at an informal social level, will be embedded in the quality of future work and the advances yet to be made in the various fields. As yet one can only go on the conviction of those who took part.

When the plans for the conference were well under way it was decided that some sort of publication should be considered. Clearly, the papers were going to be of a high order and would probably merit publication in a body. Since it was to be a working conference with as much emphasis as possible on discussion – with multiple parallel sessions – and as little as possible on formal presentation of papers, it was planned to try in this book to convey the ideas generated by these discussions. Now this could have been done by selective verbatim reporting, but we felt that there was too much risk that this would be ill structured, lengthy, and sometimes dull to read. Instead, further contributions in the form of short papers have been prepared by 'rapporteurs' for the various sessions. They were encouraged to select, to edit, and, whenever they thought fit, to make their own comments and draw their own conclusions about what was said. These, then, are not necessarily unbiased reports, but rather linking contributions. In this way, we hope that this book will stand on its own as a stimulating symposium of related papers that will help readers to achieve the degree of enthusiasm for the topics and the interactions that the conference stimulated for most of the participants. Hence this is not 'The Proceedings of the International Conference on Operational Research and the Social Sciences' for distribution to delegates in order to generate a warm glow of 'I was there', but simply 'Operational Research and the Social Sciences', a book in its own right, produced by virtue of there having been a conference, but with a far wider audience in mind.

My part began well after the plans for the conference had been made and has consisted of trying to translate it all into a coherent volume. I would like to stress my gratitude to my two ex-colleagues, John Banbury, who was

Chairman of the Programme Committee and helped me to form my view of how the task should be carried out, and Steve Cook, who was a sponsor of the first session and who provided me with invaluable help in describing the thinking of the original architects of the conference. I hope that my background in operational research has not led me to misinterpret the social scientists or to bias either this preface or the book as a whole.

2 · The Conference at Cambridge

The International Conference on Operational Research and the Social Sciences was held at Gonville and Caius College, Cambridge, from 14 to 18 September 1964.

The organization was handled by an organizing committee and a programme committee whose members were:

G. Neville Gadsby (*Chairman – Conference Committee*)
John Banbury (*Chairman – Programme Committee*)
S. L. Cook
R. T. Eddison
W. N. Jessop
S. Laner

J. R. Lawrence
P. A. Longton
G. W. Sears
R. W. Shephard
E. L. Trist
Mrs M. Kinnaird (*Secretary of the Operational Research Society*)

The success of the conference itself owed a great deal to the many people who chaired plenary sessions, syndicates, and discussion groups:

Russell Ackoff
G. A. Barnard
A. Battersby
Stafford Beer
Tom Burns
R. B. Davies
R. J. Deam
M. A. Dizy
R. L. Drew
T. E. Easterfield

Norman Fisher
C. D. Foster
A. Glaskin
Donald Hicks
Gurth Higgin
F. T. Hulswit
J. Lesourne
N. Lichfield
D. L. Marples
Don Marquis

J. McCarthy
E. F. Mellen
M. J. Moroney
B. H. P. Rivett
R. G. Stansfield
A. C. Stedry
K. D. Tocher
N. R. Tobin
A. T. M. Wilson

to those who helped the rapporteurs by acting as secretaries for discussions:

A. Battersby
D. T. Bryant

Tom Burns
M. W. G. Duff

E. A. Field
J. K. Friend

Liam Gorman
K. F. Jackson
E. A. Little
P. A. Longton
Julius Marek
J. McCarthy

Hugh Murray
R. Neate
J. V. Rosenhead
B. W. Sayer
R. W. Shephard
John Stringer

P. Thursfield
Hans van Beinum
R. A. Ward
G. G. L. Wright

and to M. Barbier, who stood in for, in presenting the paper by, S. Goldberg, and to Russell Ackoff who stood in for, in presenting the two papers by, Anatol Rapoport. We hope that these lists are complete and accurate and apologize for any inadvertent errors or omissions.

We should also give credit for their contributions to this volume to the many delegates, not already listed, who attended the conference and took part in its discussions.

The organizers are particularly grateful to the Sloan Foundation for providing substantial funds to enable a number of distinguished American delegates to attend the conference.

3 · Opening Remarks

SIR CHARLES GOODEVE

It is hardly necessary to emphasize how important it is that our knowledge of Man and society should catch up with the technical progress which has arisen from the advances in the natural sciences. Many of the Presidents of the British Association since the war have referred to the fact that science is continuing to put more and more power into the hands of Man, without at the same time learning about the minds and the social organizations which control those hands. As far back as fifty years ago the *Scientific American* had a leading article on this point and many writers before that had expressed their concern.

Few speakers or writers have, however, produced practical suggestions as to what should be done about it. Few natural scientists have gone over to a study of sociological problems since Michael Polanyi did nearly thirty years ago, or as Professor Tustin did more successfully in his introduction of the concept of feedback into economics – a concept which still has a long way to go in the social sciences. But even more surprising is the fact that a large number of physical scientists have become active in an organization under the name of Pugwash, which is indeed, I believe, meeting at this very moment. But active as they have been, they have remained outside the social sciences as if they are rather afraid of penetrating, perhaps through lack of confidence, perhaps from fear of the complexity of the subject. All the talk, therefore, of redressing the balance is in the air unless it can be followed by responsible action.

The trouble, of course, is that most of the problem areas in the social world are of a degree of complexity far beyond that of anything so far met with in the natural sciences. As de Sola Pool has pointed out, prediction in the social field is somewhat parallel to the problem of roulette; to predict what the ball will do is so impossibly hard that no one attempts to do this. This is in contrast, say, with chess, where we can predict some way ahead. In human behaviour things are so complex that we 'fall back on punditry and

11

intuition'. However, Pool's analogy cannot be carried very far because society would indeed be chaotic if human behaviour was as random as the roulette ball.

Most of us at this conference have some expectation that operational research can form a useful bridge between the natural and social sciences, largely because it has been learning how to deal with more and more complex situations. This expectation is based on success in dealing with problems of considerable complexity in industry, defence, and other spheres, aided more recently by the introduction of the computer.

Before dealing with this aspect, let me refer to a second object of the conference, and this is to see how the social sciences can contribute to operational research.

Those working in operational research have been successful in studying efficiencies, flows, inventories, problems requiring research, etc., but most of these are largely mechanical problems. The social sciences can enable operational research people to go into other important fields, such as organization and communications, with a greater chance of success. They already go into these fields, but feel the need for removing the limitations caused by ignorance of social science.

There are many possible examples. The paper by Warren Bennis deals with change, and this involves overcoming many human obstacles. Operational research people are very much concerned with change and can deal with the logic, including the economics, of it. But attitudes of people – managers, technicians, workpeople, salesmen, customers, etc. – can throw the best of predictions into confusion.

Professor Bennis's paper starts from a wealth of experience of the human aspects of such problems. I trust that it will be challenged to test the degree to which the disciplines that operational research people claim to use are behind the words and conclusions. In this way we might bring about a satisfactory combination of the two approaches, as is argued in the paper by Churchman and Emery.

Many problems attacked by operational research involve questions of 'goodwill', especially when the market aspects need to be considered. Most of us find that some of the arguments used in practice are not really related to the objectives of the company, but more often to the interests of individuals – the salespeople or the top management. In studying goodwill one hopes that the psychologists will be able to help us. We in operational research would be satisfied with a very rough measurement of goodwill, and indeed we would be pleased even if we could have a better appreciation of its component factors.

Goodwill is part of the great game of business – almost all business is a form of game. The analysis of games received an impetus from the work of Rapoport and others, but further progress here is desirable. For this, more knowledge of human behaviour as well as the logic of games is required.

Gamesmanship requires a high degree of selection in the flow of information and indeed sometimes requires the feeding of false information to one's competitors. The discipline of science, on the contrary, requires free and full communication of accurate information, and mixing science and gamesmanship presents complications to many scientists – perhaps not to all!

Many people in business prefer the sport of games to the logic of science; school playing-fields train them for this. But business men are not often enough concerned whether they are playing a zero-sum game or a positive-sum game. The difference is of particular importance in the vertical direction, that is in dealing with your customers or your suppliers. You can win at the expense of these, but only in the short term. In the long term part at least of your customers' losses will come back to you.

The problem of balancing between long-term and short-term objectives becomes even more prominent in investment problems – a common task put to operational research people. Companies like to know how much of their cash flow they should consume today and how much they should plough back through savings to produce gains in the future. The same problem faces every individual in the community – whether to spend today or save for investment in the future – that is, for gains to yourself in your old age, for your children, or just for future generations. Operational research can help in formulating this question very precisely, but cannot by itself find an answer. I believe that the social sciences can say much about this very fundamental and important problem of human behaviour and can fill in the gaps left by the logic of operational research. Indeed, I would go so far as to say that this is one of the most intriguing and important problems which faces all of us: How should people decide between consuming today and saving for the future?

I would like now to come back to the first issue – that is, the possible gains to the social sciences from links with operational research. Operational research people think that they have been good at clarifying and weighting objectives and that this is one of the reasons why they have been rather successful at the application of their science to problems of industry and government. They also believe, from their experiences in the natural sciences, that it is both desirable and possible to extract from complex situations some basic principles so that the mass of intricate detail can be put in perspective. The details can then be built in at different levels of a structure resting on basic principles.

Furthermore, operational research people claim to be good at model-building as part of the process of analysis and prediction. So much emphasis is placed on this that the outsider should be forgiven if he imagines that an operational research man spent his time with bits of balsa wood and glue. However, I will leave it to the operational research people to explain themselves to the social scientists and at the same time to learn from them.

The main object of social scientists is to increase their knowledge and in particular their ability to predict. But I should like to offer a suggestion to the social scientists that would go some way towards fulfilling two other important objectives. The first objective would be to assist in gaining collaboration with operational research people. The second, of much greater importance, is to make it possible for the knowledge of the social sciences to flow to a much wider public, and particularly to flow down the line to the generations coming along behind us. If we are to fulfil our responsibilities we should be playing our part to ensure that our knowledge reaches the man in the street, and particularly the man of tomorrow in the street. With care we can thus affect his individual behaviour for the better and reduce the tremendous amount of wasteful conflict which goes on at the present time. We shall be discussing conflict, an important dynamic force in our social structure. You have only to read the newspapers and listen to the man in the pubs to realize the enormous amount of effort that could better be spent in arguing about things that really do matter rather than about the elementary facts of life.

My suggestion to meet these objectives is that another bold attempt should be made to put part of our knowledge of man and of his social systems in a communicable form. To achieve this we must produce a basic model of a social group or community, a model that is simple enough to be understood by operational research people and sixth-formers. Life is too short and the brain too small to absorb the intricacies of the social sciences as they are today, unless one is prepared to drop everything else and become a specialist.

Many will say that this is typical of a suggestion from a physical scientist who would be lost if he were not trained in Newton's laws of motion. To those who would say I was asking for the moon, I would remind them of Lord Keynes, who pulled out such key principles from the complexity of economics that he has raised the status of the whole subject.

It is much more important, I suggest, to spread the knowledge of the social sciences than of any other science. Every driver of a car must learn the fundamentals of driving in a congested street, but he need not learn thermodynamics or how his car works. But in social life everyone must learn about living and learn it from ground level. I think we can achieve this by improving the background knowledge of people concerned with communication to the public and in particular the people in the press and broadcasting, in the churches and the schools, whose knowledge of the social sciences is limited. A further dividend is that from the flow to the coming generation we can excite new people to study social problems and thus add to our general body of knowledge of the subject.

Different people will have different ideas as to what should be considered as basic and whether we should approach model-building from a study of the individual or of the group or of both. The approach, of course, should be related to the objective that one has in mind. I prefer the approach from the individual because this allows one to introduce, or at least to think about, the concept of will, which is basic to motivation and responsibility.

It would be presumptuous of me to attempt a simple model and indeed perhaps foolish on a brief occasion such as this. But I should like to underline the suggestion by hazarding a few points.

Let us start with the most elementary of points. Every individual spends his life drawing on his surroundings – that is, on the community – for his food, clothing, etc., to meet his needs and wants.

So we have a first basic principle for our model, indeed an axiom, in that the drawings on any particular good or service by all individuals cannot exceed the contributions, except, of course, over a very short period. Indeed, as a subsidiary point, a group if it is to raise its standard of living must contribute more goods and services than it consumes, otherwise it cannot invest for the future. We know, of course, that, in order to follow this fundamental principle and law, a social group devises a system based on a concept of value and the use of money as an operator to link contributions and drawings. One might go on into details. Society usually accepts that individuals can vary about the average. They do not all need to give to the community equally, or more than they draw. Each individual has to vary over his life-span: as a baby or as an old person he contributes less than he consumes, but he makes up for this during his working life.

For almost every good there is an interval between the time when it is made and the time when it is finally consumed – a short time for cooked food, a long time for a tool or a Cambridge college. During this time interval between making and consuming it is 'owned'. Our model must have in it the basic principles of ownership, but these, I suggest, are not as complicated as the textbooks make out. You start off by owning what you learn and what you make and, of course, you can let out for hire your skill and your labour.

Another axiom that would be helpful in our model is that practically all the decisions made by individuals will be in the direction to satisfy their needs and their wants, providing these terms are interpreted on a broad basis, that is they should include non-material wants. But the wants of different individuals overlap, and thus they will lead to conflict. The society therefore introduces restraints modulating the decisions of the will referred to earlier. It is in the wide variations in the wants of individuals that much of the complexity of society is to be found, a complexity that obscures the reasons why people make decisions as they do.

Finally, I think that this model should indicate why people join together in groups. Much, of course, has been written on this point, and I need hardly elaborate on it.

With these suggestions I hope I will have irritated some people enough to provoke them to put forward their own sets of basic principles. You could well criticize my remarks by saying that a simple model will not take us very far. This is certainly true from the point of view of advancing the social sciences, but the other and very important goal is to extract a basic model or set of principles from the complexity of our social system. We need a framework of our social structure, and one simple enough to be taught to the non-specialist, but basic enough to support detail. I believe that if this goal could be realized a large part of the irrational behaviour of people today, based as it is on ignorance of simple things, would disappear.

Part II
Organization and Control

SPONSORS: S. L. COOK and W. N. JESSOP

17

human ability – the process of manufacture – noise, information, and the manufacturing process – the abstract process of automation – the human and the automaton in manufacturing – some questions of economics – the course of automation – the kinds of work that will survive – some possible lines of research – postscript

4 · Introduction

S. L. COOK

The search for organizational effectiveness

Organizations grow increasingly large and complex. The problems of designing and improving management control systems in order to increase organizational effectiveness occupy the minds of more and more people: managers, management advisers, researchers, and consultants – and scientists and technologists of all kinds.

Organizational effectiveness means efficiency in achieving the objectives of the organization, and in many organizations these objectives are taken as being closely linked with productivity. In these cases, and if the system can be made so tightly controlled or 'mechanistic' that human characteristics have no effect on its mode of operation, the design study need not encompass human variables at all.

Where human characteristics cannot be ignored, the designer may be satisfied to obtain some measure of the average and variation of human response in the appropriate circumstances, treating this characteristic as an independent random variable in the system. The situation becomes more complex, however, if this characteristic is thought to be *dependent* upon other aspects of the system. For example, in a stock control situation the storekeeper may be able to bias the use of the re-order rule to keep his stocks 'comfortably' above the safety levels; the amount of this bias could vary with the proved reliability of the re-order rules.

This simple example illustrates a general feature of the human component in a management control system. He may occasionally be there because a human being is the cheapest means of doing some set of physical operations or observations; in which case he is supposed to work to set rules all the time, and never to think. But most often he will be there because of some problem-solving requirement which comes up from time to time, and which he is expected to solve 'free style'. There is no direct measure of whether he is solving the problem well – and he will do better or worse according to his

21

motivation and general state of mind. The combined effect of the emotional and intellectual components will be hard to predict in designing a system.

In most management control systems the level of complexity is far greater than in this example, and we are dealing with interactions involving large numbers of human beings and of logical systems. Here the possibility of taking account of individual human responses becomes negligible, but instead we may perhaps consider more generalized measures which aggregate the attitudes, and hence possibly the behaviour, of the management or work force as a whole. We may call one such measure 'morale'. Most managers accept that morale is strongly influenced by some characteristics of the management control system – perhaps 'style' of management, or some more tangible aspect of the system. Many managers believe that a high level of morale can lead to higher productivity for the organization. There appears at present to be as much evidence against as for this proposition, but there seems little doubt of its truth in some circumstances. In these situations human factors cannot possibly be ignored in the search for organizational effectiveness in the sense of high productivity.

Finally, there are an increasing number of managements – usually of organizations which have become large and acquired a 'social conscience' – who will make morale (or perhaps 'employee satisfaction', or just the happiness of the members of the organization) a separate objective, and will rate their organizational effectiveness partly on the achievement of this – as well as on productivity. They will be less concerned with the effect of morale on productivity than with the effect of management control systems on morale.

These opening comments perhaps illustrate the range of factors involved in studying and improving organizational effectiveness. They barely touch on the complexity of the problem. For example, systems of formal and informal communication within an organization will greatly influence the quality of decisions taken in two distinct ways: first, by the extent to which they make available, at the right point and at the right time, the appropriate information for the decision – the 'cognitive' aspect; second, by the ways in which they motivate the individuals and groups concerned. Any study of communications within an organization which aims to increase organizational effectiveness must therefore seek to separate and measure these two kinds of influence – no easy task.

The activities of operational research and social science in organizations

Now let us consider the parts operational research and social science have played in the studies of organizational control in industry in recent years.

Since 1947 in the United Kingdom, and since the mid-1950s in other countries, operational research groups have been developing and doing significant work in industrial organizations. They have tackled a wide range of problems, from the planning of plant development and production programmes to operational studies of existing communication, transport, and production systems. In the last type of study particularly they have often found that the one-off solution to an operational problem is not very satisfactory because changing circumstances may invalidate the solution quite soon and also because operating methods tend to drift from those recommended. This has led to more and more operational research teams being greatly concerned with the design of control systems which are, to some degree at least, self-adaptive. The development has been accentuated by the rapid increase in applications of computers for control in industry. Once an organization goes to the trouble of installing computers, it is worth while to employ operational research teams to study the best logic for control, rather than to computerize existing procedures.

The same argument applies to planning whenever this is routine. Present management methods of planning can be improved by operational research studies and then incorporated in systematic routines, possibly on a computer, for regular use.

There has been a gradual change in the nature of operational research teams since their first development during the second world war. At that time they were usually made up of a number of scientists from various backgrounds, usually with considerable research experience in their own disciplines and ranging from psychology and biology to physics and engineering. The change has been due both to the lack of availability of sufficient experienced scientists and to the immediate demands of the work of the teams. Nowadays operational research groups are considerably younger, having recruited about half of their members straight from university; they are more concentrated in disciplines, being drawn mainly from the mathematical and physical sciences, with perhaps the occasional economist. They have become much more skilled at applying a certain range of techniques to a corresponding range of problems. An important casualty of this development has been the mixed-team concept in its full original meaning, and specifically the inclusion of social scientists. There are many reasons for this, and some are discussed later. In using the term 'operational research' in this book in contradistinction to 'social sciences', we refer to operational research as it is generally carried on at the present time, rather than, as it was originally and as it should perhaps become again, a broad interdisciplinary activity which includes social scientists wherever appropriate. At present, a very few distinguished groups are maintaining and developing interdisciplinary operational research.

The activities of applied social scientists in industry since the war are admirably covered by Professor Bennis's paper. In brief, industry has been increasingly using consultants for applied social science problems, and a number of leading firms, especially in the United States (such as Esso, I.B.M., Thompson Ramo-Woolridge, each in their different ways), have set up their own internal groups. Typically, such studies have arisen when a firm has found itself faced with the need for major organizational changes, because of a serious drop in performance, or a change in the market situation, or perhaps a merger. However, acceptance by industry of this contribution is far less widespread than that of operational research, and the greatest social science activities in industry are probably those of a research nature based on government-sponsored projects. Leaders in this field have been, for example, the Institute for Social Research at the University of Michigan; in the United Kingdom, the Science Research Council (and formerly D.S.I.R.) has increasingly supported such studies, of which that reported in Chapter 8 is an example.

Until very recently the operational research groups and social science groups working on industrial problems hardly knew of each other's existence, let alone feeling they had anything to say to each other. Now they are both getting deeper and deeper into the real problems of management, they are beginning to become very aware of their own shortcomings and to feel that they could perhaps help one another. As has been said, the operational research movement began with the concept of mixed teams which could very well include social scientists, but was swept along by the rapid progress in the quantifiable area, and most of the social scientists in it disappeared in the process. By the time operational research reached the level of sophistication of making control system studies and recommendations for computer applications, there was no trace or tradition of social science in most of these groups. Now, however, operational research men see the importance of human factors in at least two areas which are vital to operational research.

First, to design a good management control system which will work as predicted, they need to know much more about the likely behaviour of the human components of the system.

Second, in trying to implement operational research proposals, whether for some sophisticated management control system or for a much simpler change of method, they often find human resistance to change to be a major obstacle. They need all the help that social science skills or theories can provide.

A third area in which the operational research man is very concerned deals not with his job but the environment in which he works. The organizational structure and management style very much affect the way the operational research team can work with other members of the management and greatly preconditions the chance of satisfactory implementation.

The operational research man has at present no techniques with which to link up these three areas, but he would like to think that the social scientist, in so far as he has made any progress in the field of organization theory, can make some improvements.

The social scientist in his turn has become deeply involved with organizational structure and management style from the point of view of formal and informal roles, communications, motivation, conflict, morale, intergroup relations and so on. In these studies he has until recently treated the precise nature and content of the tasks performed, the communications made and the

decisions taken as being secondary to human relationships and the communication system. There is no doubt that this approach has met with
considerable success, but increasingly the social scientist feels the need to
take more account of these 'content' variables. He realizes that the operational research man is rather more practised in defining, classifying, and
measuring these 'cognitive' aspects than himself.

A comment is perhaps due at this point on the nature of the present contributions of operational research and of applied social science to improving
organizational effectiveness. It is occasionally suggested that operational
research (like the 'scientific management' movement preceding it) is concerned
primarily with improving productivity and profitability – sometimes to the
detriment of morale; and that social science (like the 'human relations
movement') is primarily concerned with improving morale – sometimes, but
not always, to the advantage of profitability. It would follow from this
assumption that the two groups are aiming consciously at different components of 'organizational effectiveness', and that the task of ensuring that
these components result in a net gain rather than a net loss (in terms of
overall company objectives) is left with the management of the organization.
However, in fact this is not how most operational researchers or social
scientists see their roles. Most activities of each group are directed fundamentally towards the same goal, namely the definition and optimal achievement of overall organizational objectives. The difference lies rather in those
parts of the problem that are handled implicitly and by intuition, and those
parts that are dealt with more explicitly or analytically.

The operational research man would certainly consider that he was concerned with 'the whole problem' – i.e. the effect of all aspects of a proposed
change on the performance of the organization; and although his quantitative
analysis would probably not be able to include allowance for human factors,
his demonstration and test of the proposed solution should reveal whether
these detract from the value of the solution – in the short term at least. The
applied social scientist, in any attempt to improve communications and
human relations, is normally doing so in the firm belief that these will improve effectiveness; and he often concerns himself also with such variables
as attitude to task performance, and tries to ensure that these, too, improve.

The outstanding problem for both groups is that as yet there is no satisfactory measure of organizational effectiveness, let alone a satisfactory model
of the controllable and the uncontrollable factors affecting it. Realization of
this fact is perhaps the most important corrective to 'stereotype' thinking
about the roles of operational researchers and social scientists in organizations.

Factors linking operational research and social science in organizations

There are many other professional groups concerned with the control problem in organizations; and in the practical tasks of building organizations and

systems all such groups should, of course, be included in the discussions. However, the operational research workers and the social scientists are the only two broad groups which are scientific and research-based. There seems therefore to be a particularly strong case for them to have a good scientific understanding of each other's activities, an awareness of the implications of their methods and conclusions for one another, and a will and ability to collaborate wherever this might be fruitful. It is asking too much of the line manager, at least if he is a non-scientist, to reconcile conflicting theories or proposals from the two groups if the two groups have not themselves tried to do this in a scientific manner.

It is interesting to reflect why these two groups should have stayed so far apart up till now, especially when both recognize the great value of the inter-disciplinary approach. Paradoxically, their already interdisciplinary nature may provide one answer. Each group, feeling that it is an interdisciplinary activity, has come to feel that members of the other group, if interested, should come and join in under its own banner. Moreover, each group has been heavily engaged in coping with its interdisciplinary nature, which re-quires continual effort to digest and communicate the approaches, methods, and ideas of several different disciplines. But the time has come to recognize that one interdisciplinary activity is not necessarily all possible interdisci-plinary activity. If operational research, on the one hand, and social science, on the other hand, are useful interdisciplinary groupings, then let them by all means continue as such, recognizing the considerable overlap of subject-matter. But if the two interdisciplinary groups find they need to get together to discuss and collaborate, then they must make the effort needed for this; possibly a new interdisciplinary group containing some of the activities of each of these two groups will need to form alongside the other two. And perhaps the skills and knowledge of the applied social scientists are needed to assist inter-group relations in this context.

Aims in planning this section

This, then, was the background to the preparation of this part of the con-ference. It was hoped first of all to help each group to become much more aware of the scope and nature of the activities of the other in the field of organization and control, including both research and specific applications. Second, it was hoped that each group would indicate the areas in which it was finding difficulty and in which the other might be able to assist. Third, it was hoped that both groups jointly would explore the possible obstacles to collaboration, the desirable fields of collaboration, and the priorities for further research in either field.

To this end, Professor Churchman and Dr Emery were invited to present their paper reviewing 'Various Approaches to the Study of Organizations' as an introduction to general discussion. Professor Bennis was invited to prepare his paper on 'Theory and Method in Applying Behavioural Science to

Planned Organizational Change' as a general review of the contributions of social science in industrial organizations. A comparable paper surveying the field of operational research applications to organization and control was also sought, but it transpired that so little suitable work had been published that no author could be found to undertake the detailed research that would be necessary to produce such a paper. The significance of this negative discovery is discussed in Chapter 20.

In addition to these two review papers, a number of contributed papers were invited to describe any current work relevant to organization and control and involving the application of operational research or social science or the two in combination. The twelve papers included here can to some extent be taken as a cross-section of work in the field (or at least of work that people are willing to write about) and also as examples for discussion of the desirability or effectiveness of collaboration.

A disclaimer

This is perhaps an appropriate point for the author of these three linking chapters to make a personal disclaimer. Readers will perhaps have realized already that I do not claim a background ranging evenly across the whole field of operational research and the social sciences, or of both pure and applied research. My background and viewpoint are those of an industrial operational researcher, and if this has not shown through already, I am sure it will in later sections.

To social science readers in particular, I apologize for any irritation that might be produced through my lack of detailed knowledge in their field. However, I make no excuse for attempting the task itself. I have tried to grasp the nettle and write objectively about the whole field, because the task is important and not many are willing to attempt it; because I believe that applied scientists engaged on organizational problems in industry should try to give a lead to the integration of relevant knowledge and research; and because I think that operational researchers in particular, with their considerable entrée to management problems and their potentially powerful interdisciplinary approach, must not shirk their part in this attempt.

The aim of these chapters – as of the book as a whole – is not to close the subject but to open it up; to start a discussion in non-specialist language of the main issues that can unite or divide us. For this purpose I hope any unintended bias or lack of balance in my approach will not prove a serious disadvantage.

I have not been able to separate clearly the various views as expressed at the conference, the views I took to it and came away with, my own and other discussion reporters' reactions to the ideas expressed, and so on. My comments, especially in Chapter 20, are an amalgam of all these things. If some of the comments appear naïve to those expert in particular areas this may be no loss; the comments may genuinely represent current understanding between practitioners and between disciplines, and thus provide a good starting point for further discussion.

If I have been able to show some appreciation of the social science viewpoint, credit is due especially to Professor Herbert Shepard, of Case Institute of Technology, who made many helpful comments on the plans for the conference session and on my chapters.

The review papers: preview and commentary

There is little to be said about the paper by Professor Bennis other than to advise operational research practitioners in particular, 'Read it, read it, read it!' The bibliography offers a guide to extensive further reading.

To some, the phrase 'planned change', used to describe a specialized area of applied science, may seem pretentious. After all, many kinds of change are planned in all walks of life, and the operational research man might feel he was often concerned with the planning of changes which had nothing to do with human behaviour. However, the operational research man should remember that, to non-operational-research men, the phrase 'operational research' itself sometimes sounds all-embracing and presumptuous. If we remember that either phrase is used simply as a convenient label, perhaps we can avoid 'emotional blocks'.

The paper does not, of course, claim to cover the whole range of applied social science; Professor Bennis introduced it as a 'slender slice of the field, omitting a wide range from rural sociology to applied economics'. Nevertheless, it does cover a very large part of the area of most interest to operational research men in industrial organizations. As the title implies, the paper is mainly concerned with the process of change in the organization rather than the 'normative' question of what to change to; however, there is a very clear treatment of the latter which indicates that most 'change agents' accept the desirability of some form of 'participative' management as described by Likert, McGregor, and others.

This apparently greater emphasis on the process of change than on the nature or direction of the change itself may be another stumbling-block to the operational research man. He is accustomed to thinking in terms of a preferred or optimal solution, derived through analysis and discussion, as the primary objective; the process of change involved in implementing this solution, however time-consuming and difficult it may be, is nevertheless a by-product of that objective.

It seems sensible enough to worry first about the destination, and only after this to choose the route; the operational research man may wonder why the applied social scientist does not have the same outlook.

One possible explanation is that the main human relations problems occur in conditions of change, whereas the main logistic or non-human problems relate to periods of stability. But this is unconvincing; Likert and many others indicate the importance of good 'patterns of management' and attention to human relations in the 'steady-state' condition; many logistic problems are most critical during periods of technological or market change. More likely is the explanation that the social scientist, dealing with more difficult and less tangible material than the operational research man, is that much more cautious; he tries to move step by step in the right general direction, rather than boldly attempting to define where, ideally, he would like to be. Also, paradoxically, the operational research man finds it more difficult to treat analytically the transient period (of change) than the steady state.

If at first this difference seems to increase the gulf between the operational research man and the social scientist it also gives further reason why they should come closer together. Increasingly, as the operational research man digs deeper into the complexities of management systems and management problems, he finds more situations where he must settle for evolutionary movement in the right direction rather than an optimal solution. Increasingly, social scientists are trying to define the appropriate steady-state conditions for effective management, in particular task environments. If both will struggle to understand each other's basic philosophies they may well find this an aid in their own work – quite apart from the prospect of collaborative studies, which will be discussed again in Chapter 20.

Another factor which may be linked with the social scientist's emphasis on change is undoubtedly linked with the circumstances in which organizations seek help from 'change agents'. As summarized in the conclusions of Bennis's paper, these would appear to be twofold. First, the organization has major change forced upon it by changes in the market, technical, or other environment, and needs help to cope with them in the most effective way. Second, there is a general appreciation that 'participative' forms of management meet the needs of the times, and are therefore likely to be more effective than more 'authoritarian' methods. It seems likely that the former consideration plays a larger part in the mind of the organization management at the outset, and the latter in the mind of the change agent, but that before serious work goes ahead there is general agreement between them on both points.

It is, of course, possible to restructure the second need in terms of the first. Instead of saying that the present social climate is such that it calls for a more participative form of management than exists in many organizations – thus relating our studies strictly to the present and the future – we can say that the changes in the social environment which have been and are going on are in fact forcing change upon the organization, and that this change also is one which it needs help to cope with. There is a subtle difference here between speaking of the desirability and of the inevitability of change. Here again is material for the operational research man to ponder. His own downgrading of the 'change' part of his work may be linked with the 'commonsense' view (perhaps analogous to the 'set-up cost' and 'learning curve' concepts of industrial engineers) that all change costs time, effort, and money, and should be avoided unless the end-result aimed at can be shown to be better than the present state by an amount significantly greater than this cost. He may, therefore, be a little apologetic and defensive about the changes he recommends. It might sometimes be more productive for him to think of himself instead as a kind of 'change agent', helping management to cope with the inevitable changes forced on them by the rapid rate of change of social, technological, and economic factors in the world generally – including the availability of new aids to decision-making.

If this appeared to be a valid concept, then he would indeed find himself very close in philosophy to the applied social science of which Bennis writes. Let us hope that the Bennis paper will be discussed by operational researchers and social scientists working in industry.

The paper by Professor Churchman and Dr Emery does not describe or review work in organizations, but tackles the fundamental question of the philosophical background to the applications of operational research and/or social science in organizations. It shows that many of the problems of operational researchers and applied social scientists within organizations are similar – especially the question of which values and objectives to work to. The operational researchers and social scientists approach the task with the values of their own scientific communities or maybe the scientific community at large; the organization has its own sets of values which have been developed to reconcile the objectives of the individuals making up the organization with the objectives implicit in their job roles and the aims of the organization as a whole. Operational research values will normally require, for example, that a 'rational' balance be struck between the relative achievement of the various corporate objectives of the organization, such as productivity or profitability, on the one hand, and morale or employee satisfaction, on the other. The social scientist may put less emphasis on productivity but go further in the other direction, since his values will probably require him to consider the interactions of the members of the organization with society at large.

To the operational research practitioner, the approach here may seem over-simplified. There are many other professional groups besides scientists who have their own values which interact with those of the organization – for example, accounting, sales, production, engineering. Some of these have professional values almost as strong as those of, say, the scientific community. A major difference is perhaps that the applied scientists have a greater urge to understand and to *change* the organization as a whole than have the other professions, which may be more concerned with the *status quo*. An interesting question is where, for example, the general manager and the production manager respectively stand on this issue. One might assume perhaps that the general manager must be committed to change wherever it can be shown to be beneficial. It is not so clear that this is always true of the production manager – it may depend on the professional group which he feels himself to belong to. Some production managers may feel that their main job in life is to continue operating their present facilities efficiently, tidily, and without obvious waste. Others may feel that their main job is to initiate improvement of the facilities and their operation. The values of such professional groups within the organization can be as important in the application of operational research and social science as are the overall values of the organization.

We must look particularly to the social scientists to show us more clearly how best to unify the values of all these groups, and how we can ensure a continuous meeting of minds over principles and objectives between the scientific groups concerned with organizational studies and the top management of the organization concerned.

Top management needs to understand not only the separate aims and methods of the social sciences and of operational research but also the interactions between them which are rich with potential benefits.

C

5 : Theory and Method in applying Behavioural Science to Planned Organizational Change

WARREN G. BENNIS

The nature of planned change

THE NOTION OF PLANNED CHANGE

Planned change is a method which employs social technology to help to solve the problems of society. The method encompasses the application of systematic and appropriate knowledge of human affairs for the purpose of creating intelligent action and choices. Planned change aims to relate to the basic disciplines of the behavioural sciences as engineering does to the physical sciences or as medicine does to the biological disciplines.* Thus, planned change can be viewed as a crucial linkage between theory and practice, between knowledge and action. It plays this role by converting variables from the basic disciplines into strategic instrumentation and programmes. In historical perspective the development of planned change can be viewed as the resultant of two forces: complex problems of modern (organizational) society requiring expert help and the growth and viability of the empirical behavioural sciences. 'Behavioural sciences' is a phrase of post-second-world-war vintage coined by the more empirically minded of the profession in order to 'safeguard' the social disciplines from the non-quantitative humanists and the depersonalized abstractions of the econometricists. Typically, the field is thought to contain six disciplines: psychology, sociology, anthropology, political science, history, and economics. Planned change, as it is used here, relies most heavily on the sociological and psychological disciplines.† The process of planned change involves *a change agent*, who is typically a behavioural scientist brought in to help *a client system*, which refers to the target of

* It falls far short of this aim as of today, partly due to the relatively less mature state of the behavioural sciences and even more because of the lack of tradition in the application of the behavioural sciences. (N.B. Refs 1 and 2 refer respectively to the phrase 'Rise of the Rational Spirit' and to the comment on the increase in the proportion of planned change that appear on the Synopsis on p. xiv.)

† For a recent inventory of scientific findings of the behavioural sciences, see Berelson and Steiner:[3] for the best single reference on the philosophical foundations of the behavioural sciences, see A. Kaplan.[4]

change.* The change agent, in *collaboration* with the client system, attempts to apply *operable knowledge* to the client's problems. These four elements in combination: change agent, client system, valid knowledge, and a deliberate and collaborative relationship – circumscribe the class of activities referred to as planned change. The terms are imprecise and somewhat ambiguous, but it is hoped that their meaning will be clarified upon discussion of concrete illustrations.

These four elements also help to distinguish planned change from other forms of change. Planned change differs from 'technocracy' in that it attempts to implement research results and relies more heavily on the relationship between change agent and client system. Planned change differs from most 'coercive' change programmes in that the change agent has no formal power over the client system. Planned change differs from spontaneous and secondary innovations in that it is a conscious and deliberate induction process.

Figure 1 presents a typology where eight species of change may be identified. Along the horizontal axis are shown two variables, dichotomized for convenience: mutual goal-setting and deliberateness of change. Along the vertical axis, power distribution between the change agent and client system is shown: 0·5/0·5 indicating a fairly equal distribution of power, 1/0 indicating a

Figure 1   *Typology of Change Processes*

	Collaborative		*Non-collaborative*	
	Mutual goal-setting		*Goals set by only one or by neither side*	
Power ratio	Deliberate on the part of one or both sides to the relationship	Non-deliberate on the part of both sides	Deliberate on the part of one side of the relationship	Non-deliberate on the part of both sides
0·5/0·5	*Planned*	*Interactional*	*Technocratic*	*Natural*
1/0	*Indoctrinational*	*Socialization*	*Coercive*	*Emulative*

tilted or unequal power distribution. (In other words, in a 0·5/0·5 power ratio each party has the capability of influencing the other; in a 1/0, only one party is susceptible to influence.) 'Valid knowledge' is omitted from the paradigm, since it is for the present subsumed under 'mutual goal-setting'. In a later section we will return to the question of 'operable knowledge' and its relevance to planned change.

* These terms, 'change agent' and 'client system', are awkward, but suitable substitutes which satisfy aesthetic criteria do not come to mind. And these terms are coming into wider usage. See Ronald Lippitt *et al.*[5] for a fuller account of these terms. See also the author's *The Planning of Change.*[6]

Planned change entails mutual goal-setting, an equal power ratio (eventually), and deliberateness on the part of both sides.

Indoctrination involves mutual goal-setting and is deliberate, but involves an imbalanced power ratio. Many schools, prisons, and mental hospitals or other 'total institutions' [7] fall into this category.

Coercive change is characterized by non-mutual goal-setting, an imbalanced power ratio, and only one-sided deliberateness. Coercive change, as we are using the term, may be examplified by thought-control and 'brainwashing' [8].*

Technocratic change may be distinguished from planned change by the nature of the goal-setting. The use of technocratic means to bring about change relies solely on collecting and interpreting data. Technocratic change, then, follows primarily an 'engineering' model: the client defines his difficulties as deriving from inadequate knowledge and assumes that this lack of knowledge is accidental or a matter of neglect – not something that is functional to the system itself. The technocrat colludes in this assumption and merely makes and reports his findings.†

Interactional change is characterized by mutual goal-setting, a fairly equal power distribution, but no deliberateness on either side of the relationship. (*Unconsciously* either may be committed to changing the other in some direction.) Such changes can be observed among good friends, married couples, and in various other non-deliberate transactions among people. Change does occur in such relationships, possibly with beneficial effects, but there is a lack of self-consciousness about it, thus a lack of any definite change-agent/client-system relationship.

Socialization change has a direct kinship with hierarchical controls. Parent–child relationships would be the most obvious example, although the counsellor–camper, teacher–pupil relationships would also be applicable here.

Emulative change takes place for the most part in formal organizations where there is a clear-cut superior–subordinate relationship. Change is brought about through identification with and emulation of the 'power figures' by the subordinates.

Natural change refers to that class of changes brought about with no apparent deliberateness and no goal-setting on the part of those involved in them. Primarily it is a residual category encompassing all accidents, 'quirks of fate', unanticipated consequences, spontaneous innovations, etc.

---

* The distinctions between *Indoctrination* and *Coercive* change are complex. When all is said and done, hospital administrators and P.O.W. commandants may employ similar processes and techniques. There are probably more similarities than would appear obvious between forms of 'acceptable' social influence, such as psychotherapy or teaching, and 'unacceptable' forms, such as 'brainwashing'. This paradigm, like all others, creates an ideal and abstract model to which empirical occurrences do not neatly conform. See my typology of change process. [9]

† See A. Gouldner [10] for a full discussion of the technocrat as change agent.

This typology is crude: in life we can rarely observe these change processes exemplified so neatly. In addition, the distinctions made in it are somewhat arbitrary and certainly not all-inclusive. In order to give the notion of planned change more meaning and substance it might be useful to compare it with some characteristics of operational research.

PLANNED CHANGE COMPARED WITH OPERATIONAL RESEARCH

I enter this discussion with a humility bordering on fear. My knowledge of operational research stems from three sources: lay articles on operational research that one might pick up in popular periodicals such as *Scientific American* or in Schuchman;[11] more recently, and in preparation for this paper, the basic introductory books recommended by operational research professionals; and most of all from operational research 'pros' who occasionally sit across from me at the dining-table at M.I.T. and talk mysteriously and cheerfully about their work in such a way that I hesitate to ask even the most elementary questions, like 'What do you *really* do?' And I ruefully sense a kinship, the mutual incapacity to explain to each other the basic nature of our work. But as I read over some of the literature recently I was encouraged by certain similarities between operational research and what I mean by planned change. It may be useful to discuss these now.

Some similarities between operational research and planned change

Both are relatively *recent developments*. Both were products of the second world war. As I understand it, operational research was 'founded' just before the second world war, developed its status during the war, and flourished thereafter. Planned change, as was true of almost all applied behavioural research, began in earnest following the second world war and was facilitated and promoted by practitioners who learned during the war that science could be practical.* Later on, I will have more to say about the relationship between science and action, but I should stress at this point that, while there have been in the past fruitful liaisons between the behavioural sciences and action in rural sociology, in applied economics, and in clinical psychology – to mention only a few – the quality and quantity of these linkages has taken a significant upturn since the second world war. From a pastime, the application of knowledge became a profession.

Both operational research and planned change are problem-centred, as contrasted with the basic disciplines, which emphasize *concept* or *method*. This is a matter of emphasis, only; for operational research and applied research, in general, have often provided significant inputs to the concepts and methods of their parent basic disciplines. This is not a one-way street.†

* Kurt Lewin, one of the leaders of this group, was fond of saying: 'There is nothing so practical as a good theory.'
† See A. Gouldner[12] for a brilliant exposition on the contributions of applied research to 'pure' theory.

Both operational research and planned change emphasize improvement and optimization of performance. To that extent, they are *normative* in their approach to problems: that is, they attempt to maximize goals under certain conditions.

Both operational research and planned change rely heavily on *empirical science* as their main means of influence. Ellis Johnson [13] points out that the 'majority of practitioners of operations research were trained in the basic sciences rather than in engineering or administration'. Similarly, practitioners of planned change were mostly trained in psychology, sociology, or anthropology. To both, the old maxim 'Knowledge is Power' seems appropriate as a model of action.

Both operational research and planned change rely on a relationship with clients based on *confidence* and *valid communication*.

Both operational research and planned change emphasize a *systems* approach to problems, meaning essentially an awareness of the interdependencies within the internal parts of the system as well as boundary maintenance with its environment.

Finally, both operational research and planned change appear to be most effective when working with *systems which are complex, rapidly changing, and probably science-based.* As Johnson [14] says,

'. . . in those large and complex organisations for whom once-reliable constants have now become "galloping variables" because of the impact of increasing complexity, trial and error must give way to planning, and acceptance of marginal improvement must give way to an organized search for opportunities to make major shifts in the means of achieving organizational objectives. Today, so many industrial and other organizations are so huge, and major operations are so expensive, that a single major "wrong" decision may be fatal; trial and error becomes "trial and catastrophe" '.

These characteristics, then – newness, problem orientation, normative approach, basis in science, collaborative relationship with clients, systems approach, and effectiveness in rapidly changing environments – show some of the points of common interest and approach between operational research and planned change. Let us turn now to some of the differences.

Some differences between operational research and planned change

Perhaps the most crucial difference between operational research and planned change has to do with the *identification of strategic variables*, that is, with those factors which appear to make a difference in the performance of the system under study. The marked difference in the selection of variables must undoubtedly stem from a unique 'frame of reference' which leads to divergent problem definitions. Ackoff and Rivett,[15] for example, classify operational research problems in the following way:

Inventory	Routing
Allocation	Replacement
Queueing	Competition
Sequencing	Search

A similar inventory of problems in the planned-change field would probably include:

Identification of appropriate mission and values	Utilization of human resources
Human collaboration and conflict	Communication between hierarchical ranks
Control and leadership	Rapid growth
Coping with and resistance to change	Management and career development

The divergence of problem definition leads to the selection of different variables. Operational research practitioners tend to select economic or engineering variables; most certainly variables which are quantitative, measurable, and which appear to be linked directly to the profit and efficiency of the system. Not so of the planned change practitioners. While there are vigorous attempts to measure rigorously and to conduct evaluation studies, the variables selected tend to be less amenable to statistical treatment and mathematical formulation. Upon even a superficial perusal of some of the literature on planned change and operational research, the difference is evident: a significantly lower ratio of tables and mathematical formulae in the former.

An interesting example of the difference in variable identification and selection can be seen if we compare an example of operational research with an example of planned change. Ackoff and Rivett, in their introductory chapter, report a case where operational research was called on to help a major commercial airline to decide on how often it should run a class for stewardesses and how large the class should be. This study led to a study of the following factors: cost of running the school, forecasts of future requirements, forecasting procedures, expenses and salaries of all personnel, maximum possible average number of flying hours per stewardess that could be obtained, factors in stewardesses' job satisfaction, the number of reserve stewardesses required at each air base, the number of bases and where they should be located, how flights should be assigned, etc., etc. As Ackoff and Rivett conclude:

'What originally appeared to be a simple and isolated problem turned out to be interconnected with almost all other operating problems of the airline. With extension of the problem the solutions to the parts could be interrelated to assure best overall performance. This avoided a "local" improvement which might result in overall loss of efficiency.'

Compare the airline's case with a report of C. Sofer, a sociologist who employs techniques of planned change as a social consultant to a variety of organizations. A small firm called upon him to help in the selection of a senior manager.* This 'presenting symptom' led to a series of disclosures and causal mechanisms which Sofer uncovered during a series of talks and meetings with the top management group. The case itself unravelled a complicated cat's cradle of factors including family relationships (among the top management group), fantasies and mistrust among members of the management group, management and career development, selection procedures, etc. Sofer helped the firm to overcome these problems through counselling, through devising new organizational structures, through a training programme, and through developing improved selection devices. The case was completed in about three years, with follow-up consultations from time to time.

When we compare the two cases, what differences appear? First and foremost, as we said before, the problem identified as crucial for the success of the enterprise. In the case of operational research, the problems identified appear to be more concrete, more measurable, and more obviously related (at least in the short run) to the success of the enterprise, i.e. profits and loss. Sofer identified problems and variables which were less measurable, more subjective in that they were *felt* as problems by the participants, and less obviously linked to the firm's success.

But beyond this, there appear to be some equally marked differences in their approach to organizational change. In the example given by Sofer,[17] he concerns himself directly with his relationship to the client, studies this very carefully, and attempts to 'use' this relationship both as a diagnostic instrument and as a training device. Even apparently 'trivial' decisions, such as whether or not to have lunch with his clients, come under scrutiny:

'My staying to lunch was consistent with what is now a not uncommon Institute [Tavistock] pattern of associating to a certain degree with "clients" outside the professional situation as strictly defined. Not to do so would seem unnatural to them and highly discrepant from the ordinary conventions of business relationships to which they are accustomed. There is also the more positive reason that through such association clients are more likely to remain reality-oriented in their perceptions of the social consultant and to regard him simply as another human being who brings a particular type of expertise to bear on their problems.'

So a second major difference between operational research and planned organizational change has to do with the *perceived importance* of the *relationship with the client*. The development and maintenance of this relationship is a crucial element in all planned change programmes. And *not* solely, or even more importantly, for 'good human relations'. Instead, the quality and the

---

* This example is taken from Sofer's *Organization from Within*.[16] We will return to this book later on when we take up the strategy and theory of planned organizational change.

nature of the relationship are used as indicators for the measure of progress and as valid sources of data and diagnosis. This is not to say that operational research practitioners do not concern themselves with matters of this kind. Undoubtedly they do; and probably the most successful of them operate with great sensitivity towards their clients. But if one looks at what they *say* about their work there is no question that practitioners of planned change are clearly more *self-conscious* and concerned with the human interactions between client and change agent.*

A third major difference can now be identified. In the airline case, the operational research practitioner devoted the majority of his time to *research*, to problem-solving. In the case Sofer presents, while there was some research effort and data-gathering, perhaps slightly more time was spent on *implementation through programmes* of one kind or another: counselling, training programmes, selection procedures, management development schemes, etc.

A fourth major difference has to do with the degree to which operational research and planned change practitioners take seriously the idea of a *system* in their approaches. Though I said earlier that both were systems-oriented, it seems that this is less stringently upheld in most cases of planned change. Sofer dealt almost exclusively with the top management group, and though the actions taken may have 'percolated' down to lower echelons, there is a wide zone of uncertainty regarding the effects of this programme on other parts of the system. In a case of Argyris,[18] which will be discussed later on, we will see how a particular change programme in only one part of the system may create negative disturbances and unanticipated consequences on other parts of the system.†

Two other differences should be mentioned before going on. First, the idea of an interdisciplinary team, so central to operational research, does not seem to be a part of most planned change programmes. Usually, only one or two men work on a programme. It is true that these change agents are themselves 'generalists' and are capable of bridging disciplines. Yet it is a lack, compared with operational research. Many times, for example, an economist or an engineer would add significantly to the change agent's skills – particularly as they relate to the measurement of effectiveness and performance variables.‡

One thing that emerges from a study of these two approaches to organizational change is a realization of the complexity of modern organizations. Look through the kaleidoscope one way and a configuration of the economic

---

* It may be that the extent to which science and instrumentation can be used in effecting change is directly and inversely proportional to the use of personal elements of the relationship. We will return to this speculation later on.

† See Bavelas and Strauss,[19] for a classic case where positive change in one part of a system created such perturbations in adjacent parts of the system that the entire programme was scrapped.

‡ Another factor may be that there is a greater homogeneity of theory among operational research practitioners. I do, however, mistrust this observation, no matter how valid, based on a fundamental law of social perception, i.e. the 'others' always seem more alike to the 'outsider' – the 'Well, they all look alike to me . . .' response to the natives.

and technological factors appears; tilt it and nothing appears except the pattern of external environment surrounding the firm. Tilt it again, and what emerges is a pattern of the internal human relations problems confronting the organization. The practitioners of planned organizational change more often than not tend to focus on these last-named human factors and their effects upon the performance of the system.*

A FOCUS OF CONVENIENCE FOR PLANNED ORGANIZATIONAL CHANGE

So far, I have discussed planned change in its broadest context without carefully distinguishing it from applied or developmental research in general. Let us turn to that task now and develop what George Kelley refers to as a 'focus of convenience' for planned organizational change. Earlier, I defined planned change as a deliberate and collaborative process involving a change agent and client system which are brought together to solve a problem, or, more generally, to plan and attain an improved state of functioning in the client system by utilizing and applying operable knowledge.† This is still a vague and general definition, and I will have to make two aspects of it clearer, particularly the notion of a 'collaborative relationship' and that of 'operable knowledge'.

I have implied in the last section that the outcome of a planned change effort depends to some extent on the relationship between the client and the change agent. So let us turn, first, to that. Criteria for evaluating the nature and quality of this relationship can be based on the following questions: (*a*) How well is the relationship understood and veridically construed by both parties? (*b*) To what extent do both parties determine the course and fate of the planned change programme? (*c*) To what extent is the relationship open to examination and reconstruction by one or both parties? In other words, a deliberate and collaborative relationship can be optimized in a planned change induction only when the following conditions are met:

(*a*) a joint effort that involves mutual determination of goals;
(*b*) a 'spirit of inquiry' – a relationship that is governed by data publicly shared;
(*c*) a relationship growing out of the mutual interaction of the client and the change agent;

---

* This is not the place to elaborate some of the issues involved in the identification of variables *internal* to the system or *external* to the system. This has been one of the pivotal issues dividing economists from social psychologists and other so-called 'human relationists'. It is not unlike the debate Arthur Koestler wrestles with in his distinction between the Yogi and the Commissar, between those who turn *inward* for insight, for therapy, for nirvana, and those who turn *outward* to the external environment for the location of variables of promise. This distinction seems to have lost a good deal of its impact recently owing almost primarily to the work of the Tavistock groups, particularly Emery and Trist,[20] as well as A. T. M. Wilson,[21] who have brought the *environment* and boundary-maintenance back into the mainstream of organizational theory and research.

† For a fuller treatment of some of these ideas, see my article in *Administrative Science Quarterly*.[22]

(*d*) a voluntary relationship between change agent and client, with either free to terminate the relationship after joint consultation;

(*e*) a relationship where each party has equal opportunities to influence the other.

Now, what is meant by 'operable knowledge'? Generally speaking, the criteria for operable knowledge are based on the requirements for viable applied behavioural science research. They include the following: an applied behavioural science that

(*a*) takes into consideration the behaviour of persons operating within their specific institutional environments;

(*b*) is capable of accounting for the interrelated levels (person, group, role, and larger organization) within the context of the social change;

(*c*) includes variables that the policy-maker and practitioner can understand, manipulate, and evaluate;

(*d*) in specific situations can allow selection of variables most appropriate to a specific planned change in terms of its own values, ethics, and moralities;

(*e*) accepts the premise that groups and organizations as units are as amenable to empirical and analytical treatment as the individual;

(*f*) takes into account external social processes of change as well as the interpersonal aspects of the collaborative process;

(*g*) includes propositions susceptible to empirical test, focusing on the dynamics of change.

The definition and criteria for planned change presented here must be construed as an arbitrary goal and not as an existing reality. To my knowledge, there is no programme which fulfils these requirements completely. This realization raises the final consideration in this focus of convenience: the arbitrary selection of those change agents working on organizational dynamics. This particular class of change agent was selected not only because of my greater familiarity with their work but for two other factors as well.

(*a*) First, they seem to fulfil the criteria outlined to a greater extent than any other change agents.*

(*b*) Equally important in the choice of emphasis is the belief that changes in the sphere of organizations – primarily *industrial* – in patterns of work and

---

* There are others, from an assortment of fields, who undoubtedly deserve discussion here but have to be omitted primarily for space reasons. I am referring to the work of rural sociologists such as Loomis and Sower (see E. M. Rogers[23] for a recent summary of this work); to community and hospital and psychiatric change agents such as Caplan, Lindemann, S. Levine, L. Howe, B. Paul, D. Klein, the Cummings, and the Rapoports; to applied anthropologists working on directed culture change such as Holmberg, Goodenough, Kimball, Barnett; and to those change-oriented economists: Hagen, Hoselitz, Rosenstein-Rodan, and Eckaus. Each of these branches implies a research and theoretical tradition which falls beyond the scope of this paper but which will be touched on briefly in the next section.

relationships, in structure, technology, and administration, promise some of the most significant changes in our society.*

Planned organizational change in perspective

It is important at this juncture to recognize some aspects, theoretical, social, and historical, of planned organizational change which may not be obvious to the general reader and which should be illuminated before going on to the main portion of the paper.

RELATIONSHIP BETWEEN SYSTEMS OF KNOWLEDGE AND ACTION

It is probably true that in the United States there is a more practical attitude towards knowledge than exists elsewhere. [25] Harrison Salisbury was impressed with the disdain European intellectuals seem to show for practical matters. Even in Russia, he reported, where one would least expect it, there is little interest in the 'merely useful'. [26] He was struck during his recent travels by the almost total absence of liaison between research and practical application. He saw only one great agricultural experimental station on the American model. In that case, professors were working in the fields. They told Salisbury: 'People call us Americans.'

There may not be many American professors working in the fields, but they can be found almost everywhere else: in factories; [27] in the government; [28] in underdeveloped countries; [29] even in backward areas of the United States; [30] in mental hospitals; [31] on international matters; [32] in educational systems; [33] and in practically all the institutional crevices that Ph.D. candidates can worm their way in. They are advising, counselling, researching, recruiting, developing, consulting, training, and working for the widest variety of clients imaginable. This is not to say that the deep ambivalence which Americans have towards the intellectual has disappeared – witness the recent nomination of Goldwater – but it does indicate that the academic intellectual has become *engagé* with spheres of action in greater numbers, with more diligence, and with higher aspirations than at any other time in history.†

The behavioural sciences have been directly implicated in this trend. Recent additions to the vocabulary of the behavioural scientist, which reflect this,

---

* I do not exclude socialist societies from this statement. As Parsons pointed out, the one common feature between so-called capitalist systems and socialist systems is the presence of bureaucracy. In the United States it is my guess that industrial bureaucracies are the most radical, innovative, and adventurous in adapting new ways of organizing – far ahead, it seems to me, of the government, universities, and trade unions, who appear rigid and stodgy in the face of rapid change. Industrial bureaucracies, at least in the United States, are acting with a verve and imagination regarding rapid change which, I wager, will not only be copied but will also be a model for future organizational change programmes in other institutions. For an elaboration of this point, see P. Slater and the author's paper 'Democracy is Inevitable.' [24]

† To the point where other intellectuals have questioned this hyperactivity on behalf of the 'Establishment'. See L. Baritz [34] for one such statement.

are the following terms: clinical sociology, policy sciences, action research, action anthropology, change agents, social catalysts, human and social engineers, sociotherapy, milieu therapy, knowledge centres, and others. Also, within the past three years, the three primary professional associations of psychology, sociology, and anthropology have been devoting more and more annual meeting time to the problems of application and utilization. The University of Michigan's Institute of Social Research has within the year added a third major division under Floyd Mann's direction: a Center for the Utilization of Scientific Knowledge. There has also been a growing literature on planned social change through the uses of the behavioural sciences.[35] Finally, a more subtle trend can be detected; a growing concern with normative planning, with new forms of social architecture, with 'realistic' and 'vivid' utopias, with more radical assumptions about social values.[36]

These signs and activities all point in the same direction: towards an emerging *action* role for the behavioural scientist. The *manipulative standpoint*, as Lasswell calls it, is becoming distinguished from the *contemplative standpoint* and is increasingly ascendant in so far as knowledge utilization is concerned.*

SOME REASONS FOR THE EMERGENCE OF THE ACTION ROLE

It may be useful to speculate about the reasons for this shift of emphasis, this tendency towards a more direct role of action, intervention, and manipulation on the part of the behavioural scientist. Most important, but trickiest to identify, are those causative factors bound up in the warp and woof of 'our times and age' what is often known as the *Zeitgeist*. There has been a shift in the intellectual climate of opinion, perhaps aroused by the threat of atomic destruction and reinforced by the exigencies of our time. 'The world community of scientists', according to C. P. Snow,[39] 'has a final responsibility upon it – a greater responsibility than is pressing on any other body of men. . . . I cannot prove it, but I believe that, simply because scientists cannot escape their own knowledge, they won't be able to avoid showing themselves disposed to good.' And from my own vantage point, more and more behavioural scientists are committed to action programmes and research projects of significance, pertaining to war and peace, problems of Negro–White relations, problems of economic development, etc. So there seems to be a growing disenchantment with the moral neutrality of the scientist and a willingness to risk scientific method on urgent social problems.

Related to shift in *Zeitgeist*, and possibly caused by it, may be a general tendency to regard the applied social sciences with less condescension. To be sure, 'pure' research still implies that applied research is somehow 'impure';

* It is beyond the scope of this paper to discuss some of the *value* implications of the manipulative standpoint. Certainly, science suffers when it becomes the servant of any higher authority. And though it is alive with problems, unless we can discover ways of utilizing science to influence policy formulations without losing its soul, then science cannot realize its full potential. For excellent discussions of the 'value' issues, see A. Kaplan,[37] whose point of view I follow, and Benne and Swanson.[38]

but while still not as honorific as pure research, applied or action research does not carry the same opprobrium it once did.

A third reason for this shift of emphasis, perhaps the most crucial, is simply that we know more. Since the second world war, when the results of applied research could not be brushed aside, and following post-war developments, when the impetus for application accelerated, we have obtained large bodies of research and diverse reports on the application of research. Writing in 1951, Merton and Lerner [40] commented on the lack of codified and systematic experience on application. Today, we are in a better position to assess the results and potentialities of applied social sciences precisely because there are more complete reports and analyses available to us.*

Finally, we must mention a fourth factor which has played a key role in the action orientation of the behavioural scientist and which will be of special concern to us throughout the paper. It has to do with the fate and viability of human organization, particularly as it has been discussed and conceptualized as 'bureaucracy'. I use that term in its true sociological sense, not as an epithet or a metaphor *à la* Kafka's *The Castle* to connote 'red tape', impotency, inefficiency, and despair. Bureaucracy, as a form of government, was developed in order to co-ordinate the divisions of labour brought about by the Industrial Revolution and in order to bring order, precision, and rationality to man's burden. To Max Weber, we owe a tremendous debt, for it was he, more than any other scholar, who saw and conceptualized the idea of this form of organization. In a telling passage he likened bureaucracy to a machine (like a computer) and wrote: 'Organisation is like a modern judge who is a vending machine into which the pleadings are inserted together with a fee and which then disgorges the judgement together with its reasons mechanically derived from the code.' †

In the past three decades Weber's vision of organization has been increasingly scrutinized and censured. Not only by practitioners who are facing, first-hand, some problems that current practices and policies of organization cannot cope with but by the behavioural scientists as well. On page 38 above I presented an inventory of organizational problems as perceived by the managers. A catalogue of problems and short-comings of bureaucracy, as perceived by the behavioural scientists, would include the following:‡

(*a*) It does not adequately allow for personal growth and the development of mature personalities. [43]

* During the writing of this paper, for example, the Foundation for Research on Human Behavior sponsored a conference on 'Organizational Change and the Behavioral Sciences'. Over a period of five days, about a dozen behavioural scientists and an equal number of industrial practitioners concerned with organizational improvement, reported on change programmes utilizing the behavioural sciences. These papers are currently being edited for publication by D. Zand and P. Buchanan. [41]
† This passage was cited in Bendix's intellectual protrait of Max Weber, a book I recommend to all who would like to become more familiar with Weber's contributions. [42]
‡ Note the similarity and overlap.

(b) It develops conformity and 'group-think'.[44]

(c) Its systems of control and authority are hopelessly outdated.[45]

(d) It does not take into account the 'informal organization' and the emergent and unanticipated problems of the human side of the enterprise.[46]

(e) It cannot adequately cope with rapid change.[47]

(f) It has no adequate juridical process.[20]

(g) It may not be the optimum organization for 'turbulent environments.'[48]

(h) It has inadequate and 'dysfunctional' means for resolving differences and conflicts between ranks, and most particularly, between functionary groups.[49]

(i) The full human resources of the organization are not being utilized owing to mistrust, fear of reprisals, etc.[50]

(j) It cannot assimilate the influx of new technology or of scientists entering the organization.[51]

The general meaning of this list should be clear: managers and practitioners, on the one hand, and organized theorists and researchers, on the other, are dissatisfied with the current practices of organizational behaviour and are searching for new forms and patterns of organizing work. However wrong their diagnosis may be (and there is no firm evidence for their prognostications), a good deal of activity and many change programmes are being generated by this impetus to revise and supplement the idea of bureaucracy in the face of these perceived theoretical and practical exigencies.

THE CONTEMPORARY STATE OF THEORIES OF SOCIAL CHANGE

If there is one truth upon which all social theorists agree and can arrive at a quick consensus it is the lack of a viable theory of social change.

Wilbert E. Moore,[52] an intrepid sociologist, says: 'The mention of "theory of social change" will make most social scientists appear defensive, furtive, guilt-ridden, or frightened.'

Kaspar D. Naegele,[53] in the introductory essay on social change in the monumental *Theories of Society*, Vol. II, says: 'At the gate of the study of social change stands a host of half-truths.'

Finally, Martindale[54] reports an admission made by 'leading sociologists that its theory of social change *is the weakest branch of sociological theory*' (emphasis his). He goes on to say:

'This confession by some of the most highly placed persons in American sociology has usually been accompanied by the assurance that sociology's lack of an adequate theory of change is either of no great importance or merely a temporary state of affairs. One cannot but wonder whether this confession and smug reassurance proceed from breath-taking *naïveté* or from an unctuous philistinism.'

Sherlock Holmes was reviewing the case. 'Then, of course,' he reflected, 'there is the curious incident of the dog barking in the night.'

'But,' said Watson, 'there was no dog barking in the night.'

'Precisely, my dear Watson,' said Holmes. 'That is what I find so curious.'

What Holmes might find so curious about the present state of theories of social change – what I find so curious – is that they are silent on matters of *directing* and *implementing* change. What I object to – and I include the 'newer' theories of neo-conflict,[55] neo-functionalism,[56] and neo-evolution-ary theories[57] – is that they tend to identify and explain the dynamic inter-actions of a system without providing a clue pertaining to the identification of strategic leverages for alteration. They are theories suitable only for *observers* of social change, not theories for *participants* or practitioners of social change. They are theories of *change* and not theories of *changing*.

PREREQUISITES FOR A THEORY OF CHANGING

According to Robert Chin, a theory of changing must include the following factors:*

1 A theory of changing which provides levers or handles for influencing the direction, tempo, and quality of change and improvement, i.e. variables that are accessible to control. Variables which 'explain' and are causal may be the *least alterable*; hence a science of 'causes' may not be adequate for a theory of changing. For example, we do know that urbanization causes population explosion, but the applied demographer can do little to reduce the birth-rate by manipulating the degree of urbanization. Demographers can, however, control contraceptive materials and information. So, most of all, a theory of changing must include manipulable variables.

2 A theory of changing which can take into account the roles of a change agent and a client system, each with its own system of values, perceptions, and rights of self-determination. For example, in the preceding example it may be that the use of contraceptives in a Catholic country will render this independent variable virtually useless because it conflicts with the client system's values. In addition to manipulability, then, the variable must not violate the client system's values.

3 A theory of changing which can take into account the cost of usage. Prohibitive costs may again rule out a highly controllable and value-resonant variable.

4 A theory of changing which provides a reliable basis for diagnosing the strength and weakness of the conditions facing the client system.

5 A theory of changing which accounts for phases of intervention so that the change agent can develop estimates for termination of his relationship with the client system, self-'take-off' points, etc.

6 A theory of changing which can be communicated with minimum distor-tion to the client system without destroying its effectiveness.

* I am deeply indebted to my colleague, Robert Chin, for many of the ideas here. See his articles.[58] See also A. Gouldner.[59]

7 A theory of changing which can assess its own appropriateness for different client systems.

Such a theory does not now exist, and this probably explains why the change agents, whom we will discuss in the next main section (p. 54), appear to write like 'theoretical orphans'. More important, it also explains why so many change programmes based on theories of social change have been inadequate. Let us turn now to some of the most commonly used models of knowledge utilization and assess their effectiveness.

TRADITIONAL CHANGE PROGRAMMES BASED ON SOCIAL KNOWLEDGE

The term 'traditional' is used here because it describes the thinking of most scholars concerned with adapting knowledge to social change programmes. I would also wager that these so-called traditional ideas are accepted as conventional wisdom and 'common sense' in our society. I shall describe eight of the most commonly used programmes and then question the assumptions on which they are based.

Eight types of change programme*

It is possible to identify eight types of change programme if we examine their strategic rationale: exposition and propagation, elite corps, human relations training, staff, scholarly consultations, circulation of ideas to the elite, development research, and action research.

Exposition and propagation may be the most popular type of change programme. It rests almost entirely on the assumption that knowledge is power, that ideas change the world, and that the men who possess Truth will ultimately lead the world. Myrdal [61] presents the case for this method:

> 'My thesis is that, while there was little participation on the part of social scientists in the actual technical preparation of legislation and still less in administering induced social change, *their influence was due in the main to their exposition and propagation of certain general thoughts and theories*' (emphasis added).

Elite corps programme is based on the idea of 'getting the *right man* in the job'. Perhaps the best-known contemporary version of this programme is the one advocated by C. P. Snow [62]: Get scientists in government. And in a recent *Encounter*, R. H. S. Crossman [63] writes in a manner supporting Snow. The elite corps idea grows from the justified realization that ideas by themselves (exposition and propagation) do not constitute action and that a strategic *role* (Civil Service, M.P.) is a necessity for ideas to be implemented.

---

* For a fuller exposition of these ideas, see my paper, 'A New Role for the Behavioural Sciences: Effecting Organizational Change'. [60]

A version of the elite corps idea can be observed in a good deal of the writings in the 'human relations' training field. It is similar to the elite corps idea in that it depends upon the knowledge and skills of men in power positions; its difference lies in the type of knowledge it requires of the elite. The programme of *human relations training* hopes to inculcate key executives with necessary insight, wisdom, and diagnostic sensitivity. In other words, human relations training attempts to translate concepts from the behavioural sciences in such a way that they take on personal referents for the executives.*

The idea of *staff* is to provide a source of intelligence within the client system so that the appropriate intelligence is available when needed. As Myrdal [66] says, the strategy of the staff idea: 'is to observe and to analyse actual situations and short and long term developments and, on this basis, to plan rationally the immediate policy reactions to events of a government, an interest organization, or a business firm.'

Examples of staff are the work of social anthropologists advising military governors after the second world war, staff work in large organizations, etc.†

Zetterberg [67] uses the phrase *scholarly consultations* to describe a procedure whereby science can be made useful to clients. It includes exploratory inquiry, scholarly understanding, scholarly confrontation, discovery of solutions, and, finally, scientific advice to the client. It is an unusual approach compared with the others. For rather than taking a research orientation towards the client's problems, the adviser considers the problem in terms of available sociological theory and literature and deduces solutions from combinations of propositions already known.

A strategy which can be called *circulation of ideas to the elite* is based on a very early idea in American history. The American Revolution, according to historians, was partly triggered by the Council for Correspondence, a remarkable chain letter linking the recipient rebels to a programme of action. The idea is simple: 'If you want to change things, then get your ideas to the people in power, or people who influence someone who can influence someone in power.'‡

The idea of a *developmental research*, as a counterpart to the developmental research of the research and development laboratories was advanced recently by Mason Haire: [69]

'The one thing which, more than any other, seems to keep the social sciences from being socially useful is the lack of developmental research. By "developmental research" I mean a kind of work midway between the

---

* In addition to human relations training, some advise forms of psychotherapy and psycho-analysis for the translation of theory into practice. See Levinson *et al.* [64] and Holt. [65]

† For a survey of the role of staff in administration, see Barnett's *Anthropology in Administration*. [28]

‡ A recent example of this strategy is *The Liberal Papers*, [68] a series of papers inspired by a group of intellectuals who communicated their ideas to a receptive congressional audience.

rarefied aloofness of laboratory tests of theoretical propositions and the somewhat pebble-picking particularity of applied research. It is the research that asks the question, "If this proposition is true in principle, how does it find expression in the operational context of action?" . . . Developmental research would be directed exactly toward the problem of helping people to see, given new theoretical insights, *how* something could be done substantially differently or better.'

Like Zetterberg's scholarly confrontation method, developmental research has to do with seeing whether an idea can be brought to an engineering stage. Unlike the former method, developmental research is directed towards a particular problem, not necessarily a client, and is concerned more with implementation and programme. (Incidentally, I would wager that *no* developmental research is being done today in the behavioural sciences.)

Action research (or applied research) is the last programme we will discuss that aims to apply the behavioural sciences to improve systems performance. The term was coined by Kurt Lewin, and the best statement of its methods and aims can be found in an article by three of his followers.[70] 'It is a field,' according to them, 'which developed to satisfy the needs of the socio-political-individual who recognises that, in science, he can find the most reliable guide to effective action, and the needs of the scientist who wants his labors to be of maximal social utility as well as of theoretical significance.'

In all but one respect, action research is identical with the traditional functions of applied research; that is, it is research undertaken to solve a problem for a client. What distinguishes action research is the nature of the roles of researchers and subjects in the research endeavour. In the typical applied research project the roles are differentiated and static. In action research the roles may change and reverse. For example, it is not uncommon in action research programmes for the subjects to become researchers and for the researchers to engage in action steps in place of the subjects whom they are studying.

Critique of the eight change programmes

Although the eight change programmes differ in objectives, in values, in means of influence, and although each has its own programmatic implications, they are similar in wanting to use knowledge to gain some socially desirable end. Each seems successful or promising, if current usage is any criterion, and each has its avid supporters and detractors. Intrinsic to each of the eight programmes, I believe, is a bias or flaw which can be questioned and which probably weakens its full impact. Four biases are particularly visible.

Rationalistic bias: no implementation of programmes. Present to a greater or less degree in all the schemes is the belief that knowledge equals power. Obviously there is some truth in this. But why should the dissemination o knowledge by itself lead to influence, particularly if the knowledge affects deeply held motives, beliefs, and attitudes, particularly those reinforced by group norms and power blocs? I do not want to minimize the importance of facts and knowledge – certainly, they do play a role in social change; yet in most of the strategies discussed there is an almost total reliance on rationality. Knowledge *about* something does *not* lead automatically to intelligent action, no matter how 'right' the idea. Intelligent action requires *commitment* and *programmes* as well as truth.

Technocratic bias: no spirit of collaboration. Related to the rationalistic bias is the assumption that, if a programme is presented, the client can carry it out with dispatch. We see this most clearly in the strategies related to action research: scholarly consultation and developmental and applied research. Zetterberg,[71] for example, says: 'The client is presented with a translation of the theoretical solutions into the client's language and with references to his specific situation. In short he is told what to do.' But this technocratic approach to planned change rarely works without some form of collaboration between the change agent and the client. And the degree to which collaboration is required is probably related to the type of change anticipated: the more it involves social psychological factors – as opposed to technical – the more collaboration required. Elliott Jaques[72] is worth quoting in this regard:

> 'In practice the problem usually boils down to the relationship between the "expert" and the administrator or the executive responsible. We already know how difficult this relationship becomes even in the domain of the physical sciences and engineer; how much farmers, for example, often resent the intrusion of the government agriculture expert with his new and supposedly superior methods. *How much more difficult does the problem of establishing a satisfactory relationship become, however, where not crops but the changing of human behavior itself become the target of scientific endeavor?*' (emphasis added).

F. L. W. Richardson,[73] the action anthropologist, puts it more strongly: 'One conclusion, however, is certain; namely, a social scientist's success in an action role, similar to that of a practising psychiatrist, often depends more on inter-personal than on rational skills.'

Why are collaboration and interpersonal skills so necessary in facilitating social change? Because any significant change in human organization involves a rearrangement of patterns of power, association, status, skills, and values. Some individuals and groups may benefit, others may lose. Some may view an anticipated change as 'threatening' and reject it, and others may view it as 'enhancing' and embrace it.* In any case, change typically involves risk and fear. The trust and support of the change agent during the period of greatest stress may help to 'ready' the client for the change.

* For the best discussion on 'resistance to change' see ref. 74.

Another crucial reason lies at the foundation of this need for collaboration. It has to do with important value differences between change agents and clients. For the most part, clients are practitioners, managers, men-of-action. Change agents tend to be academicians, scholars, researchers, men-of-contemplation. Inevitably, there are bound to be value conflicts between these two orientations; inevitably, there are bound to be ambivalences, false starts, worries, and concerns about the other party to the relationship. Without an opportunity for these fears and worries to be discussed and 'worked through', without an opportunity for each party to 'test' the competence and confidence of the other, it is doubtful if the change programme can realize its full intent.*

Individualistic bias: no organization strategy. The trouble with those strategies associated with C. P. Snow and G. Myrdal, as well as human relations training programmes, is their assumption that if men in power possess the right ideas they will act in accordance with those ideas. Undoubtedly there is some truth in this, as there is in the rationalistic strategy. But it denies completely the organizational *forces* and *roles* surrounding the individual; in short, this strategy tends to place altogether too much reliance on the individual.

There is a great deal of evidence which questions this assumption. For example, there is simply no guarantee that a wise individual who attains power will act wisely. The noted political scientist Hans Morgenthau [75] (in his review of a book written by an intellectual economic historian who took a highly placed job with the U.S. State Department) writes:

'How could such a mind produce such trash? The answer lies in the corruption of power and the defenselessness of the intellectual in the face of it. The intellectual as a social type is singularly deprived of the enjoyment of power and eminently qualified to understand its importance and what it means not to have it. Thus campuses and literary circles abound with empire-builders, petty politicians, and sordid intriguers – all seekers after power, the substance of which eludes them. When an intellectual finds himself in the seat of power he is tempted to equate the power of his intellect with the power of his office. As he could mould the printed word to suit his ideas so he now expects the real world to respond to his actions.'

* Perhaps the most glaring example in recent history of the failure to develop (or even consider!) the required form of collaboration between client and change agent can be seen in the early work of F. W. Taylor and his colleagues in *Scientific Management*. To this day, in some government bureaux, stop watches – the hated emblem of the 'time and motion boys' – are not allowed to be used by a government industrial engineer. The trouble with Taylor was that he was not *scientific* enough; that is, he did not consider the relationship between the engineer and the client as falling within the domain of scientific management. Another corollary of this can be seen within the Freudian psycho-analytic movement. In the early days, Freud considered it adequate to examine the unconscious of his patients and to tell them what he learned. In some cases he even analysed dreams by mail. It turned out that this was not the way to help patients, at least not permanently. Later on, the analysis of relationship and resistance became the hallmark of successful treatment.

Perhaps *role corrupts*: both the role of powerlessness and the role of power. For example, Unilever Limited, if I understand their management development programme, aims at early selection of talent, an elite corps of bright, young men. But mindful of the fact that bureaucratic norms may corrupt or mistrain the cadre, Unilever attempts to accelerate their progress through the bureaucratic structure and rush them to the top.[76]

The point of all this is that there is no guarantee that placing certain types of people in management – or training them or psycho-analysing them or making scientists of them – leads to more effective action. Psycho-analytic institutes, according to Clara Thompson,[77] are stricken with the same human predicaments as any other organization; scientists act like administrators – or even more so – when they gain power;* and graduates of human relations training programmes tend to act like non-alumni shortly after their return to their organizational base.†

The staff idea, proposed by Myrdal, is limited by the unresolved tensions in the staff-line dilemma noted by students of organizational behaviour. This solution ignores, as well, something touched on earlier: the conflicts derived from the role of the intellectual working in bureaucratic structures. Merton[80] catalogues some of these conflicts in his treatment of the problem. He also suggests that the high turnover of expert personnel in public bureaucracies is not only a matter of *client* dissatisfaction but also the 'product of the cumulative frustrations experienced by the intellectual who has been previously conditioned to a sense of personal autonomy and cannot abide the visible constraints imposed by a formal organisation'.[81]

For all these reasons – organization norms, influence of role pressures, naïveté with respect to power, 'fade-out' effects, value collisions – the idea of getting the right man in the job, the elite strategy has serious drawbacks, primarily because it focuses on the individual and not on the organization.

Insight bias: no manipulability. Many of these strategies, but particularly those associated with human relations training programmes, reflect a bias held by most clinical psychologists: insight leads to more effective functioning. This is a more sophisticated solution than the purely rationalistic model, because insight, though usually ill defined, implies an emotional as well as an intellectual grasp of an issue. My major quarrel is not with the formulation: insight leads to change, though this is presently being challenged by some.[82] What is more serious in the insight approach is the lack of provision of strategic variables, i.e. those accessible to control. How does personal insight get translated into effective programmes of change? It is not obvious that insight leads directly to sophistication in rearranging social systems or in

* See R. Jungk's *Brighter than a Thousand Suns*:[78] e.g. how scientists, such as Oppenheimer, acted more like administrators, forsaking personal and scientific moral imperatives for imperatives of the organization, against their colleagues' expectations.

† This 'fade-out' effect has been frequently commented upon and studied. See Fleishman and Argyris.[79]

making strategic organizational interventions. If anything, planned change depends on the policy-maker's controlling the relevant variables. Insight provides these as far as personal manipulation goes, but the question still remains: how can that lead directly to the external manipulation of social factors?

The foregoing discussion outlines some of the biases that are inherent in traditional models of social change. They will serve as terms of comparison and evaluation in what follows. Now with these preliminary considerations and background factors out of the way, let us turn directly to our main business in hand.

The elements of planned organizational change

THE CHANGE AGENTS

In the edition of the *New York Times* dated 7 October 1963, a large classified ad. was printed announcing a search for 'change agents'. It read:

'WHAT'S A CHANGE AGENT?
A result oriented individual able to accurately and quickly resolve complex tangible and intangible problems. Energy and ambition necessary for success. . . .'

Whatever doubts I had had up to this point about Madison Avenue's gifts of simplification and polish were lost. For I realized then and do now that any description of a change agent I would advance would have to include more factors than 'energy and ambition', though these two are probably also required.

The change agents I have in mind are *professionals*, men who, for the most part, have been trained and hold doctorates in the behavioural sciences. Many of them hold university posts and others work as full-time consultants, but they owe their professional allegiance to one of the behavioural science disciplines.

While change agents are not a very homogeneous group, it may be useful to sketch out in broad terms some of their similarities:

(a) *Their assumptions*. They take for granted the *centrality of work* in our culture, to men and women at work in highly organized instrumental settings such as industries, hospitals, universities. They are concerned with *organizational effectiveness*, however intangibly defined or measured. So they are concerned with improvement, development, and enhancement. While their prescriptions vary, their diagnosis of organizational health pivots on *interpersonal or group relationships* and the implications of these for changes in technology, structure, and task. Although they are aware of these three nonpersonal factors and occasionally focus on them, their main preoccupation is with people and the processes of human interaction.* Along these lines, it is

* Contrast this with another approach, of an engineering type, proposed by Chapple and Sayles,[83] where task, structure, and technology are utilized as independent variables.

important to point out that they are not interested in the changing (or trans-ferring) *personnel*, but the relationships, attitudes, perceptions, and values of the existing personnel.

(b) *Their roles.* They play a variety of roles as change agents: researchers, trainers, consultants, counsellors, teachers, and in some cases as line mana-gers. Some specialize in one, but for the most part, they shift and switch from one to another.

Frequently, the change agents are not actual members of the client system; in other cases they are. There are some who say that significant change depends on the impetus generated by an external agent.[84] They argue that only a skilled outsider-consultant can provide the perspective, detachment, and energy so necessary to effect a true alteration of existing patterns. Advo-cates of the internal model take the opposite stance. They argue that the insider possesses the intimate knowledge of the client system (and the legiti-mization) that the external change agent lacks. In addition, the internal change agent does not generate the suspicion and mistrust that the outsider often does. His acceptance and credibility are guaranteed, it is argued, by his organizational status.*

Change agents tend to be self-conscious about their roles and their role-changes *vis-à-vis* their clients. They go into instructive detail describing their interventions.

(c) *Their interventions.* Change agents intervene at different structural points in the organizations (person, group, inter-group, etc.) and at different times. Blake and Mouton [85] list nine major kinds of intervention which facilitate organizational development:

Discrepancy: Calls attention to a contradiction in action or attitudes.
Theory: Research findings or conceptual understanding which helps the client system to gain perspective.
Procedural: A critique of existing methods of solving problems.
Relationships: Focuses attention on tensions growing out of group and interpersonal relationships.
Experimentation: Setting up comparisons and testing of several actions *before* decision is made.
Dilemma: Identifies significant choice points or exigencies in problem-solving, and attempts to understand assumptions and search for alter-natives, if necessary.
Perspective: An attempt to provide situational and historical understanding of problems through a detached study.

* Thus, General Electric in its change programme uses internal change agents (to gain credibility and to eliminate the typical fear that behavioural scientists are 'headshrinkers', 'brainwashers', etc.). However, these internal men are not placed within their own company department.

Organizational structure: Identifies source of problem as bound in the
structure and organizational arrangements.

Cultural: Focuses on an examination of traditions.

(d) *Their normative goals.* These are stated with varying clarity and specificity,
but there is unmistakable evidence that their goals imply a particular vision
of man and organization and a particular set of values which lay the base for
this version.

To a large extent, these normative goals are aroused by dissatisfaction with
the effectiveness of bureaucratic organizations set out above. These objections were probably most cogently articulated and given the greatest force by
the writings of McGregor, Likert, and Argyris.[86] Their three books are often
cited as 'evidence' and used by change agents as the foundations for various
change programmes.

Though each change agent has in mind a set of unique goals, based on his
own theoretical position and competencies as well as the needs of the client
system, roughly speaking there are some general aims which most change
agents would agree to. Argyris provides a graphic model which can serve us as
an example. In *Figure* 2 [87] he shows (at the far left) the purported value
system which dominates modern organizations; i.e. bureaucratic values.
These values, basically impersonal and task-oriented and denying humanistic
and democratic values, lead to poor, shallow, and mistrustful relationships
between members of the organization. Argyris calls these 'non-authentic'
relationships and they tend to be 'phony', unhelpful, and basically incomplete;
that is, they do not permit the natural and free expression of feelings which
must often accompany task efforts. These non-authentic relationships lead to
a state which Argyris calls 'decreased interpersonal competence', a result of
the shallow and threatening state of the relationship. Finally, without
effective interpersonal competence among the managerial class, the organization is a breeding ground for mistrust, intergroup conflict, rigidity, etc., which
in turn lead to a decrease in whatever criteria the organization is using to
measure its effectiveness.

This is the paradigm: bureaucratic values tend to stress the rational task aspects of the work and to ignore the basic human factors which relate to the task
and which, if ignored, tend to reduce task competence. Managers brought up
under this system of values are badly cast to play the intricate human roles now
required of them. Their ineptitude and anxieties lead to systems of discord and
defence which interfere with the problem-solving capacity of the organization.

Generally speaking, the normative goals of change agents derive in one way
or another (explicitly or not) from this paradigm. Most commonly strived for
are the following:

(*a*) Improving interpersonal competence of managers.

(*b*) Effecting a change in values so that human factors and feelings come to be
considered legitimate.

Figure 2 *The Managerial Grid*

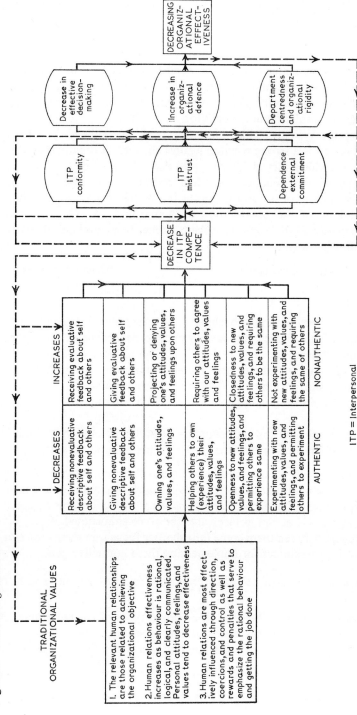

ITP = Interpersonal

(c) Developing increased understanding between and within working groups in order to reduce tension.

(d) Developing more effective 'team management', i.e. the capacity for functional groups to work competently.

(e) Developing better methods of 'conflict resolution'; rather than the usual bureaucratic methods, which include suppression, denial, and the use of naked and unprincipled power, more rational and open methods of conflict resolution are sought for.

(f) Organic systems. This normative goal, as outlined by Shepard and Blake,[88] is a strong reaction against the idea of organizations as mechanisms, which, they claim, has given rise to false conceptions (such as static equilibria, frictional concepts like 'resistance to change', etc.) and worse, false notions of social engineering and change, e.g. pushing social buttons, thinking of the organization as a machine, etc. Organic systems, as Shepard and Blake conceive them,* differ from mechanical systems in the following ways:

Mechanical systems	*Organic systems*
Individual skills	Relationships between and within groups
Authority–obedience relationships	Mutual confidence and trust
Delegated and divided responsibility rigidly adhered to	Interdependencies and shared responsibility
Strict division of labour and hierarchical supervision	Multi-group membership and responsibility
Centralized decision-making	Wide sharing of control and responsibility
Conflict resolution through suppression, arbitration, or warfare	Conflict resolution through bargaining or problem-solving.

Change agents conceptualize and discuss their normative goals in different ways; occasionally they work towards the same goal under different labels and for different goals under similar labels. But allowing for some exceptions, they would probably accept at face value the goals enumerated above. Where the differences between them come into sharper focus is in their choice of instruments or programmes for implementing these normative goals.

PROGRAMMES FOR IMPLEMENTING PLANNED ORGANIZATIONAL CHANGE

Discussion here will focus on three broad types of change programme that seem to be most widely used: training, consulting, and research. Most frequently they are used in some combination depending on the needs of the

---

* Burns and Stalker [89] also develop the idea of organic and mechanical systems in their *The Management of Innovation*. They state, however, in contradiction to Shepard that both may be appropriate under differing environmental and organizational conditions.

client system and the particular skills of the change agent. For our purposes, we shall consider each of them separately.

Training

Training is an inadequate and possibly misleading word to use in this context, since its dictionary meaning denotes 'drill', 'exercise', and the general notion of imparting skills through habit and rote learning. As the term is used here, it has a widely different meaning. It is used here to describe a particular variety of training which has been called laboratory training or education or sensitivity or group dynamics training, and in most quarters T-Group training.* The idea of laboratory training originated at Bethel, Maine, in 1947 under the guidance of L. Bradford, K. Benne, and R. Lippitt, all of whom were influenced by Kurt Lewin. This group shared a common concern for the application of the behavioural sciences to practice and policy. The T-Group emerged as one of the most important components of laboratory training and has evolved over the past eighteen years into one of the main instruments for organizational change. Bradford, as director of the National Training Laboratories, has played a central role in the development of laboratory training; its growth was facilitated through the active participation of a number of university-based behavioural scientists and practitioners.† Its main objective at first was *personal change*, or self-insight. Since the late 1950s or so, the emphasis has shifted away from personal growth to organizational development.‡

As evidence of this shift, more and more laboratory training is conducted for specific organizations, using groups which follow organizational patterns rather than so-called 'stranger labs' where people come together from a variety of organizations and professions.

This is not the place to go deeply into the subject of laboratory training, but it might be useful to say a word or two more about it. It unfolds in an unstructured group setting where the participants examine their interpersonal relationships. The training process relies primarily and almost exclusively on the behaviour experienced by the participants, i.e. the *group itself* becomes the focus of inquiry. Conditions are promoted whereby group members, by examining data generated by themselves, attempt to understand the dynamics

---

* For a popular account of laboratory training as it is used to implement organizational improvement, see Argyris's recent paper in the *Harvard Business Review*.[90] For other writings on the same subject, see Schein and Bennis,[91] Blake and Mouton,[92] and Argyris.[93] For a theoretical background of laboratory training, see the recent book edited by Bradford, Gibb, and Benne.[94]

† The Tavistock Institute has played a similar role in England. Recently a group of European behavioural scientists have set up their own counterpart to the National Training Laboratories in the United States.

‡ I date this more precisely as 1958, because at about this time the Employee Relations Department of the Esso Company, under the leadership of Blake and Shepard, inaugurated a series of laboratory training programmes in their refineries throughout the country. Other companies followed suit, but the original Esso programmes laid the groundwork for future developments. See ref. 95.

of group behaviour; e.g. decision processes, leadership and influence processes, norms, roles, communication distortions, the effects of authority on a
number of behavioural patterns, personality and coping mechanisms, etc. In
short, the participants learn to analyse and become more sensitive to the
processes of human interaction and acquire concepts to order and control
these phenomena.

T-Groups are used in organizations today in the following ways:

Stranger labs. Executives from organizations attend labs as 'delegates'
representing their organization. The parent organization hopes to improve
the organization in this way by 'seeding' a sufficient number of managers.

'*Cousin labs.*' Organizations set up labs for individuals with a similar organizational rank but from different functional groups, e.g. all first-line supervisors
or all general foremen.

'*Diagonal slices.*' T-Groups are composed of members from the same company, but of different ranks and from different departments. No man is in the
same group with anyone from his own work group.

'*Family*' or *Functional groups.* These groups are identical with the intact group
as indicated by the formal organization, i.e. a particular supervisor with his
work group.

Decisions about type of composition of T-Group training are based on a
variety of factors: e.g. the state of organizational development of the client
system; particular exigencies facing the client system, and the competencies
of the change agent. The extent to which laboratory training affects the
organizational value system and structure is related to the T-Group strategy
utilized: the more it approaches the family group, the more the total organizational system is affected.

Consulting

For every type and style of training, there is an equivalent type of consulting.
The type we will be concerned with here is practised by a number of change
agents and is perhaps best exemplified by the work of the Tavistock Institute.*

The change agent *qua* consultant operates in a manner very like the practising physician or psycho-analyst: 'In undertaking my work,' writes Sofer,[98] 'I
entered the same moral order as my respondents, helping them to maintain
what was positive in their situation and to alter what was negative.' So the

---

* The work of Jaques, Sofer, and Rice [96] in particular. Sofer has been the most articulate
in the sense of adumbrating the principles and assumptions behind this style of social
consultancy, so I have used his book, *The Organization from Within*, most profitably for
this paper. Richard Beckhard [97] in the United States has also developed a procedure and
unique style with respect to the role of the management consultant.

consultant starts from the chief 'presenting symptom' of the client, articulates it in such a way that the causal and underlying mechanisms of the problem are understood, and then takes remedial action.

He employs an extensive repertory of instrumentation which he uses as flexibly as possible. Using himself, most of all, he aims to detect and get close to the important 'data', to exploit every encounter he can in order to help the client system to see 'reality'. He uses situations, as they develop spontaneously, to work through the tensions and resistances associated with them. Most of all, he uses *himself* as a *role model*. More important than the expertise and methodological help they can contribute – and it is substantial – is the '*manner* in which my colleagues and I defined and reconceptualized the problems'. To the extent that this role model is emulated by the management group, change can occur.

Heavy emphasis is placed on the strategy of role model because the main instrument is the change agent himself: his skills, insight, expertise. Sofer reveals this when he suggests that psychotherapy or some form of clinical experience in a mental hospital is necessary preparation for the change agent.

Argyris provides an interesting example of change agent *qua* consultant. He writes about two possible reactions displayed by clients when their attempts to 'seduce' him into giving the 'solutions' fail. One is the expression by the executives of sorrow and dismay. Another reaction is their insistence that, since he is the 'expert' consultant, he *should* provide some answers. Argyris [99] writes:

> 'Moreover, if their expectation of the researcher is that he should give some answers, because in the feed-back situation he is the leader, what does this expectation imply concerning what they probably do to their subordinates? Perhaps this indicates that when they (as leaders) make a diagnosis, they feel they must make a prognosis. But if the above analysis is valid, what positive value is a unilateral prognosis? At best it gives their subordinates something to shoot at (just as they are behaving toward the researcher). But as they just experienced, if the leader (in this case, the researcher) is skilled enough to answer all their objections, he succeeds in making the diagnosis *his* and not theirs. Perhaps, this also occurs when they succeed in answering all the questions of their subordinates when they, as superiors, are "selling" a new policy or practice.'

So Argyris, as consultant, confronts the group with their behaviour towards him as an analogue of their behaviour *vis-à-vis* their own subordinates. He continually searches for experiential referents in the existential ('here-and now') encounters with his client system, which can be used as a heuristic for the fuller understanding of the client.

If, from this description, consultancy sounds more ambiguous and vague than the training process this probably reflects reality. Because in the consultant approach the processes of change and the change agent's interventions are less systematic and less programmed than in either the training or the applied research programme. Let us now turn to the latter.

Applied research: the utilization of survey data as feedback

Almost all planned change programmes utilize research results in one way or another. The particular form of applied or action research I am referring to now is where research results are used systematically as an *intervention*. This type of programme was developed primarily by the researchers at the University of Michigan's Institute for Social Research, most particularly by Floyd Mann and his associates.[100] Here is the way it works: survey data are collected and then reported back to the particular departments (subjects) in 'feedback' meetings, where the subjects become clients and have a chance to review the findings, test them against their own experiences, and even ask the researchers to test some of their hypotheses. In contrast with the traditional uses of research of the technocratic variety, where the findings are submitted 'in triplicate' and probably ignored, this method strives for the active participation of the subjects.

In other words, most methods of research application collect information and report it. There the relationship ends. In the survey-feedback approach the collection and reporting of results is only the *beginning* of the relationship. On the basis of the research results – and partly because of them – the involvement and participation in the planning, collection, analysis, and interpretation of more data is activated. Objective information, knowledge of results, is the first step in planned change. But more than intellectual commitment is usually required. The survey-feedback approach is utilized in order to gain this extra commitment *via* active participation in the research process.

Richard Beckhard, too, utilizes data as the first step in his work as a change agent, both as a means of diagnosing the initial state of the client system and as a springboard for discussions with the executive staff. His procedure is very similar to the work of Mann and his associates, except that the data are collected through informal, non-structured interviews, which he then codes by themes about the managerial activities of the client. He then convenes a meeting at an off-site resort with the particular sub-system on whom the data were collected and uses the research headings as the basis for discussion. An example of these themes are the following:

(*a*) communications between president and line (or staff);
(*b*) line/staff communications;
(*c*) location of decision-making;
(*d*) role clarification or confusion;
(*e*) communication procedures. [101]

I should reiterate that most planned change inductions involve all three processes: training, consulting, and researching. In most cases the change agent, himself, tries to utilize all these functions. Some change agents report, however, that they work in collaboration with others and that they divide their functions. For example, Argyris used L. Bradford as trainer and Roger Harrison as researcher.[102] Sofer employed his colleagues at Tavistock to augment the services he could perform. It is also true that some change agents possess distinctive competencies which tend to direct their activities in certain directions.

What should be clear from the foregoing discussions are these three points: (*a*) change agents play a variety of roles; (*b*) clients play a variety of roles: subject, initiator and planner, client, and participant-researcher; and (*c*) the final shape of the change agent's role is not as yet clear, and it is hazardous to describe exactly what they do on the basis of their own reports.*

STRATEGIC MODELS EMPLOYED BY CHANGE AGENTS

In order to gain a deeper understanding of how these change programmes are used in practice, it might be useful to sample some of the strategies employed by change agents. This turns out to be somewhat more difficult than one might think, because change agents more often than not fail to report their strategy or fail to make it explicit – even to themselves. However, two quite different strategic models are available to us, one developed by R. R. Blake in his 'Managerial Grid' scheme and one through some work I was associated with at an Esso Refinery.†

R. R. Blake [103] has developed a change programme based on his analytic framework of managerial styles. On the basis of this twofold analytic framework, it is possible to locate eight types of managerial strategy. One dimension is 'concern for people'; the other dimension is 'concern for production'. As Blake points out, the term 'concern for' represents the degree of concern, not the *actual* production or people activities. *Figure* 3 shows his grid and the eight managerial styles. Blake and his colleagues attempt to change the organization in the 9,9 direction.

In their strategic model employed to induce changes in the direction of 'team management' (9,9), Blake and his colleagues specify six phases, which represent their most thorough and systematic work so far. Their strategy is based on experience with fifteen different factories, ranging in size from 500 to 5,000 employees.

* There are other matters with respect to these three functions which limitations of space make it impossible to more than mention. For example, in *choosing* one particular intervention over another, one would have to consider the following factors: cost, time, degree of collaboration between the change agent and client system required, ease of measurement of effects, state of target system, whether internal or external change agent is required, and the degree to which the programme is 'instrumented' (for example, Blake's change programme is so precisely programmed and 'laid out' that first-level line managers within the client system can conduct their own programme based on Blake's ideas without his presence); and the relationship between the type of change sought and the change indication process.

† It might interest the reader to know that in this case the strategy – if it can be called that – was strictly a *post hoc recapitulation* of what was done. It was not developed by the change agents themselves, but by Chris Argyris, who was asked to evaluate the programme several years after its termination.

D

Phase 1 takes place away from the plant location where factory members are exposed to behavioural science theory (managerial grid, etc.), take part in structural experiments, and participate in face-to-face feedback experiments and sessions of the T-Group variety. All members of the managerial organization participate in the laboratory for a session lasting one or two weeks.

Figure 3   *The Managerial Grid* (after Blake et al.[103])

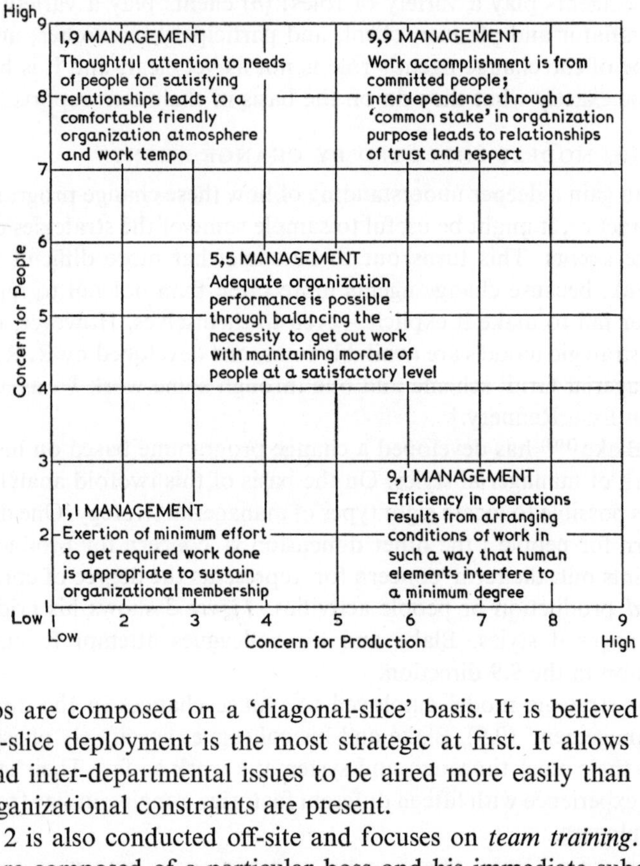

Groups are composed on a 'diagonal-slice' basis. It is believed that this diagonal-slice deployment is the most strategic at first. It allows organizational and inter-departmental issues to be aired more easily than when the usual organizational constraints are present.

Phase 2 is also conducted off-site and focuses on *team training*. Training groups are composed of a particular boss and his immediate subordinates, starting with the top team and reaching lower levels later on. Thus, the unit of grouping is the actual 'family' group, and actual conditions become the focus of analysis. This phase is based on the principle that if organizational change is to take place it must be supported by the actual organizational groupings and must be exemplified and reinforced by top management.

Phase 3 is designed to achieve better *integration between functional groups* and between various organizational divisions, such as staff and line, technical and practical, sales and production, and so on. The normative goal of this horizontal linking is to create an organizational 'culture' which can link relationships and articulate between departments in a more effective way than the bureaucratic model. In this phase pairs of functional groups work together in order to solve the problems that exist between them. First they work as groups apart from each other, testing their image and stereotypes of their own group *vis-à-vis* the other, and identifying obstacles to better integration. Then they get together and attempt to develop better ways for joint problem-solving. This activity takes place, unlike the two previous phases, in the plant location.

Phase 4 gives real meaning to the concept of *planned change* – for it provides the mechanism for insuring that the changes sought after are planned. In this phase groups of ten–twelve managers get together to *set goals for the total organization*. This composition is used at this stage in order to set targets that reflect the variety of forces present in the organization. After this, issues, plans, and goal implementations are discussed by the various groups; they are summarized and used as the basis for an intensive effort towards organizational change.

Blake and his colleagues estimate that the time required for the first four phases, appreciation sessions, team training, horizontal linking, and setting of organizational goals, may be two years or longer. Implementing them may require an additional two years or so.

In Phase 5 the change agent attempts to *help the organization to realize the goals* established in Phase 4. He deals with the organization in much the same way as a psycho-analyst would deal with a patient; in fact, the programme during this phase resembles the consulting approach discussed earlier.

Phase 6, the final one, is directed towards *stabilizing the changes* brought about during the prior phases. Blake estimates this period as taking a year. The role of the change agent is more passive during this period, and he is called upon for help less and less frequently. Rather than living with the client system, he is available upon request. The main effort during this phase is to ensure the maintenance of the present state of functioning.

Figure 4[104] presents another strategy: a recapitulation of a change programme used by a New York headquarters team of a large oil company to improve the functioning of one of its smaller refineries in New England. For some years, owing to certain market changes, the refinery's profits had been declining and there had been talk about closing down the refinery. The first change brought about was the recognition by headquarters that a new manager was needed, with the necessary technical skills and administrative experience *plus* assurance, for the future operation of the refinery (see CHANGES). This man was sent to a T-Group training session in order to gain some AWARENESS of the human problems existing in the refinery. Following this, the N.Y. headquarters' organizational development staff came on the scene and conducted a DIAGNOSIS through a survey and interviews of the total managerial staff (70) and a sample of the hourly employees (40/350). About that time I was asked to consult with and help the N.Y.

headquarters' staff and the refinery manager. Thus, departmental feedback meetings with supervisors were held and a RE-EVALUATION OF NEEDS was taken in co-ordination with the consulting group and top management (which at this point consisted only of the new refinery manager).

Figure 4 *Elements in a One-year Programme in Refinery C*

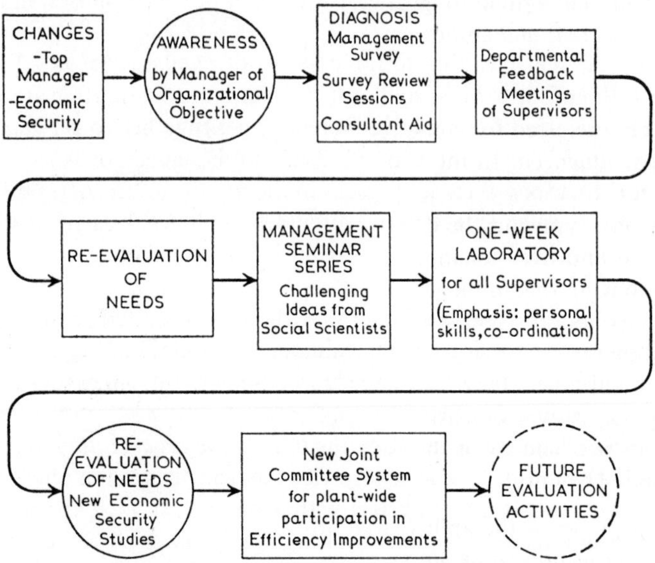

It was decided at this point that a laboratory programme or T-Group might be effective but possibly premature. So a series of weekly seminars were held with the top management group (about twenty executives) focusing on new developments in human relations. Speakers ranged over a wide variety of subjects, going from the Scanlon Plan to individual psychology. Following this a one-week laboratory training programme was held for all supervisors in diagonal slice groupings and then another RE-EVALUATION OF NEEDS was undertaken.

At this point some structural innovations were suggested and implemented. These included a top management committee consisting of all functional managers and a variety of project groupings working on a number of efficiency programmes. During the very last phase of the programme (not shown on the diagram) the Scanlon Plan was adapted and installed at the refinery (incidentally, this was the first time the Scanlon Program was undertaken in a 'process' industry and the first time that a union agreed to the Scanlon Plan without a bonus automatically guaranteed.)

It is difficult to know how typical or unusual these two planned change strategies are – insufficient experience and reports dilute any generalizations that I would hazard – but if they *are* typical, certain features of the strategies can be identified: (*a*) the length of time – Blake estimates five years – the refinery programme up to the point of the Scanlon Plan took two years; (*b*) the variety of programme utilized – research, consulting, training, teaching, planning; (*c*) the necessity for co-operation with top management and the parent organization; (*d*) approaching the organization as a system – rather than as a collection of individuals; (*e*) phasing the programme so that it evolves from individual to group to inter-group to overall organization; (*f*) the intellectual *and* emotional content of the programme.

POWER AND THE ROLE OF THE CHANGE AGENT

I have been interested for some time in the age-old question of how and why people are influenced. In the various planned change programmes discussed the question becomes even more intriguing: how and why do people and organizations change in the direction prescribed? Assuming for the moment that they do improve – change – let us try to examine the role of the change agent in exerting this influence.

Most behavioural scientists agree that power is the ability to influence: so, in effect, power is an independent variable which leads to *influence*, the dependent variable. There is still further agreement, and happily, some evidence, that power consists of at least five components; that is, if said components are held by *A* they can lead to the influence of *B*, other things being equal. They are:

(*a*) *coercive power* or the ability of *A* to reward and/or punish *B*;
(*b*) *referent or identification power* or the influence which accrues to *A* because he (or the group) is attractive, a person whom *B* wants to like and be liked by – in short, a role model;
(*c*) *expert power* or the power that we associate with science and Truth;
(*d*) *legitimate or traditional power*, that is, power which stems from society's norms and practices and from historical/legal traditions;
(*e*) *value power* or influence which is gained on the basis of attraction to the values of *A*.

Which of these five sources of power does the change agent possess? In fact, this is a question we have to guess at and make some inferences about, because the change agents themselves tend to ignore (or are silent about) the sources of their own influence. It is not coercive power; for we can guess with some confidence that unless the change agent is himself a manager or an influential member of the organization, he does not possess the means to exert coercive power. In fact, most change agents are external to the organization and do not hold any formal title. More to the point, the change agents discussed in this paper would prefer, at least intellectually, not to wield coercive power, whether or not they in fact possessed it. This is true for at least two reasons. First, coercive power appears to be at variance with their normative goals and values and, second, there is some evidence that coercive power is not as durable as other types except under conditions of vigilant surveillance over the influenced.[105]

Traditional power? Almost certainly not. The change agents are, in fact, continually working without legitimization. Quite often, they are perceived as odd men out, strangers, as quite marginal to the enterprise (or as a 'committed nut' according to one manager). So little influence redounds to them on the basis of traditional norms and precedent.

Expert power? Possibly some, but it is not obvious that the change agent is perceived as a source of really 'useful' knowledge. True, in varying degrees, he does possess useful information about the human side of the enterprise and about methods of investigating these phenomena. But it is doubtful whether this type of knowledge is considered 'expert' enough – in the sense that an engineer or doctor or lawyer is seen as a source of expertise.

Referent or identification power? Apparently so. Some change agents, like Sofer, talk directly to this point and attribute some indefinite amount of their influence to the client system's ability and desire to emulate the change agent. Still, members will probably identify with the change agent to different degrees and some, perhaps, not at all. By itself, it would appear that identification or referent power would have to work in concert with another source of power.

So that leaves us with value power; and while I cannot prove it, the most likely candidate, it seems, of the possible sources of power, would be this one, the ability to influence through representing and transmitting values which are admired and desired by the client system. Most of the change agents in their work do embody a set of values which are certainly communicated to the client system verbally or otherwise. Argyris makes his own value position very clear, and most of the other change agents tend to emit cues of one kind or another which provide a consistent value system. These values are based on Western civilization's notion of a scientific humanism: concern for our fellow-men, experimentalism, openness and honesty, flexibility, co-operation, democracy.

If what I have said about power is correct it is significant (at least in the United States) that this set of values seems to be extremely potent in influencing top management circles.

CHARACTERISTICS OF CLIENT SYSTEMS

Are there any particular characteristics of client systems? For the most part they appear to be sub-systems of relatively large-scale international operations who find themselves in increasingly competitive situations. Also, they are almost always found in rapidly changing environments. They are subjected to what Johnson called 'galloping variables', not comfortable and stable conditions. Quite often, it appears that the enterprise was founded, developed, and achieved success through a particular innovation or monopolistic advantage which is thought to be in jeopardy. In any case, the type of client system most typically looking for organizational change programmes seems to be eminently appropriate for an organic form of organization *à la* Burns and Stalker.[(106)]

Third, there is always some exigency, dissatisfaction, tension, dilemma, crisis – some discrepancy between the ideal and the actual – confronting the organization which seems to activate the programme. It may emanate from the rapidly changing environment or from the internal processes within the system. Change may be forced upon management through survival fears or from problems connected with growth. Some of the exigency states which have initiated planned change programmes can be observed in a recent seminar on organizational improvement sponsored in July 1964 by the Foundation for Research on Human Behaviour. Seen as causing the change programmes were the following: employee cutbacks and various retrenchment measures, a merger, significant growth and high rates of change, competitive situation worsening, new departures, union–management conflicts and strikes, leadership succession, lack of sufficient management personnel, and a failing product. These problems give some idea of the general range of problems confronting client systems.

One last characteristic of client systems should be mentioned: all of them put some faith in the idea that an indeterminate proportion of their effectiveness is determined by social and psychological factors. Improvements in this sphere of action, they reason, no matter how vague or immeasurable, may be able to bring about an increment in organizational effectiveness.

THE MEASUREMENT OF EFFECTS

Until very recently, change agents, if they did any evaluation research at all, concentrated almost exclusively on attitudinal and subjective factors. Even so-called 'hard' behavioural variables, such as absentee rates, sickness and accident rates, personnel turnover, etc., were rarely investigated. Relating change programmes to harder criteria, such as productivity, economic and cost factors, was rarely attempted and never, to my knowledge, successful.

And again, the research that was conducted – even on the attitudinal measures – was far from conclusive. Roger Harrison[(107)] attempted an evaluation study of Argyris's work and found that, while there was a significant improvement in the individual executive's interpersonal ability compared with a control group, there was no significant 'transfer' of this acuity to the real-life organizational setting. In short, there was a fairly rapid 'fade-out' of effects obtained in a T-Group training upon return to the organization. This study also shows that new tensions were generated between those individuals who attended the training programmes and those who did not, an example of the lack of a *systems* approach that I mentioned early in the paper. Shepard's evaluation [(108)] on the Esso organization shows that the impact of laboratory training was greatest on personal and interpersonal learning, but it was 'slightly more helpful than useless' in changing the organization.

More recently, though, some studies have been undertaken which measure more meaningful, less subjective, criterion variables of organizational effectiveness. Blake and Mouton,[109] for example, 'sub-contracted' out an evaluation study of their work in a very large (4,000 employees) petro-chemical plant. They found not only significant changes in the values, morale, and inter-personal behaviour of the employees but also significant improvements in productivity, profits, and cost reduction. David,[110] a change agent working on a programme that attempts to facilitate a large and complicated merger, attributed the following effects to the programmes: increased productivity and reduced turnover and absenteeism, in addition to a significant improvement in the area of attitudes and subjective feelings.*

While these new research approaches show genuine promise, much more has to be done. The research effort has somehow to equal all the energy that goes into developing the planned change programmes themselves.

SOME CRITICISMS AND QUALIFICATIONS OF PLANNED ORGANIZA-TIONAL CHANGE

The work and direction of the change agents reported here are new, and occur, for better or worse, without the benefit of methodological and strategic precedents. The role of the change agent also is new and still settling; its final shape has not fully emerged. So it has the advantage of freedom from the constraints and pressures facing most men of knowledge and, at the same time, suffers from lack of guidelines and structure. With this as background, let us touch quickly on some problems and criticisms which I see as facing the change agents in the years to come:

Relationship to other social theories of change. The closest approximation to a theory of change is Argyris's systems model. And, again, this is a theory of change, not a theory of changing. The methods of change employed by Argyris and his co-workers seem to be heavily – and justifiably – based on engineering models, heavy on techniques and methods of change, but less strong on a theory of change. Though they cite esteemed sources, like Freud and Lewin, their formulations do not really figure in their models of change. Blake[111] states this most forcibly: 'The behavioural sciences have accomplished little of systematic character in the direction of achieving change in situations of organised human activity.' So they write, perhaps inevitably, as 'theoretical orphans' developing, on occasion, some autonomous verbalizations and rarely linking their ideas with theories of personal and social change.

Neglect of problem-solving models. All the approaches mentioned here tend to emphasize interpersonal and group factors as causal variables in blocking problem-solving activities, and tend to de-emphasize the cognitive processes of problem-solving.

* A staff from the University of Michigan, including Dr S. Seashore and D. Bowers, conducted the research and operated independently of the change agent.

Planned change and organizational effectiveness. What criteria of organizational effectiveness are change agents attempting to optimize? I can identify six dimensions of organizational effectiveness: legal, political, economic, technological, social, and personal. Which of these do change agents hope to affect? There is a good deal of fuzziness on this issue and the data are inconclusive. Argyris, who is the most explicit about the relationship between performance and interpersonal competence, is still hoping to develop good measures to establish a positive relationship. The connexion has to be made, or the field will have to change its normative goal, which is to construct not only a *better* world but a more *effective* one.

A question of values. It is not all obvious to me that the types of change induced by the change agents are: (*a*) compatible with 'human nature' or in accord with 'findings from the behavioural sciences' as some change agents assert, or (*b*) desirable, even if they are in tune with man's need structure, or (*c*) functional.

These new values which are espoused indicate a certain way of *behaving and feeling*; for example, they emphasize openness rather than secrecy, superior-subordinate collaboration rather than dependence or rebellion, co-operation rather than competition, consensus rather than individual rule, rewards based on self-control rather than externally induced rewards, team leadership rather than a one-to-one relationship with the boss, authentic relationships rather than those based on political manoeuverings, and so on.

Are they natural? desirable? functional? What, then, happens to status or power drives? What about those individuals who have a low need for participation and/or a high need for structure and dependence?[112] And what about those personal needs which seem to be incompatible with these images of man, such as a high need for aggression and a low need for affiliation? In short, what about those needs which can be expressed and best realized through bureaucratic systems? or benevolent autocracies? Are these individuals expected to be changed through some transformation of needs, or are they expected to yield to and comply with a conception of human nature incompatible with their own needs?

This problem of values is an important one and deserves thorough discussion. One of the problems in holding such a discussion is the emotional and value overtones which interfere with rational dialogue. This is exacerbated by a particularly unfortunate manner in which advocates and antagonists phrase the argument. More often than not, one is plunged into a polarized, black-and-white debate which converts ideas into ideology and inquiry into dogma. So we hear of 'theory *X vs.* theory *Y*', personality *vs.* organization, people *vs.* pyramids, participation *vs.* great men, democratic *vs.* autocratic, task *vs.* maintenance, achievement *vs.* socialization, hard *vs.* soft, human relations *vs.* scientific management, external *vs.* internal, and on and on.

Surely life is more complicated than these paired dualities suggest and surely these dualities must imply a *continuum* – not only extremes – along which, given certain criteria, different points may be optimized.*

Lack of systems approach. Up to this point, I have used the phrase 'organizational change' rather loosely. In Argyris's case, for example, organizational change refers to a change in values of eleven top executives, a change which was not necessarily of an enduring kind and which apparently brought about some conflict with other interfaces. In most other cases of planned organizational change, the change induction was limited to a small elite group. Only in the work of Blake can we confidently talk about organizational change – in a systems way; his programme includes the training of the entire management organization, and at several locations he has carried this step to include wage-earners.

Sometimes the changes brought about simply 'fade out' because there is no carefully worked-out procedure to ensure co-ordination with other interacting parts of the system. In other cases the changes have 'backfired' and have had to be terminated because of their conflict with interface units.[113] In any case, a good deal more has to be learned about the interlocking and stabilizing changes so that the total system is affected.

Planned organizational change: in conclusion

Now that I have discussed in some detail the background, elements, and processes of planned organizational change and placed it in its perspective as a special case of the utilization of social knowledge, it may be useful, both as peroration and conclusion, to state in the most general and tentative manner some generalizations. They are derived or implied, for the most part, from the foregoing discussion, and anchored in experience, and wherever possible, in research and theory.

First, a forecast: I suspect that we shall see an increase in the number of planned change programmes along the lines discussed in this paper: towards *less* bureaucratic and *more* participative 'open system' and adaptive structures. This prophecy is based on a number of factors, the most important of which is the *rate* of change confronting organizations today. Given that pronounced rate of change, the growing reliance on science for the success of the industrial enterprise, the growing number of professionals joining these enterprises, and the 'turbulent contextual environment' facing the firm, we can expect more and more demand for social inventions to supplement and revise significantly our traditional notions of organized effort: bureaucracy, greatman theories, and 'the Club'.

As far as adopting and acceptance go, we already know a good deal.†

---

* Burns and Stalker deserve my gratitude for stressing over and over again the importance of appropriateness of management work systems under differing conditions.
† See, in particular, E. Rogers[114] and Miles.[115]

Before any change of a consequential human kind can be accepted and adopted, the *type* of change should be of proven quality, easily demonstrable in its effects, and with information easily available. Its cost and accessibility to control by the client system as well as its value accord have to be carefully considered.

Acceptance also depends on the relationship between the change agent and the client system: the more profound and anxiety-producing the change, the more collaborative and close the relationship required. In addition, we can predict that an anticipated change will be resisted to the degree that the client system possesses little or incorrect knowledge about the change, has relatively little trust in the source of the change, and has relatively low influence in controlling the nature and direction of the change.

What we know least about – and what continually vexes those of us who are vitally concerned with the effective utilization of knowledge is *implementation*.[116] As I use the term, implementation encompasses a process which includes the creation of understanding and commitment in a client system towards a particular change which can solve problems, and devices whereby it can become integral to the client system's operations. It bears to organizational theory the same relationship as the term *internalization* does to personality theory, i.e. it is a process which leads to automatic self-generation and integral functioning.

When it comes to implementation of organizational changes, most practitioners seem to overemphasize the importance of intellectual *understanding* or the *informational* status of the intended change. Now, as I have said, information and understanding are a necessary, but not a sufficient, component for inducing change. More than that is required *if* the change affects important human responses. For human changes are bound up in the self-image and its maintenance and the complicated context of the social life and groupings which help to define and give meaning to the individual's existence. If an intended change is perceived to threaten (or enhance) the self-image, then we can expect differential effects. If an intended change is perceived as threatening the social 'life space' of the individual, then safeguards must be undertaken which ensure new forms of gratification and evaluation. In short, I am saying that human changes affect not only the individual but also the social fabric and norms from which he gains his evaluation and definition of self. It means, quite probably, that thinking solely about the *individual's understanding* of the change and its consequences is not enough.

From this vantage point, I shall try to summarize the necessary elements in implementation:

(*a*) The *client system* should have as much understanding of the change and its consequences, as much influence in developing and controlling the fate of the change, and as much trust in the initiator of the change as possible.

(*b*) The *change effort* should be perceived as as self-motivated and voluntary as possible. This is made possible through the legitimization and reinforcement of the change by the top management group as well as the significant reference groups adjacent to the client system. This is also made possible by providing as much true volition as possible.

(c) The *change programme* must include emotional and value as well as cognitive (informational) elements for successful implementation. It is doubtful whether relying solely on rational persuasion (expert power) is sufficient. Too often, rational elements are denied or rendered impotent because they conflict with a strongly ingrained belief, consciously or unconsciously held. Intellectual commitment is a first step, but not a guarantee to action. Most organizations know what ails them or what could help them; it is utilization where the rub is.

(d) The *change agent* can be crucial in reducing the resistance to change by providing consultation and psychological support during the transitional phase of the change. As I have stressed over and over again, the quality of the relationship is pivotal to the success of the change programme. As long as the change agent acts congruently with the principles of the programme and as long as the client system has a chance to test his competence and motives (and its own), he should be able to provide the support so necessary during the risky phases of change.*

REFERENCES

1 R. K. Merton & D. Lerner (1951)
2 W. E. Moore (1964) Chapter 1
3 B. Berelson & G. A. Steiner (1964)
4 A. Kaplan (1964)
5 R. Lippitt, J. Watson & B. Westley (1958)
6 W. G. Bennis, K. D. Benne & R. Chin (1961)
7 E. Goffman (1961)
8 E. H. Schein, I. Schneier & C. H. Braker (1961)
9 W. G. Bennis, K. D. Benne & R. Chin (1961), p. 154
10 A. W. Gouldner (1961a), pp. 643–53
11 A. Schuchman (1963)
12 A. W. Gouldner (1961b), pp. 83–95
13 E. A. Johnson (1954), p. xii.
14 E. A. Johnson (1954), p. xix
15 R. L. Ackoff & B. H. P. Rivett (1963), p. 34
16 C. Sofer (1961)
17 C. Sofer (1961), p. 8
18 C. Argyris (1962)
19 A. Bavelas & G. Strauss (1961), pp. 587–91
20 F. E. Emery & E. L. Trist (1963)
21 A. T. M. Wilson (1961)
22 W. G. Bennis (1963)
23 E. M. Rogers (1962)
24 P. E. Slater & W. G. Bennis (1964)
25 P. F. Lazarsfeld & S. S. Spivack (1961)
26 H. E. Salisbury (1960), p. 136
27 C. Argyris (1962)
   R. R. Blake & J. S. Mouton (1964)
   T. Burns & G. M. Stalker (1961)
   E. Jaques (1951)
   P. Lawrence (1958)
   A. K. Rice (1963)
   P. Spencer & C. Sofer (1964)
   C. Walker (1962)
   R. J. Smith (1962)
28 H. G. Barnett (1956)

* For a fuller discussion of these issues, see the author's recent book *Changing Organizations*.

R. Hilsman (1956)
29 G. M. Foster (1962)
W. H. Goodenough (1963)
E. Hagen (1962)
D. C. McClelland (1961)
E. H. Spicer (1952)
S. Tax (1964)
G. A. Almond & J. S. Coleman (1960)
30 S. T. Kimball & M. Pearsall (1954)
31 A. H. Stanton & M. S. Schwartz (1954)
W. Caudill (1958)
32 O. Klineberg (1964)
33 M. B. Miles (1964)
34 L. Baritz (1960)
35 W. G. Bennis (1963)
H. E. Freeman (1963), pp. 143–60
H. Zetterberg (1962)
J. R. Gibb & R. Lippitt (1959a)
R. Leeds & T. Smith (1963)
R. Likert & S. P. Hayes, Jr. (1957)
C. Glock *et al.* (1960)
36 J. Friedman (1963)
M. Mead (1957)
L. Mumford (1956)
G. Myrdal (1958)
37 A. Kaplan (1964), Chapter 10, especially section 45
38 K. D. Benne & G. Swanson (1950)
39 C. P. Snow (1962)
40 R. K. Merton & D. Lerner (1951), p. 56
41 D. Zand & P. Buchanan (1965)
42 R. Bendix & M. Weber (1960)
43 C. Argyris (1957)
C. Argyris (1964a)
44 C. Argyris (1962)
W. H. Whyte, Jr. (1956)
45 R. Likert (1961)
D. McGregor (1960)
46 A. W. Gouldner (1959), pp. 404–12
F. J. Roethlisberger & W. J. Dickson (1941)
47 H. A. Shepard (1960)
H. A. Shepard (1964)
P. E. Slater & W. G. Bennis (1964)

48 W. Evan (1962)
49 R. R. Blake, H. A. Shepard & J. S. Mouton (1964)
50 C. Argyris (1964a)
R. R. Blake & J. S. Mouton (1964)
R. Likert (1961)
51 H. J. Leavitt (1964), pp. 542–56
H. J. Leavitt & R. L. Whisler (1958)
52 W. E. Moore (1960)
53 K. D. Naegele (1961), p. 1207
54 D. Martindale (1964), p. xii
55 L. Coser (1956)
R. Dahrendorf (1961), pp. 445–51
56 A. Boskoff (1964), pp. 213–43
57 R. T. Parsons (1964)
58 R. Chin (1963)
R. Chin (1961)
59 A. W. Gouldner (1961b), op. cit.
60 W. G. Bennis (1963), op. cit.
61 G. Myrdal (1958), op. cit., p. 26
62 C. P. Snow (1961)
63 R. H. S. Crossman (1964)
64 H. Levinson *et al.* (1962)
65 H. Holt (1964), pp. 68–84
66 G. Myrdal (1958), p. 29
67 H. Zetterberg (1962)
68 J. Roosevelt (1962)
69 M. Haire (1962)
70 I. Chein, S. W. Cook & J. Harding (1948)
71 H. Zetterberg (1962), p. 136
72 E. Jaques (1961), pp. 162–8
73 F. L. W. Richardson (1962), p. 61
74 F. C. Mann & F. W. Neff (1961)
A. Zander (1961)
75 H. Morgenthau (1964)
76 A. T. M. Wilson (1961)
77 C. Thompson (1958)
78 R. Jungk (1958)
79 C. Argyris (1962)
E. A. Fleishman (1953)
80 R. K. Merton (1949)
81 R. K. Merton (1949), p. 174
82 N. Hobbs (1962)
83 E. D. Chapple & L. R. Sayles (1961)
L. Sayles (1961), pp. 62–7
84 R. Lippitt, J. Watson & B. Westley (1958)

S. E. Seashore & E. Van Egmond (1961)

85 R. R. Blake & J. S. Mouton (1965)
86 D. McGregor (1960)
   R. Likert (1961)
   C. Argyris (1962)
87 C. Argyris (1962), p. 43
88 H. A. Shepard & R. R. Blake (1962), pp. 88–96
89 T. Burns & G. M. Stalker (1961)
90 C. Argyris (1964b)
91 E. H. Schein & W. G. Bennis (1965)
92 R. R. Blake & J. S. Mouton (1964)
93 C. Argyris (1962)
94 L. P. Bradford, J. R. Gibb & K. D. Benne (1964)
95 H. A. Shepard (1960)
96 H. A. Shepard (1960)
97 R. Beckhard (1965)
   J. R. Gibb & R. Lippitt (1959b), pp. 13–19
98 C. Sofer (1961)
99 C. Argyris (1962)
100 F. Mann (1957)
   F. Mann & H. Baumgartel (1964)
   F. Mann & R. Likert (1952)

101 R. Beckhard (1965)
102 C. Argyris (1962)
103 R. R. Blake, J. S. Mouton, L. B. Barnes & L. E. Greiner (1964)
104 C. Argyris (1960)
105 J. R. P. French & B. Raven (1959) pp. 150–67
   H. C. Kelman (1958)
106 T. Burns & G. M. Stalker (1961), p. 121
107 R. Harrison (1962), Chapter 11
108 Foundation for Research on Human Behaviour (1960) p. 31
109 R. R. Blake, J. S. Mouton, L. B. Barnes & L. E. Greiner (1964)
110 G. David (1965)
111 R. R. Blake & J. S. Mouton (1962b)
112 V. H. Vroom (1960)
113 R. S. Jenks (1965)
   E. H. Schein & W. G. Bennis (1965), Chapter 10
114 E. M. Rogers (1962)
115 M. B. Miles (1964)
116 C. W. Churchman & P. Ratoosh (1960)
117 W. G. Bennis (1966)

6 · On Various Approaches to the Study of Organizations

C. WEST CHURCHMAN and F. E. EMERY

Our assignment is to classify and compare the ways in which social scientists attempt to study human organizations. It is reasonable to ask why such classification and comparison should be made. In considering how to frame a reply we were convinced that papers prepared for discussion meetings are usually much too long, because they attempt to include all the discussion the writers can conceive of. We have adopted the policy of simply stating some theses, and providing a few clues as to how we arrived at them. This policy (*a*) guarantees that we finish the paper although our thinking is unfinished and (*b*) maximizes the probability that it will be read and (*c*) minimizes the redundancy of the idiosyncratic steps in our reasoning.

Our first theses defend our right to discuss the topic covered by the title of the paper:

T 1 *There are different approaches to the study of human organizations.*
T 2 *Each approach has a positive value.*
T 3 *Each approach is essentially incomplete relative to the ideal of a satisfactory study of human organizations.*
T 4 *There is a reasonable possibility that the different approaches are complementary, in the sense that some combination of two or more of them will prove better than any one of them alone.*

What we mean by 'combination' is evidently not clear, even to us. 'Combining' is itself an organizational concept, and hence we are faced here and throughout the paper with the need to use organization theory in order to discuss different approaches to the study of organizations. Organizations can be combined by setting up new by-laws, new committees, new hierarchies, etc. None of these familiar meanings of combination is very helpful in explaining the concept of combining different kinds of research effort.

T 5 *Two distinct research approaches are combined only if the differences between them produce in the two together a difference in the research behaviour of the individuals and/or the whole organization.*

77

We do not need to remind our readers that combination rarely occurs in academic circles, but that in the arena of applied social science the environment often forces different research approaches to combine.

So much for our motivation. What are the distinct approaches to the study of organizations? The commonly adopted classification is given in terms of empirical sociology, mathematical social science, and social philosophy. Each of these approaches is usually defined in terms of the methodology that is used. Thus empirical sociology uses interview schedules, statistical analysis, and the like. Mathematical social science uses mathematical models and searches for data to 'realize' the models. Social philosophy uses intuition and broad frameworks.

Instead of following the usual patterns of discussing social science, we adopt a more radical approach. This approach is based on a thesis about groups of people such as those who call themselves social scientists.*

T 6 *There exists a framework of concepts of organizational structure and behaviour such that the properties of any human group can be defined completely within the framework.*

This somewhat outrageous thesis says, in effect, that whatever we are as social scientists we are by virtue of our relations within and to some organizations; whatever we want to say about ourselves as social scientists we can say within the framework of the concepts we use to describe human organizations. Of course the thesis is rather weak, because it says nothing specific about the framework, nor does it commit itself on the meaning of 'definition'. From this thesis we arrive at

T 7 *The distinct approaches can be characterized in terms of organizational concepts by*
   (a) *the way in which the pursuers of these approaches are organizationally related to the organizations they study;*
   (b) *the way in which their preferred subject-matter is embedded in an organizational context.*

The question that first concerns us is the relationship between the organization to which the researcher belongs and the organization which he is studying. We note that only in the study of human organizations does this question become obviously important.

We shall consider three different answers to this question, and these constitute the classification of different approaches to the study of organizations. First there is the approach which asserts that the researcher belongs to a completely independent organization:

T 8 *One approach to the study of organizations is to regard the researcher as a member of an organization completely independent of the organization being observed.*

* By social group we mean 'any number of human beings who are in potential (or actual) communication, "potential" meaning some significant level of probability'.[1]

This thesis means that the researcher accepts norms of behaviour, his role and his goals, from an entirely different organization from the ones he observes. In so far as he studies their goals and conflicts, he is indifferent to how far they achieve their goals or resolve their conflicts. We generally call the researcher a member of the research community. This community is not well understood in organizational terms as yet. It evidently places a high value on honesty, objectivity, and something vaguely called intellectual interest. Its members thrive on channels of communication, and a member's value to the organization depends on how strong a link he is in the communication network. The communication nets of the research community tend at times to separate, so that only very weak flows exist between the separate parts. The separation is accomplished by giving certain sub-goals a greater value. Thus, empirical sociology emphasizes the importance of good bits of input from the organization being studied; mathematical social science emphasizes the importance of excellent communication between researchers in which finer and more elegant questions and replies can be given; and social philosophy emphasizes the importance of a 'total input' from the observed organization. Their analogues in business organizations are the marketing man, the systems man, and the policy-makers. Of course, the meaning of the independent approach depends on how one defines independence.

For our purposes

T 9 *One organization* A *is independent of another* B, *if* B's *behaviour does not influence the goals* (*or standards*) *of* A.

It will be noted that *A* may, by its observational activity, introduce irreversible changes in the goal structure of *B*; the independence only goes one way.

We said at the outset that each approach to the study of organizations is incomplete. What's incomplete about this one?

T 10 *The 'independent' approach is incomplete because the independent research community has no adequate way of judging whether its focus of interest or its output are of any real concern or value to any other organization.*

This is certainly a debatable thesis, as we hope all the other theses are. Of course the independent research community could observe the problems with which an organization appears to be concerned; but the point is that the organizational problem may well manifest itself in misidentification of the organization's problems. Similarly, the independent research community could observe how an outside organization responds to its output of research reports; but the point here is that this response never makes any significant difference in the plans and policies of the research organization. Furthermore, although there are some interesting attempts to combine empirical sociology and mathematical social science within the independent approach, it could not itself be studied by this approach, for then the research would be part of the organization being studied. Perhaps this is a dilemma that the leaders of university development might consider?

T 11 *A second approach to the study of organizations is to regard the researcher as both a member of an independent research community and a member* pro tem *of another organization that includes the one being observed.*

This approach is common to a great deal of applied social science in industry and commerce and in industrial or government operational research. Here the researcher tries to 'optimize' or 'suboptimize' and uses as his criterion the value structure or at least the stated objectives of the controlling interests of that organization. 'The traditional formulation of operations research problems (is) in terms of ends and means – how can I maximise the achievement of an objective or a set of objectives for a given cost? or alternatively, how can I minimise the cost of achieving a certain set of objectives?' [2] The operational research man typically regards costs as 'opportunity costs', the value to the controlling interests of the alternative means that have to be sacrificed. The applied social scientist will typically also go to the sublevels, and especially the individual, to establish ethical constraints on his *pro tem* participation in the organization under study.

The incompleteness of the dual approach is obvious and not essentially affected by the difference just noted between operational research practice and applied social science.

T 12 *The dual organization approach is incomplete because the researcher has no adequate basis for resolving conflicts of interest and values within the organization under study or between it and the research community.*

At best the researcher can look for activities where the conflict is minimized, e.g. areas of a technical, administrative character. The applied social scientist can hardly avoid the problems of administration-of-men, and hence his concern to restrict his involvement by assuming ethical constraints of a very general nature. Thus does the researcher find himself edged away from problems of great intrinsic interest to his science and of central importance to the organization he studies. [3]

Not only this, but he must always worry about where to spend his time. He knows that the process of implementation of recommendations is long and tedious; should he drop the matter at the point where the research community nods approval, or carry on until the observed organization accepts and understands? Also, he wants to carry back a message to the research community; he wants to say that its standards of acceptance are defective, because its ideas do not work out in practice. He is getting ready to do 'research on research', but he does not see clearly how this is possible.

There is another approach, of course. It is most difficult to enunciate because it is less frequently pursued and requires for its definition a conceptual framework somewhat more advanced than we have.

T 13 *A third approach to the study of organizations is to regard the researcher as a member* pro tem *of a third organization sufficiently greater than the organization under study to encompass the conflicting interests and yet sufficiently close to it to permit its values to be related to the concrete issues of conflict.*

Ideally, this third organization would be sufficiently broad to encompass also the interests and values of the research community. However, this implies such a general level of human organization – almost certainly supranational – that it is difficult to understand how one would work back to agreed-upon objectives in concrete conflict situations. It might be that there are not enough in-between levels at which sufficient community of interests and values exists to justify search for agreed research objectives and criteria. This seems unlikely. Societies as admittedly full of conflict as ours, could hardly hang together unless there were very pervasive strands of common interest. Our own experience is that community of interest can usually be found at the next higher level of social organization. The practical difficulty is more likely to be that the researcher pursuing this third approach will have to engage in institution-building so that agreement about his research concerns can be actively pursued and powerfully sanctioned. It should be noted that when in this approach the researcher obtains his value standards from the next higher level he does not have a privileged objective standing as a member of this level. He can claim neither special knowledge of the value structure of this level nor special power to sanction things on its behalf.

These differences in approach may help somewhat towards understanding the differences between 'academic studies', the typical applications of social science and operational research to part-systems, and the emerging promise of these latter at the level of overall system policy.*

There is no obvious way in which one could combine these approaches to yield other and better approaches. At best one may recognize that circumstances make a weaker approach unavoidable, or that a circumscribed interest may make it justifiable.

As between applied social science and operational research we can simply note that

T 14 *Applied social science and operational research have a common interest in the second and third approaches* (T 11, T 13).

This is not in itself a compelling ground for a closer relationship. If there is complementary relation (T 4) this must be sought in the way their preferred subject-matters are embedded in an organizational context (T 7).

* There seems little need to follow Enthoven in his use of the term 'systems analysis' to describe this broader application of operational research. Whatever restrictions may have been imposed on the practice of operational research since its wartime hey-day there appears to be nothing intrinsic in operational research that confines it to part-systems.

We approach this question with another thesis about individuals and organizations

T 15 *The properties of some groups might be defined in terms of a single organization, but an individual can be so defined only in terms of more than one organization.*

This is putting it mildly. If any individual could be described in terms of one organization we would have 'organization man', pure and simple. We do not think that he would be even humanoid. The individuals who carry out the work of an organization are related as individuals and as groups to a multitude of other organizations.[4] They cannot be defined as persons without reference to these varied interpenetrating relations. For an organization this means more than a well-thumbed personnel file on each of its members.

T 16 *Any organization, in tying together individuals, whose properties are partly determined by their relations to a multiplicity of different organizations, creates for itself a statistical aggregate that has properties of its own – an internal environment with field properties.*

It is not as if we have all been blind to this. We have tapped away its cruder manifestations in turnover and absentee problems. We have gone into the more complex manifestations in morale and informal group structures. We have been perplexed and fascinated by the Bionesque phenomena of the group relations laboratories.[5]

However, we have consistently tried to refer these phenomena to either the organization or the individual. There has been a marked reluctance to recognize that which is obvious to any who has had to directly command a body of men. An aggregate of stones has such extremely weak field properties that we can usually ignore them. An aggregate of human beings readily constitutes a powerful contagious social field, more or less inclined to shared emotions and behaviour of hostility, docility, loyalty, flight, etc.[6]

What is perhaps even less well recognized is that

T 17 *The dual characteristic of human organizations, as structured role-sets and as statistical aggregates of persons, demands of organizational research the joint consideration of two research strategies, not just the employment of two methodologies.*

Historically, social science has evolved about the traditional scientific strategy of identifying particular cause–effect relations of a high degree of probability. That scientific truths can be discovered in the penumbra of complex relative indeterminacies is a very recent insight for which we are indebted to the mathematical theories of probability and error. To this insight operational research owes the possibility of its existence.

The difference between social science and operational research is no more a difference simply of methodology than is the difference between Cartesian geometry and probability theory. Appropriate methodological biases have certainly emerged, but the crux of the difference is the strategic one of the direction from which one may hope to approach the common scientific goal of understanding. This difference has involved the usual array of unexpressed assumptions and operational research, despite its attempts to formulate its opposing assumptions as multivariate, etc., has shown itself particularly susceptible to hidden assumptions that are more closely related to the traditional mechanical but quantitative models than to its own parentage; the strategic difference has involved also the formulation of the basic questions that tend to mould the character of any discipline, the concepts that give to these questions the shape of an answer, and, only within this, a process that selects methodological procedures, which however, once adopted, themselves modify assumptions, questions, and concepts. This is perhaps simply to restate T 17 as meaning that it is not enough for the understanding of organizations that the social scientists use methods appropriate to statistical aggregates or that they open up the black box with structural keys. It seems necessary to consider organizations from both of these perspectives. One must seriously challenge any quick assumption that a particular organizational problem belongs to one perspective.

Such a caveat would be pious indeed if the duality of organizations affected only minor aspects of their behaviour. We do not think this is the case for reasons that are best indicated by the interim conclusions we reach.

T 18 *An adaptive behavioural system must be pre-set to exclude, magnify, or attenuate informational inputs if it is to remain adaptive.*[7]

Assuming that an organizational structure is such a system (without specifying how adaptive), we assert:

T 19 *The state of the aggregate of individual persons (the internal environment) is a primary factor in pre-setting the communication that is possible within the organization.*[8]

T 20 *Organizations seek to relate this state of the aggregate to their organizational requirement by the development of so-called organizational values.*

T 21 *The embodiment of organizational values is thus a constant preoccupation permeating not only such personnel tasks as selection training, promotion, but also the exercise of authority, operating doctrine, and marketing policies.*[9]

T 22 *Like other values, organizational values emerge to cope with relevant uncertainties and gain their authority from their reference to the requirements of larger systems within which people's interests are largely concordant.*

These last theses are no better founded and no more compelling than our earlier ones. Nevertheless, they do suggest that the duality of organizations enters into the central regions of their behaviour.

The problem of organizational values emerges as critical for both operational research and applied social science. From whichever perspective one approaches the study of an organization, one will be questioned about these values. Furthermore, if we return to our earlier problem of how the researcher relates to the organization under study we find that in seeking to identify 'the next higher level', he is engaging in the search that the organization must undertake in finding its appropriate values.

It is interesting to speculate that the fate of research projects within the organization may have more to do with the maturity of the organization's values than with the value of the findings.

REFERENCES

1 C. W. Churchman & R. L. Ackoff (1950), p. 503
2 A. C. Enthoven (1963)
3 P. Selznick (1957)
4 P. Selznick (1948)
5 W. R. Bion (1961)
6 S. L. A. Marshall (1947)
7 W. T. Powers et al. (1963)
8 W. T. Powers et al. (1963), see his discussion of the role of the N-system
9 P. Selznick (1957)

7 · Connective introducing Chapters 8–19

S. L. COOK

The twelve contributed papers which constitute Chapters 8–19 are reviewed under four main headings:

Observation of organizational behaviour.

Theoretical models of organizational control.

Specific applications of operational research or social science to organization design.

Factors affecting implementation of operational research studies.

Observation of organizational behaviour. Papers by Woodward and Eilon, Churchill and Cooper, and Radnor

These three papers record painstaking and systematic observation of the behaviour and attitudes of certain functional components of the management system in a number of organizations.

Woodward and Eilon's paper reports a pilot study on three firms. It suggests that various control systems build up which operate independently and may not be compatible with one another or with company goals. Attitudes to these systems are ambivalent. 'Multiple goals' have to be met and the operator reaches a compromise among them; this may result in far from optimal performance.

Industries can be classified according to the frequency of changes in production. At one extreme of the scale are the processing industries, which make long runs of a single product, and at the other are the industries in which every product is different. The behaviour of the people in these two groups is very predictable. In the middle of the range the pattern breaks down, and it appears that another dimension of classification is necessary – which type of control system is used in the firm.

The authors emphasize that this is an early paper on the study and that an enormous amount of analysis remains to be done on the material collected. Present conclusions are therefore speculative. Eventually it is hoped to make a classification of control systems taking into account such features as the degree of formalization, the degree of definition of objectives, adaptiveness, the amount of feedback, and whether there is a single system or a series of systems.

This study used the 'tracer' technique. This means that particular items under production are followed through from one department to another as a means of linking activities of the departments.

In the discussion of this paper it was mentioned that even the separate control systems existing were often not well designed. Using the quality control chart, there is often no reward for doing well, only a punishment for doing badly. Where controls are based on past performance there is a built-in penalty for operators who do too well because they set themselves a higher standard of acceptance for the future. Some felt that a properly displayed control chart would be its own reward, but others that interest in such charts inevitably waned.

It was also noted that psychologically there is an optimum level of control. With too much external control, a person may feel persecuted and that not enough is being left to his initiative. With too little control, he may feel insecure and that not enough notice is being taken of his activities.

Churchill and Cooper's paper describes a study on eight firms. It explores attitudes to internal auditing and auditors within the firm, and the perceived effects of internal auditing. Senior managers thought that auditing aimed mainly at checking clerical procedures, while clerks thought it aimed at checking the overall system. Nevertheless, most thought auditors were more like policemen than teachers or lawyers. The importance of this study goes beyond the conventional auditing function, because, in designing complex management control systems, it will be essential to provide 'preventive maintenance' to components of the system to check that the procedures laid down are indeed being followed. For example, at present most companies try to exert from the centre some crude overall pressure to keep stock levels below some arbitrary figure; this often clashes with established 'optimal' and inventory control rules in use by local managements. It might be better for the centre to 'audit' these local rules and their application.

The authors stressed during discussion that this paper represented the results of only preliminary work in a major study the aim of which was to assess the value of auditing procedures as a substitute for more normal supervisory methods of control. The next step would be to do an experiment in a firm, or management game, of which the aim would be to examine and compare different structures of audit procedure and to test the way in which people reacted to them.

There was general agreement that, if audits were to be part of control, it was essential that the minimum of extra work should be done to provide documents for such a procedure. It could be that, if an eye were not kept on this, the cost of preparing for an audit might exceed the money that could be saved by using such a method of control. On no account must the audit be allowed to become an inhibiting function.

This method of control was apparently under consideration by the U.S. Armed Forces in connexion with research and development contracts, as an alternative to the more usual methods of progress reports and budgetry control.

There was some discussion on the problem of who was to 'audit the auditors' if they themselves became in effect advisers to management. Clearly the paper introduces some novel and challenging ideas about the 'management of management methods' which could have great relevance to the place of operational research in the organization.

Radnor's paper reports a study of forty-eight large industrial firms. This inquired into top management attitudes to research and development and the relation between these and the methods of control used.

It is of particular interest from three aspects. First, it reports management attitudes to research and development and to its organization and control; these may have some parallels to management attitudes to the use of operational research and of social science.

Second, it illustrates the possibility of getting some general description of management attitudes to the general control problem in an organization. The study uses the 'internal rationality' model, also used by Woodward and Eilon and commented on favourably by Burns during the Conference. This means that it collects and synthesizes managers' views on the basis that they will act rationally on the beliefs they state.

Third, there is a methodological interest. As the authors said in introducing the paper, it gives some idea of the amount and reliability of information that can be collected by quick interview techniques, and the value and limitations of the open interview.

All three papers under this heading offer insights into organizational behaviour, but suggest further research rather than results immediately applicable in management systems design and development. They all illustrate the combined operational research/social science approach to descriptive research in organizations and, incidentally, the amount of effort required in such studies.

Theoretical models of organizational control. Papers by Charnes and Stedry, Burns, Sewell, and Whinston

The papers by Charnes and Stedry, Sewell, and Whinston deal with mathematical models of the 'cognitive' elements of control. In Sewell and Whinston any reference to behavioural aspects is implicit only. Decentralization is looked on as a means of reducing the information-handling load to reasonable proportions, not as a way of improving motivation. The models developed seek to provide a framework within which decentralized decisions can come close to being optimal for the organization. The methods proposed involve operational research studies at the centre which are used intuitively to establish the 'transfer prices', interest rates, or other parameters which must be used by the decentralized managements when trying to optimize local performance. These parameters are set at such levels that the best local decisions are best for the whole organization.

These papers will illustrate to the social scientist the approach of the really research-oriented operational research man to organization studies.

The paper by Charnes and Stedry moves farther towards recognizing behavioural elements and indicates several ways in which they might be incorporated in mathematical models of the control system. The paper 'departs from certain kinds of utility and transfer pricing treatments' in that it 'admits limits on both cognitive capacity and rationality', and uses basically the 'satisficing' concept of Simon. However (unlike the descriptive 'behavioural theory of the firm'), it attempts to show how operational research methods could be used to improve organizational performance. The paper gives an excellent review of current thought in this area and explores current models of behaviour – such as ensuring a given probability of achieving a set goal, equalizing the probability of achieving a set of multiple goals, and so on. It concludes that 'the goals of the sub-unit need not and probably cannot be the same as, or smaller scale replicates of, the organization goals. Rather, the goals of the sub-unit and the reward structure accompanying goal attainment should be so constructed that by working towards its own aspirations, it will unavoidably work toward organizational goal attainment as well.'

Burns's paper complements that of Charnes and Stedry. The model presented is entirely non-mathematical and is concerned primarily with behavioural rather than cognitive elements in organizational control. It postulates three parallel interacting systems in the organization; the working or task system, the political system, and the career system. The difference between this approach and previous attempts to build human characteristics into the organization model is that most of these have assumed these characteristics to be independent of the state of the decision system, simply supplying a certain element of 'noise', 'friction', or 'distortion'. The Burns model is clearly more complex, involving interaction between three dynamic systems. The paper offers no suggestion as to how to use this concept to improve organizations; it is rather a warning that simpler approaches are not likely to represent reality.

In discussion, a general comment on the papers of Charnes and Stedry, Sewell, and Whinston was that mathematical models for such complex organizations seem themselves to be so complex that they might not be manageable in practice unless the whole job was turned over to a computer. There is also the question whether such systems could be made to be adaptable. In connexion with the Sewell paper it was suggested that, in setting up a pricing system in the way described, one might be making grave assumptions that the rational or economic man existed in the military context.

Much of the discussion of the Charnes and Stedry paper was concerned with relative merits of 'satisficing' or operating within fixed constraints, operating within probabilistic constraints, and maximizing utility, treating all variables as continuously variable with no absolute constraints.

In discussion of the Burns paper the main criticisms were that the paper was negative in that it put forward the arguments against all the present manageable approaches to optimization, and all the complicating factors that had to be allowed for, without showing how in fact the job could be done. Burns himself commented that he was a strong supporter of the Simon/Cyert/March school of organization theory.

All the papers in this session should give much food for thought to operational research men working on the development of management control systems. The paper by Charnes and Stedry, in particular, provides one of the most thoughtful contributions yet towards the combination of behavioural and 'cognitive' concepts of organization, and many of the ideas should be testable by operational research in applied studies. Let us hope that any such tests will be fully documented.

Specific applications of operational research or social science to organization design. Papers by Geisler, Brink, and Brown

Geisler and Brink describe specific studies, and Brown's paper is based on a specific study.

All use operational research concepts without presenting any very formal models; all appear to have used some intuitive behavioural understanding and have probably involved social scientists as members of an operational research team, but have not used formal social science.

Geisler's paper describes simulations which *demonstrate* and *test* the results of operational research studies for the U.S. Air Force on inventory policy, missile system logic, missile support management, and maintenance management.

The operational research studies themselves had used mainly all-computer simulations, which are much cheaper and quicker for exploring the logical properties of different solutions. In the man–machine simulations the main human roles are performed by men who normally have such roles in real life and/or who will have the same role to perform in the new system. The purpose of *demonstration* is to give all these participants confidence that the proposed system is workable, together with a general feeling for the logic of the system, so that they can start up with some synthetic 'previous experience' of the system. The purpose of *test* is to discover what human difficulties may arise in operating the system and to adjust it to overcome them. There is also a *research* purpose, since the exploration of interactions between the proposed system and the human beings could be expected to improve general understanding in this field; however, the paper draws no formal conclusions of this nature.

Brink's paper describes the first stages of an ambitious attempt to map the entire decision-making system of a complex organization – a university. He refers to the approach to this problem as 'boring a tunnel through a mountain from opposite sides and hoping to meet in the middle'. The two sides are monetary values, on the one hand, and ultimate social values, on the other. The latter side involves the social sciences; the emphasis here appears to be on organizational goals and values rather than on the behavioural aspects of operating the organization, although clearly in a university there will be an exceptionally high interaction between personal goals (and hence motivation and behaviour) and the aggregate goals of the organization.

Brown's paper is a speculative paper based on a study of automation potential in an electronics factory. He discusses human ability in terms of information theory, and assumes that humans are happiest when most fully using their abilities – and that this is likely to be when 'processing a high amount of information'.

Factors affecting implementation of operational research studies. Papers by Ratoosh and Lewis

These two papers, superficially very different, both discuss conditions necessary for successful application of operational research. Ratoosh describes a range of experiments in which a team is set a problem and an individual within it has the task of persuading the team to adopt the correct solution which he alone knows. They 'investigate the resistance to the solution and consider ways of presenting the solution that will increase the likelihood of its being accepted'. The author concludes by referring to the widespread neglect by operational researchers of the social sciences. He says:

> 'It seems to me that there is another reason that problems pertinent to the social sciences attract little interest among most operational research workers. It is intimately related to the reasons that our experimental groups reject the solution. It is that the recognition that something that seems as complicated and uncontrollable as human psychology plays an essential role in operational research would lead to very grave doubts on the part of operational researchers about the potency of their techniques; and these doubts operational research workers are no more willing to entertain than were our chief executives willing to accept a solution when the acceptance would lead to doubts about their own competence.'

Lewis discusses the way in which operational research must operate 'in the area of command as opposed to control', in order to be effective. He argues strongly *against* the feasibility of overall rational models to link objectives, goals, strategies, and tactical decision, and *for* an evolutionary process by which the 'student of operations' must interleave his work with the ongoing management, deferring efforts to change any component of the current system until he understands the present mode of operations. Methods are more often qualitative than quantitative. He makes no specific allusions to social science, and in the main the reasons for recommending evolution, not revolution, are to ensure that solutions are 'relevant, useful, and convenient'. The effort goes into getting good solutions, rather than getting solutions accepted. However, there is one reference to behavioural patterns: '. . . the law of the conservation of power – if an accretion of power occurs in one place, it came from somewhere else. The flow of power will be resisted by those who are losing it, or think they are.'

Discussion on the Ratoosh paper centred upon the factors that affected the readiness with which a group was likely to accept a rational solution of their problems – the solution that, in the experiments quoted, was put forward by the confederate introduced into the group. The results of additional work, not reported in this paper, were made available by the author to clarify some of the questions raised.

For instance, it had been found that where a group could 'purchase' a document prepared by the control staff which gave them the optimum solution to the problem they had been set they were more likely to act upon it than when they were advised verbally by a consultant; but that they were more likely to accept the word of the latter than that of a member of their own hierarchy, since this jeopardized their personal prestige much less. The tightness of the group had little effect on their readiness to accept such proposals; tests had been carried out on this using groups ranging from one in which the chief executive had complete power to 'hire and fire' and distribute profits to one in which there was no structure imposed at all. It was remarked in parenthesis that the latter type of group had in fact spent most of their time trying to set up an organization for themselves, but that this result might have been mainly due to the fact that the majority of the group were students at a business school!

It was generally agreed that to present too much detail was a disadvantage in getting ideas accepted. Rationality was not the only factor that affected the chance that this would occur, and as much emphasis needed to be given to the method of advocacy adopted. The general approach of 'You made an interesting remark a little while ago (even if he hadn't) that I have managed to develop into something . . .' was, as might be expected, much more likely to produce results than 'Here is the answer: take it or leave it'. Again, the 'confederate' must in practice be someone who is preferably well known to and trusted by the group if his ideas are to be accepted. Operational research workers in particular seemed to have an important role to play in this – some experiments had demonstrated that their ideas were often well accepted – but that there was perhaps a tendency for them merely to present an optimal solution, rather than going on to describe the ways that were available to reach such a goal without losing face or committing irretrievable steps; jointly working out a path to the goal was in practice as important as describing the goal itself.

The advantages of using a formal language for communication were discussed briefly. Here the questions revolved around the idea that if the use of a formal language reduces the communication of stresses within the group these stresses must show themselves in other ways. There was no general agreement on this, however.

Discussion of the Lewis paper led to the following points:

(*a*) Organizations are in a state of continual change. These changes can occur quite quickly; so much so that the effects are often outside the experience of the typical organization member. Weapon systems can become obsolete in the research and development phase.

(*b*) If operational research is to provide useful support it must be available on a continuous basis. The organization must look upon operational research as a part of itself. Only in this way can new support procedures be continuously evaluated and, as appropriate, implemented with full assistance of the operations people.

(*c*) Operational research analysts must take full cognizance of the human problem in implementing a new support system. Almost all changes involve a redistribution of power. The consequent resentment of some individuals can prevent effective implementation or cause complete abandonment of the project; it is often better to proceed in short steps.

(*d*) In a rapidly changing organizational environment it is necessary to get changes made in the financing system. Reviews need to be arranged as and when required. More success has been achieved in obtaining funds for operational research work than in general financing.

Further comments on the content of contributed papers: participative versus authoritative management

The sponsors of the session on organization and control had expected some reference to the applicability of the McGregor–Likert–Haire school of social science – or Theory *Y* (*vs.* Theory *X*). In terms of control a possible application would deal, for example, with the use of information systems to enhance self-control rather than control down the hierarchy. In terms of the use of operational research and other staffs to design and improve management control systems, it would favour collaborative project teams, involving 'line' and 'staff' men without distinction, rather than strict division of responsibility between line and staff. No such explicit reference appeared in the contributed papers for the session, but there is some implicit reference in two papers already discussed – in Woodward and Eilon, and in the introductory discussion in Charnes and Stedry. Explicit reference does, however, appear in two papers, in other sections, those by Revans and Walton.

Revans, in 'Hospital Attitudes and Communications' (Part VI, Chapter 45), offers further evidence to support Likert and others that 'participation' does, in a wide range of circumstances, appear substantially to improve organizational effectiveness. In presenting the paper, he drew some strong analogies with industrial organizations and mentioned recent extensions of the work into industry. Further news of this work will be awaited with interest, because the question of whether or in what circumstances increased participation does lead to increased operating efficiency remains controversial.

Walton, in 'Conflict in Lateral Organizational Relationships' (Part IV, Chapter 30), deals very thoroughly with the concept of horizontal collaboration in an organization – as the alternative to horizontal conflict. The treatment is non-quantitative – a review of work in the field, a restatement of concepts, and some logically deduced conclusions. These are interesting if not revolutionary; their clear statement may lead to fruitful measurement studies within organizations. They appear to be relevant both in the design of formal management control systems and in management of staff departments such as operational research. Walton does not say conflict is bad, and collaboration good; he does not judge them (except here and there by implication). He says that most horizontal decision-making relationships in organizations contain components of both conflict and collaboration, and he redefines the relationships concerned under the names 'distributive' and 'integrative' relationships. He then states the 'concepts which identify the divergent syndromes of behaviour'.

'A *distributive relationship* has the following components:

'1 A bargaining form of decision-making where information is carefully rationed and deliberately distorted.
'2 A structure of interaction which is rigid, formal, and circumscribed.
'3 Negative attitudes towards the other unit.

'The *integrative relationship* has these components:

'1 A problem-solving form of joint decision-making in which accurate information is freely exchanged.
'2 A flexible, informal, and open pattern of inter-unit interaction.
'3 Positive sentiments between the two units.'

8 · A Field Study of Management Control in Manufacturing Industry

JOAN WOODWARD and SAMUEL EILON

Introduction

The Human Sciences Committee* of the Department of Scientific and Industrial Research is sponsoring and financing a research project into the human and social implications of control, with particular reference to production control in manufacturing situations. This project is based on the assumption that when the management of a firm makes a decision to manufacture a product or series of products a control system is brought into existence. Objectives have to be determined in relation to the product and a sequence of activities planned in order to achieve those objectives. Plans then have to be executed and information generated to enable the results to be assessed. If the activities are to be repeated, corrective action may have to be taken or the objectives modified in the light of the results obtained. For those concerned with the product at all levels of the hierarchy, the control system is the framework in which they operate and determines the amount of discretion they have in the organization of their own activities.

The control system may be neither complex nor formalized. In some manufacturing firms objectives are not defined with any degree of precision. The stated aim may be no more than to avoid making a loss, to remain in existence, or to try to meet a particular delivery date, and the assessment of results may be no more than the production of an annual balance sheet.

The complexity of the control system is linked with, but not entirely dependent on, the technological and economic situation of the firm. In continuous flow and single-purpose plant production objectives have to be precisely defined. The 'how', 'how much', 'where', 'when', and 'at what cost' of production usually have to be determined before the plant is designed and built. At the other end of the scale, where products are subject to rapid development and variety and results are not predictable, precise definition of objectives is rarely possible. Between these two extremes, however, the nature of the control system and the complexity of the planning and control

* This part of the work of D.S.I.R. was taken over by the Science Research Council in 1965.

procedures depend as much upon the outlook and sophistication of the management of the firm as upon the technological or economic circumstances.

Work on management organization already undertaken [1] had indicated that there is a link between technology and behaviour. It had also suggested that organizational and behavioural patterns are more consistent and predictable at the extremes of the technological scale than in the middle ranges. Moreover, the variations in behaviour observed in the batch and mass production firms studies appeared to be related to the nature of the control system, in particular to the precision with which objectives were defined and to the limitations imposed on discretion at the different levels in the hierarchy.

It was felt, therefore, that the description and classification of the different kinds of control system in batch and standardized production and the observations of the behaviour associated with them constituted a logical follow-up to the earlier project. The project completed by Lisl Klein [2] had also led in the same direction; one of her findings had been that work study has at least as important and far-reaching effects on operator behaviour as part of a control system as it has as the basis of a system of wage determination.

Methods of research

THE TRACER METHOD

As a preliminary to determining a framework for the description and classification of control systems, it was decided to carry out a series of case studies in manufacturing firms, concentrating on control and the behaviour patterns of those involved. It was felt that a useful approach would be to isolate an order, product, batch, or process as a 'tracer' and follow its progress through the control system of a firm, observing the way in which people become involved in plans, decisions, and tasks in relation to it. The first problem, therefore, was to locate and obtain the co-operation of firms in which this could be done; it was necessary to be able to identify the 'tracer' and its component parts right through the manufacturing process. Moreover, the period of time taken from the initiation to the completion of the 'tracer' had to be sufficiently short to fit into the research programme.

Three studies were undertaken, one research worker being responsible for each study, and the fieldwork for these is now being completed. Peripheral studies have also been made in several other firms, and some useful comparative information has been obtained. The fieldwork, observations, and interviewing and the analysis of the data collected were carried out by Angela Barnard, Peter Combey, Lisl Klein, and Jeffrey Rackham.

THE FIRMS STUDIED

Case 1 is the study of the building of an analogue computer, approximately 90 per cent of its contents being standard sub-assemblies or 'modules' and 10 per cent being specifically designed for the customer. There was some delay in getting the fieldwork started in this firm owing to the fact that a complete reorganization took place following a change of ownership in August 1962. This change, together with the fact that the industry was becoming more competitive, set in motion a rationalization process, and during the nine months that the research assistant has been 'chasing' the analogue computer through the factory a number of changes have taken place in the control procedure. Budgetary control, costing, and estimating procedures have all been restated or changed during this period, cost feedback to the production floor has been introduced, a new Engineering Department has been set up as a buffer between development and production, a production bonus scheme has been introduced, and quality control initiated. Case 1, therefore, has become a study of the effects of increased formalization of the control system on behaviour and relationships.

Case II followed through an order for 200 receivers that formed part of a comprehensive communication, navigation, and automatic direction-finding system for aircraft. This equipment had been designed and developed by the firm, and twenty receivers had already been made on a jobbing basis. By the time the order was complete, three more orders had been received and more were expected. The scheduled delivery date for the batch being studied was approximately nine months after the receipt of the order. The control system was formalized. Interestingly enough, fifteen years ago, and before the building of the production unit in which the research was carried out, this firm had gone through a process very similar to that now in progress in the firm covered in Case I; thus, the long-term could be compared with the short-term effects of formalization of control procedures.

Case III covered the production of 'Brand X' household soap. The product was a long-established one, with infrequent modifications in design of product or methods of production and only slow changes in demand. This created a technical and economic situation in which few things were unpredictable. This, together with the fact that the management was sophisticated, had led to the development of an extremely complex control system. Procedures were laid down – sometimes in very great detail – for determining targets and controlling results for the parameters of quantity, quality, methods, and costs. Production was scheduled in four-weekly periods, and the study covered three phases: first, the scheduling phase isolating the various factors taken into consideration in setting the schedule, second, the month's production was observed in detail, and, finally, the assessment and feedback stage, when results were known and discussed. The control system in this firm is likely to become even more formalized in the near future, for a computer is to be used for planning. It may be possible to repeat the study after the computer is in operation.

The three case studies cover three different technical situations within the batch and standardized product area; unit assembly based on standardized parts; batch production, and mass production. The three control systems varied in the extent to which they were formalized and detailed. But it should be borne in mind that the firms were not chosen systematically. Apart from the general desire to keep within the batch or mass-production fields, the only criteria on which the choice was based were willingness to co-operate and the fact that the 'tracer' could be isolated. Later, the firms to be studied will have to be more purposively chosen in the light of the information obtained from these preliminary studies.

THE COLLECTION OF INFORMATION

The 'tracer' approach implies a very detailed study of part of a firm's total activities over a period of time: the methods used were based on social anthropology, the direct and prolonged observation of the daily behaviour of people towards each other until patterns of interaction were identified.

As a first step, preliminary interviews were held with all the people likely to be involved in the policy-making, planning, production, or control activities relating to the product chosen. The purpose of the research was explained to them. A danger that was foreseen was that the identification of a particular product for study might change the behaviour of the people associated with it. In Case III this was no more of a problem than in any piece of social science research, for the people concerned with the scheduling and production of the soap being used as a 'tracer' would be unlikely to realize that there was anything special about a particular four weeks' production. In Cases I and II the research workers deliberately tried to avoid making too obvious the products in which they were interested. In both cases they were helped in doing this by extraneous circumstances. In Case I the original order was cancelled after about three months' work had been done and the completed modules were reallocated among new orders. In Case II the factory manager was concerned about the organization, layout, and general attitudes of the operators in the main assembly workshop, and he asked whether, in return for the research facilities provided, an attitude survey could be carried out covering the entire shop, when the research worker reached this point in the investigations. The interviewing involved was done by two post-graduate students under the direction of the research worker; its effect was to broaden the study and to obscure, at least at shop-floor level, its immediate purpose.

At the preliminary interviews information was obtained about the formal procedures involved in each individual's contribution to the progress of an order through the factory and about what he considered to be his main problems in this connexion. The relevant paper work was also collected at this stage. From these preliminary interviews and the documents obtained it was possible to compile a detailed description of the control system, of all the work that went into the product and all the procedures, policies, and conditions impinging on it.

From the point at which the 'tracer' began to move through the system a detailed diary of events was kept; the idea being to compare what happened in practice with the way the control system was supposed to work in theory. At the outset all three research assistants used the 'milk round' technique, going daily to all the people who were involved with the 'tracer' and asking what had happened since the previous day. In the firm covered in Case III it was possible to do this for the month in which the schedule was being followed and also to spend two hours a day in direct observation of the production department concerned. In the other two cases, however, the number of people involved with the product simultaneously became so large that it was necessary to supplement direct observation and interviewing by asking people to keep records of what happened. At shop-floor level these were very simple memory schedules; a sheet of foolscap was divided into three columns, and the name of the person contacted, the time of contact, and the reason for the contact entered. The research worker went through the sheets with the people concerned each time he saw them. These sheets were kept for periods varying from two days to twelve weeks, depending on the length of time the operator was concerned with the 'tracer'.

In the firm studied in Case II forty-three people holding senior positions in all departments likely to be concerned with the receivers in which we were interested kept more complicated diaries for the period in which the order was progressing through the factory.

In all three cases the research workers also attended all planning, progress, and evaluation meetings at which the 'tracer' was likely to be referred to.

THE GROUND COVERED

In order to make it possible to compare the information arising from the three case studies, the research workers were given some guide-lines to indicate the ground they were expected to cover. Beyond this, they were encouraged to develop their case study as they wished, pursuing points of special interest to them.

They were asked to obtain information under the following headings:

(a) *The history of the 'tracer' in relation to the total activity of the firm.* Here it was important to get the chief executive's definition of the firm's objectives as he saw them in relation to the 'tracer', to find out how these objectives had evolved in time, and to try to assess the firm's achievement in relation either to the 'tracer' or to similar products.

(b) *The relationship between planning, execution, and control activities.* The particular points to look for here were the extent to which these activities were separated organizationally and the area of discretion of those responsible for the execution of the plans. In what circumstances would line supervision modify plans, and were they able to take corrective action if things were obviously going wrong at the production stage?

(c) *The setting of standards.* In this connexion it was important to find out not only who was responsible for the setting of standards relating to time, quality, cost but also on what criteria the standards were based. Was there anything in the way of a master plan discernible, or was any deliberate action taken to ensure that all the standards set could be met simultaneously? If conflict arose between, for example, quality and cost, whose responsibility was it to fix priorities and how were the conflicts reconciled?

(d) *The awareness of standards.* To what extent were those responsible for and concerned with production at shop-floor level aware of the standards being aimed at? If they were aware of the standards, did they accept them and have faith in the accuracy and relevance of the tools used for measurement? To what extent were people conscious of the fact that they were falling behind, and did this cause anxiety?

(e) *The use made of control tools.* The main question here was what happened to control information. Was it fed back to the chief executive, and if so, how did he use it? In particular, did he use it either to develop and modify policy or as a basis for the assessment of the performance of individual managers? The research workers were also asked to note the time-lag between measurement and any necessary corrective action being taken.

(f) *Informal controls.* The research workers were also asked to find out as much as they could about the informal control mechanisms individuals and departments create for themselves to supplement or circumvent the formal control mechanisms. Were subsidiary objectives built into the control system at various stages in the cycle and, if so, were these subsidiary objectives compatible with overall objectives?

(g) *The relationship between the control system and the social system of the firms being studied.* Having followed their 'tracers' through the firms concerned, the research workers were asked to turn their attention to the wider social structure of the firm and to identify the sections and departments with which they had or had not been brought into contact during the course of their study.

Obviously, these production departments not concerned with either the 'tracer' or its components would not have been studied in detail, although the manager of such departments might have been present at planning or progress meetings, and there might have been exchanges of information between departments. These could be important, since the elements of competition between departments so introduced could increase the pressures associated with the control system. It was also important to indicate the extent to which departments such as Sales, Development, Personnel, Training, and Public Relations came into the picture and how far the broader aspects of company policy were linked with the techniques and procedures of control. For example, it was known that the firm studied in Case III operated a guaranteed employment plan; did this have any real significance when production schedules were being worked out.

Interim results

The project has now reached the stage at which a considerable amount of detailed information has to be organized and analysed. It is probably a very bad time, therefore, to make assumptions about what is likely to come out of the research. From discussions with the research workers and from their progress reports, however, it seems that, among a mass of interesting information collected under the headings given above, the following are points of particular significance.

THE USE OF THE 'TRACER' METHOD

All three research workers felt that the use of a 'tracer' was helpful in finding out what happened inside a factory. Its disadvantage, particularly relevant to Case II, where the main control problem was to fit a number of different orders into an overall production programme, was that the concentration on one order meant losing some of the significance of the different orders on each other. This was outweighed by its advantages, however. The first of these was that it was possible to compare objectives and attitudes at all levels of the hierarchy and between line and staff departments in relation to the same task, and to see how the same task created different problems for and offered different satisfactions to the various individuals and groups concerned with it. Second, the 'tracer' provided a valuable reference or 'homing' point for the research workers themselves during a long and complex investigation. It would have been impossible to make such a detailed study and to ask the same questions of the same people so many times without having this reference point to which the answers could be related.

Third, following the 'tracer' through the firm at the pace at which it was being made enabled the research workers to see the evolvement of the control system and the relationships associated with it in a 'real' time context. The fact that an individual, asked at a progress meeting to follow up a certain component, did so on the morning before the next progress meeting, could have significant implications not only for the control system itself but also for the human relations associated with it. It was also possible to see how time ebbed away in the politics of decision-making, and how and when a sense of urgency was introduced into the control system. In this respect the 'tracer' method has advantages over the more generalized organization study and gets round the difficulty so often encountered in attitude surveys of relating what is said to the events taking place in the factory at the time the survey is being carried out.

THE EMERGENCE OF THE INDEPENDENT CONTROL SYSTEM

The limitations on behaviour imposed by the emergence of a control system independent of technology and the adaptations made to the system have been interesting in all three studies. At the operator level there is the curious two-dimensional effect on industrial relations. Operators can have an attitude to and an involvement with the control system within which they work that is distinct from and sometimes in conflict with their attitude towards their employer in a broader sense. The attitude survey carried out in Case II shows how people react to the shop-floor organization and the restrictions imposed by the control system. It would appear that a person's attitude to his firm, the feeling of whether the firm is a good or bad firm to work for is not necessarily determined by day-to-day experience of working on the shop floor. On the other hand, experience on the shop floor seems to be more important than the image of the firm, both in determining how hard he works and whether he stays or leaves it. The realization of this two-dimensional effect has already been useful in interpreting attitude survey material obtained in other connexions.

A particularly interesting aspect of Case III is the effect that working in a formalized framework has on the manager's attitude to his job. The extreme detail in which procedures are laid down, techniques made explicit, and contingencies provided for, means that the area of discretion of managers is very limited. Linked with this is a lot of movement of managers; the manager's job is often a transitional one, part of a training programme or part of a planned progress up the firm. One result is that the manager becomes more involved with his career as a manager than with the job he happens to be doing at the moment. By the time someone recruited as a university graduate is about twenty-six or so he may have held what appear on paper to be three or four responsible management posts. He will certainly have been running a department, but in one sense his control has been nominal because in this highly formalized framework the department has probably been running itself. The inevitable narrowing of the pyramid at the top of the management hierarchy means that quite a lot of people in this age group go elsewhere, many of them to firms in which the work of the manager is less predictable and decisions less circumscribed. The research worker was told that in general the managers who move find it very difficult to adjust to what appears to them to be inefficient management and lack of adequate control, and that a high proportion leave their second jobs after a very short time. A follow-up study of these managers would be important from the management-training point of view.

THE CONTROL SYSTEM AND PERSONNEL MANAGEMENT

The setting of the control system inside the total social structure of the firm indicated that there were a number of interesting differences between firms. There was, for example, a difference between the firm studied in Case I and that studied in Case II in the extent to which the Personnel Department became involved in control and manufacturing problems. In Case I, where formalization of control was currently taking place, the Personnel Department was not called upon when shop-floor problems arose; in Case II it was deeply involved in both the planning and execution stages of the control cycle.

This raises the question of what the role of personnel management should be in relation to the control system. With the extension of control techniques it certainly seems to be important for someone knowledgeable about human behaviour to come into the picture at the programming stage, to make sure that what appears to be the most profitable and economic way of producing is also a way that the people involved will accept. One way of involving the personnel manager is to bring him into planning and progress meetings, not as a formality but to get expert opinion on what is likely to be the impact of a particular decision on the people concerned.

The personnel manager can, however, also become involved in the control system in a very much less desirable way. Reference has already been made to the fact that one of the characteristics of highly formalized control procedures is that loopholes are blocked up. Probably the most difficult loophole to block up is the industrial relations one. In the industrial relations field it is very difficult to foresee all contingencies. In a highly formalized control system, therefore, stoppages of work, overtime bans, restrictive practices, and other failures on the part of operators can become line supervision's only excuse acceptable to top management for failure to reach the standards set. To a harassed foreman aware that he is falling behind his schedule, a stoppage of work could be a godsend. The desire to keep this loophole open encourages line supervision to opt out of labour problems, the personnel department becoming the scapegoat. Industrial disputes as loopholes in the control system might be an interesting subject for further study. Line management in a strike-prone industry may have a vested interest in perpetuating their industry's bad reputation.

INCOMPATIBILITY OF STANDARDS AND RECONCILIATION OF MULTIPLE GOALS

The studies are demonstrating the extent to which functional controls are exercised in parallel rather than in unison. This was particularly so in one of the firms studied; here, over the years, production itself had seemed to become completely separated from the planning and control elements in the system. The setting of the various standards and the measurement of actual against anticipated results seem to have become self-contained activities, ends in themselves rather than integral parts of the control system.

Because so many functional control systems are found to be operating in parallel, rather than in unison, there are a number of goals that people in the organization are trying to attain at one and the same time: a certain task has to be completed by a pre-determined date to satisfy the production controller; it should involve certain methods and perhaps given man-power, to satisfy the work-study man; it has to comply with quality standards, to satisfy the inspector; it should not involve more than certain costs, to satisfy the cost accountant; and so on. With these control mechanisms operating in parallel, and different goals not always being compatible with each other, the operator's main objective becomes to violate these standards as infrequently as possible. Furthermore, he will presumably rank the goals in a diminishing order of nuisance value, depending on the expected outcome of failure, frequency of past failures, and the latitude that each goal provides. Lesser goals may be sacrificed at times to ensure that other critical ones are attained, and there is no incentive to do better than the goal in any one field. This has a serious implication for the operational research concept of maximizing the use of resources. In an industrial environment which is subjected to a set of control systems, each having its own standards, the attainment of all goals may well be entirely divorced from this concept.

INFORMAL CONTROLS

A considerable amount of information has also been collected about informal controls and how and why they develop. In some instances the informal controls are necessary because the formal controls were inadequate or insufficiently well known. In others, the lack of acceptance of the standards set leads to various forms of evasive action being taken. Even where standards were accepted and known, as was the situation in Case III, informal controls seem to be necessary so that those involved in the system could retain the initiative in some respects and thereby increase their own discretionary powers.

INFORMATION FLOW

The following of a product through the control system has produced a comprehensive picture of how information is passed between individuals involved in that system and has shown how in some channels blockages exist and how in other areas channels are duplicated.

THE ASSESSMENT OF MANAGEMENT PERFORMANCE

The research has shown that one problem resulting from the formalization of the control system is that managers can no longer succeed, they can only fail. If a chief executive is satisfied that the standards set are reasonable and based on valid criteria he sees no great virtue in his subordinates meeting them. In some cases, too, it is as bad to do 'better' than the standard as not to achieve it. This means that in industrial organizations where there is formalized control, sticks are more important than carrots. There is also better provision for the transmission of information about failures than about successes. One manager expressed this succinctly to a research worker in discussing the control system and showing how every contingency had been foreseen and every loophole blocked, by saying, 'You can't win.' Added to this, the principle of control by exception means that contacts between people are usually brought about by things going wrong. Where and how things go wrong certainly seems to determine patterns of interaction.

In this situation it becomes extremely important to meet the formal standards, even if in doing so hidden costs are generated or the primary objectives of the firm overlooked. Several examples of the kind of behaviour reported by Jasinski [3] were observed; of foremen rushing all work in progress through the measuring point, of procrastination in making decisions about operating repairs and protective maintenance, of switching components to an order that was being chased.

Not only does working inside this framework lead inevitably to strains and stresses in interpersonal relationships but the dampening effect of being concerned only with not losing the game seems to make it difficult for management to take the initiative when they are required to do so, and to encourage conformity with the letter and evasion of the spirit of the controls.

THE ANALOGY OF CONTROL ENGINEERING PROCEDURES

This assessment of management performance is too akin to procedures in control engineering to be brushed aside as a mere coincidence. In a closed-loop control circuit a feedback signal provides the basis for an adjustment in the input. But as long as no adjustments are required and the system operates according to the pre-determined plans, the only 'reward' is in the absence of warning signals.

Similarly, in quality control the use of control charts relies on the relation between results and predetermined control limits. No action is called for as long as these results remain within the limits, but a point on the chart which falls outside the limits constitutes a warning that something has gone wrong with the process or the product. If this situation persists, an investigation into possible causes is undertaken and a corrective action is called for. In fact, as long as the control limits are not violated, the process is said to be 'under control', and when they are it is 'getting out of control'. In quality control there are special charts which record the number of defectives produced and the number of defects found in inspection, and these charts too have control limits. They imply that a certain amount of defective work is unavoidable and that no action need be taken, provided a certain limit is not exceeded. It is when this predetermined limit is exceeded that a procedure of investigation and corrective action is initiated.

There is nothing in these formalized procedures to provide a reward for good performance. It is only deviations from the standard that are noted and investigated. Furthermore, it is interesting to note that this standard performance as defined by control limits is determined on the basis of past performance: samples of products are measured and recorded and statistical methods are then used to indicate the variability that would be acceptable. Thus, past performance is interpreted as the capability of a production process to work to given tolerances, and designers are urged to bear these in mind when specifying dimensions of components. 'It is no use,' they are told, 'to specify too tight tolerances, since the process will not be able to withstand them, and if you insist on too high a standard the production will have to be 100 per cent inspected to segregate the defects, causing extra costs in inspection and scrap (and by implication you are responsible for taking a decision that causes this inevitable state of affairs).'

It is conceivable that the essentially similar approach which prevails in production control stems from management accepting, sometimes unwittingly, the principles of control engineering as the basis for any formal system for managerial control. This may well provide a better understanding of the way in which schedules and target performance standards are set.

Possible further studies

To make the analogy of control engineering more meaningful, there are a number of problems that could benefit from further investigation, and the following list is not meant to be exhaustive.

(a) Feedback in a system can be used either as a continuous or as a discrete warning signal. The latter still implies continuous monitoring, but if the measured variable exceeds a critical value, a signal is given for corrective action. In production control, too, monitoring of performance is continuous, though reporting is confined to given time intervals and warning signals may either be included in these reports or set separately when breakdown or some other crisis occurs. A further study of the procedures for initiating these signals (both formal and informal) could be rewarding.

(b) A highly formalized but essentially simple control system requires a consistent reaction to feedback; that is, given the same circumstances and the same warning, the system will resort to the same corrective action. Circumstances in practice, however, are not repeated in quite the same way, and an adaptive system will learn from past failures to react in some cases more vigorously to the same stimulus, in other cases to ignore it. Characteristics of adaptive systems could provide an interesting insight into the study of reactions to warning signals in production control.

(c) If goals and standards are indeed determined by past performance a secondary and far more intricate control system may be initiated, namely the adaptation of a performance level with deliberate latitudes built in, so as to prevent high standards from being set up in the future. This implies that incentives can have only a limited effect on improving performance, which increasingly limits the area of discretion and leads to more frequent failures to achieve the standard.

(d) The tacit or often bargaining situation which evolves in setting standards is also highly relevant here. The production planner who sets or suggests a standard gets to know about slack in performance. Now, if he deliberately sets a standard much higher than the level suggested by past performance he runs the risk of incurring a high failure rate and perhaps even slacker performance as a reaction. His objective could be then to take as much slack out of the system without getting it out of control, and the study of standards can perhaps be viewed in this light.

REFERENCES

1 J. Woodward (1965)
2 L. Klein (1964)

3 S. J. Jasinski (1959)

9 · A Field Study of Auditing as a Mechanism for Organizational Control

NEIL CHURCHILL and WILLIAM W. COOPER

Introduction

MOTIVATION AND PURPOSE

This paper reports on one of a series of studies sponsored by the Office of Naval Research directed towards control (as distinguished from planning) in management. One aspect of this study series is concerned with audits, auditing, and auditors as vehicles for influencing the activities of managers and, in particular, it is concerned with a field inquiry directed to ascertaining the perceptions of persons who have been subjected to one or more phases of an audit process.

The need for such a field study was highlighted by experiments which were to be conducted to ascertain ways in which an audit might affect the performance of laboratory subjects. Important parts of the design of this experiment were evidently contingent upon ways in which subjects might be expected to perceive any audit to which they might be exposed. Thus, a precise structuring of the 'audit variable' was necessary. Recourse to the literature of accounting and psychology produced only vague or tangential suggestions, apparently because no previous studies had been directed to this particular topic.

Thus, only to secure the pointed insights which were wanted for the experiment,[1] an investigation was initiated in two firms. Results obtained from this inquiry were sufficiently interesting, however, to suggest that it might be worth extending this line of inquiry in its own right. This was done, and a 'second-phase' field study was initiated by extending the original inquiry to include a total of eight firms.[2] The objective was still one of securing insight, and no attempt was made to secure representative samples from which statistically valid inferences might be drawn. Furthermore, given the state of knowledge on this subject, it seemed best to conduct these as face-to-face, unstructured interviews.

This kind of research produced results which were not as precise as might

109

be desired for the kind of content analysis techniques we employed. Particular difficulty was experienced in attempts to classify or categorize some of the responses. Hence it was deemed necessary to extend the study to a 'third phase' by means of a postal questionnaire to approximately 20 per cent of the respondents who had previously been contacted in phase two. It is these last two phases of the total study with which the present paper is mainly concerned.

THE SUBJECT UNDER INVESTIGATION

Subsequent sections of this paper will be concerned with methodological issues that arose during the course of this inquiry, as well as the nature of the results secured and the conclusions that can be drawn. This section describes some aspects of the audit environment which are of particular relevance to the study. It also raises some questions which, from the outset, were deemed to be of interest.

From one standpoint the audit process can be viewed as a sociological 'influence function'.[3] As such, the effects should be expected to flow both ways: i.e. from the auditor to the persons audited, as well as from the latter to the former – and possibly to third parties as well. Except for interviews with three internal auditors, this study focused on the effects flowing *from* the auditor. Even with the internal auditors, the focus was upon what they thought the audit process did. Nevertheless, the potential effects which might be produced on the auditor were kept in mind.*

The laboratory experiments on audit effects [1] indicated that an audit can exert its influence in two ways: one, through an audit report, whose preparation is a focus towards which audits are customarily pointed: two, through an auditor's actions as seen or heard about by those audited – e.g. what the auditor looks at, what he ignores, what he pursues vigorously, how he behaves, etc. It therefore seemed desirable to investigate situations where no report was rendered to the person under audit as well as situations in which the audit report was reviewed with the person audited prior to its being forwarded to the auditor's superior and then, possibly, to others higher in the company hierarchy.

The laboratory experiment also indicated two distinct effects of the audit process. One occurs in anticipation of an auditor's arrival – in response to the *expectation* of the audit. The other occurs in response to the actual audit experience – the audit *occurrence*. This aspect of the audit's influence is difficult to measure without a sequence of interviews before and after actual instances of audits. We hoped, however, to be able to make some inferences on this effect by cataloguing the attitudes towards the audit of people who had experienced different intensities of audit contact. These attitudes might be reflected, for instance, by an auditee's perception of whom the auditors

* Consideration is being given to an additional study which will be focused on the auditor.

check on, and whether the auditee regarded the auditors as advisors or as policemen representing a third-party control which is imposed from above.

Attitudes towards an auditor might also be influenced by the way an audit is conducted.* For instance, one part of an audit might require an auditor to make observations on the way in which assigned tasks are currently being performed. At another time, or simultaneously, another auditor might restrict himself only to inspections of selected records of past performance. In addition, such a 'record check' might be made at one time for verification of procedures utilized, and at another time it might be directed to fact-finding which is concerned with the way in which a particular transaction was handled. Finally, these checks, studies, and tests occur at a number of organization levels, with differing emphases, and they may be performed by different auditors upon a variety of people. Thus, one would expect compound effects, if only because the different persons involved with our audit often communicate with one another.

One way of approaching the information transmission and control aspects of an audit would be: (*a*) to obtain information on a respondent's view of the audit relative to his own immediate tasks and objectives, and then (*b*) to distinguish these feelings from the respondent's views towards the tasks, objectives, and requirements of the total organization. This can be done in the usual way as, say, by opinion-polling directly. It can also be done indirectly by reference to accounting tasks (related to audit) which the organization requires. For instance, the latter may involve record-keeping and reporting requirements which are generally imposed upon an employee for reasons that are not necessarily directly related in an obvious manner to the immediate performance of his job.

At one extreme organizational record-keeping or reporting requirements might be regarded as a hindrance to the auditee's own operations. Their maintenance may then be perceived as necessary only as an aid to the audit process. At another extreme the records which are maintained may be of assistance or even vitally necessary to immediate task performance. An intermediate view, finally, might have an auditee maintaining records or rendering reports which he perceives as only tangentially of use in immediate tasks but which he also perceives, perhaps with some favour, as being needed for overall organizational control.

In this latter connexion, the auditor might be regarded as an emissary servicing others. He might also be regarded as one controlling the actions of others. Thus, for instance, an auditor's test check of the records might be regarded as one part of the policing imposed upon the auditee. It might also be regarded as policing designed to check on others as much as or more than the auditee. For instance, as we shall see, auditees sometimes regard the

---

* And, of course, the auditor's personality can be influential. This was kept in mind during our study, but an inquiry of the type we employed does not lend itself to observations of this variable.

audit process in just this manner, especially when their own expertise tells them that the amount of test checking which is being performed is not sufficient to enable an auditor to understand and evaluate all aspects of the auditee's job. In this latter case those audited may regard an audit as being performed on them for purposes of checking the behaviour of their superiors. In any case, the audit conveys information and exerts an influence which can affect many aspects of job performance and organizational behaviour.

Because of the complexity and multiple interactions which stem from such organizational activity, it is evident that rather complicated and sometimes delicate techniques of inquiry and analysis are required if one is to ascertain and understand significant parts of an auditee's perceptions relative to this process.

The study design

METHODOLOGY

The study was conducted by means of open-ended interviews applied to a number of people in eight different firms. These eight enterprises were selected to include a wide range of characteristics (size, type, geographical dispersion, form of management, etc.). Some had large internal audit departments, others had small audit staffs or none at all. Most were audited by Certified Public Accountants; some were audited by governmental agencies; but all had one thing in common – they were subject to audits of one type or another.

Within each firm, people were chosen for interviews at different levels of the organizational hierarchy. Selection was made by reference only to job level in the organization and the requirement that each individual had been previously exposed to some kind of audit.

Each interview was open-ended and exploratory in character. Some direction was given to the interview, however, to ensure that each respondent would focus on the somewhat subtle and complex processes that are involved when an audit is being examined for its behavioural consequences.* Detailed records were compiled and maintained for each interview and then, subsequently, submitted to 'content analysis'.

Neither the nature of the research technique nor the exploratory character of the study lent itself to ready summarization. Although the methodology of content analysis is still somewhat embryonic, this approach seemed to offer an appropriate mechanism for obtaining insights into the interview data. A search of the literature on content analysis (e.g. refs. 5 and 6) revealed no instance where it had been applied to the results of interviews, but, *ab initio*,

---

* As the interviewing progressed, the interviewers developed increased insight into the area examined and consequently guided the discussion in later interviews somewhat differently from the earlier ones. This, it will be noted, is permissible for studies, like this one, which are conducted to secure insight rather than to validate already specified hypotheses or to obtain statistical estimates – ones which can be assigned a significance by reference to states of knowledge which have become sufficiently articulate to admit of a solid basis for further progress by reference to the numerical results achieved. See, e.g., remarks by Irwin Bross.[4]

there seemed to be no especially new methodological problem involved for the indicated application.

For the analysis, a number of variables were selected which dealt with internal audits.* This restriction was made for two reasons. First, internal audit is, at present, more of a tool of managerial control and is more easily perceived as such than are the audits conducted by firms of C.P.A.s or governmental bodies. In addition, perception of the latter as a tool of control would only be arrived at, in general, if an auditee possessed considerable sophistication or insight into the audit process. Second, a greater portion of the respondents had experienced contact with internal auditors than with others and, again, we could rely on direct experience, such as arises from personal experience, instead of more abstract ideas, such as would arise from a familiarity with management literature and precepts.

Eighteen variables were chosen for interview guidance and, possibly, subsequent analysis. The interviews were conducted by two persons working in close co-operation. The eighteen designated variables did not, however, represent explicit questions asked by the interviewers.† Also, not all of the variables were chosen in advance. Some were chosen, rather, as representative of types of comment made by respondents in prior interviews. The designated variables, however, did not exhaust the content of the interviews. In the final analysis the indicated eighteen variables were selected, in the main, to give some insights and to impose some order on the analyses which were applied to a large set of complex unstructured data.

Each variable was deemed to represent a potentially significant area for analysis and inference. Within each area a further division was affected by reference to ordered values which might be assigned to the relevant variable. Two coders independently went through the record of each interview, one variable at a time, searching for the category that most reasonably characterized each interviewee's position with respect to the variable being examined.

It is usual in content analysis for different coders to differ at times with respect to how a particular item should be classified even when employing the same code. This occurred to a limited extent in this study. Whenever this happened, however, the two coders examined the reasons for each other's choice and then re-examined the interview data. In all cases agreement was obtained on the second examination and, for further safeguard, these agreements were checked by a third coder on a sample basis. In all cases agreement was secured. The results of the 'consensus' were put on punched cards. These cards were analysed by a computer programme that:

1 Listed by variable the number of responses in each category.
2 Analysed the variables in all possible two-way classifications.

* I.e. audits conducted by persons on full-time company account – as distinguished from external audits conducted, say, by independent certified public accountants.
† With the exception of number twelve, which was asked of many of the respondents by one of the interviewers.

3 Computed a chi-square value for each of the eighteen combinations above.

4 For selected combinations, presented the variables in three-way classification tables.

The chi-square statistic was not considered to apply for testing in a rigorous statistical sense. Rather, it was used as a classification device which could systematically indicate situations that warranted further examination. On the other hand, it was desired to avoid undue reliance on this statistical tool. Thus, for instance, an extension was effected beyond the usual two-way classification and a chi-square analysis for three-way combinations was developed. The resulting matrices tended to be sparse, and where this was so the extension was not used.

THE VARIABLE USED

The eighteen variables, see *Table 1*, fall into five general groups:

The first group contains only variable 1, the variable reflecting the position of the respondent, R, in his organization. The categories of this variable are described in *Table 2*.

The second group, variables 2–5, deals with the involvement of the respondent with the internal audit function.

The third group, variables 6–12, deals mainly with the attitude of the respondent towards the internal audit and the internal auditor.

The fourth group, variables 13 and 14, are concerned with the internal auditor's report.

The final group of variables are the ones of primary interest from the behavioural side. They deal with effects which the internal audit is perceived to have on the respondent and to a lesser extent on the respondent's organization.

A content analysis categorization into these eighteen variables must, of course, lose some information from such unstructured interviews. On the other hand, even if a content analysis cannot produce the ingredients of a complete analysis, it does provide a means of systematically capturing certain significant aspects of the total study, which can then be expanded by reference to a general outline of the material.

Results

THE RESPONDENT'S POSITION IN HIS ORGANIZATION

The sixty-six people interviewed occupied positions at all levels in the eight firms (see *Table 2*). Five of the people interviewed belonged to an organization that had no internal audit staff. Four others – two in each of two other firms – were interviewed but are not included for discussion in this report, since they had no contact with internal auditors, and the interviews with them yielded no data on any of the variables under examination with respect to internal auditing. Finally, three of those interviewed were themselves internal

Table 1 Content Analysis Variables and the Categories of Each

Variable Number	Variable name	Category 1	Category 2	Category 3	Category 4
1	Position of respondent (R) in organization	See Table 2			
2	Extent of R's contact with internal auditors	None	Limited	Extensive	—
3	Does the internal auditor review his report with R?	Yes	No	—	—
4	Does R's supervisor review the I.A. report with R?	Yes	No	—	—
5	Does R have knowledge of the nature of the I.A. report?	Yes	No	Don't know	—
6	Attitude of R towards the internal audit	Negative	Neutral	Positive	Mixed
7	Attitude of R towards the internal auditors	Negative	Neutral	Positive	Mixed
8	Level of education R sees as necessary for Int. Auditing	High school Graduate	College graduate	—	—
9	Extent of changes in internal auditing past 3–5 years	Little	None	Substantial	—
10	Extent of changes in internal auditing next 3–5 years	Little	None	Substantial	—
11	Extent I.A.s are used or seen as useful as consultants	None	Little	Substantial	—
12	Who the internal auditor is most like	Teacher	Policeman	Attorney	Mixed
13	Is it desirable for R to see the I.A.'s report?	Yes	No	Don't know	—
14	The most important part of the I.A.s report	Findings	Recommendations	—	—
15	Internal audit as an information flow	1-way	2-way	—	—
16	The primary purpose of the internal auditing	Procedural check	System evaluation	Accuracy check	Other
17	Who the internal auditors are checking on	Self	Boss	Others	No one individual
18	Extent to which I.A.s are seen by R as influencing his behaviour	None	Limited	Substantial	—

auditors. The remaining fifty-four people formed the basis for the content analysis. The total for each of the twelve categories is shown in the far right-hand column of *Table 2*.

Table 2 *Positions of Respondents in Their Organizations*
Variable Number 1

Function and position			Description of position	Total number of respondents	Number of respondents categorized
Accounting	Upper level		Vice-presidents of finance	5	4
			Controllers	5	4
	Middle level		Accounting supervisors of over 200 employees	4	4
			Accounting supervisors of from 50 to 200 employees	7	6
			Accounting supervisors of from 10 to 50 employees	8	7
	Lower level		First-level accounting supervisors – less than 10 employees	7	6
			Accounting personnel – no subordinates (clerks)	9	8
Non-accounting			Upper-level executives	6	5
			Middle-level executives	8	6
			Lower-level personnel – with some supervisory responsibility	2	2
Special and technical			General 'corporate' accounting supervisors	2	2
			Internal auditors	3	0
			Total	66	54

THE RESPONDENT'S INVOLVEMENT WITH INTERNAL AUDITING

The interviews with fifty-two of the fifty-four individuals included in this study produced reports which allowed the content coder to classify the extent of each respondent's contact with internal auditors. Of these 52 persons, 43, or 83 per cent, had some contact with internal auditing. This is shown in *Table 3* along with the statistics on the other three variables dealing with audit involvement.

The extent of audit contact, variable 2, seemed to be a function of the respondent's position in the firm. None of the eight vice-presidents of finance or controllers indicated even limited professional contact with internal auditors. All but one of the twenty-three accounting supervisors and all of the accounting clerks indicated either limited or extensive contact. The intensity

Table 3 *Respondent's Involvement with Internal Auditors*

Variable number	Number of respondents categorized	Variable name	Categorized responses (percentages)		
2	52	Extent of *R*'s contacts with internal auditors	*None* 17	*Limited* 44	*Extensive* 39
3	29	Does the internal auditor review the audit report with *R*?		*Yes* 55	*No* 45
4	25	Does *R*'s supervisor review the internal audit report with *R*?		*Yes* 64	*No* 36
5	36	Does *R* have knowledge of the nature of the internal audit report?	*Yes* 91	*No* 6	*Don't know* 3

varied with the respondent's level in his organization. Because this information is of interest for its bearing on the overall results, a weighted index of audit contacts by organizational level was synthesized by using the following as ordered weights according to extent of contact reported: 1 = none, 2 = limited, 3 = extensive. Using this set of weights, then, we can arrive at the following as indices of contact at various levels:

	Accounting	Non-accounting
Vice-presidents and controllers	1·00	—
Supervisors of over 200 employees	2·33	2·20
Supervisors of 50–200	2·83⎫	2·33
Supervisors of 10–50	2·67⎭	
Supervisors of less than 10	2·57	2·00
Accounting, non-supervisory	2·12	—

It is thus seen that the internal auditors in this study are generally perceived as being most heavily involved with middle-level supervisors. The extent of contact diminishes systematically for both executives at the top and for 'non-supervisory' personnel at the bottom of the organization.

The above indices were synthesized by reference to contact in general. Another measure of audit contact is whether or not the auditor's report is reviewed with the respondent. This, too, was found to be related to the respondent's position. It does not appear necessary, however, to display the results in detail. The respondent's supervisor is indicated as reviewing the audit report with the respondent at all levels but clerical. The internal auditor is indicated as reviewing his report with practically all the respondents except at the first-line supervisory and the clerical levels.

The indicated degree of audit contact is influenced by these reviews.* Sixty-five per cent of those indicating limited audit contact did not have the

* Significant with the internal audit review at the 2·5 per cent level.

auditor review his report with them, while only 17 per cent of those with extensive contact had no such review.

Still another aspect of audit contact (hence familiarity with audit) is embedded in variable number 5. Knowledge of the contents of an audit report is also related to the audit review. Not surprisingly, all those who had experienced either a supervisor's or an auditor's review of a report indicated knowledge of its contents – as did several others who did not give any information on the audit reviews. The 9 per cent (see variable 5, *Table 3*) who indicated 'no' or 'don't know' had not had a review of the report by either an auditor or a supervisor.

The importance of the internal auditor is sometimes equated with his role as an adviser to management – top management if possible – with respect to formulation of plans, choices to be effected between alternatives, etc. To be sure, our sampling of interviewees was not restricted to examining only this (planning) aspect of accounting but, in fact, was primarily oriented to an investigation of control features of the audit. Nevertheless, the interview generally had sufficient scope for it to be reasonable to suppose that planning would appear, if present in any significant degree. We shall touch on this topic later by reference to whether respondents regarded the internal auditors as advisers or assigned them to other categories – policemen. At present we need only observe that the results covered, at least to this point, do not bear out an assertion that internal auditors play (or even should play) a strong role as planning advisers. On the other hand, we need not consider this as definitive, since much may depend on the way in which management uses such audits to effect, i.e. control, the decisions of others as well as the ways in which management might use reports received from the auditors.

The latter topics will be addressed again, but we should note at this point that very complex and detailed analyses would be required for any general investigation into these dimensions of the audit process. For the present, we may note several salient, if simple, items such as: contact with internal auditors varied with the level of the respondent's position in the organization. Even here, a distinction must be made between the auditor's work *vis-à-vis* the accounting department and this work relative to other, non-accounting departments. Audit contacts outside the accounting department appeared to be less extensive. On the other hand, the audit report is more often reviewed with and explained to the auditee who is not in the accounting department – perhaps because such outside contacts have more of a managerial and advisory flavour or perhaps because a lack of accounting background in the respondents is deemed to make such reviews and explanations necessary.*

Finally, we should observe that the accounting departments were ones in which the more extensive contacts were reported between middle management

---

* For example, in the latter capacity the auditor would, presumably, be viewed as performing a teaching function, whereas in the former capacity he would function as a consultant.

and the internal auditor. At lower levels in these departments, however, as in the case of clerks and first-line supervisors, there was less knowledge of the results of an audit and of the general nature of an audit report.

RESPONDENTS' ATTITUDES TOWARDS INTERNAL AUDITING

Seventy-four per cent of the respondents indicated either a neutral or a positive attitude towards the internal auditor and the internal audit. Of course, a direct response to this kind of question would generally need heavy qualification, and even a content analysis applied to unstructured interview data should also be approached with caution if a solid basis for inference is wanted. Other variables would also need to be considered along with higher-order interaction analysis. This was one consideration in structuring the third group of variables.

As shown in *Table 4*, the respondents were almost evenly divided on the amount of education they deemed to be desirable for internal auditors. The respondents also felt that the internal audit function was changing, and changing at an increasing rate. Less than a third of the respondents, however, thought that the changes were substantial. The internal auditors were viewed as having a function similar to that of a policeman. They were not seen as having consulting type of work as a major part of their duties.

Not only are these attitudes influenced by one another but they also depend on the respondents' position in their firms and the extent of each respondent's involvement with the internal auditors.

It does not require any deep analysis to see that many of the variables are overlapping. This was, in part, deliberate, since we wanted to assure ourselves that major points being addressed were uncovered in spite of the terminological or other vagaries which are generally to be expected in unstructured interviews. Thus, for example, we wanted to ascertain whether distinctions were made between the *audit* as a process and the *auditor* as a person. The attitude the respondent expressed towards the internal audit was highly correlated with his attitude towards the internal auditor.* Some difference did appear, however, in that there was displayed a more neutral attitude towards the auditor and a more positive attitude towards the audit.

Attitudes towards changes in the audit which have taken place in the past and the changes expected to take place in the future are also highly correlated.† The major differences are a shift from 'none' in the past to 'little' or 'substantial' in the future – see variables 9 and 10 in *Table 4*. A dramatic difference‡ emerges, however, when the analysis is extended and the education perceived as desirable is compared with the extent of the respondent's contact with auditors. This aspect of the study is displayed for separate

* When put into a two-way classification, 71 per cent of the responses lie on the diagonal. The chi-square is significant at the 0·5 per cent level.

† With 75 per cent of the responses on the diagonal and a chi-square significance at the 0·5 per cent level.

‡ Significant at the 0·5 per cent level.

Table 4 *Respondent's Attitude Towards Internal Auditing*

Variable number	Number of respondents categorized	Variable name	Categorized responses (*percentages*)			
6	43	*R*'s attitude towards internal audit	*Negative* 26	*Neutral* 37	*Positive* 37	*Mixed* 0
7	42	*R*'s attitude towards internal auditors	*Negative* 26	*Neutral* 48	*Positive* 24	*Mixed* 2
8	36	Education seen as desirable for internal audit work	*High School Graduate* 47		*College Graduate* 53	
9	31	Change in internal audit seen in past 3–5 years	*None* 32	*Little* 45	*Substantial* 23	
10	39	Change in internal audit predicted in next 3–5 years	*None* 13	*Little* 56	*Substantial* 31	
11	30	Extent to which internal auditors are seen as useful as consultants	*None* 57	*Little* 40	*Substantial* 3	
12	26	Who the internal auditor is most like	*Teacher* 11	*Police-man* 58	*Attorney* 23	*Mixed* 8

analysis in *Table 5*, which shows the relationship between these two variables.

The attitude of a respondent towards internal audit, variable 6, influences the respondent's perception of the desirable level of education in the same manner as audit contact. Of those who have a neutral attitude, 90 per cent see

Table 5

Extent of respondent's contact with internal auditing	Education needed by internal auditors	
	High-school graduates	*College graduates*
None	0·80	0·20
Limited	0·14	0·86
Extensive	0·71	0·29

a college degree as desirable while among those who have either positive or negative attitudes towards auditing, 67 per cent and 75 per cent, respectively, see a high-school degree as sufficient.*

It thus appears that where a respondent either has little contact with auditors and/or possesses a neutral attitude towards them he thinks that a college education is appropriate. Where he knows the internal auditors well, ir-

* While the extent of a respondent's contact with auditing and his attitude towards the audit are not highly correlated, 50 per cent of those with limited or no contact are neutral, while only 17 per cent of those with extensive contact feel this way.

respective of whether he is positive or negative in his view of them, he thinks that a high-school education is sufficient.*

Two other variables included here have a possible bearing on the attitudes towards internal auditing. The first, the perceived usefulness of internal auditors as consultants, increases somewhat with the level of a respondent in his organization. This variable is more sensitive, however, to whether or not the internal auditor's report was reviewed with the respondent – particularly if the review was conducted by the supervisor.† The second variable has a somewhat different status. The results on this variable were secured by means of a forced-choice question which required the respondent to categorize the internal auditor by reference to one of four roles which provided the greatest similarity to their view of an auditor. The responses to this question seem unrelated to the respondent's position, the extent of his audit contacts, or his feeling about the audit or the auditor. The majority response is 'policeman' – but this is perhaps best discussed in the next two sections of this report, where its possible bearing on 'audit effects' can be made apparent.

RESPONDENTS' ATTITUDE TOWARDS THE INTERNAL AUDIT REPORT

Two variables are used to measure respondents' attitudes towards the internal auditor's report. The first measures the desirability of respondents' seeing the internal auditor's report. The response was overwhelmingly 'yes' with only two people in middle accounting management saying no – see *Table 6*. This was, of course, an expected result.

Table 6 *Respondent's Attitude Towards the Internal Audit Report*

Variable number	*Number of respondents categorized*	*Variable name*	*Categorized responses (percentages)*		
13	21	Is it desirable for *R* to see the internal audit report?	*Yes* 90	*No* 10	*Don't know* 0
14	17	The most important part of the internal audit report	*Findings* 53	*Recommendations* 47	

Another variable was also included in the study so that we could investigate the extent to which people who are audited see the auditor as a person trying to exert pressure towards change or whether they see him as a person who is mainly interested in reporting the state of things. For the former, the tendency

* Another reinforcement of this point comes from: (a) 64 per cent of those who see substantial changes in the future still see high school as sufficient compared with 33 per cent of those who see little or no changes in the offing, and (b) 57 per cent of those who have had the auditor review his report with them see high school as sufficient, while 80 per cent of those without such a review vote for college.

† Over 64 per cent of those who had both reviews of the audit report – i.e. a supervisory review and an auditor review – indicate internal auditors to be useful as consultants. None of those who reported that they had neither review felt this way.

would be for the auditor to be seen in a supervisory or quasi-supervisory capacity which derives from the perception of pressures directed towards specific change. This could also include a 'self-supervision' function in so far as the pressure is perceived by the auditee as being directed only in a manner which would cause him to make his own changes. The latter is perhaps especially interesting, since its occurrence would enable the audit to function as an alternative to more usual methods of supervision.

Of course, an auditor's 'findings' can generate supervisory and self-supervisory pressures on those who are audited – e.g. in the form of a reaction to the auditor's expressed or implied criteria. Conversely, a 'recommendation' may have an exactly opposite effect. The problem of effecting distinctions in these factors is a difficult one, and only a beginning towards its analysis was attempted in this study. For this purpose a rough guess at the indicated distinctions was made between a report of 'findings' as distinguished from 'recommendations' and then the supposition was made that these might reflect, respectively, (a) mere reporting with no particular pressure towards change, and (b) explicit recommendations which could result in supervised or self-imposed adjustments.

The data indicate that the internal auditor's review affected the respondent's perception of his report. Here it will be noted that we are distinguishing between the findings of the audit examination as to what is being done and the recommendations that might flow from the audit examination. For instance, a 'finding' might result if a prescribed procedure was not followed. A recommendation might also be made to the effect that the prescribed procedure should be altered or revoked. Thus, it is of interest to observe that 67 per cent of those who *did not* have the auditor review his report indicated audit *findings* as most important, while 72 per cent of those who *did* have the auditor's review thought the audit *recommendations* were most important. This relationship did not hold true, however, when it was the supervisor who conducted the review. No perceivable difference was reported between the importance assigned to 'findings' and 'recommendations' in the latter case.

This correlates with the points made on p. 118. The literature on internal auditing stresses the role of the internal auditor as an aid to management and an effort is made to minimize the role of the auditor as a 'policeman'. We previously noted that there was direct testimony to the effect that internal auditors were, in the main, regarded as 'policemen'. This is not conclusive, however, and as the relationship between findings and recommendations (above) indicate there is some reason to suppose that the auditor had implicitly communicated his role as an adviser to those who were audited when he reviewed his report with them. On the other hand, many of these recommendations were perhaps specific and procedural rather than evidencing a concern with the broad aspects of management planning, selection between alternative courses of action, etc. To this extent, the distinction noted between findings and recommendations may be deceptive, and no exact relationship could be deduced between the use of the auditor as a consultant and the importance of his recommendations.

THE PERCEIVED EFFECTS OF INTERNAL AUDITING

This fifth group of variables is intended to measure, in some degree, the effects that, in the respondent's perception, are exerted by internal audits and auditors. One variable, number 18, is an attempt to measure these effects directly. The others approach the respondent's reactions more indirectly.

The audit as a mechanism for transmitting information is perhaps the least obvious of the variables shown in *Table 7*. The audit could serve as a vehicle for communication, even if no report were rendered. This point, made above, is further corroborated by the laboratory study,[2] which indicated that a flow in two or more directions could be expected. On the other hand, a post-experimental questionnaire used in the laboratory study indicated that subjects generally did not accord explicit recognition to the information flow process as such. They did not see the audit process communicating information to themselves as distinguished from a communication upward of the results of the audit findings. Thus, it was natural to devote some further attention to this point in the field study analysis. This is done in variable 15.

Table 7 *The Perceived Effects of Internal Auditing*

Variable number	Number of respondents categorized	Variable name	Categorized responses (percentages)			
15	30	The internal audit as an information flow	*1-Way* 83		*2-Way* 17	
16	53	The purpose of the internal audit as seen by R	*Procedural System Accuracy* *Check.* 76	*Eval.* 4	*Check* 11	*Other* 9
17	26	Who the internal auditors are perceived as checking on	*Self* 23	*Boss* 4	*Other individual* 8	*No one individual* 65
18	40	Perceived effect of internal auditing on respondent	*None* 60	*Limited* 32	*Substantial* 8	

It was anticipated that most respondents would, at best, see the internal audit as a one-way mechanism for information transmittal. Actually no one outside the accounting department at or below the first-supervisory level saw the audit as other than a vehicle for one-way communication. It was viewed as a communication process in which, *via* the audit report, information was transmitted from the bottom of the organization upward. These results were not statistically significant, and neither was the further finding that 42 per cent of those from the controller level through middle-level accounting supervisors perceived the audit to be a vehicle for two-way communication. That is, two-way communication was perceived as occurring only if: the respondent was (a) in an accounting function, and (b) above the first level of supervision.*

We now consider variable 16. Virtually everyone in the top and middle levels of management, both accountants and non-accountants, perceived procedural check as the most relevant purpose of internal auditing. Even with 'no audit contact', six out of eight top managers interviewed indicated the internal audit was mainly a procedural check.†

All respondents who thought 'accuracy check' was the most relevant characterization were in the clerical and first-level supervisory class. In addition, they all indicated that they had experienced only limited contact with the internal auditors.‡ Thus, the respondent's position and the extent of his contact with internal auditing in the broad sense were quite influential in his perception of the audit's purpose – the greater the contact and the higher the position, the more the respondent tended towards viewing the internal audit as a procedural examination.

Further insight comes from relating variables 12 and 16 (see *Tables 4* and *7*). Sixty-three per cent of those who characterized the audit as, in the main, a procedural check also felt that the auditor was most similar to a policeman. This was 87 per cent of the selections of 'policeman'. It suggests a possible correspondence in which the respondents mentally related *looking* to see if things are going according to plan and *ensuring* that the plan was followed. That is, the auditor was here being viewed as policing all actions to ensure that the plans of higher management were, in fact, being followed.

It is desirable, however, to consider this in the light of the other variables in the analysis. Thus, for instance, variable 17 shows that, for the most part, the respondents did not perceive the internal auditor as checking on any one individual. By the term 'no one individual', the content coders meant that an overall organization check was deemed to be the pertinent characterization rather than an individual-by-individual check throughout the organization. Hence the policing function may, in this sense, be viewed as a higher-order abstraction than the term 'policeman' might suggest. To this extent, the image of the auditor is projected in a way that accords with the ones recommended in the accounting literature.§

At another level of analysis it would be necessary to relate variables 16 and 17 through further breakdowns of their categories. Half of the 23 per cent

---

* On the other hand, two vice-presidents of finance and one internal auditor indicated that they perceived the audit as only a unidirectional communication device. This is understandable, perhaps, with reference to the vice-presidents in so far as they have contact only with the reports and not with the internal audit process *per se*. It is more difficult to understand the perception of the internal auditor except as either personal inclination or a manifestation of a particular company's policy.

† Two of the three internal auditors chose 'other', however.

‡ Audit contact and perceived purpose of the audit had a chi-square statistic significant at the 2·5 per cent level, while the corresponding value of the auditor's review and the perceived purpose of the audit was significant at the 5 per cent level.

§ See the discussion of this point in Churchill [1 and 7] and Mautz and Sharaf. [8]

indicating the auditor as checking on 'self' (see *Table 7*) were at the clerical accounting level. Furthermore, as we previously observed, these persons reported that, in general, they had not experienced any review of an audit report with either the internal auditor or their supervisor. In fact, *no one* who had been a party to either review indicated 'self'.*

Finally, we come to variable 18, which attempts to provide a direct measure of the extent to which respondents perceived the internal audit as influencing their behaviour. Seventy-four per cent of those interviewed expressed themselves in a way which could be entered into this category of our analysis. Their comments indicate that the audit had little, if any, such perceived effect. The perception and the actuality probably differ, however, as we may surmise from the laboratory studies which have already been conducted.[2] Thus the result was not unexpected, given the subtleties involved in an audit influence function.† That is, a simple, direct measure of this kind cannot be relied upon without further, and deeper, supplementary inquiries.

Neither the level of the respondent in his firm nor the extent of his dealings with the auditors seemed to exert any influence on the perceived effects of an audit. There is some indication that upper and middle management in both accounting and non-accounting functions perceived a stronger influence than those above or below them in their firms.

One would suppose that there might be some relation between behavioural effects and the attitudes towards audits and auditors held by the respondents. The attitudes reported by respondents do not bear this out in an unambiguous manner, however. For instance, a neutral attitude towards the auditors appears to be accompanied by a perception of little, if any, audit effect. On the other hand, negative or positive attitudes as expressed in variables 6 and 7 are accompanied by a response for variable 18, in which 67 per cent of those who indicated 'negative' or 'positive' attitudes also reported 'little' or 'substantial' effects on their behaviour. By way of contrast, only 17 per cent of those reporting a 'neutral' attitude also reported 'little' or 'substantial' audit influences on their behaviour.‡ It is not advisable, however, to infer anything significant from these cross-relations without further supplementary studies.

Conclusions

We have here attempted to report some findings from a limited field inquiry. This inquiry was mainly pointed towards sharpening the issues so that this

---

* Ninety-two per cent who had experienced a review with either an auditor or a supervisor indicated a 'no one individual' response for variable 17.

† As a concrete illustration, we can refer to the report of one interviewee who stated that the auditor had no effect on his behaviour and that he didn't care whether the auditor came in or not. Later in the conversation, however, he stated that, '. . . he was a busy man with more things to do than he had time for and when he knew the auditor was coming he got those things done which he thought the auditor would look for in order to minimize the amount of time the auditor would be in his hair.'

‡ Both negative and positive attitudes generated similar perceived effects.

rather subtle area of management can be made the subject of further and better research.[9] First, we observe that the area of managerial control has not been a subject of systematic scientific inquiry. Second, we observe that a further evolution of scientific method will probably be needed before many of the significant dimensions of the audit-control function can be adequately studied in a broad context such as face-to-face field interviews, questionnaires, etc. This was illustrated at many points in the preceding analysis and brought sharply into focus by our discussion of perceived 'behavioural effects' at the close of the last section.

To be sure, controlled laboratory investigations, such as those referred to above, are in order. These, too, are only pointers, however, and further elaboration and assistance will be required from suitable mathematical–statistical models which can be developed to handle the numerous and complex interactions that are involved in such control procedures. On the other hand, as we have already observed, a good deal more is needed in the way of preliminary study before the task of synthesizing such models can be fruitfully undertaken. Indeed, even the laboratory investigations require recourse to field inquiries even to define the pertinent variables for study.

The field inquiry reported here was itself a product of this need. It is hoped that the continuation, of which this present study is a part, will ultimately indicate areas where research in mathematics, management, and the social sciences may be joined, to the end that new scientific knowledge and new methods of management will emerge. Just as the advent of operational research has produced a more easily tapped field of inquiry in the area of management planning, so may we anticipate a similar evolution in the more subtle activity of management control in symbiosis with the behavioural sciences. The methodology which such research may produce can then, perhaps, lend itself to social inquiry as well. It may also facilitate the reporting and study of the kinds of 'social fact' which can emerge from managerial applications which are effected by means of these same tools and constructs.

ACKNOWLEDGEMENT

This paper was written as part of the contract 'Planning and Control of Industrial Operations', with the Office of Naval Research at the Graduate School of Industrial Administration, Carnegie Institute of Technology, Management Sciences Research Group. Reproduction of this paper in whole or in part is permitted for any purpose of the United States Government. Contract NONR 27 TO24.

REFERENCES

1 N. C. Churchill (1962)
2 N. C. Churchill, W. W. Cooper & T. Sainsbury (1964)
3 J. G. March (1955)
4 I. Bross (1964)
5 B. Berelson (1952)
6 I. de Sola Pool (1959)
7 N. C. Churchill & W. W. Cooper (1964), pp. 250-75
8 R. K. Mautz & H. A. Sharaf (1961)
9 W. W. Cooper (1961)

F

10 · Control of Research and Development by Top Managers in Forty-eight Very Large Companies

MICHAEL RADNOR

Introduction

This is an abbreviated report on a study that was conducted at Northwestern University as part of a larger programme of research on the organization and management of research and development activities in large decentralized companies. For more complete analyses and/or data presentations see references 1–5. In addition, a full report on our ten-year research programme in the area is in preparation for publication by these authors.

We consider here the problem of control of the research and development activity by the highest level of the organization hierarchy. This is examined in the complex environment of very large decentralized companies. We shall attempt to illustrate several of the characteristics of this control situation as it is perceived by the top managers of such firms. We will also present and partially test a theory which indicates the form of top managerial control responses to this perceived situation.

The field study

The data presented in this paper were obtained primarily from a series of interviews with top managers of forty-eight very large industrial companies

Table 1

Industry	Number of companies
Engineered products	15
Chemical and pharmaceuticals	6
Primary materials	3
Electronics	12
Metals	1
Food	7
Miscellaneous	4

129

which had research and development activities. The combined sales of these companies was approximately fifty thousand million dollars in 1963, ranging from one hundred million to approximately ten thousand million dollars. The distribution of companies between industries was as shown in *Table 1*.

The interviews, which lasted from one and a half to four hours each, were in two sections.*

1 A free interview in which the top managers were guided through a series of topics concerning their attitudes regarding research and development control problems and the various types of controls and changes they had effected or were considering.

2 A series of ratings obtained through a Q-sort procedure. These ratings were designed to measure what were hypothesized to be three principal components of top managerial perceptions of their control situations. These measurements were obtained for the divisional and central research and development programmes in most of the forty-eight companies, as of the time of the interview and as it was reported to have been three to five years previously. The ratings were on a five-point scale. While the top managers were performing the sortings (or ratings) they were also asked to comment on the reasons for their ratings, on actions they had taken or were planning, on changes they had made and so on, for each sub-unit in their firms.

There was also available for each company previous interview data as well as various types of documentary data – annual reports, organization charts, memoranda, etc. – which had been obtained over the eight years of the study. These both provided additional sources for this present aspect of our research and also enabled the interviewer to go into the meetings prepared on the history and organization of the company and its research and development activities.

The control system

Our concept of control and evaluation can be conceptualized by the system control model shown in *Figure 1*.

Our focus is on the top manager viewing the organizational system as an instrument for his goal achievement. Specifically, we shall be concerned with the perceptions of the top manager conceived as the system designer and controller. These perceptions are concerned with the characteristics of the organizational system and its performance, the environment, the adequacy and reliability of the information feedback, the perceived ability to evaluate this feedback, the perceptions of ability to effect the desired controls, and the form of the top managerial control attempts. We have hypothesized that these attempts will be an internally rational response to the stimulus of their

---

* For complete information on the interview schedule, see Radnor. [1, pp. 119-28]

perceived control situations. We have further focused on that sub-set of these top managerial attitudes and behaviours which are related to the research and development and allied areas.

Figure 1   *Conceptual Control Model**

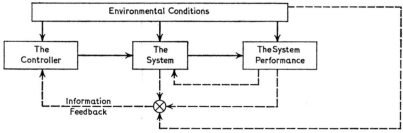

* This will be seen as analogous to the Shewart [6] quality control concept. We recognize in this model the complex nature of the phenomena and the fact that our theories must of necessity be partial.

The organizational form of the decentralized company may be noted as consisting of a number of semi-autonomous operating divisions reporting to a top corporate management and supported with corporate staff functions. Research and development activities have been found to be deployed, generally, either at these divisions and/or with a corporate research and development function.[4] This central research and development function could also be looked upon as having had delegated to it a measure of decision-making autonomy. Thus, the location of operating responsibility for research and development decision making in decentralized companies may be:

1 in the divisions – under the division managers;
2 in the central laboratory – under the corporate research manager.

We are consequently interested in the top managerial control perceptions and attempts at these two levels.

Top management attitudes to research and development

RESEARCH AND DEVELOPMENT GOAL DIFFERENCES AS PERCEIVED BY TOP MANAGERS

In Radnor and Rubenstein [2] and Radnor [1] we theorized that the existence of often diverse and dispersed semi-autonomous sub-units each with their own emergent social systems, and the effects of the methods used to control, evaluate, and reward their managements, could lead to unintended consequences for the top manager. These might be manifested in perceived differences, or lack of agreement, between top managers and either, or both, their division managers and corporate research managers with respect to goals, values, attitudes, orientations, and abilities. In the case of the division managers, as it concerns research and development and related areas, this could be perceived by top managers to appear as shorter time horizons than desirable, tendencies towards supporting divisional rather than corporate objectives, lack of co-operation with or even opposition towards the corporate research laboratory, and so on. For the research personnel and management, this may be viewed as resulting from a lack of commercial and managerial orientations and abilities on the part of such scientific personnel.

In order to test for the existence of such top managerial perceptions of research and development and similar goal differences with their division managers, the following proposition was tested. This contains a set of examples of perceived goal differences as related to the corporate viewpoint on research and development and on long-range activities.

'Many top managers come to believe that there are research and development goal differences between themselves and their division managers, as manifested by perceptions that the division managers:

'(a) have shorter-range objectives (time horizon) than would be preferred by these top managers;

'(b) tend to support divisional rather than corporate objectives;

'(c) will only do long-range planning under pressure;

'(d) will not tend to support basic research;

'(e) will give only reluctant support or even opposition to a corporate research and development function.'

The following findings were drawn from the interview data and indicate the proportions of top managers who expressed perceptions agreeing, to various degrees, with those stated in the proposition.

Table 2

Top managers with	No.	%
All known perceptions* agreeing	28	58½
The majority of known perceptions agreeing	2	4
The majority of known perceptions disagreeing	1	2
All known perceptions disagreeing	11	23
Other	6	12½
Total	48	100

* Because of the inevitable time constraints encountered when attempting to interview top managers of large companies, not every respondent expressed an opinion on every topic.

These findings* would seem to indicate that a substantial proportion of the top managers felt, to some degree, that such research and develop-

* For more detailed findings see Radnor.[1]

ment goal differences did exist between themselves and their division managers.

Similarly, we hypothesized, for the other end of the continuum, that:

'Many top managers come to believe that there are research and development goal differences between themselves and their research personnel and managers as manifested by perceptions that:

'(a) such personnel do not have a commercial or business orientation;
'(b) it is difficult to find research managers who think and behave as they do;
'(c) they have problems integrating a corporate research laboratory into the company.'

Our findings were as shown in *Table 3*.

Table 3

Top managers with	No.	%
All known perceptions agreeing	28	58½
The majority of known perceptions agreeing	3	6
The majority of known perceptions disagreeing	0	0
All known perceptions disagreeing	3	6
Other	4	8½
Not known	10*	21
Total	48	100

* Time did not allow the asking of these questions in these 10 companies.

Thus, there are indications that a substantial proportion of top managers also appeared to have such perceptions of their research personnel.

'VISIBILITY' OF THE RESEARCH AND DEVELOPMENT AREA FOR TOP MANAGERS

We further hypothesized that most top managers have had a relatively low level of training and experience in the research and development area. Also that, in general, they recognize that the research and development area is one of low 'visibility' for themselves – both because of this lack of direct exposure to it and because of its inherent complexities and uncertainties.

'Many top managers involved in research and development decision-making come to believe that the research and development area is one:

'(a) that they need to know more about;
'(b) for which they have need of better information and reporting concerning what is happening in their companies;
'(c) in which it is hard to evaluate performance.'

Our findings were as shown in *Table 4*.

Table 4

Top managers with	No.	%
All known perceptions agreeing	24	50
The majority of known perceptions agreeing	1	2
The majority of known perceptions disagreeing	0	0
All known perceptions disagreeing	4	$8\frac{1}{2}$
Other	0	0
Not known	19	$39\frac{1}{2}$
Total	48	100

Most top managers did appear to agree, then, that the research and development area was one which we may describe as having relatively low 'visibility' for them.

We have so far seen that, in general, top managers perceive themselves to be faced with these problems: (*a*) they have subordinates who are responsible for the operating research and development decision-making who do not have the same research and development goals and orientations as themselves; and (*b*) this occurs in a situation in which they themselves feel that they do not understand the processes and requirements as well as they might wish. Let us now turn to the form of their responses to this situation.

Top managerial control responses

We have theorized [1, pp. 84-90] that top managerial control behaviour responses (CBRS) are a function of: perceived need to control (PNC), perceived ability to control (PACS), and the perceived level of understanding and appreciation of the situation – the 'visibility' – (PLOV), i.e.:

$$CBRS = f[PNC, PACS, PLOV]*$$

We have also theorized that the precise form of the response will be an internally rational attempt by the top manager to overcome the constraints on his improving his present and potential research and development outcomes from the organizational system.

If we conceptually represent the three variables PNC, PACS, and PLOV along three axes we could attempt to predict the CBRS at, or near, the extreme points.

* This may be noted as being closely related to the Hull–Spence stimulus–response formulation as stated in Campbell.[7]

Figure 2 *Control Perceptions*

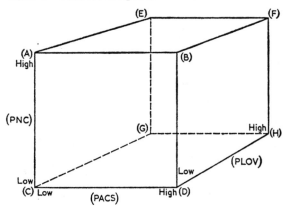

The conditions at these extreme points may be tabulated as follows: High to Low.

Table 5

Location	Variable		
	PNC	PACS	PLOV
A	High	Low	Low
B	High	High	Low
C	Low	Low	Low
D	Low	High	Low
E	High	Low	High
F	High	High	High
G	Low	Low	High
H	Low	High	High

We have hypothesized that all three of these variables, together, represent a set of necessary and sufficient conditions for determining the form of the managers' control responses. We have not, in this study, attempted to examine the relative weights of these variables in this determination. We were, therefore, looking to the extreme values of the dimensions to test for the occurrence of the predicted behaviours as they will be described below.

As a secondary hypothesis, we would expect that weaker predictions could be made where any two of the three variables fell near the extremes. In these cases we would expect the responses to be more similar to those which are typical at the closest locations than to those at the other extremities. Thus, for example, we would expect a high, high, medium rating-set to be more likely to show behaviours typical of either a *B* or an *F* location than the others. In a geometrical sense, such a rating situation would be closer to a *B* and/or an *F* than to any other point.

The following are the specific predictions which, in conformity with our conceptual hypothesis, show the top manager attempting to overcome the actual and potential constraints on his ability to achieve his research and development goals through a sub-unit, a division, or a corporate laboratory.

Expected CBRS when an organizational unit is perceived to be at location:

A – Frustration, a desire to do something, but perhaps not knowing what to do. The top managers will try various types of controls to see what happens. They will make attempts to learn more. Where the control and visibility constraints seem, to the top manager, to have arisen because the unit is 'too different', there may be divestiture attempts.

B – The top managers will make attempts to learn more about the situation. They may attempt to make compliance demands. They may be optimistic of improvements.

C – The top managers will leave the unit alone, but will watch it warily. They will try to learn more.

D – The top managers will leave such units strictly alone. They will try to learn more as the opportunity arises.

E – The top managers will try to make major structural changes – such as changes in unit management and/or personnel, or amalgamation with other units.

F – The top managers will try direct compliance demands. There will be attempts to work things out, and optimism for improvement. Where the difficulties are perceived as being due to external factors, this could lead to direction changes or even divestiture attempts. Where they are thought to be due to inability of the unit managers to perform, personnel changes may be attempted.

G – There may be attempts when opportunity arises – perhaps with retirements – to gain control.

H – The top managers will leave such units alone. With their high level of control ability and visibility, they could attempt experiments to further improve their outcomes, in contrast to *D*.

In looking at the form of the top managerial responses we must note that we are unlikely to be able to find the type of clear-cut cause-and-effect relationships that seem to be implied above. Thus, for one example, top management may institute a change because it is fashionable, but which turns out to be most functional, preventing problems that might otherwise have occurred. We would be able to observe the mechanism being used but not able to see it as a response to a previous need. Thus, the use of a mechanism can be in response to an actually perceived existing or potentially expected need. It can also be used for other, possibly idiosyncratic reasons, which nevertheless save the top managers from ever experiencing that particular need – i.e. they may remain in ignorance of it, to some degree.

It was more likely that we would be able to associate specific behaviour responses with needs that occur at a sub-unit level rather than at a total organizational system level, where many more variables could affect the top manager's behaviours. We therefore, in the empirical phase of our study, worked at the sub-unit level in attempting to predict and explain specific behaviours against measurements of the PNC, PACS, and PLOV as above.

The measurements for the PNC, PACS, and PLOV variables were obtained from the Q-sort ratings, for the present and past situations. A total of more than four hundred sets of ratings of sub-units by top managers was so obtained.

The form of the ratings was such that the set could fall near one of the extreme locations, between any two such locations, or in mid-location. In some cases we were able to obtain measurements of only two of the three variables. In the following tables:

Single ratings – as *A*, *B*, etc. – represent sets of ratings at an extreme location.

Double ratings – as (*A–B*) or (*A–*?) – represent sets between two extremes or between one extreme and the mid-location.

? ratings are sets at the mid-location.

Together with each set of ratings, we also had the data on top managerial control behaviours, if any, in the past and in the present or on any plans that they had, relative to each sub-unit. It was on the association of the composite ratings and these behaviours that the analysis was based.

The primary analysis was from the association of present ratings with present and planned behaviours. The use of ratings of the past presented some added problems. Thus, the rating by an executive today of the manner in which he perceived the world some years ago may be subject to the influence of all events that have occurred since that time. We therefore utilized data on the past as secondary and possibly confirmatory, bearing in mind the possibilities of such distortion.

To partially test our theory, we selected two of the more extreme types of behaviour as follows:

(a) *Major structural changes made for technical activity reasons**

From our theory the expectation for such events was that they would occur for the most part in *E*-type situations.

In the following table the percentage figure shown is the proportion of all occurrence of the indicated location (*A* to *H*) which appeared in association with the event being investigated. Thus, 78 per cent of all *E*-type rated situations in the present were associated with major structural changes. Chance alone would lead to equal distribution of such proportions between locations. We had, however, no *a priori* basis for determining the size of this proportion in terms of our present theory.

---

* E.g. elimination or formation of a central research laboratory, replacement of a division manager, reorganizations.

As expected, for the single ratings, the *E*-type situation was found to be associated with major structural changes several times more frequently than was any other location.* In fact, approximately three-quarters of all *E* situations were associated with such control behaviours.

Table 6

Location	Present occurrences			
	Single ratings		Double ratings	
	No.	%	No.	%
A	1	33	7	54
B	—	—	4	21
C	0	0	0	0
D	1	$12\frac{1}{2}$	1	3
E	7	78	14	$58\frac{1}{2}$
F	2	33	8	17
G	1	33	7	$53\frac{1}{2}$
H	1	$2\frac{1}{2}$	5	$7\frac{1}{2}$
?	5	7	5	$18\frac{1}{2}$
No rating	1	20	—	—

That this finding is not merely a reflection of the high perceived need to control in these cases can be seen by comparing the *E*-occurrences with the other high PNC locations, namely *A*, *B*, and *F*.

It does not even appear that high PNC is a necessary condition for such structural changes. Thus under *G*-type conditions, which have low PNC and for which we predicted opportunistic changes to gain control, it appears that top managers may even be willing to make deliberate changes to obtain such control, even though the overall performance is satisfactory, i.e. they respond not only to system output, but also to their perceptions of the nature of the system. Further, although they have a high PNC, we had not predicted structural changes for *B*-type situations, and they did not appear. As expected for the *C*, *D*, and *H* situations, in which we had predicted that managers would leave the units alone, there were no such changes.

If we look to the double ratings we find, as expected, that while *E*-type ratings were still strongly associated with major structural changes, in approximately half of such locations resulting in changes, the predictive ability had in fact become weaker. Thus, *A*-type situations were as highly associated with structural changes as were *E*. Again we note the emergence of the *G*-type location in association with such changes. We also again observe the lesser showings of the high PNC *B*-type situation, as expected. *C*, *D*, and *H* locations repeat the previous findings in their relative absence. Thus, while the

---

* The hypothesis of a difference between the proportions of *E* ratings and the others can be accepted at better than the 0·05 risk level.

findings are weaker, as expected, these double ratings do confirm the findings for the single ratings.

Let us now examine the findings based on ratings of the past.

Table 7

Location	Past occurrences			
	Single ratings		Double ratings	
	No.	%	No.	%
A	0	0	16	50
B	—	—	3	43
C	—	—	2	28½
D	0	0	1	11
E	17	71	16	40
F	1	11	3	14½
G	1	33	3	43
H	0	0	1	11
?	2	9	4	20
No rating	3	2½	—	—

For the most part, the same picture has emerged for the past ratings. The findings are strongest for the single ratings and weaker, but in the same direction in the double ratings – showing that E-type situations are the most highly associable with such changes. The C, D, and H locations are, again, for the most part absent. (The hypothesis of a difference between the proportions of the E ratings and the others can be accepted at the 0.05 level of risk, for the single ratings.)

The one exception seems to lie in the B and F locations, which appear with greater and lesser prominence respectively in these past occurrences. A possible explanation is that this is because of distortion due to changes in perspective, or level of aspiration. Thus, several years ago a top manager may have felt that his level of understanding of a given operation was fairly high, but several years later he feels that he really did not have such a level at that time – given normal learning in the interim. This could alter past F situations to present perceptions of them as B's. This could account both for the small reduction in F-type ratings and for a consequent increase in B's. With only a low N ($= 1$ for single ratings and $= 3$ for doubles) such a distortion in a small number of cases could change the overall picture to coincide with that found in the present ratings.

The difference between A and E situations also seemed to diminish somewhat between the two periods, and this might be explained by the same distortion.

To return to the present ratings, it is of interest to consider differences between behaviour in the E and A situations. Both show high need to control and low ability to do so, but visibility is higher in E than in A. We predicted an initial reaction of frustration in A situations and we would expect to find, as we did, a lower level of major structural changes. This may be a demonstration of the importance of the PLOV variable in the system.

In summary, for structural changes, we have observed that our theoretical scheme has enabled us to show a high degree of association between situations of high perceived need to control, low ability to control, and a high perceived level of understanding (E), and the making of a major structural change as a response. Conversely, a lower association was shown under most other conditions. In comparing the findings for the various locations, we have observed that each variable is able to differentiate between behaviours. As a consequence, strong predictions could be made only when all three variables were in the prescribed locations. The fact that the associations based on only two variables were weaker further confirmed this.

(b) *Leaving a sub-unit 'alone'*

We now turn to the other extreme of behaviour, namely 'the leaving of a sub-unit alone'. From our hypothesis we would expect such top managerial behaviour to be associated with D, H, and C locations, in that order.

Table 8

| Location | Present occurrences | | | |
| | Single ratings | | Double ratings | |
	No.	%	No.	%
A	1	33	3	23
B	—	—	9	47½
C	1	100	2	40
D	8	100	27	92
E	0	0	6	25
F	3	50	31	64½
G	1	33½	7	54
H	38	88½	54	82
?	51	72	18	66½

In this case we operationized 'leave alone' behaviour by the incidence of no known behaviours of any other kind. The number of cases involved made this the only practical method of approaching such a concept.

For single ratings in the present, we find that almost all D, H, and C are associated with no action relative to the sub-units involved. By contrast, E situations are non-existent. This diverges very sharply from our previous finding for structural changes and further demonstrates the ability of this application of our theory to differentiate between these diverse control behaviours under extreme conditions. As previously, these associations weaken considerably for the double ratings, although they still indicate the same effect. As expected, *D* location was the most consistent in its demonstration of top management leaving units 'strictly alone'.*

Of the other locations, only the *F*- and *G*-types appeared. We predicted compliance demands in the *F* situation, and changes under limited circumstances. It was not altogether surprising, therefore, to find the incidence of no action for this type of situation. It was most unlikely that we would be able to pick up all instances of compliance pressures on sub-units. This would require studies in depth. Thus, it is possible that a number of the events recorded as no action would actually show the existence of compliance pressure by top management. Given such a data loss, we would expect to find *F* somewhat more highly associated with 'leave alone' situations. Similarly for *G* situations, the lack of opportunity to make control attempts could appear, in part, as no action.

Table 9

| Location | Past occurrences | | | |
| | Single ratings | | Double ratings | |
	No.	%	No.	%
A	1	25	6	$19\frac{1}{4}$
B	—	—	1	$14\frac{1}{4}$
C	—	—	4	57
D	1	100	6	67
E	2	$8\frac{1}{2}$	9	$22\frac{1}{2}$
F	4	$44\frac{1}{2}$	8	38
G	1	33	1	$14\frac{1}{4}$
H	2	50	5	$55\frac{1}{2}$
?	11	50	5	25

These data confirm our findings for the present-day ratings. *C*-type did not occur in the single ratings and could not therefore be tested for in that case.†

For both sets of data, the low PNC situations are more reliable in their association than are the high PNC cases. Within this we do, however, note that the low PNC situation of *G* is not any more reliable in association with no action than is the high PNC situation of *F*, again confirming that we have more than a high–low satisfaction dichotomy.

We have so far seen that our theory has enabled us to differentiate between general types of control behaviour to be expected from top managers in response to their perceptions of the research and development control

---

* The hypothesis of a difference between the proportions of the *C*, *D*, and *H* ratings and the others can be accepted at the 0·05 level of risk.

† The hypothesis of a difference between the proportions of the *C*, *D*, and *H* ratings and the others can be accepted at the 0·05 level of risk.

situation. Further, that this control situation can be usefully described in terms of the variables PNC, PACS, and PLOV.

We now turn to an examination of the repertoire of control responses and the prevalence of various mechanisms that are utilized by top managers.

The repertoire of responses

The repertoire of responses available to the top manager may be ascertained by reference to the control model in *Figure 1*. These may be categorized as: attempts to control the characteristics of the system – the design function; attempts to control the behaviour of the system – the control function; attempts to improve the visibility levels – the information feedback; and finally, where perceived necessary, attempts to make goal changes.

The top managerial attempts, based on their system design and control functions, to influence the first-level subordinate research and development decision-making, can be operationally restated in terms of three modes of control:

1 Control attempts through demands for compliance from either or both division managers and corporate research managers with research and development decisions made by themselves (decision compliance);
2 Control attempts to structure the situations in which these subordinate managers make their decisions (situation structuring);
3 Control attempts to regulate the decision premises used by these subordinate managers in making their research and development decisions (premise regulation); through either or both:

    (*a*) changing the research and development decision-makers at a given location – divisional or corporate research;
    (*b*) changing the location at which certain research and development decisions are made – from divisional to corporate research, or vice versa.

We have attempted to demonstrate the use of these three modes of control by top managers and the prevalence of particular mechanisms, out of the repertoire available to them. We have also taken note of top managerial attempts to improve the visibility to them of the research and development area in their firms, in terms both of their capacity to perceive and their access to these activities, and we have also noted the possibility of their making goal changes.

The following findings will be presented in summary form – for the full tabulated data, sample sizes, and significance levels see Radnor.[1] The proportions shown are of the companies interviewed who reported the use of the mechanism concerned.

1 COMPLIANCE DEMANDS

We found that 86 per cent ($N = 48$) of the top managers reported using various mechanisms that applied compliance demand pressures on their division managers in relation to research and development activities. Examples of such mechanisms were: the giving of direct instructions (81 per cent; $N = 41$); making performance in the research and development area part of the evaluation criteria for judging division managers (70 per cent; $N = 20$); calling for reports from the divisions on their research and development activities (94 per cent; $N = 32$) and the utilization of corporate research managers to audit divisional research and development to some degree (77 per cent; $N = 34$).

The use by top managers of direct compliance demands on their corporate research managers was found to be less prevalent (54 per cent; $N = 37$) than for division managers. Two possible explanations seemed to suggest themselves. These were: (*a*) that top managers may have experienced fewer problems, relatively, with their corporate research managers as regards research and development activities than with their division managers; and (*b*) that because of both a felt lack of common language with their research managers and a deficiency in their own perceived level of understanding of the research and development process, the top managers felt constrained in their attempts to use compliance demands on their research managers. Of specific interest was the finding that a number of companies (30 per cent; $N = 37$) had delegated the control of their corporate research and development activity to a commercially oriented executive who might be found heading both corporate research and corporate marketing, with the objective of giving the corporate research and development activity a more commercial orientation. While this was not widely prevalent at this time, these types of appointment were all of relatively recent origin, indicating a possible developing trend.

2 SITUATION STRUCTURING

Several examples were noted of top managerial attempts to structure the research and development situations of their subordinates. An example at the divisional level, having the objective of encouraging broader-scoped research and development, was allowing the division managers to use corporate funds on favourable terms to finance longer-range or larger research and development programmes than they would normally undertake (62 per cent; $N = 21$ for companies with central laboratories and 75 per cent; $N = 8$ for those without such laboratories – and who presumably would have greater need for such programmes in the divisions). A number of companies (57 per cent; $N = 28$) charge their divisions for service work performed for them in the central laboratory, to discourage excessive use of such a facility in this manner. As an example at the corporate research level, we observed a greater tendency to change the funding of a corporate research laboratory from corporate to divisionally supported in those situations where top managers had reported having experienced problems in integrating such laboratories than where no such problems had occurred (27 per cent; $N = 15$ to 0 per cent; $N = 7$).

3 PREMISE REGULATION

The use of 'premise regulation' of the research and development decision-makers as a mode of control was found to be widely prevalent at the divisional level. Specifically, most companies had utilized various types of formal and informal educational programmes to change the thinking of their division managers on research and development (93 per cent; $N = 45$). Many had added 'new blood' to division manager staffs (86 per cent; $N = 28$). Less common was the addition of complete 'new products organizations' (34 per cent; $N = 15$), and the utilization of technical centres where corporate and divisional laboratories are located together as a means to influence divisional research thinking (4 per cent; $N = 48$). Many companies had made, or were planning to make, changes in division management, or had 'welcomed' retirements, etc., entirely or in part as a consequence of research and development behaviour and performance (91 per cent; $N = 32$). Further, in some companies (37 per cent; $N = 33$) technically oriented or young division managers had been put in or were being groomed as replacements.

The use of premise regulation over corporate research managers was also noted to be widely prevalent (95 per cent; $N = 41$). We found that, in those cases where there had been deliberate changes in corporate research managers, there was something of a tendency to replace them with commercially oriented men (64 per cent; $N = 11$).

The relocation of some aspects of research and development decision-making from divisional to corporate sites was widely used (92 per cent; $N = 48$). Many companies had set up a corporate research and development function (73 per cent; $N = 48$), and of these, 83 per cent ($N = 29$) had longer-range missions. In most cases central research and development laboratories were found to be wholly or partly corporately funded (78 per cent; $N = 32$), and there were observed some slight tendencies towards changes in this direction and away from divisional funding, particularly for those central laboratories with stated longer-range missions. Most companies were also found to have a corporate planning function (81 per cent; $N = 48$). Corporate co-ordination of divisional research and development activities was also found to be widely used (70 per cent; $N = 47$). Very little support, however, was seen for the possible mechanism of using a top corporate research manager or similar as a direct controller over division research and development project selection, etc. (27 per cent; $N = 37$). We have suggested that this may be related to the relatively lower observed status of the corporate research manager as compared with the division managers in many situations.

The use of this mechanism in the other direction, i.e. the moving of the location of aspects of research and development decision-making from the corporate to the divisional level, was found to be less prevalent at this time than for the above finding, but it was seen to be utilized (52 per cent; $N = 33$). Only 16 per cent ($N = 37$) of the companies were seen to have discontinued or reduced the scope of their central laboratories in recent years. There was, however, a slight tendency for this to occur more often in companies that had reported having had problems of integrating such a laboratory than among those companies that had not reported having had such problems. Only a few division managers were found to have direct decision-making authority over central laboratory activities (20 per cent plus 14 per cent partly; $N = 30$).

4 ATTEMPTS TO CHANGE RESEARCH AND DEVELOPMENT 'VISIBILITY'

We now turn to a consideration of the top managerial attempts to remedy the relatively low perceived visibility to them of the research and development activities in their companies. We found that many top managers had attempted to take steps to improve their levels of understanding of the research and development activities, and that there was a weak indication that such behaviour was more prevalent among those top managers who were categorized as being less technically trained than among those with more research and development experience (74 per cent; $N = 23$ for top managers without technical training, 67 per cent; $N = 9$ for an intermediate group and 60 per cent; $N = 10$ for those with technical training). We further saw that most top managers had taken steps to improve the visibility to them of the research and development activities in their companies, or wished to take such steps (91 per cent; $N = 23$).

5 GOAL CHANGES

Finally, we observed situations in which top managers made changes in their research and development goals, where they had encountered problems in achieving their overall objectives through research and development or alternative routes. Thus, we found an indication that top managers who had reported having had problems in integrating a central laboratory into their company were also somewhat more likely to report that they had changed their emphasis in growth routes from research and development to some other means. This compares with those who had not reported on such integration problems (29 per cent; $N = 7$ compared with 0 per cent; $N = 3$), although the finding was not conclusive. We also found an indication that many top managers were trying to concentrate in their fields of activity (54 per cent plus 20 per cent partially; $N = 41$), and that, of these, the top managers of companies who had attempted to diversify in the past and had not completed their programmes were the most likely to emphasize such concentration as against diversification.

Conclusion

Some data have been presented on how top managers in forty-eight very large companies view research and development. Data, gathered largely by interviews, were presented on several aspects of top managerial perceptions of their need to control research and development, their ability to take control action, and their understanding of and familiarity with the research and development activities. In a quasi-experimental study we showed that it was possible to make successful predictions of broad categories of control responses that top managers would make, given a knowledge of their perceptions of the research and development situation as stated above. A summary was presented of the types of control mechanism found to be in use among these top managers.

ACKNOWLEDGEMENT

This work was supported by grants from The National Aeronautics and Space Administration, the McKinsey Foundation, and the Irwin Foundation.

REFERENCES

1 M. Radnor (1964)
2 M. Radnor & A. H. Rubenstein (1964)
3 A. H. Rubenstein & M. Radnor (1963), pp. 505–19
4 A. H. Rubenstein (1960)
5 A. H. Rubenstein (1959)
6 W. A. Shewart (1931)
7 D. T. Campbell (1963)

11 · The Attainment of Organization Goals through Appropriate Selection of Sub-unit Goals

ABRAHAM CHARNES and ANDREW C. STEDRY

Introduction

In the growing body of research dedicated to increasing knowledge of organizational behaviour many approaches and disciplines may be involved in the investigation of even a single problem. In this paper we are concerned with two approaches to organizational behaviour, both of which possess a fairly high degree of internal consistency. The disparities which exist between these two bodies of thought, however, appear to exceed the level of a multifaceted approach to a problem that might be considered to have beneficial results. While these disparities cover the entire area of organizational research, our emphasis will be on the problems of organizational control – i.e. the co-ordination of the activities of various sub-units in the organization in order to attain the aims of the organization as a whole.

One body of thought in organizational research has evolved from theoretical economics but remains quite closely related to that discipline. Starting from an assumption that firms do (or should) maximize long-run profits, the focus of research is on the means for attaining this aim. For example, some work of Koopmans [1] deals with the design of transfer pricing systems for optimal production and distribution scheduling by sub-units within the firm; Arrow [2] deals with the design of internal organizational control schemes for profit maximization. Shubik, [3] treating the various sub-units as players in a game, investigates the properties of different kinds of game rules – i.e. organization structures in game-theoretic terms – as they relate to overall profitability. Marschak [4] investigates requirements for the optimal behaviour of teams. This list could be made quite long and varied, but we shall attempt a generalization. We take as included in this body of thought research which has the following characteristics: (i) explicit long-run profitability maximization assumed for the firm as a whole; (ii) focus on the design of internal systems to achieve this aim; and (iii) the rigorous use of mathematical tools in the solution of the organizational problems posed.

The second body of thought of particular interest here goes under the heading of the behavioural theory of the firm. Described in detail by Cyert and March,[5] it draws on the descriptive hypotheses of organizational behaviour presented by Barnard,[6] March and Simon,[7] and others. The focus of this research is on the description and understanding of organizational behaviour rather than on its improvement. Although dependent in part on mathematical modelling, the research has utilized observation, simulation, and laboratory experimentation extensively. The differences between these two bodies of thought can be conveniently classified into those of purpose and of underlying assumptions. The first has already been alluded to. The body of research which is most closely related to the traditional assumptions of economic theory has been devoted to the design of optimal systems; it is essentially normative, focusing on the best way of doing things, with the behaviour of individuals within organizations and the aims of organizations to be known. The behavioural theory of the firm approach, however, is essentially descriptive in character where the efficacy of extant organizations is taken as given but the actual behaviour of individuals and the organization as a whole assumed as the subject for investigation.

It is not unusual, of course, in the physical sciences for one body of researchers to be concerned with the description and understanding of phenomena and another with the design of devices to utilize the phenomena. Nor is the problem simply that of degree of abstraction – e.g. the simplicity of the maximization assumptions compared with the relatively more complex behavioural descriptions hypothesized in the theory of the firm model. Much engineering design can be perceived as a process of using highly abstracted notions – e.g. the law of gravity – to extrapolate from a limited number of empirical observations a series of design curves for a variety of conditions whose effects were not observed. The problem in organization research arises from a disparity between the abstraction used and empirical observation which cannot be explained as a result of simplification or approximation.

The abstraction that firms maximize profit is generally coupled with an assumption that individuals within the firm are 'rational'. That is, individuals act in such a way as to maximize their own gain. This gain, although in early economic studies it was assumed to be entirely expressible in monetary terms, has generally been broadened to the concept of 'utility maximization'. Utility is defined as the value to an individual of all the things he can possibly enjoy or possess – including status, prestige, power, etc. – beyond mere income or monetary worth. All of the non-monetary components are assumed, however, to be translatable into a single utility scale which, in essence, allows trade-offs between the non-monetary and monetary components to be made.* That is, it is assumed that an individual could pay for additional prestige by taking a cut in income of an amount equivalent in

---

* Notwithstanding some work in the construction of certain kinds of multidimensional utility functions. See, e.g., Chipman.[8]

'utiles' to the change in prestige without altering his total utility or satisfaction. The behavioural theory of the firm by contrast is rooted in the 'satisficing' concept of individual behaviour presented by Simon.[9] He argues convincingly that individuals search until a satisfactory solution is found (not an optimal solution) and that, because of the limits on human cognitive powers, are not likely to combine their various sources of satisfaction into a single function, and are certainly not able to maximize such a function. They are likely to seek for satisfactory solutions in the several areas of their activities and, if trade-offs between areas occur at all, they are likely to be quite limited in range.

These differences in assumptions carry over into the organizational behaviour sphere not only in terms of the internal working of the firm but in terms of the aims assumed for organizations as a whole. In the behavioural theory of the firm, it is assumed that a 'ruling coalition' formulates goals for organizational activity in several areas. The 'rational man' assumption of economics at the individual level becomes profit maximization at the organizational level, in the maximization approach. If organizational aims are to be extended beyond profit maximization* an organizational utility function incorporating performance in these other areas is assumed, and assumed to be maximized.

If, indeed, individuals are 'satisficers' rather than 'maximizers' and organizations are goal-striving rather than profit- (or utility) maximizing, then the normative models for organizational design are lacking in two ways. The first is that their prescriptions are based upon faulty assumptions as to the way in which individuals and collections of individuals within an organization will respond to them. The second is that they are designs for the attainment of an organizational aim which organizations do not have, and are thus unlikely to be operational in their present form. On the other hand, for those who consider normative research to be a valid endeavour, the economics/behavioural science amalgam of research known as 'the behavioural theory of the firm' is disappointing in view of its almost complete absence of interest in the evaluation and improvement of organizational behaviour. Organizational behaviours of certain kinds are postulated – in particular certain satisfactory levels of performance – but no great amount of attention has been paid to developing mechanisms for formulating better goals or better means to attain them. In the sections that follow, we shall attempt to show how the assumptions of long-run profit or utility maximization are non-operational if, logically or tautologically, they can be shown to be valid. Without attempting to trace their complexities of development, we shall describe certain outgrowths of the profit maximization theory of organization as they conflict

* Opinion on this is mixed. Some writers will not admit any valid aim of the firm other than to maximize long-run profit. Others, while still adhering to the general tenets of organizational maximization, will allow a broader conception of organizational aims subsumed under a utility function.

with the realities faced by the business firms, even in those areas which are generally considered the province of economic research. Finally, we shall present some examples of a line of research which a few workers have been following in an attempt to gain some knowledge in the area of organizational designs for goal-oriented organizations.

Short-run goals formulated by organizations

It seems reasonable to accept, as a descriptive proposition, the notion that the ruling coalitions* of an organization and sub-units within the organization formulate certain goals for the future activities of these organizational units. It is obvious from the pronouncement of corporations that goals may be stated in the context of profit – the traditional measure of organizational performance in economic theory – or other variables which albeit possibly translatable into the context of long-run profit are rarely explicitly formulated in profitability terms. It is quite possible that a stated goal to 'increase our share of the market from ten to twelve per cent' is more closely related to long-run profit than a goal to 'increase our profit from ten to eleven million dollars' over the same period. It is, however, simply impossible to find evidence that firms do construct explicit long-run profit functions from which they derive these short-run statements of purpose.†

Other short-run goals found to be formulated by organizations are even less easily translated into profitability terms than are those of the order of 'share of market' goal. Goals which are related to employee satisfaction and morale are a case in point. These may take the form of a policy – e.g. 'we will not lay off employees', or 'we will not reduce an employee's salary if we reclassify a job' – which places constraints on the organization's ability to maximize short-run profits. Although it has frequently been suggested that morale is related to productivity,‡ the overwhelming weight of the evidence suggests that while certain constraints on a level below which certain 'morale variables' should not fall may be advisable,§ the relationship between morale and productivity is, at best, highly conditioned by other situational factors.¶ Whether or not corporate executives feel that the long-run effects of policies designed to promote employee security and welfare are felt in increased

---

* This term is in the context of the 'behavioural theory of the firm' as developed by Cyert and March.[5]
† See, for example, Cyert, Dill, and March.[10]
‡ See Likert,[11] for a summary of the empirical studies whose aim was to confirm a positive relationship between morale and productivity.
§ Hertzberg, Mausner, and Snyderman [12] provide a form of evidence on this point.
¶ Brayfield and Crockett [13] present a 'box-score' of the studies pro and con based on the hypotheses that morale and productivity are positively related. Hertzberg, Mausner, and Snyderman [12] suggest that satisfaction of some needs is required but, above these minimum levels, increases are not accompanied by better performance; Stedry [14] discusses the relevance of particular studies which failed to find a positive relationship to the problems of organizational control. Vroom [15] presents an excellent summary of the available evidence in this area.

profitability, it is clear that a 'no-layoff' policy, for example, may be extraordinarily costly in the short run and may limit severely the flexibility available in organizational planning in the longer run.* While frequently rationalized to stockholders and others as contributory to organizational effectiveness, the evidence that such limiting policies are necessary to ensure profitable companies does not exist. The current generation of corporate executives may simply prefer to have secure, reasonably contented employees than insecure, unhappy ones. There are probably very few who will send a worker with thirty years' service 'out on the streets' no matter how ineffectual he has become, although it would be impossible to assess the dollar cost or contribution to long-run profit of a policy which is probably best described as 'simply humane'. In order to be consistent with the evidence (or lack of it) concerning a relationship between policies and constraints aimed at a high level of employee morale and the traditional profitability measures, one must treat such policies as separate, and perhaps independent, goals.

Such policies are only examples of organizational aims which may be more conveniently considered as *ipso facto* goals rather than as a part of an all-encompassing utility function. Goals which may have a direct, but quantifiable role in the determination of organizational profitability may be discerned. Company 'image', community relations, civic pride, patriotic endeavour have all, at one time or another, been among the stated goals of corporate managements. Whether or not such aims actually do, or are perceived to, contribute to corporate profits, may be irrelevant. What is quite obvious is that, given the present capacity to predict the effect of changing such variables on profitability, any *precise* formulation of corporate objectives depends upon the specific statement of the objectives *per se* rather than inclusion in a profit function rendered markedly subject to error thereby.

The normative relevance of short-run goals

It is not sufficient, of course, to show examples of non-optimal behaviour. The neo-classical economic model would *require* that a firm should maximize long-run profit subject to technological constraints, i.e. eliminate irrationality. If, however, the demands of the market, or society, or technology preclude rationality as a viable concept at the organizational level a stronger case may be made for a need for new kinds of normative models. It will be instructive to examine some of these demands – generally considered within the province of economic analysis – in detail as examples in support of this need.

The financial community, perhaps 'irrationally', places constraints on the

---

* As, for example, the model of Holt, Modigliani, Muth, and Simon.[16] In their model, work force is seen as a variable with specified costs of layoff, retraining, and training of new employees. While they do not include possible costs of deleterious effects of layoffs on the morale of the remaining employees, it is clear that assuming an infinite cost of layoff – i.e. a 'no-layoff' policy – could produce a substantial departure from optimality.

firm's ability to borrow.* A firm may simply be unable, no matter what interest rate it is willing to pay, to borrow beyond a modest percentage of its total equity.† Furthermore, it is reasonable to believe that what is considered 'good risk' leverage in one period may be a 'poor risk' in another. A firm may thus desire to maintain a degree of leverage well below that of the maximum it can borrow at a time when additional funds would be 'nice to have' in order to maintain a reserve against a time when funds will be desperately needed. Since the latter is not unlikely to come at a time when leverage requirements of lenders are most stringent, the relevance of a current borrowing limit for long-term debt is unclear. While possibly evidence of 'irrationality', numerous examples of companies with no long-term debt in their capital structures exist.

It is certainly not difficult to envisage a policy that long-term debt should not exceed some percentage of total equity, even if the current borrowing limit has not been reached and investment opportunities exceed the cost of capital. While such a policy *may* reflect inadequate understanding of the dynamic processes underlying future investment opportunities, the normative theorist is generally faced with the problem of maximizing (or satisficing) relative to known, rather than unknown, parameters in his models.

Yet, the predictability of the effects of capital budgeting decisions would seem to be of an order much greater than that in other areas – e.g. personnel policy. When, in an area as seemingly well defined as capital budgeting, no satisfactory dynamic model for optimal decision-making exists except where deterministic returns may be assumed,‡ of what use, in a normative sense, are models which assume the capacity to make long-run optimal decisions 'across the board' in all areas of management endeavour?

We are, we think, not attempting to provide a justification for formulating models whose purpose is to 'hold the line' while bridging temporary gaps in our knowledge of the world and the predictability of future events. Rather it appears that, as our knowledge is growing, so is the number of areas which will be included in a definition of organizational 'welfare'. Performance measurements and determination of causality may well be more difficult in the new areas which seem to be emerging. It is feasible, if perhaps undesirable, that the future corporation will endeavour to satisfy more and more individual needs of satisfaction and fulfilment. Selznick,[22] for example,

---

* Chambers and Charnes[17] have shown, for example, the extremely low loss ratio allowed by a bank's policy in obvious contradistinction to a policy of charging higher interest rates to compensate for making loans with more risk. Clarkson's[18] simulation of a trust officer shows similar 'cut rules' as opposed to a rate-risk continuum.

† While Modigliani and Miller[19] have demonstrated that assumptions relating leverage to cost of capital can be shown, through use of aggregated data, to produce empirically verifiable hypotheses, the possibility that the relatively restricted ranges of both equity and the cost of capital observed are attributable to constraints on the extent of leverage remains. Other investigations such as Farrar's[20] have provided evidence for quite severe limitations on risky investments in the portfolios of certain classes of investors.

‡ See Weingartner.[21]

suggests that individuals in future generations should obtain a greater share of their satisfactions, social intercourse, needs for self-esteem and achievement, etc., from the organization in which they work. Should Selznick's criteria, for example, be adopted by an enterprise, much more specific knowledge of individual needs – psychologically and psychiatrically – would be required for implementation than for the more modest aims of profit, market share, and a modicum of employee security. It is not inconceivable that the monetary gains made through automation, advanced information-processing, and optimal programming schema will be used in part to increase the 'affluence' of organizational employees in non-monetary as well as monetary terms. These may, of course, be looked upon as 'by-products' of long-run profit maximization or as candidates for incorporation in an 'organizational utility' function.

But are we to assume that future generations of corporate management could (or would want to) formulate complex 'organizational utility' functions which include these additional individual rewards? The complexity of such (hypothetical) functions, including interdependencies introduced by the dependence of one person's satisfaction with his lot on another's rewards and the not-soon-to-be-understood relationship between individual satisfaction and other aspects of organizational performance, is awesome. The task of formulating such complex utility functions would seem to provide an insurmountable obstacle even if computationally feasible solutions may be shown to exist for finding their optima. It would seem that to adopt, as a normative construct, the premise that each individual firm *should* maximize an 'organizational utility' function would be to require each firm to formulate and maximize a welfare function of an order of complexity not appreciably less than that of a social welfare function for the society as a whole.

The practical difficulties confronting an attempt to construct an all-inclusive long-run profit or utility function can, of course, be explained away by assuming a 'cost of information'. That is, one can construct as simple a function as one chooses, provided one assumes that the cost of formulating a more complex one, or finding its optimum, is prohibitive. On this basis, *all behaviour* can be (and has been) described as 'rational',* although our observations tell us, to paraphrase George Orwell, that some behaviours are more rational than others. Moreover, if all behaviour is rational, of what use are normative models of rationality? It would seem, then, that in order to adopt long-run profit or utility maximization as a normative construct one must either assume a level of knowledge far in excess of that which exists or will exist in the foreseeable future or adopt a prohibitive cost of information which negates the need for normative constructs.

We have attempted to argue that little convincing evidence exists that would imply that organizations maximize profit or utility. We have also

---

* See, for example, Luce and Raiffa,[23] particularly Chapter 2, for a discussion of the ways in which utility theory may be made to fit all behaviours.

attempted to argue that at least one common justification for a proposition that they can maximize expected utility rests upon an assumption which, carried to its logical conclusion, also implies that they do. We do not mean to imply that insights gained from long-run maximization models are not of value. Rather, we are attempting to provide for the admissibility of normative models of organizational behaviour which incorporate the tools developed in the process of economic analysis but which do not focus on an all-inclusive utility function. Such models might define an organization's (or its ruling coalition's) criteria in terms of its desires to attain certain short-run goals and achieve conformity to organizational policies without attempting to justify these short-run aims or policies in terms of a long-run utility function.

Assumptions of normative decision-making models

The development of normative models for the purpose of making better decisions as to, for example, production and distribution schedules – generally classified as operational research – may be perceived as occupying a place somewhere between the two extremes of profit maximization for the firm as a whole and entirely descriptive research. Their purpose is normative, but in the course of formulating models the processes with which the models deal must be described in considerable detail. Furthermore, these models have generally been developed in response to real problems observed to be extant in industrial organizations. These models most often have maximization of criteria function as their aim, but, unlike maximization of profit or utility at organizational level, the criterion function is credible. Intuitively, there is little to be gained by having a non-optimal petrol-blending operation when an optimal solution is readily available. The problems of organizational aims noted in the earlier sections of the paper are not particularly relevant in the selection of a criterion function for many kinds of models; it is better to have less than more cost – given constraints on the availability of inputs, blending capacity, etc.

The departure of such models from the quest for global optima (for the organization as a whole), however, should be clear. The constraints of the organizational sub-problems are not derived from a decomposition of a global maximization problem. They are derived from externalities to the problem which are not themselves optimally determined. Although certain techniques used – e.g. linear programming – provide information about the cost or profit advantage to be derived from altering the constraints, no real claim can be made that the problem solution is part of an optimum 'in the large'. The constraint set is not optimally determined nor will alterations in that set undertaken on the basis of information obtained from the model render the set optimal, even if increases in profitability can be clearly demonstrated.

Needless to say, the applications of operational research have gone far beyond cases where the constraints and parameters of the problem chosen for the solution were or could be derived from decomposition of an all-inclusive optimization problem. Indeed, such cases are probably non-existent. The application of operational research models which provide only optima 'in the small' can be encompassed within global maximization assumptions on the basis of a 'prohibitive cost' of constructing an integrated model or even a model larger than those applied. Alternatively, one can take, as a management aim, the optimization of certain aspects of its operations without the desire to maximize some global organizational criterion. This latter construction avoids the necessity to assume or compute the (frequently unestimable) cost of constructing larger models. Also, consider the obvious paradox which arises when a cost of additional modelling under existing technology is 'prohibitive' at one point in time, but, by management decision, is undertaken without substantial advance in technology at another. The introduction of optimization models into a 'satisficing' organization does in fact seem to avoid some of the circuitous reasoning required to introduce them into a 'rational' organization.

Although it would seem obvious that most operational research modelling and application have occurred in situations where the constraints and parameters of the models used have resulted from management decisions external to the models, *explicit* recognition of this fact has been rare. Indeed, large classes of models, such as the S,s inventory models typified by the research of Arrow, Harris, and Marschak,[24] have been formulated as though they were global maximization problems: a 'cost of capital' has been assumed rather than limitations on capital that could be invested in inventory; a 'storage cost' rather than a warehouse constraint has been utilized. Other models as, for example, the great bulk of linear programming models, have been less imitative of the assumptions of classical economics but fall short of explicit recognition of some kinds of management decision. They allow technological constraints – machine capacities, required sequences, etc. – rather than incorporating additional capacity 'at a cost' or an infinity of different possible operations to replace the current one at some cost or another. However, although most technological constraints result from a management decision of one kind or another – e.g. a decision not to buy a bigger machine – specification of constraints whose tangible physical properties are not *a priori* apparent is infrequent, at least in the published literature.

Explicit recognition of the validity of management's imposing, by fiat as it were, policy constraints on the maximization problem is an important step in increasing the usefulness of operational research models in the context of management decision problems of broad scope. An example is provided by Charnes, Cooper, and Miller,[25] who specify a minimum cash balance constraint as a management *desideratum* in addition to the usual technological constraints. The short-run cost of capital implied by the constraint may then be *imputed* by using the dual variable associated with the cash balance constraint, thus serving as a guide to future management decisions. Explicit recognition is thus made of the fact that, in the final analysis, it is management, rather than the linear programming model, which must decide what price it is willing to pay to maintain a liquidity position.

The models described below are closely related to the operational research methodology. They represent, however, further extensions of the principle of attaching validity to management decisions made as to goals and policies with or without explicit recognition of the economic impact of those policies. The solutions derived using these models are, like operational research models, prescriptions for behaviour. However, based upon actual goals that managements do set for their organizations, they are prescriptions for optimal behaviour *vis-à-vis* the stated and observed desires of management rather than a hypothetical long-run profit or utility maximization.

Chance-constrained programming

Management goals are frequently stated in terms such as 'we aim to' or 'our policy is' rather than 'we must'. The deterministic constraints of usual linear-programming models are stated, by contrast, as requirements – absolute constraints. A minimum cash balance, for example, would need to be stated as 'we aim to keep cash at or above \$100,000 with probability equal to 1'. In order to make this into a goal or policy as we normally understand these terms, the requirement of the unit probability must be relaxed. It is quite clear that there would be circumstances in which a firm might violate any policy or forgo the attainment of a goal. The frequency with which these violations occur is, in some sense, a measure of the degree of adherence desired to a particular aim. In response to this problem, Charnes and Cooper [26] have developed models incorporating 'chance constraints' which replace, in a linear-programming framework, some of the usual constraints of the form:

$$\sum_{j=1}^{n} a_{ij} X_j \geqslant b_i$$

where the X_j are the variables, the a_{ij} parameters and the b_i requirements with probabilistic constraints of the form:

$$P\left\{ \sum_{j=1}^{n} a_{ij} X_j \geqslant b_i \right\} \geqslant 1 - \alpha_i$$

where $P\{X\}$ is the probability of occurrence of X and α_i the maximum probability allowed for non-satisfaction of the constraint. In this form the b_i become goals. Charnes and Cooper refer to the expression in this form as the statement of a 'policy'; e.g. a 'policy' of satisfying all customers from stock (i.e. no order backlog) is not taken seriously as a zero probability of stockout but a *low* probability of stockout.

It may well be easier to assess the tolerance limit of customers in terms of the proportion of times they will tolerate being turned away than to assess a 'cost of stockout'. One of the authors observed [27] that, in constructing an optimal inventory scheme for a military supply system, 'cost of stockout' was essentially an unestimable quantity, while the establishment of tolerable stockout probabilities for different classes of items was eminently practicable. In other situations a firm may desire to have satisfied customers even if it is costly to short-term profit or even long-run profits (if, of course, the benefit of having 'satisfied customers' could be adequately assessed).

Examples of inventory control policies are familiar, but chance constraints can express policies – such as 'no' layoff – as well. The dual variables provide the benefit or cost to the optimal solution of altering the percentage of non-conformity with policy that will be tolerated. Whether or not organizations should (from the standpoint of 'rationality') formulate policies, or, in the language of this paper, set goals, they apparently do. Chance-constrained programming offers one method of expressing policies or goals in such a way that optimization of short-run profits, or profits over a finite horizon, can be maximized while offering an evaluation of the costs of these policies as well. A policy which is found to be extremely costly may be re-examined and, perhaps, altered to an equally desirable policy (on the basis of other criteria), or eliminated.

Goal programming

In another approach to the goal-setting or policy formulation problem, Ijiri [28] and Charnes, Cooper, and Ijiri [29] have stated an optimization problem entirely in terms of minimization of the extent of nonconformity with goals. Their goal-programming models include, in addition to the usual linear-programming constraints, deterministic constraints of the form:

$$\sum_{j=1}^{n} a_{ij} X_j + Y_i = b_i$$

where Y_i is the distance from adherence to the policy:

$$\sum_{j=1}^{n} a_{ij} X_j \geqslant b_i$$

The functional in the problem can be an unweighted sum of the nonconformities or a weighted sum such as

$$Z = \sum_{i=1}^{n} C_i Y_i$$

to be minimized, assuming that all policies are not viewed as equally important. If all of the goals can be attained a trivial solution is obtained with $Z = 0$. The applicability of these models is to problems where goals conflict and cannot all be simultaneously attained.

Many variations of these models are possible, such as combining a profit function with the goal conformity function. Combining this concept with that of chance-constrained programming could yield interesting models in which a function of the X_i, or the Y_i, or both could be minimized. The concept retains, however, the perception of several goals to be attained or policies adhered to rather than simply a single profit or utility function.

Multiple-goal models

The authors [30,31,32] have presented elsewhere models which combine the stochastic character of chance constraints with the concept of goal programming. In these models we have specified the probabilities of attainment of independent goals as functions of the managerial effort allocated to attainment. In particular, functions of the form:

$$P\{X_j \geq a_j\} = k_j (1 - e^{-\alpha_j \rho_j})$$

have been used where P is the probability operator, X_j the actual performance, a_j the performance goal, ρ_j the effort allocated to attaining the jth goal, α_j an arbitrary constant, and k_j a limiting probability of attainment as ρ_j grows large. This function has certain desirable properties for representing response to effort – diminishing returns to scale and asymptotic approach to a limiting probability – and because it is monotically increasing and concave, it is mathematically convenient. Other functions are possible, of course, but our investigations to date have been concentrated on this one to provide examples of what can be done with several kinds of criterion function.

One possible criterion of success of a programme involving goal attainment is obtained by assuming that goal attainment carries a reward, r_j, and non-attainment a penalty, p_j. Then a reward function may be formulated as:

$$R = \sum_{j=1}^{n} r_j z_j^+ - \sum_{j=1}^{n} p_j z_j^-$$

where $z_j^+ = 1$ where $X_j \geq a_j$ (i.e. where the goal has been attained) and 0 elsewhere and $z_j^- = 1$ where $X_j < a_j$, 0 elsewhere. If one wishes to maximize expected reward, it is readily perceived that:

$$E(z_j^+) = (1)[P(X_j \geq a_j)] + (0)[1 - P(X_j \geq a_j)]$$

and

$$E(z_j^-) = (1)[1 - P(X_j \geq a_j)] + (0)[P(X_j \geq a_j)]$$

so that the expected reward function may be expressed as:

$$E(R) = \sum_{j=1}^{n} [(r_j + p_j)P(X_j \geq a_j) - p_j]$$

A function such as this may be perceived as similar to one faced by a supervisor in an organization who has budgets to meet in several areas – labour cost, material cost, overhead, etc. – with differing levels of importance attaching to each budget as reflected by the weights $(r_j + p_j)$. We have presented a solution to this maximization problem in ref. 30, and shown in ref. 32 that for the exponential density by appropriate choice of $r_j + p_j$ and a_j, a supervisor who would set out to maximize the expected reward function would allocate his effort so as to maximize the function:

$$E(\pi) = \sum_{j=1}^{n} \beta_j E(X_j)$$

where the β_j are the contributions to profit of a unit of X_j. This kind of equivalence suggests the possibility that a supervisor who 'irrationally' looks at budget attainment rather than expected profit as related to his reward and a management which 'irrationally' sets budgets rather than telling him to maximize expected profit can combine to produce 'rational' behaviour in the economic sense. A possible solution to some of the problems of a disparity between normative and descriptive organizational models may be one of utilization of patterns of observed 'irrational' behaviour to produce, through using instructions more meaningful to individuals than profit maximization, behaviour which is closer to 'rational' behaviour in the economic sense, if this is considered desirable.

Other forms of goal attainment criteria found in practice are conceptually farther removed from expected utility models. A list of specifications for a new product is a case in point. In order to be acceptable, a plane must fly X miles per hour, have a range of Y miles, an altitude of Z miles, etc. Trade-offs among such specifications are no doubt possible, but if a transatlantic airliner cannot fly across the ocean without refuelling no increase in speed or altitude will render the craft suitable for its intended use. Given a set of contract specifications, minimum acceptable performance in the jth area denoted by a_j and actual performance by X_j, a performance criterion might be the maximization of the joint probability of occurrence of attainment of all goals, or:

$$P = P\{X_1 \geqslant a_1, X_2 \geqslant a_2, \ldots X_n \geqslant a_n\}$$

One can, of course, transform this into an expected utility maximization model by denoting the utility of joint attainment as 1 and of non-attainment as 0. Then, denoting utility by U, we have:

$$E(U) = (1)(P) + (0)(1 - P) = P$$

This *ex post facto* transformation, however, adds nothing to understanding of the criterion function. The explicit recognition that the various performance levels are of no value unless all of them attain some minimal standard can only be obscured by imposing discontinuous utility functions, even though this can be done and, in some cases, might be convenient for computational purposes.

We have developed an algorithm for an approximate solution to the probability maximization problem in ref. 31, where the attainment of each of the several goals is viewed as stochastically independent of the others, with

G

functional independence introduced through constraint on total effort. The problem, using the exponential form of effort response, is stated as:

Maximize:

$$P = \prod_{j=1}^{n} [k_j(1 - e^{-\alpha_j\rho_j})]$$

Subject to:

$$\sum_{j=1}^{n} \rho_j \leqslant \rho$$

The precise form of the solution, which, because no readily available analytical solution exists, involves tedious application of methods for finding approximate solution and error limits on the approximation, is beyond the scope of this paper. Variations of this model are of interest, one of which we have investigated in ref. 32. There we postulate one set of levels as 'minimum standards', a_j, all of which must be attained with probability at least W, as well as 'desirable levels', a'_j whose attainment is associated with reward.* This problem can be stated as:

Maximize:

$$E(R) = \sum_{j=1}^{n} r_j P\{X_j \geqslant a'_j\} = \sum_{j=1}^{n} r_j k'_j(1 - e^{-\alpha'_j\rho_j})$$

Subject to:

$$P = \prod_{j=1}^{n} P\{X_j \geqslant a_j\} = \prod_{j=1}^{n} k_j[(1 - e^{-\alpha_j\rho_j})] \geqslant W$$

$$\sum_{j=1}^{n} \rho_j \leqslant \rho$$

where the primed parameters relate to 'desirable' levels of performance, the unprimed to 'minimum acceptable' levels. This may be comprehended as representing the not unfamiliar situation where 'kudos' is given for performing at a level noticeably higher than 'minimum acceptable' but where failing to achieve acceptable performance in any area can cancel out the benefits of good or exceptional performance in others.

Other variations, of course, are of interest. With relatively little increase in complexity, chance constraints can be placed on levels of attainment in individual areas. Although we have not investigated a vast array of goal structures observed in practice, our investigations have shown the feasibility of formulating optimal solutions to problems couched in terms of goal attainment. While these models share with profit and utility maximization models the optimization of a single criterion function, the resulting solutions

---

* Through the possible construction of equivalent expected reward maximization and profit maximization models indicated above, this problem could also be comprehended as expected profit maximization subject to a minimum standard constraint.

can frequently be reduced to heuristics sufficiently simple for an individual to be able to use them in lieu of the maximization model.

For example, for the reward maximization model the supervisor faced with a budget should allocate effort to areas where $a_j(r_j + p_j)k_j$ is large, before those where this product is small. He should not allocate effort to any area where he does not have a 'reasonable' probability of attainment. Once he has decided which areas are on his 'list', a first approximation to the optimum allocation within the list is to make $\alpha_j\rho_j$ a constant. A somewhat better one is to make the ρ_j proportional to $1/\alpha_j$ or $[a_j(r_j + p_j)k_j]$ – although at this level of complexity we seem to be sufficiently beyond 'simple heuristics' for a computerized decision rule which need not be limited in its complexity to seem desirable. For the probability maximization model a good heuristic would be to allocate effort so as to equate the probabilities of attainment of the individual goals.

While such heuristic solutions are not capable of providing optimal allocations of effort, they may serve as a guide to formulating behavioural hypotheses for test. It is unlikely that a supervisor in a manufacturing plant will find the optimum solution and allocate his effort accordingly. However, he may operate according to a heuristic which roughly equates the probabilities of attainment of his various budgets. If so, budget-setting might then be accomplished with the aid of the mathematical model which corresponds to this heuristic – the probability maximization model – setting budgets which would provide optimal allocations if the optimal solution were used but providing sufficiently good allocations with the simple heuristic.*

The exponential functions we have used, borrowed from the theory of search (see Koopman [34]) and embellished, can be viewed only as an example of the existence of solutions to certain types of problem. The vast possibilities extant in the investigation of individuals' response to goals in the design of optimal or quasi-optimal goal structures have only begun to be recognized.

Experimental investigation

A necessary concomitant of the modelling of behaviour is the reality-testing of models which might be fruitful for expanding goal-oriented theories of organization. Of particular interest is an experiment performed by Churchill [35] which dealt with conflicting goals. Acting as supervisor to his subjects, he directed them both to find the best solution to the problem and to follow a procedure which gave 'good' solutions (but not the best solution). He examined the effects of subjects' performance when an audit (of procedure) was announced and did not take place, was announced and did take place, etc. He worked with two different subject groups – students and clerks – with

* Attempting to alter effort allocation directly would seem to be of limited value. In a study reported by Rubin [33] it was found that 'time spent' in various substantive activities was badly communicated through an organization and that little correspondence existed between how supervisors wanted subordinates to allocate their time and what subordinates thought their superiors wanted them to do.

whom the effects of audit differed. The student subjects, who were generally capable of finding better solutions than the procedure would provide (although they made errors which they would not have made following the procedure), gave poorer overall performance as the emphasis on audit increased. The clerks, however, benefited from procedural emphasis, which caused them to conform more closely to procedures which gave good solutions, although 'too much' emphasis seemed to result in a deterioration of performance (perhaps from nervousness resulting from repeated audits). Although this study was oriented towards investigating the role of the auditor, generally considered external to the day-to-day business operation, it is a pioneering effort in using the psychological laboratory to study the effect on performance of techniques for enforcing conformity to policy and procedure – techniques which are ubiquitously used in contemporary organizations.

An example of an entirely different approach to the study of goal response is an experiment carried out in a field situation in an attempt to study the effect of the difficulty of attainment of goals set for production foremen on their performance. Although the sample size was too small to provide conclusive findings, Stedry and Kay's [36] results suggest that difficult goals may produce extremes in performance. Foremen in their study who had difficult goals generally showed large improvements or large decrements in performance, while those with 'normal' goals generally showed modest improvement or decrement. Those who stated that they perceived their goals as impossible showed large decrements in performance, but so did a few who perceived their goals as challenging. Strong correlation (negative) between performance improvement and age among foremen with difficult goals suggests that individual differences in response must be considered in the design of any goal-setting procedures.

In another field experiment, French, Kay, and Meyer [37] found that where specific performance goals were set, performance improvement was recorded while admonitions to improve performance had no effect.

In still another type of investigation Haberstroh [38] took advantage of a 'natural' experiment – i.e. a change which takes place in the organization which allows before and after measures but is not under direct control of the experimenter – to investigate the response to changes in safety goals in a steel mill.

The number of systematic investigations of performance response to goals and the usual techniques of managerial control is small but increasing. Human response to goals individually, in groups, and in large organizations is a relatively new area to receive rigorous empirical investigation. These initial steps provide encouraging results.

Some possible directions of future research

In this paper we have attempted to bring together some of the work which is directed towards closing the gap between descriptive theories and normative models of organizational behaviour. This work shares a focus on the processes with which organizations are observed to operate – setting separate goals, formulating policies, setting budgets – but with an emphasis on the means of doing these things more systematically.

Integration of the experimental and model-building approaches is difficult. We can observe phenomena much more complex than we can model. On the other hand, to vary conditions in the laboratory systematically is extraordinarily more difficult than varying parameters in a model. Experiments conducted under actual organizational conditions and designs which vary more than one thing at a time are incredibly costly to implement. This makes the random testing of behavioural hypotheses for the purpose of designing improved organizational control systems prohibitively costly. It is probably economical to pursue extensive model-building activity in an attempt to find out in advance what behavioural propositions are sufficiently promising to justify the cost of experimental testing.

The direction in which this research will lead us is at present unclear. Just how much will be learned about human behaviour is, of course, an open question, as is the limit to which one can use this knowledge to attain organizational goals without infringing individual rights. Perhaps an ultimate goal is an organization whose control system is so designed that attainment of goals set for employees at all levels contributes to organizational goals. This is not to say that all employees in an organization need be committed to organizational goals – e.g. it is not necessary for the lathe operator to be committed to increasing the company's market share. Rather, it is necessary to design for that lathe operator a set of goals and rewards of such a kind that his pursuit of what he considers to be his own best interests whatever the form of rational or irrational decision rules he follows will contribute as much as possible to the attainment of organizational goals. It is probable that goals and policies which contribute to employee and community welfare, whether or not justified on profitability grounds, will continue to exist – at least among organizations sufficiently affluent to afford them.

In any event, more research must be done before any claim to a satisfactory system of controls or designs for sub-goals at the various levels in the organizational hierarchy can be made. At present our control systems are hampered both by an inadequate knowledge of their behavioural effects and by an absence of techniques fitting these probabilistic response patterns into a co-ordinated pattern for the organization as a whole. It is hoped that these areas will be subject to extensive investigation.

ACKNOWLEDGEMENT

The research for this paper was supported by the U.S. Office of Naval Research Contracts Nonr-1228(10), Project NR 047-021 at Northwestern University and Nonr-760(01), Project NR 047-011 at Carnegie Institute of Technology and by the

National Aeronautics and Space Administration under Research Grant No. NsG 235-62 at Massachusetts Institute of Technology. Reproduction in whole or in part is permitted for any purpose of the United States Government.

REFERENCES

1 T. C. Koopmans (1951)
2 K. J. Arrow (1964)
3 M. Shubik (1964)
4 J. Marschak (1954)
5 R. M. Cyert & J. G. March (1963)
6 C. I. Barnard (1938)
7 J. G. March & H. A. Simon (1958)
8 J. S. Chipman (1960)
9 H. A. Simon (1957)
10 R. M. Cyert, W. R. Dill & J. G. March (1958)
11 R. Likert (1961)
12 F. Hertzberg, B. Mausner & B. Snyderman (1959)
13 A. H. Brayfield & W. H. Crockett (1955)
14 A. C. Stedry (1964)
15 V. H. Vroom (1964)
16 C. C. Holt, F. Modigliani, J. F. Muth & H. A. Simon (1960)
17 D. Chambers & A. Charnes (1961)
18 G. P. E. Clarkson (1962)
19 F. Modigliani & M. H. Miller (1958)

20 D. Farrar (1962)
21 H. M. Weingartner (1963)
22 P. Selznick (1963)
23 R. D. Luce & H. Raiffa (1958)
24 K. J. Arrow, T. Harris & J. Marschak (1951)
25 A. Charnes, W. W. Cooper & M. H. Miller (1959)
26 A. Charnes & W. W. Cooper (1962)
27 A. C. Stedry & J. Griswold (1962)
28 Y. Ijiri (1963)
29 A. Charnes, W. W. Cooper & Y. Ijiri (1963)
30 A. Charnes & A. C. Stedry (1964b)
31 A. Charnes & A. C. Stedry (1964a)
32 A. C. Stedry & A. Charnes (1962)
33 I. Rubin (1963)
34 B. O. Koopman (1957)
35 N. C. Churchill (1962)
36 A. C. Stedry & E. Kay (1964)
37 J. R. P. French, Jr., E. Kay & H. H. Meyer (1962)
38 C. J. Haberstroh (1961)

12 · On the Plurality of Social Systems

TOM BURNS

The partial nature of social systems

Business enterprises are co-operative systems assembled out of the usable attributes of people.* They are also places in which people compete for advancement. Thus, members of a business concern are at one and the same time co-operators in a common enterprise and rivals for the material and intangible rewards of successful competition with each other. The hierarchical order of rank and power, realized in the organization chart, which prevails in all organizations, is both a control system and a career ladder.

This dualism reflects the order prevailing in society at large. There is a sense in which a national society is organized as a co-operative system. Nevertheless, complex societies such as our own depend for their survival on maintaining a flow of the best-qualified people to the top places in society where the best talents are most needed. To do this, a complex system of educational and occupational promotions open to merit has been set up. But beyond this it is essential for every member of the society to enter the race and compete as best he can and to regard success in these terms as one of the highest personal goals of his life. This indoctrination is usually fairly successfully carried out, especially because the distribution of utilities and privileges accords more and more with the social position achieved in this way.

However, in the nature of things, few people can actually succeed out of the total numbers who have to try. Thus, a Western society is composed of people almost all of whom are frequently confronted with the possibility of failure. In many cases, therefore, people will try to increase their own chances of success by illegitimate means and will impute the same desire to others who are or may at some time be in competition with them. All social milieux in which such competition occurs have codes of rules, explicit and implicit, which distinguish illegitimate behaviour from legitimate, and apply

* Passages in this paper draw on work previously published.[1,2,3,4]

sanctions of some kind to transgressors. Moral codes of this kind are specific to individual occupational milieux and even to individual organizations; overt references to the failures and deficiencies of one's rivals of the kind which are unexceptionable in the clothing trade would damage oneself rather than them in the B.B.C., although, if we are to believe C. P. Snow, they may also go unquestioned in the less genteel social climate of a Cambridge college. The existence of such codes, and of such definitions, bespeaks the presence of a specific class of acts and relationships, with its own normative rules governing relationships – i.e. of a social system, existing in juxtaposition with the social system represented by the formal organization, with *its* own norms, relationships, and acts.

But there are also, frequently, disputes about the criteria which determine success, about the justice or logic with which they are applied, and about the relevance of the criteria of career success to the capacity of the organization or society as a whole to survive. In addition, the ends and means formulated by previous or existing leaders as goals and procedures for the organization as a co-operative system may be challenged. In short, the rules of the game being played in the two social systems I have already mentioned – the formal organization and the career system – may themselves be the subject of conflict. Major decisions about changing the rules of the game usually require much antecedent search and discussion, not so much to accumulate information as to test out and align consensus; decisions about 'policy matters', therefore, ordinarily involve the formation of groups and sections concerned with the advocacy of one or other course of action. But such groupings are more enduring than this suggests. The individual may be, and usually is, concerned to extend the control he has over his own situation and prospects, to increase the value of the resource which he represents to the organization. He may be, and often is, able to increase his personal power by attaching himself to parties or sections of people who represent the same kind of resource and wish to enhance its exchange value, or to cabals who seek to control or influence the exercise of patronage in the organization. Such formations have to do with what are commonly, and rightly, regarded as the 'internal politics' of organizations. Interest-groups are often identical with departments, or with dominant groups in them, and their political leaders are heads of departments, or accepted activists, or elected representatives (e.g. shop stewards). The issues in which they are involved arise from the conflicting demands on the rewards of the enterprise, its uncommitted resources (the allocation of new capital), the direction of the activities of others (the authority to propose or sanction action by other departments, groups or individuals), and patronage (promotions, new appointments, and the distribution of rights and privileges).

The systems of relationships and the kinds of behaviour which can be designated political are also subject to the same kind of normative regulation that obtains for the formal organization and the career system. It is this which enables us to recognize political activity when we see it. Normally each side in any conflict called 'political' by observers claims to speak in the interests of the organization as a whole. Indeed, the only feasible way of advancing sectional interests is to present them in terms of improved welfare or efficiency, as contributing to the organization's capacity to perform its tasks and to prosper. In managerial, as well as other, legislatures both sides claim to speak in the interests of the community as a whole. It is only backstage, so to speak, that the imputations of empire-building, log-rolling, and obstructionism occur. The terminological division is particularly marked in universities, where mutually exclusive frames of reference exist for discussion in faculty meetings or committees and in clubs, common-rooms, and parties. In the first the only legitimate reference is to the needs of students and to the advancement of approved branches of learning. Allegations, or even hints, of careerism or of pressure-group politics are entirely improper in faculty meetings, yet may be entirely acceptable and legitimate in other settings. Indeed, in certain gatherings it might be imprudent to the point of social suicide to impute higher motives than self-interest and aggrandizement to reformers and claimants for larger funds or more staff.

Rationality models

I have begun with a preliminary statement about the more obvious and familiar social systems which co-exist with the formal organization in workplaces because it seems that a number of influences are combining to re-establish the conception of organizations as monolithic, or at least homogeneous, structures. The influences are of three kinds. One emanates from the exhaustion, for heuristic purposes, of the concept of the 'informal organization'. For a generation since the Hawthorne studies the notion of the informal organization has served as a receptacle for observations about the behaviour, the relationships, the sentiments and beliefs, the commitments and self-identifications of workers and managers which were seen as irrelevant to the 'formal organization' or incompatible with it and its purpose. The dualism of formal and informal attracted the related notions of rational and irrational. This engendered a view of the informal organization as pathological, comprehending all that had defeated Taylorite attempts at human engineering. In much of the literature of industrial studies it appears as a kind of Freudian unconscious which 'human relations' research could explore, bringing its hidden activities and commitments and conflicts into the light of consciousness (i.e. to the notice of management) and enabling its misdirected effects to be checked or harnessed to ends consonant with those of the enterprise.

The decline of interest in informal organization in terms of organizational pathology has been matched by the growth of interest in the field designated as formal organization, beginning with Gouldner's[5] and Blau's[6] studies, and implemented by the rediscovery of Weber and his establishment as the founding father of organizational theory. If, as Gouldner suggests, managers and workers can devise more than one way in which they can interpret a given organizational structure, and institute for each a system of working relationships in which they mutually sustain each others' beliefs, expectations, status, and self-regard, then, although new questions arise about organizational goals, there is little point in continuing to regard the informal organization, values, and objectives of workers as existing on a different plane, and requiring a different conceptual framework, from that of the formal organization of management.

There are two directions which have been taken by organizational studies since this new synthesis was established. The first consists in attempts to formulate typologies of bureaucratic forms; the key variable being technology for some,[7,8,9,10] the rate of environmental change for others,[11,12] the characteristic form of utility produced, for a third group,[13] and the kind of authority structure, or rather, of sanctions employed, for a fourth.[14,15]

The second direction is more visibly pertinent to the set of topics which may be presumed to lie in the intersection of the interests of both operational researchers and industrial sociologists. This is the development of the behavioural theory of organizations by the Carnegie Institute of Technology group (March and Simon,[16] Cyert and March,[17] Simon[18]) and of a system theory of organizations by the Tavistock Institute group. Couched in very different terms, both are endeavours to elaborate a rational model of the business concern, the American using a conceptual framework derived from the conventions of the computer simulation of business decision-making, the English starting from a basis of the organicist system theory developed by Bertalanffy and exploiting some of the ramifications and junctions with system theory in other sciences which have occurred in recent years. Both, one should add, are put forward as attempts at constructing a general theory which will relate to, and presumably make sense of, a very considerable fund of empirical experience of business concerns obtained through research and consultancy work. Both are, nevertheless, models in the sense of analogues rather than constructs derived from concrete or conceptual units and relationships abstracted from data specific to industrial studies or, indeed, to any social science.*

Rationality models imply that organizations exist as instruments for the attainment of valued future states, which are construed as goals. This has attracted the criticism that to specify organizational goals one has to postulate an 'organizational mind', as Cyert and March[17] have remarked. There have been four ways put forward for handling this problem of misplaced concreteness and the allied problem of reconciling the unity of aims posited in the model and the empirical fact of disunity of purpose among the individual members and groups who make up an organization.

(i) March and Simon[16] suggest that sub-goals are generated by groups and

* Herbert A. Simon[18] is clearest of all on this point.

individuals within organizations. These sub-goals may be discrepant from those of the organization. Perception of the total situation of the concern and awareness of its goals may be deficient or selective, in any case partial; in addition, individual and group motives may be at variance with those required for the organization as a whole.

(ii) Trist and Emery[12] suggest that the notion of goal is best subsumed under the general heading of an endeavour to establish an interaction between the organization and its environment (i.e. market; external resources of capital and labour; social, cultural, and technological milieu) which will maximize an organization's capacities; in other words, the open system which the organization and its environment constitute has a steady state as its goal. In this endeavour, the variance which has to be 'managed' within the organizations in order to achieve this end is distributed unevenly among its members. It will, moreover, impinge upon them in various ways, and thus prompt differing action and the setting of differing sub-goals.

(iii) Cyert and March [17] have detected in both these kinds of formulation the contraband of hypostatization in the idea of organizations having goals but not the familiar outlines of the corpse of 'informal organization' being smuggled through inside the costume of 'divergent sub-goals and motives'. Instead, they rather cleverly throw the critics off the trail of their own model by getting it to walk on its hands upside down. The unit is now the individual's goal, and organizational goals, like group and section goals, are merely the product of 'coalitions' – i.e. the co-ordinated acceptance of (temporary) common goals. They write (p. 28):

'Studies of organisational objectives suggest that agreement on objectives is usually agreement on highly ambiguous goals. Such agreement is undoubtedly important to choice within the organisation, but it is far from the clear preference ordering usually assumed. The studies suggest further that behind this agreement on rather vague objectives there is considerable disagreement and uncertainty about sub-goals, that organisations appear to be pursuing different goals at the same time. Finally, the studies suggest that most organisation objectives take the form of an aspiration level rather than an imperative to "maximize" or "minimize", and that the aspiration level changes in response to experience.

'Unless we choose to ignore such observations, we need to reconsider our conceptions of objectives. Since the existence of unresolved conflict is a conspicuous feature of organisations, it is exceedingly difficult to construct a useful positive theory of organisational decision making if we insist on internal goal consistency. As a result, recent theories of organisation objectives describe goals as the result of a continuous bargaining-learning process. Such a process will not necessarily produce consistent goals.'

A critical coach and horses could still be driven through this formulation, although I believe it to be the best defence against empirical realities yet devised for a rationality model. But before trying to do so, there is: (iv) Simon's latest re-draft of his formulation [18] to consider. In this return to the problem of organizational goals, Simon resorts again to the analogy of computational methods, but this time from the standpoint of linear programming merely. Solutions to orthodox programming problems, he argues, take the form of providing sets of constraints within which action is 'satisficing' – i.e. will satisfy all the requirements laid down by the programmer. We could define the course of behaviour followed by a business concern as a complex programme of decision-making involving both the generation and the testing of alternatives. Within this general programme sub-programmes are written (sometimes for the performers, sometimes by them) which accord with the constraints laid down by the overall programme. The link is the acceptance by each programmed performer (sc. member of an organization) of the constraints which determine his goal (i.e. his organizational role). In so far as the constraints are tightly set, there will be less room for the manipulation by the performer of criteria so as to allow of interpersonal differences. But, more fundamentally, adopting an organizational role (taking a job) means that he steps into a cognitive framework and accepts a set of constraints on purposive action which are consonant with those of the organization. This is a facility provided by the psychological make-up of human beings (at least of socialized members of Western societies).

'An individual can assume a wide variety of roles when these are evoked by appropriate circumstances, each of which may interact only weakly with the others. At one time he may be a father, at another a machinist, at another a chess player. Current information processing theories of human cognition postulate that there is only a modest overlap of the subjects of memory contents – information and programs – that are evoked by these several roles. . . . The ability of a single individual to shift from one role to another as a function of the environment in which he finds himself thus helps to explain the extent to which organizational goals become internalized, that is, are automatically evoked and applied during performance of the role. By whatever means the individual was originally motivated to adopt the role in the first place, the goals and constraints appropriate to the role become a part of the decision-making program, stored in his memory, that defines role behavior' (Simon,[18] pp. 12–13).

This pronouncement spells, I think, a return to the traditional, pre-Hawthorne, notion of the organization as containing a single system – the formal structure – with all behaviour which cannot be contained within the definition of formally constituted roles being treated as frictional elements. Individual goals, action which is distinguishable from those prescribed (by organizational role, or by a part in a coalition, or by a function within a system) are all treated by Cyert and March, Simon, and, by implication, Trist and Emery as a residual category. Cyert and March are most forthcoming on this issue, as indeed they are on most, and it is clear (pp. 29–38) that although the bargaining and learning process may be observable in unmistakable terms in the decision-making procedures which take place within the frame of reference of the organization as a rational instrument (they cite the institution of budgetary systems and the allocation of functions as instances of the kind of mutual control system evolved through the process of bargaining-learning) those activities and goals which cannot be comprehended within the rational model are seen not only as residual but as random. The same view is implicit in Simon's 'abstraction of organizational role from personal goals' (p. 12). Certainly, this issue appears in rationality models in terms of the side payments which are the 'inducements' (in Barnard's terms) offered for the 'contributions' made by individuals, but here again, although side payments cover 'personal treatment, authority and so forth in addition to money', the effect is that only those aspects of individual behaviour and goals which bear on the assumption and maintenance of an organizational role, and only the specific relationships derived from a position in the formal organization are treated as relevant.

The interaction of organizational and other social systems in the same milieu

The position I want to adopt in this paper, and for which I hope the two previous sections have provided some kind of preparation, if only of a very flimsy kind, is that rationality models of organizations are both too simple and too complex for them to be other than dangerous instruments for research, or as a guide to consultative work, or for managerial practice itself.

They are too simple because of the assumption, explicit at times but implicit throughout, that a single system of interaction, or structure of relationships, provides an adequate frame of reference for the study of organizations or the practice of management, and because, although other kinds of interactive behaviour and other relationships are recognized as existing, they are regarded as residual and random.

They are too complex because there remains the problem of determining what does and what does not fall within the compass of the model. It is misleading to suggest, as Simon does: (i) that this is a question that resolves itself into simply a division between questions about joining and staying in organizations (personal) and questions about decision-making within organizations which are composed of people who have committed themselves to organizational roles (p. 11), or (ii) that behaviour is easily apportioned between that to which the first kind of question is appropriate and that to which the second kind applies (ibid.). In some organizations goals are undefined and susceptible to rapid changes; the goals of teaching hospitals and universities may be defined in substantially different ways by administrators, governors, teaching staff, researchers, and clients (students or patients). The incompatibilities between them may not necessarily be reconciled either by bargaining processes leading to mutual control systems or by the authority inherent in the organizational structure. Decisions of this kind are reached through the organizing of consensus and the manipulation of sanctions, legitimate and illegitimate, within a systematic framework of political action; and such organizing and manipulative activity may be regarded as in the interests of the organization as a whole or of interested individuals, or, indeed, both.

This paper began by discussing the interaction of the social systems existing within the concern. These systems are built out of the conduct (and the relationships which conduct involves, and values which the relationships specify) of individuals as they act in pursuit of the different ends to which they commit themselves, and find themselves committed, as members of the concern.

I have referred to three such social systems: the working organization, the political system, and the career structure. None of these is necessarily to be taken as the substructure of the totality of systems existing within the concern, since each *may* be manipulated so as to further the interests of one of the others.

The total membership of a concern – directors, managers, and operatives – represents the human resources assembled as instruments for use in achieving its ends. These resources and their systematic use represent the working organization. So far as the ends of the concern are considered in isolation, each individual member contributes part of his total capacities as a resource in return for a share of the rewards of the enterprise.

The systematic exploitation of these resources in order to realize the ends of the enterprise has been perceived traditionally in terms of bureaucracy. It appears, however, that this formulation is as time-bound as other generalizations, being appropriate to the second phase of industrialism.[3] In attempting to elucidate the situation of concerns in the electronics industry which were confronted with rapidly changing commercial circumstances and a much faster rate of technical progress than had previously been experienced within industry itself, it was necessary to posit two 'ideal types' of working organization, the one mechanistic, adapted to relatively stable conditions, the other, 'organic', to conditions of change.[4,11]

Mechanistic systems reveal most of the characteristics of the formulation given by Weber to bureaucracy, a formulation curiously, and significantly, similar to that arrived at independently by Fayol and developed later by writers on management techniques and by consultants. The problems and tasks which face the concern as a whole are, typically, broken down into specialisms. Each individual carries out his assigned task as something apart from the real tasks of the concern as a whole; it is as if his task were the subject of a sub-contract. 'Somebody at the top' is responsible for seeing to the relevance of his work to that of others, and to the needs of the concern. The technical methods, duties, and powers attached to each post are precisely defined, and a high value is placed on precision and demarcation. Interaction within the working organization follows vertical lines – i.e. between superiors and subordinates. Within the prescription of functional roles operations and working behaviour are governed by instructions and decisions issued by superiors. This hierarchy of command is maintained by the assumption that all knowledge about the situation of the concern and its tasks, and therefore of the proper disposition of the human resources committed to its service, is – or should be – available only to its head. The management system, usually visualized as the complex hierarchy familiar in organization charts, operates as a simple control system, with information flowing upwards through a succession of filters, and decisions and instructions flowing downwards through a succession of amplifiers.

Organic systems are adapted to unstable conditions, when new and unfamiliar problems and requirements for action continually arise which cannot be broken down and distributed among specialist roles within a hierarchy. Jobs lose much of their formal definition of methods, responsibilities, and powers, and the definitive or enduring demarcation of functions becomes impossible to prescribe. Responsibilities and functions, and even methods and powers, have to be constantly redefined through interaction with others participating in the discharge of common tasks or the solution of common problems. These tasks, and each individual's share, have to be discharged in the light of knowledge of the tasks and situation of the concern as a whole. Interaction runs laterally as much as vertically, and communication between people of different rank tends to resemble 'lateral' consultation rather than 'vertical' command. Omniscience can no longer be imputed to the head of the concern.

For the individual, much of the importance of the difference lies in the difference in the extent of his commitment to the working organization. Mechanistic systems (sc. 'bureaucracies') define his functions, together with the methods, responsibilities, and powers appropriate to them; in other words, however, this means that boundaries are set. That is to say, in being told what he has to attend to, and how, he is also told what he does *not* have to bother with, what is *not* his affair, what is *not* expected of him, what he can post elsewhere as the responsibility of others. In organic systems the boundaries of feasible demands on the individual disappear. The greatest stress is placed on his regarding himself as fully implicated in the discharge of any task appearing over his horizon, as involved not merely in the exercise of a special competence but in commitment to the success of the concern's undertakings approximating closely to that of the doctor or scientist in the discharge of their professional functions.

In studying the electronics industry in Britain, I was occupied for the most part with concerns which had been started a generation or more ago, well within the time-period of the second phase of industrialization, and equipped at the outset with working organizations designed in accordance with mechanistic principles.

Enlarging the commitment of the individual to the concern so as to admit of the adaption of the working organization to its own larger commitment to the new situation confronting it proved only partially possible to most firms. Indeed, the ideology of formal bureaucracy seemed so deeply ingrained in industrial management that the common reaction to unfamiliar and novel conditions was to redefine, in more precise and rigorous terms, the roles and working relationships obtaining within management, along orthodox lines of 'organization charts' and 'organization manuals', and to reinforce the formal structure. In these concerns the effort to make the orthodox bureaucratic system work (because it was seen as the only possible mode of organization, and because the enlargement of commitments to the concern was abandoned as hopeless or never seriously contemplated) produced what can best be described as pathological forms of the mechanistic system.

Three of these pathological systems may be mentioned. All three were responses to the need for finding answers to new and unfamiliar problems and for making decisions in new circumstances of uncertainty.

I In a bureaucracy the normal, prescribed procedure for dealing with any matter lying outside the boundaries of anyone's functional responsibility is to refer it to the point in the system where such responsibility is known to reside, or, failing that, to lay it before one's superior. If conditions are changing rapidly, in comparison with what obtained in the past, such episodes occur frequently; moreover, in many instances the immediate superior has to put such matters higher up still. A sizeable volume of matters for solution and decision can thus find their way to the head of the concern. There can, and frequently does, develop a system by which a large number of executives find – or claim – that they can get matters settled only in direct consultation with the head of the concern.

So in some concerns an ambiguous system developed of an official hierarchy of power and responsibility, and a more or less clandestine system of pair relationships between the head of the concern and some dozens of persons at different positions below him in the management. The head of the concern would be overloaded with work, and senior managers whose standing depended on the operation of the formal system would feel aggrieved at being by-passed. The managing director would tell himself, or brought in consultants to tell him, to delegate responsibility and decision-making. The organization chart would be redrawn. But inevitably, this strategy promoted its own counter-measures from the beneficiaries of the latent system as the stream of novel and unfamiliar problems built up anew.

Disparities between the two systems had their effect on the operational effectiveness of the concern. The conflict between managers who saw their standing and prospects depending on the ascendancy of one system or the other deflected attention and effort into internal politics. Both processes bore heavily on the time and effective effort the head of the concern was free to apply to the tasks proper to his position, the more so because political moves focused on controlling access to him.

II The preferred solution in other concerns was to grow more branches of the bureaucratic hierarchy. Most of the problems which appeared in the firms under discussion manifested themselves as difficulties in communications. These were met, typically, by creating special intermediaries and interpreters: methods engineers, standardization groups, contract managers, post-design engineers. Underlying this familiar strategy were two equally familiar characteristics of managerial thinking. The first is to look for the solution of a problem, especially a problem of communication, in 'bringing somebody in' to deal with it. A new job, or possibly a whole new department, may then be created, which depends for its survival on the perpetuation of the difficulty. The second attitude probably derived from the traditions of production management, which cannot bring itself to believe that a development engineer is doing the job he is paid for unless he is at a bench doing something with his hands; a draughtsman isn't doing his job unless he is at his drawing-board, drawing, and so on. Higher management in many firms are also worried when they find people moving about the works, when individuals they want are not 'in their place'. They cannot again bring themselves to trust subordinates to be occupied with matters directly related to their jobs when they are not demonstrably and physically 'on the job'. Their response, therefore, when there was an admitted need for 'better communication' was to tether functionaries to their posts and to appoint persons who would specialize in 'liaison'.

III The third kind of pathological response was encountered only rarely in the firms included in the study; it appeared sporadically in many of them, but was feared as the characteristic disease of government administration. It is nevertheless of particular interest, since, as the word indeed makes clear, the committee is a traditional device whereby commitments over and above those encapsulated in a single functional role may be contained within the system and discharged without enlarging the bounds of feasible demands which may be made on individual functionaries, and so upsetting the balance of commitments.

The appearance of new kinds of task and of unfamiliar problems may seem either a temporary phenomenon or to involve decisions, responsibilities, and powers of a kind which cannot properly be committed to one man or one department and handled by them. This is particularly the case in bureaucratic hierarchies in which most considerations, most of the time, are subordinated to the career structure afforded by the concern (a situation by no means confined to the civil service or even to universities). The aim is to overcome the difficulty caused by an apparent need for a job calling for unfamiliar responsibility by creating a super-person – a committee.

The problem of analysis only begins, of course, with the predication of two polar ideal types of working organization and the suggestion of the existence of a taxonomy of variants and pathological types. The question that immediately poses itself is why some concerns – indeed, most of the

concerns studied – do not change their working organization from mechanistic to organic as the general context of circumstances, technical and commercial, moves from stability to change. The answer has seemed to lie in the
fact that the commitments of the individual member of the concern are not
limited to those which enlist him as a resource of the working organization.
In addition, he is a member of a group or a section with sectional interests
in conflict with those of other groups or sections, and he is also one individual
among many to whom the position they occupy, relative to others, and their
future security or betterment are matters of deep concern.

Both these latter commitments involve him in means–end systems which
exist as alternative ways of serving his self-interests to the mode which is
defined by his entry into the contractual relationship of employment, and in
which he is committed to the use of himself as a resource in the interests of
the concern in exchange for a specified return in monetary and other rewards.

What I am suggesting here is that this is the other horn of the dilemma
presented by the rationality model. The notion either of a hierarchy of
sub-goals which, although generated within, and by the existence of, the
organization, wander out of line so far as organizational goals are concerned,
or of an organizational goal generated by the consensus reached by individuals, each with personal goals, bargaining and learning their way towards a
satisfactory equilibrium between their goals and those of the working community (sc. organization) can *itself* only be realized and made operational if
we accept the fact that the organization represents only one of several means–
end systems for realizing the goals of the individual, even if we restrict consideration of the latter to the activities, propensities, and goals composed by
his occupational role.

Second, if we accept the notion that a large number, if not all, of the
members of a working organization have commitments of this kind to themselves, then it is apparent that the relationships and conduct which relate to
these commitments are adjusted to other relationships and conduct of the
same kind existing throughout the concern, and that we can therefore speak
of the career structure of the concern, as well as of its working organization
and political system. Any concern will contain these three systems. All three
will act upon and react to the others; particularly, the political system and
career structure will influence the constitution and operation of the working
organization.

There are other social systems built out of other commitments of the
individual at work; there are organizations in which professional and quasi-
professional commitment seems of greater significance for the individual, and
to subsume a more considerable social system, than careerist commitments.
Again, the increased sub-cultural differences observable in people of different
ages in contemporary Western society is reflected in the commitments and
relationships of individuals in organizations, and gives rise to social systems
in which age-grading is the dominant feature.

The interaction of all these systems rests on the fact that an individual may invoke any one of them as the dominant reference system for this or that action, decision, or plan, even though an outside observer, or the individual himself, for that matter, may see other manifest relevance of what he is doing to all or any of the other systems. What I have called systems exist for the individual as social 'Gestalten', without which acts cannot be seen as items in means–end or cause–effect chains, and decisions cannot be given any preference ordering.

What is also argued in this paper is that these systems are best treated as separate and distinct – i.e. not as sub-systems of some total system. Clearly, the variety of commitments into which an individual enters is bounded by the individual and his career. Equally, the variety of social systems obtaining in a work place is nothing other than the finite set of social systems within or affecting the working community.

But I hope enough has been said to indicate that the connexions between these systems must be realized in terms which are categorically different from those applying within the systems. They relate to the value systems of the individual and of the culture. This means that any preference ordering *between* systems (which must be a moral ordering*) has to be in accordance with fundamentally different criteria from those which obtain within systems (which can be a technical ordering). In other words, when an individual acts he is selecting, or determining, a performance as well as merely acting a role, or (passively) carrying it out. The *ability* of the individual to determine the social significance of his behaviour in this way presupposes a plurality of action systems available to him, and the *fact* of determination by him presupposes that he can order these action systems preferentially.

REFERENCES

1 T. Burns (1961)
2 T. Burns (1962b), pp. 185–215
3 T. Burns (1962a)
4 T. Burns (1958)
5 A. V. Gouldner (1955)
6 P. M. Blau (1955)
7 J. Woodward (1958)
8 S. H. Udy (1959)
9 S. H. Udy (1961)
10 J. S. Thompson & F. L. Bates (1957)
11 T. Burns & G. M. Stalker (1961)
12 E. Trist & F. E. Emery (1962–3)
13 P. M. Blau & W. R. Scott (1962)
14 A. Etzioni (1961)
15 W. R. Scott (1964)
16 J. G. March & H. A. Simon (1958)
17 R. M. Cyert & J. G. March (1963)
18 H. A. Simon (1964)
19 R. B. Braithwaite (1955)
20 C. W. Churchman (1961)
21 D. Emmett (1966)

* The reference here is to a sociology of values, or perhaps a calculus of values, which is more than merely experiential. The scattered beginnings of such an approach are already visible.[19,20,21]

13 · Internal Pricing for Optimal Capacity of Air Transport Fleets Subject to Diversified Uses

WADE P. SEWELL

Introduction

The purpose of this paper is to outline the conditions under which the size and structure of the United States Military Air Transport Service (MATS) fleet is currently determined and to suggest how internal pricing techniques can make certain aspects of this decision more effective. Because the projected aircraft purchasing programme contains a very large and expensive addition to air transport capacity, a re-examination of the methods of rationalizing the programme may prove quite useful.

The study that underlies the paper was made possible by the contractual support of the Office of the Assistant Secretary of Defense (Comptroller) of the U.S. Department of Defense and by the substantive advice and assistance of a number of people in that Office and in Headquarters, MATS. However, the views and the analysis contained in the paper are not necessarily endorsed by the Department of Defense or any of its constituent parts. Particular thanks are gratefully proffered to my colleagues Stanley M. Besen and John G. Cross, whose contributions to the overall study are at least as great as mine.

At present MATS is concerned solely with the efficient satisfaction of air transport demands in both peacetime and wartime – that is, the determination of the relative importance of various requirements is not part of MATS's responsibility. All decisions regarding the importance of requirements are made elsewhere by authorities who have, at least implicitly, taken into account all reasonable wartime contingencies, the relative priorities of various missions, and whatever chances of success they wish to achieve in the light of the overall budget that has been made available to them. Thus, MATS is provided, and is expected to maintain, sufficient capacity to meet any air transport requirements arising from contingency plans approved by the Joint Chiefs of Staff. In practice, of course, current capacity as well as the costs of increasing it are also taken into account when air transport procurement programmes are fixed.

179

The formulation of requirements is not an entirely centralized process, however. In effect, the commands are given a portion of the available Department of Defense resources with the expectation that they will fully prepare themselves to carry out the missions that are assigned to them under the contingency plans. There is considerable leeway available to these commands for achieving their missions, however. In this paper the interest centres on the freedom of choice pertaining to transport and its alternatives. For example, equipment and personnel may reach battle areas by pre-positioning at each potential front, pre-positioning at nearby points and using sea, air, or overland transport, or by air transport from some more distant centre in the United States. Naturally, some of these alternatives involve the use of different types of equipment. Ultimately, the final decisions depend on relative *costs*; if air transport and pre-positioning can be made to serve the same purpose the cheaper will naturally be chosen. Thus, at least the preliminary decisions as to what kind of air transport to use and, indeed, whether or not to use air transport at all, are made at the command level. This is as it should be; part of the responsibility of each command is, after all, to plan the conduct of its own missions as efficiently as possible.

Unfortunately, the structure of costs as seen in such decentralized decision-making need not lead to decisions that are optimal – i.e. least-cost relative to the overall structure of Department of Defense costs. Air transport, to the Air Force, is a programme responsibility, and transport aircraft procurement is charged to the Air Force budget. The other services (and, in effect, parts of the Air Force) are able to obtain such transport for contingency purposes on a substantially costless basis – that is, at no expenditure from their own budgets. This contrasts sharply with most alternative modes of accomplishing the same missions. Pre-positioning, overland transport, and the use of more mobile, more easily transported equipment (all of which are budgetary expenditures to the using services) appear to be unduly expensive when compared to air transport which, at least in a budgetary sense, is free to all services but the Air Force. Air transport is not free to the Defense Department as a whole, however, and in many cases it may well be a significantly more expensive alternative. When the commands make up their mission plans, therefore, they are likely to make too much use of costly air transport. Of course, a comparison and co-ordination of these plans takes place at the level of the Joint Chiefs, and here it is possible to rectify some of these difficulties. But it would be impossible to obtain the greatest possible efficiency without completely reformulating all of the plans at the highest level. The total centralization which this would require would be grossly inefficient and complex in its own right. If possible at all, it must entail some loss of the detailed knowledge available only at the lower planning levels.

The internal pricing concept presents a less formidable approach, however. The difficulties outlined above arise solely from the fact that air transport costs appear, to some users, to be lower than the true costs to the Department of Defense. Correct internal pricing results in equality of the costs borne by each user of air transport and the costs incurred by the Department of Defense as a result of the users' decisions between air transport and its alternatives. Furthermore, a decentralized decision-making structure is devised so that if each user minimizes cost for a given effectiveness in his mission the overall Department of Defense cost is minimized as well. In designing the decision-making structure, an explicit effort is also made to utilize fully the detailed expertise available in each of the concerned operating and planning units; thus, the advantages of decentralization are retained and perhaps extended.

In brief, appropriate prices for using, or for the right to use, air transport in an emergency will lead the commands to compare correctly the cost of air transport with that of its alternatives in making their decisions. If the prices are chosen so as to reflect MATS's capacity costs the final mission plans may be expected to make far more efficient use of resources than they would otherwise.

A decentralized decision-making structure

Four basically different kinds of specialized information affect the proper choice of MATS's fleet structure. These are: (*a*) the nature of the contingencies and the desired objectives in dealing with them; (*b*) the requirements in personnel and equipment, as well as the timing of their arrival at their destinations, imposed by the various contingencies in which air transport may play a role; (*c*) the costs of the alternatives to air transport in meeting these requirements, and (*d*) the least-cost methods of fulfilling all or part of the contingency requirements with air transport.

Contingency definition and the formulation of objectives take place at the highest national levels and are outside the scope of this analysis. It is assumed, however, that these decisions are taken in a way that removes all uncertainty regarding mode and level of response from the calculations at the planning levels considered in this paper. Also, it is supposed that where conditional probability considerations link contingencies, they are consolidated by redefinition into a single contingency. Simultaneous occurrence of contingencies does not, in these circumstances, enter as a consideration in the planning process described.

For a particular contingency the second and third types of information are possessed by the commands charged with the operational responsibility of coping with that contingency. Furthermore, the detailed knowledge of how to plan and carry out the effective use of the forces in particular circumstances is likely to be found *only* in these commands. In other words, for given modes of transport and pre-positioning, least-cost methods of obtaining a given effectiveness in a contingency can be most efficiently sought by planners intimately associated with the commands. These planners may be expected to be resourceful in seeking out alternatives to air transport, as well, provided they are confronted with prices that adequately reflect the true costs of these alternatives to the Department of Defense. In some instances, e.g. the Military Sea Transport Service, presenting planners with correct prices for alternatives will involve problems similar to those for MATS. Alternatives such as pre-positioning, on the other hand, will yield to more traditional costing and planning procedures. In what follows, the term 'contingency planners' will refer to those who collect and apply the varieties of information and experience described in this paragraph.

MATS, on the other hand, has experience regarding efficient planning and operation of air transport that should be utilized in a decentralized planning arrangement. Furthermore, there are interactions among the requirements for different contingencies that can best be taken into account by MATS in planning for an optimal fleet composition. These interactions result from the fact that, because the mix of aircraft types appropriate in one situation, time frame, geographical context, etc., is unlikely to be as useful in another, there are no single contingencies so overwhelming in requirements that the air transport required for them is also sufficient for any other contingency. Nevertheless, substitution is possible, with some loss of efficiency in each contingency considered singly, and with *increased efficiency for all contingencies taken collectively*. Put differently, the least-cost fleet for a mix of contingencies is unlikely to be the least-cost fleet for any single contingency. This complication can be taken into account adequately if MATS is introduced into the planning process in the way envisaged in this study.

Price formation

TYPES OF PRICES

The purpose of the following paragraphs is to describe methods by which the appropriate 'internal prices' may be chosen. To a limited extent, of course, any reasonable, positive set of prices would be better than the zero prices now in use, simply because it is certain that air transport is not really free. This problem is approached here, however, by using a modification of linear programming,[1] the desired prices being derived from the L.P. 'shadow prices'.

It is evident that when the commands propose to use the services of air transport in various contingencies they are not demanding aircraft as such, but rather that some mission or part of a mission be carried out with certain degrees of speed and effectiveness. The *time* of accomplishment (i.e. one, two, or more days after the beginning of a crisis) is an important dimension of the problem. It is appropriate therefore that prices be placed not on aircraft but upon the missions themselves. For example, X dollars must be charged for transporting so many men from 'here' to 'there' within H hours of the inception of the contingency, rather than charging for the actual capacity to be utilized. Naturally, the price that is charged will be closely related to the capacity the mission requires.

Uncertainty considerations also influence the precise form of the prices to be charged. Among the many important kinds of uncertainty surrounding contingencies are those regarding the possibility and the timing of their occurrence. Indeed, it is almost certain that not all the contingencies contemplated in the contingency plans will occur during the lifetime of an air transport fleet. This consideration alone suffices to rule out prices based on the realization of the mission requirements or on the utilization of aircraft during contingencies. Instead, the prices of this study will be charges, levied in advance, for the right to claim desired levels of requirements fulfilment in the event that the contingency occurs. In other words, because the costs associated with a decision to employ air transport in a contingency are certain, although the contingency occurrence is not, the prices must be certain to the contingency planner.

TENTATIVE PRICES FOR GIVEN REQUIREMENTS

The method of determining prices may be briefly sketched as follows. As has been emphasized earlier, *minimization of overall Department of Defense costs* for achieving the desired levels of effectiveness in all contingencies is the objective. What is desired is an arrangement that causes *cost minimization for each contingency to coincide with this goal.* Suppose that for each requirement in each contingency the incremental gross saving resulting from the use of air transport is a known function of the quantity of air transport employed. Denote this incremental saving for the jth requirement of the ith contingency by $s_{ij}(r_{ij})$. For each quantity this saving should be precisely the minimum incremental cost of fulfilling the requirement by an alternative to air transport. If a set of r_{ij}, that is, quantities of each kind of air transport requirement in each contingency, are given, a least-cost MATS fleet for satisfying those r_{ij} can be computed by the linear programme described in Appendix 1. A set of prices, P_{ij}, is associated with a least-cost fleet. A particular one of these prices, e.g. P_{12}, is the increment to the fleet cost that would result from an increase of one unit in r_{12}. Now there are three possibilities. If $s_{ij}(r_{ij}) > P_{ij}$, the Department of Defense cost can be reduced by increasing r_{ij}, that is, by increasing the use of air transport in satisfying that requirement. If $s_{ij}(r_{ij}) < P_{ij}$, the cost can be reduced by decreasing r_{ij}. Finally, if $s_{ij}(r_{ij}) = P_{ij}$, no change in r_{ij} will reduce the overall Department of Defense cost. A systematic adjustment of the choice of the r_{ij} and recomputation of the least-cost fleet until $s_{ij}(r_{ij}) = P_{ij}$ for all i and j leads to the desired set of prices consistent with the goal of minimizing Department of Defense costs.*

ADJUSTMENT OF REQUIREMENTS AND PRICES

It is to be expected that the users of air transport will change their contingency plans somewhat in the light of internal prices if they are effectively

* Actually, matters are a bit more complicated than this description indicates. A more thorough discussion is given later.

charged to the user. For example, one of the dimensions of these demands is time, and the prices of transport services during the first few days of an emergency will be higher than the prices of services on less critical days. Then we would expect less essential materials to be shipped relatively late in an emergency as a result of the avoidance of the higher prices. In some cases, pre-positioning and overland transport may appear now to be relatively cheaper than aircraft. Others, of course, might find air transport to be cheaper than they expected and increase their planned use of it. These changed plans will have to be introduced into the programme and a new optimal fleet structure and set of prices obtained; that is, the process just described is repeated. Further adjustments should be continued until relative stability in the contingency requirements is obtained; that is, until the requirements desired at a set of prices are equal to those that can be satisfied by the least-cost fleet associated with those prices.

Properties of the prices

The prices obtained in this manner, when quoted to contingency planners, go a long way towards inducing planners to demand the sets of requirements that are necessary for an optimal fleet. Adjustment of the shadow prices is necessary in some cases, however, to obtain the set of prices that will lead to this result. In this section some such adjustments and other properties of the prices are discussed.

Despite the fact that the same type of aircraft may be used to satisfy several different requirements, it is *not* necessarily true that the same charges should be levied on all users if their requirements arise in different contingencies. For example, suppose that it costs $10 per passenger to expand MATS's capability for carrying soldiers into the Middle East during the first twenty-four hours of a crisis (call this contingency No. 1). This capability will be enlarged until the services which require the air transport in a Middle East emergency are no longer willing to pay $10 a man for additional air transport potential. Now imagine another contingency (No. 2) in which very little use is planned for air transport, but which would require the presence of support personnel in the Middle East within a week of the beginning of the crisis. Perhaps there would be enough time to plan to send them by sea at a capital cost (i.e. the number of troop ships would have to be increased) of $5 per man. It would surely be cheaper to plan to send these men by air, utilizing the excess MATS capacity, instead of incurring the cost of building additional ships. This will only occur, however, if MATS quotes a price lower than $5 to the planners of contingency No. 2. In fact, it is a characteristic of the linear programming shadow prices that so long as excess capacity is expected to exist in such a contingency, *zero* prices will be quoted (reflecting the fact that expansion of air transport requirements in this situation imposes no additional capital costs on MATS), and hence the user will be induced to employ air transport.

Suppose, however, that the lower air transport price quoted in the second contingency induces the users to increase their requirements so as to utilize the whole of MATS capacity. Since a further expansion in air transport requirements in *either* contingency would force MATS to enlarge its fleet (at the cost of $10 per passenger), a shadow price of $10 will be associated with both requirements. Because at this price neither user will want to enlarge his requirements, MATS will retain its fleet size if this price is quoted. This clearly may be wrong, however. The two users together may be willing to pay just under $15 for the expansion in capacity ($10 from contingency No. 1 and $5 from contingency No. 2), since each user would benefit. Thus, MATS should expand its fleet until both users *together* are no longer willing to pay $10 for additional capacity. As it happens, this kind of problem can arise only when a requirement imposed on MATS from one contingency is identical, qualitatively and quantitatively, with that imposed by another contingency. Fortunately, such a condition is readily identifiable from the linear programme, so that appropriate adjustments in the internal prices may be made.*

Finally, it should be emphasized that this technique of quoting internal prices and permitting the services to adjust their requirements will often lead to an allocation of *all* the available air transport resources in each contingency. That is, if the requirements do not exhaust capacity, prices will be lowered until either no more air transport is desired at any price or the whole supply is used. This device serves two purposes: first, it is more efficient than any allocation which would leave some aircraft idle, and second, it discourages the services from misrepresenting their actual requirements in order to obtain free air transport. If some planes were to be left unused the 'buyers' would have an incentive to understate their requirements, using the free capacity if the contingency ever came up. With capacity fully utilized, and air transport introduced into all contingency plans, this possibility no longer exists. If the capacity is not entirely used, requirements are costless anyway (and have a zero price), so that there is still no incentive to misrepresent requirements.

Typically, however, the function $s_{ij}(\,\cdot\,)$ will be known only to the planner for the ith contingency. This fact necessitates the introduction, in the case of identical requirements, of bargaining among planners over prices. In the absence of bargaining, each planner may be tempted to understate requirements because he does not know what strategy of misrepresentation may be employed by the other planners. In the presence of communication and bargaining, however, the jointly optimal solution, i.e. the least-cost solution for each planner, is to agree on the correct overall allocation of prices. Indeed, each planner will then be able to see that understatement of his

---

* In the notation previously used let the identical requirements be r_{1k} and r_{2k}, i.e. $r_{1k} = r_{2k}$. Then the sum of the quoted prices should be $s_{1k}(r_{1k}) + s_{2k}(r_{2k})$ and, indeed, the planner for the first contingency should be quoted $P_{1k} = s_{1k}(r_{1k})$ and for the second $P_{2k} = s_{2k}(r_{2k})$.

requirements will lead to their under-fulfilment unless his $s_{ij}(r_{ij}) = 0$ at the r_{ij} in question.

Resale markets

Naturally, the internal prices and the associated requirements will have to be recomputed periodically in order to adjust to changing military, technological, and financial circumstances. At the same time, however, it must be remembered that aircraft have relatively long lifetimes and that it would not be efficient to permit requirements to be made which necessitate expansions in the MATS's fleet and which later could be costlessly revoked, leaving MATS with uncompensated and unused capacity. That is, the requirements must be permanent in the sense that full payment to MATS must be guaranteed. The total cost of the capacity would then be spread over the useful life of the aircraft, the users paying annually. If some demander wishes to reduce an established requirement he may ask MATS to lower the quoted internal prices until other demanders absorb the excess capacity. The original user must then pay only the difference between the amount which he guaranteed and what others are willing to pay. In effect, the original user is *selling* his right to aircraft capacity. This device has the desirable effect of preventing users from formulating inefficient requirements which they intend later to reduce. It also permits exchange of aircraft uses as technology and needs change over time.

MATS should stand ready to repurchase requirements at prices that equal the savings in training and maintenance costs yet to be incurred less the value of the aircraft in non-contingency uses. In this way the economic life of aircraft in the MATS fleet is properly determined and the aircraft may be retired or refitted for other uses.

Possible institutional limitations

A rather substantial institutional analysis accompanies the more formal analysis in a study of this kind. There are a number of institutional considerations that may represent substantial limitations to the applicability of the analysis. In this rather truncated discussion two potential limitations deserve mention.

The objective used, in this case, for contingency planners has been cost minimization for achieving fixed effectiveness. In point of fact, the planner's problem is often overdetermined by the existence of a more or less implicit budget constraint. Some incentive to bargain over budget levels, rather than attend to cost minimization, may result from the presence of such a partially flexible, imperfectly revealed constraint. This effect can be rendered unlikely in practice, however, if the following situation prevails. Suppose it is true, and believed, that rationally determined implicit initial effectiveness and budget estimates underlie the specification of contingency definitions and objectives. Then an adjustment based on an upward revision of the cost estimate will, save for quite exceptional cases, result in diminution of the desired objectives. The planner would then be faced with either (i) the embarrassment of a lower level of capability at a higher unit cost and some more or less easily detectable inefficiency or with (ii) attempting a belated cost minimization that would belie his original contention by yielding a higher capability.

There are indications, based largely on casual observation, that changes in military plans in response to price changes are often not very rapid or of the right magnitude. Such effects can result from factors such as the loose connexion between job-performance ratings and economic efficiency, the short job-rotation period, and various institutional rigidities. The introduction of market mechanisms and internal prices should, however, result in increased awareness of and attention to cost considerations. Coupled with a realization that economic efficiency, properly measured, is an appropriate basis for performance ratings and with the introduction of appropriate incentive measures, internal pricing mechanisms may contribute to alleviating this difficulty.

Appendix: A linear programme for least-cost fleet determination

For a single contingency, say the first, with a given row vector $R_1 = (r_{11}, \ldots r_{1n})$ of requirements, a least-cost fleet may be determined as follows.

The requirements are stated in terms of man-miles or ton-miles of movement to be accomplished in specified periods of time. In some instances there will be restrictions relating to cargo size and weight, landing conditions, requirements for parachuting troops or equipment, and the like. Now, MATS will be able to construct at least one way of performing each requirement. Typically, however, there will be more than one way, because several different aircraft or several routes or other variations in operational mode will satisfy the requirement. Each method of satisfying a requirement is an activity, and associated with each activity is an activity vector and an activity level.

Naturally, an activity may contribute to satisfying more than one requirement since, e.g., some aircraft configurations will accommodate both troops and cargo. An activity vector contains an entry for each requirement in the contingency. If a requirement cannot be satisfied by the activity the entry is zero; if it can, the entry is the quantity of the requirement that can be fulfilled at the unit activity level. Usually a one-way trip or round trip by the aircraft type will be a convenient choice of unit for the activity level. Denote the matrix of activity column vectors by A_1 and the column vector of activity levels by Y_1. Then the inequalities

$$A_1 Y_1 \geq R_1, \ Y_1 \geq 0$$

express the conditions that all the requirements be satisfied and that the activity levels cannot be negative. Of course, the vector Y_1 is as yet unknown.

Each activity will employ some aircraft, in most instances only one type, and if unit activity levels are defined as above exactly one aircraft will be used at the unit level. Let X_0 be a vector of quantities of aircraft types in the existing fleet; that is, there is an entry for each type at present available. Also let $X = (x_1, \ldots x_k)$ be a vector of the quantities of aircraft types that can be procured. Both X_0 and X contain entries for all aircraft types, with zeros where necessary. Finally, let B_1 be a matrix with one as the (i, j) entry if the ith type of aircraft is used in the jth activity and zero otherwise. Now the inequalities

$$X - B_1 Y_1 \geqslant -X_0, \ X \geqslant 0$$

express the conditions that the number of aircraft used cannot exceed those available and to be procured and that the quantities produced cannot be negative. The vector, X, of quantities to be procured is also unknown at this stage.

Finally, the costs must be considered. Let C_0' be a row vector with entries that express the present values of the costs of procurement, training, and maintenance of emergency capability per unit of each type of aircraft. Let C_1' be a row vector of the present values of the costs of operating activities during the contingency.*

Now the total cost

$$C'_0 X + C'_1 Y_1$$

is to be minimized subject to the conditions already described:†

$$A_1 Y_1 \geqslant R_1$$
$$X - B_1 Y_1 \geqslant - X_0$$
$$X \geqslant 0, \ Y_1 \geqslant 0$$

Similar considerations apply for all contingencies, of course. If there are m contingencies, k types of aircraft, and if I_k denotes the k-order identity matrix, then the computation of the least-cost fleet over all contingencies consists of minimizing

$$C'_0 X + \sum_{i=1}^{m} C'_i Y_i,$$

over variations in X and the Y_i, subject to the conditions

$$\begin{bmatrix} A_1 & 0 & \ldots 0 & 0 \\ 0 & A_2 & \ldots 0 & 0 \\ \cdots & \cdots & \cdots & \cdots \\ 0 & 0 & \ldots A_m & 0 \\ -B_1 & 0 & \ldots 0 & I_k \\ 0 & -B_2 & \ldots 0 & I_k \\ \cdots & \cdots & \cdots & \cdots \\ 0 & 0 & \ldots -B_m & I_k \end{bmatrix} \begin{bmatrix} Y_1 \\ Y_2 \\ \cdot \cdot \\ Y_m \\ X \end{bmatrix} \geqslant \left. \begin{bmatrix} R_1 \\ R_2 \\ \cdots \\ R_m \\ -X_0 \\ \cdots \\ -X_0 \end{bmatrix} \right\} \text{repeated } m \text{ times}$$

$$X \geqslant 0, \ Y_i \geqslant 0, \ i = 1, \ldots, m$$

This apparently formidable linear programme can, in fact, be computed quite efficiently using the 'decomposition principle' (see ref. 1).

* Operating costs are included for completeness. However, they will typically be quite small relative to the costs C_0 and will also involve considerable estimation difficulties owing to uncertainty and discounting problems. It may therefore be convenient to take them as zero with negligible loss of accuracy.

† In those cases where contractual obligations for procurement have already been entered into, some modifications are necessary. Suppose, for example, that fifty of the first type of aircraft are on order and that a unit price $C_{01}^\star$ must be paid if delivery is made or not. Then the type must be split into two types with quantities x'_1 and $x_1^\star$, say, and the term $C_{01} x_1$ in the cost function replaced by $C_{01} x'_1 + (C_{01} - C_{01}^\star) x_1^\star$. The constraint $x_1^\star \leqslant 50$ must also be added.

The programme determines a least-cost capacity when the capacity is to be employed for diversified uses. This use of linear programming can be viewed as introducing a set of activities for the production of aircraft (the columns in the activity matrix containing the identity matrices) in each contingency's activities coupled with costs in the objective function that charge only once for aircraft production.

A least-cost fleet over all contingencies exploits the substitutability of aircraft in a way that guarantees that the least-cost fleet is unlikely to be least-cost for any contingency taken separately. Therefore, the prices must have the property that, when quoted to contingency planners, they make the optimal fleet appear to each planner to be least-cost for his contingency. The situation is closely analogous to one found in welfare economics where it is shown that pricing to account for such interactions involves a system of taxes and subsidies.* It can be shown that the shadow prices from the dual compute the necessary taxes and subsidies correctly.

REFERENCE

1 G. Dantzig & P. Wolfe (1961)

* Economists will recognize that the analogy is valid only on a decentralized interpretation of contingency planning so that the external effects are not internalized.

14 · Theoretical and Computational Problems in Organizational Decision-making

ANDREW WHINSTON

Introduction

The purpose of this paper is to examine specific procedures according to which large organizations may organize their planning process. The structure and complexity of a large organization are such that no one person or group can hope to assemble all the useful information and then form a plan of action. Some way must be developed to co-ordinate and evaluate various proposals from different parts of the organization.

This is a very large and important area of organization theory, but yet, it has not received commensurate attention. Organization theorists have discussed concepts such as communication and authority structure of large organizations while economists have mainly considered various optimality conditions for idealized organizations. Yet relatively little effort has been devoted to studying the role of the organization theorists' concepts to the possible achievement of the optimality conditions of the economist.*

The type of planning procedures envisaged here are based on a systematic exchange of information between a central staff group and various subordinate divisions. After a certain amount of exchange of information, final decisions are made. For certain decisions, final authority may rest with a central staff, while other decisions may be decentralized so that the final authority rests with divisional heads.

The first part of the paper presents an algorithm to study a specific convex programming problem. In the second part we present a discussion of various aspects of organizational decision-making. In this context the algorithm presented in the early part of the paper is shown to be interpretable as a specific model of organizational decision-making.

---

* A notable exception has been the work of T. Marschak.[1] He has studied several different decision procedures and attempted to rank them in terms of desirability. A recent paper of M. Gordon[2] discussed several points in this area. Actual planning procedures found in several large organizations were reported by A. Whinston.[3]

A decomposition algorithm for quadratic programming*

In this part of the paper we consider a direct extension of the Dantzig and Wolfe[5] decomposition algorithm for linear programming to the case of a quadratic criterion function. First presented by Dantzig[6] and further elaborated by Van de Panne and Whinston,[4] the quadratic algorithm we shall use is itself a direct extension of the simplex method. Thus, if the quadratic part of the criterion function is zero, i.e. if we, in fact, have a linear criterion function, the decomposition algorithm is reduced to the one given by Dantzig and Wolfe.

In their paper, Dantzig and Wolfe suggested an extension of their algorithm to the case of a non-linear convex criterion function. This is discussed in more detail by Dantzig.[7] Their suggestion differs from the method being presented here in several ways. First, in the quadratic case our method leads to a finite procedure while their method yields an infinite convergent algorithm. Second, in the solution of the sub-problems we must solve linear programming problems, while their method requires the solution of the same number of quadratic programming problems. Finally, the method discussed here does not require that the criterion function should be separable. Since extension beyond the quadratic case would not possess the characteristics indicated above, we present the argument for the quadratic case only.

The use of a separable criterion function, where the value or pay-off of a process is a function solely of the level of the particular process, has been studied extensively in the welfare literature in economics. Allocation models incorporating this assumption have been shown to be capable of achieving an optimal solution via a pricing mechanism.[8] Where the separability condition is no longer maintained, e.g. where the pay-off for one process is dependent on the levels of other processes, the question as to the manner of operating an informationally decentralized system successfully has not been fully explored. In the following pages we shall attempt to first discuss a formal mechanism for finding an optimal solution to a model possessing a non-separable criterion function. In a later section an interpretation of the model and process will be given in organizational terms, including explicit attention to the exchange of information.

THE ALGORITHM

In presenting the algorithm we shall attempt to illustrate the basic differences between this case and the linear programming problem. With this in mind, we consider only two sub-sectors in the following problem

$$\max_{x_1, x_2} f(x_1, x_2) = p'_1 x_1 + p'_2 x_2 - \tfrac{1}{2}[x'_1 \, x'_2] \begin{bmatrix} C_{11} & C_{12} \\ C_{21} & C_{22} \end{bmatrix} \begin{bmatrix} x_1 \\ x_2 \end{bmatrix}$$

$$= p'_1 x_1 + p'_2 x_2 - \tfrac{1}{2} x'_1 C_{11} x_1 - x'_1 C_{12} x_2 - \tfrac{1}{2} x'_2 C_{22} x_2$$

* This discussion is an outgrowth of some joint work with C. Van de Panne as reported by C. Van de Panne and A. Whinston.[4]

(1) $$A_1 x_1 + A_2 x_2 = b_0$$

(2) $$B_1 x_1 \leqslant b_1$$

(3) $$B_2 x_2 \leqslant b_2$$

$$x_1 \geqslant 0 \quad x_2 \geqslant 0$$

$$x'_1 = (x_1^1 \ldots x_1^{q_2}) \qquad x'_2 = (x_2^1 \ldots x_2^{q_2}) \qquad b'_0 = (b_{01} \ldots b_{0l})$$

$$p'_1 = (p_1^1 \ldots p_1^{q_1}) \qquad p'_2 = (p_2^1 \ldots p_2^{q_2})$$

The matrix $\begin{bmatrix} C_{11} & C_{12} \\ C_{21} & C_{22} \end{bmatrix}$ is symmetric positive semidefinite matrix of dimension $(q_1 + q_2)$. We shall assume that the convex sets described by the inequalities (2) and (3) are each bounded, in order to simplify the exposition.*

Let $\{x_{k1}\}$ be the set of extreme points for the constraints of (2), and $\{x_{k2}\}$ the set of extreme points for the constraints of (3). Then any point x_1 satisfying the constraints of (2) can be written as

(4) $$x_1 = \sum_{k=1}^{k_1} \rho_{k1} x_{k1}$$

$$\Sigma \rho_{k1} = 1$$

$$\rho_{k1} \geqslant 0$$

Correspondingly we have for (3)

(5) $$x_2 = \sum_{k=1}^{k_2} \rho_{k2} x_{k2}$$

$$\Sigma \rho_{k2} = 1$$

$$\rho_{k2} \geqslant 0$$

Substituting (4) and (5) into the programming problem we have the equivalent problem

$$\text{Max}_{\rho_{ki}} \; p'_1 \Sigma \rho_{k1} x_{k1} + p'_2 \Sigma \rho_{k2} x_{k2} - \tfrac{1}{2} \Sigma \rho_{k1} x'_{k1} C_{11} \Sigma \rho_{k1} x_{k1}$$

$$- \Sigma \rho_{k1} x'_{k1} C_{12} \Sigma \rho_{k2} x_{k2} - \tfrac{1}{2} \Sigma \rho_{k2} x'_{k2} C_{22} \Sigma \rho_{k2} x_{k2}$$

(6) $$A_1 \Sigma \rho_{k1} x_{k1} + A_2 \Sigma \rho_{k2} x_{k2} = b_0$$

(7) $$\Sigma \rho_{k1} = 1 \qquad \Sigma \rho_{k2} = 1$$

(8) $$\rho_{ki} \geqslant 0 \qquad i = 1, 2 \quad \text{for all } k$$

The Kuhn–Tucker† conditions for this problem are (6), (7), (8), and

(9) $$p'_1 x_{k1} - x'_{k1} C_{11} \Sigma \rho_{k1} x_{k1} - x'_{k1} C_{12} \Sigma \rho_{k2} x_{k2} - v' A_1 x_{k1} - \eta_1 + u_{k1}$$
$$= 0$$

(10) $$u'_{k1} \rho_{k1} = 0$$

(11) $$u_{k1} \geqslant 0,$$

* Without this assumption we would follow the argument as developed by Dantzig and Wolfe [9] as it pertains to this point.

† See Dantzig, [6] for a discussion of this topic.

(12) $\quad p'_2\, x_{k2} - x_{k2}\, C_{22}\, \Sigma_{\rho k2}\, x_{k2} - x'_{k2}\, C_{21}\, \Sigma_{\rho k1}\, x_{k1} - v'A_2\, x_{k2} - \eta_2 + u_{k2}$
$$= 0$$

(13) $\quad u'_{k2}\, \rho_{k2} = 0$

(14) $\quad u_{k2} \geqslant 0 \quad$ for all k

We must show that the transformed problem is still a concave programming problem. We write

$$f(x_1, x_2) = p'_1\, x_1 + p'_2\, x_2 - [x'_1, x'_2] \begin{bmatrix} C_{11} & C_{12} \\ C_{21} & C_{22} \end{bmatrix} \begin{bmatrix} x_1 \\ x_2 \end{bmatrix}$$

and show the following:

Theorem. The criterion function $f(\Sigma_{\rho k1}\, x_{k1}, \Sigma_{\rho k2}\, x_{k2})$ is a concave function of $(\rho_1, \rho_2) = (\rho_{11} \ldots \rho_{k_11}, \rho_{12} \ldots \rho_{k_22})$.

Proof. Since $f(x_1, x_2)$ is concave we have

(15) $\qquad\qquad f(\lambda \tilde{x} + (1 - \lambda)\hat{x}) \geqslant \lambda f(\tilde{x}) + (1 - \lambda)f(\hat{x})$

where $\tilde{x} = (\tilde{x}_1, \tilde{x}_2)$ and $\hat{x} = (\hat{x}_1, \hat{x}_2)$ are given points. We have

$$\tilde{x} = T\tilde{\rho}$$
$$\hat{x} = T\hat{\rho}$$

where T is a linear transformation. Define

(16) $\qquad\qquad\qquad g(\rho) = f(T\rho)$

Then

(17) $\qquad g(\lambda \tilde{\rho} + (1 - \lambda)\hat{\rho})$

(18) $\qquad = f(T(\lambda \tilde{\rho} + (1 - \lambda)\hat{\rho}))$

(19) $\qquad = f(\lambda T\tilde{\rho} + (1 - \lambda)T\hat{\rho})$

(20) $\qquad \geqslant \lambda f(T\tilde{\rho}) + (1 - \lambda)f(T\hat{\rho}) = \lambda g(\tilde{\rho}) + (1 - \lambda)g(\hat{\rho})$

DESCRIPTION OF THE ALGORITHM

In this section we shall describe in some detail the working of the algorithm. After certain preliminary definitions we shall give a description of the algorithm in terms of the quadratic programming tableau. Then various aspects of the algorithm will be explored in some detail.

Dantzig and Wolfe have pointed out that an important aspect of the algorithm is the sequential generation of the extreme points and resulting columns of the tableau as they are required. To initiate the algorithm, we must have $l + 2$ 'ρ_{ki}' variables, where l is the dimension of b_0, which are positive and satisfy (6), (7), and (8).* We also have l 'v' variables and η_1 and

---

* We assume that the constraint matrix has rank $l + 2$ and that the initial set of p_{ki} variables are associated with an independent set of columns. It should be observed that degeneracy can be handled exactly as in the case of linear programming.

η_2 in the basis. Note that these variables appear in every tableau, since their values are unconstrained. Finally, we will have $m + n - 1 - 2$ 'u_{kt}' in the basis corresponding to ρ_{kt} not in the basis. In general, the initial set of u_{kt} in the basis will not satisfy (11) and (14), but will satisfy (10) and (13). When conditions (10) and (13) are satisfied, then we say that the tableau is in standard form; otherwise, it is a non-standard tableau. The initial solution constitutes a feasible, standard form tableau which is not optimal, i.e. satisfies conditions (6), (7), (8), (9), (10), (12), and (13), but not necessarily (11) and (14). A feasible solution is one that satisfies (6), (7), and (8). The algorithm proceeds by moving from a feasible solution which is either in standard or non-standard form to an optimal solution, i.e. a tableau also satisfying (11) and (14) besides the conditions (6), (7), (8), (9), (10), (12), and (13).

Let $\{z_i\}$ be the values of the set of basic variables which are permitted to leave the basis in a particular iteration and let $\{l_{ij}\}$ be the elements in the jth

Set up Tableau for the Algorithm*

Basic variables	Value of basic variables	u_1	u_2	v	ρ_1	ρ_2	γ_1	γ_2	y_1	y_2	y_3
u'_1	$-P'_1$	I	0	$-\bar{A}'_1$	$-\bar{C}_{11}$	$-\bar{C}_{12}$	$-l'_1$	0	0	0	0
u'_2	$-P'_2$	0	I	$-\bar{A}'_2$	$-\bar{C}_{21}$	$-\bar{C}_{22}$	0	$-l'_2$	0	0	0
y'_1	b'_0	0	0	0	$\bar{A}_1$	$\bar{A}_2$	0	0	I	0	0
y'_2	1	0	0	0	l_1	0	0	0	0	1	0
y'_3	1	0	0	0	0	l_2	0	0	0	0	1

$$u_1 = (u_{k1} \ldots u_{k_11}) \qquad \rho_1 = (\rho_{11} \ldots \rho_{k_11})$$
$$u_2 = (u_{k2} \ldots u_{k_22}) \qquad \rho_2 = (\rho_{12} \ldots \rho_{k_22})$$
$$v = (v_1 \ldots v_l)$$
$$\bar{A}_1 = (A_1 x_{11} \ldots A_1 x_{k_11}) \qquad P_1 = (p'_1 x_{11} \ldots p'_1 x_{k_11})$$
$$\bar{A}_2 = (A_2 x_{12} \ldots A_2 x_{k_22}) \qquad P_2 = (p'_2 x_{12} \ldots p'_2 x_{k_22})$$
$$l_1 = (1 \ldots 1_{k_1})$$
$$l_2 = (1 \ldots 1_{k_2})$$

$$\bar{C}_{11} = \begin{bmatrix} x'_{11} C_{11} x_{11} \ldots x'_{11} C_{11} x_{k_11} \\ \cdot \qquad\qquad \cdot \\ \cdot \qquad\qquad \cdot \\ \cdot \qquad\qquad \cdot \\ \cdot \qquad\qquad \cdot \\ \cdot \qquad\qquad \cdot \\ x'_{k_11} C_{11} x_{11} \ldots x'_{k_11} C_{11} x_{k_11} \end{bmatrix}$$

* We add the artificial variables $y = (y_1, y_2, y_3)$ to the constraints in order to write the tableau in this form. 'I' refers to an identity matrix of appropriate dimension.

$$\bar{C}_{12} = \begin{bmatrix} x'_{11}\,C_{12}\,x_{12} \ldots x'_{11}\,C_{12}\,x_{k_22} \\ \cdot \qquad\qquad \cdot \\ \cdot \qquad\qquad \cdot \\ \cdot \qquad\qquad \cdot \\ \cdot \qquad\qquad \cdot \\ \cdot \qquad\qquad \cdot \\ x'_{k_11}\,C_{12}\,x_{12} \ldots x'_{k_11}\,C_{12}\,x_{k_22} \end{bmatrix}$$

$$\bar{C}_{21} = \begin{bmatrix} x'_{12}\,C_{21}\,x_{11} \ldots x'_{12}\,C_{21}\,x_{k_11} \\ \cdot \qquad\qquad \cdot \\ \cdot \qquad\qquad \cdot \\ \cdot \qquad\qquad \cdot \\ \cdot \qquad\qquad \cdot \\ \cdot \qquad\qquad \cdot \\ x'_{k_22}\,C_{21}\,x_{11} \ldots x'_{k_22}\,C_{21}\,x_{k_11} \end{bmatrix}$$

$$\bar{C}_{22} = \begin{bmatrix} x'_{12}\,C_{22}\,x_{12} \ldots x'_{12}\,C_{22}\,x_{k_22} \\ \cdot \qquad\qquad \cdot \\ \cdot \qquad\qquad \cdot \\ \cdot \qquad\qquad \cdot \\ \cdot \qquad\qquad \cdot \\ \cdot \qquad\qquad \cdot \\ x'_{k_22}\,C_{22}\,x_{12} \ldots x'_{k_22}\,C_{22}\,x_{k_22} \end{bmatrix}$$

column of the tableau which is the column of the variable to come in the basis. Then the variable to leave the basis is the one whose value z_i is such that

$$\underset{i}{\text{Min}}\left\{\frac{z_i}{l_{ij}} \;\middle|\; \frac{z_i}{l_{ij}} \geqslant 0 \qquad l_{ij} \neq 0\right\}$$

Starting from a basic feasible solution which is not necessarily optimal, the algorithm proceeds in the following manner:*

1 Determine the most negative u_{ki} variable. If there is none the algorithm is terminated.

2 Introduce into the basis the complementary ρ_{ki} to the u_{ki} chosen in Step 1. The variable to be removed from the basis is chosen from among the 'ρ_{ki}' variables in the basis and the 'u_{ki}' variable designated in Step 1. If the variable designated in Step 1 is removed return to Step 1; if not, go to Step 3.

3 Introduce the 'u_{ki}' variable corresponding to the 'ρ_{ki}' variable which was just taken out of the basis. The variable to be eliminated from the basis is chosen from the ρ_{ki} in the basis and the variable designated in Step 1. If a ρ_{ki} is eliminated repeat Step 3, if not go back to Step 1.

* These rules are based on C. Van de Panne and A. Whinston.[4]

We now wish to show that given the values of the $l + 2$ 'ρ_{ki}' variables in the initial basis, we may determine $v = (v_1 \ldots v_l)$ and η_1 and η_2. From the tableau we have the following $l + 2$ equations involving v, η_1, η_2, and ρ_{ki} which are in the basis:

$$(21) \quad p'_1 x_{k1} = v' A_1 x_{k1} + \sum_{j \varepsilon J_1} \rho_{j1} x'_{j1} C_{11} x_{k1} + \sum_{j \varepsilon J_2} x'_{k1} C_{12} \rho_{j2} x_{j2} + \eta_1$$

$$(22) \quad p'_2 x_{k2} = v' A_2 x_{k2} + \sum_{j \varepsilon J_1} x'_{k2} C_{21} \rho_{j1} x_{j1} + \sum_{j \varepsilon J_2} x'_{k2} C_{22} \rho_{j2} x_{j2} + \eta_2$$

where

$$J_1 = \{j \mid \rho_{j1} > 0\} \quad \text{and} \quad J_2 = \{j \mid \rho_{j2} > 0\}$$

Each of the equations corresponds to a particular $\rho_{ki} > 0$, and consequently there are $l + 2$ equations. The set of extreme points indexed $\{x_{k1}\}$ which appears in these equations is associated with $\rho_{k1} > 0$. As a result, these points are known. The extreme points indexed $\{x_{k2}\}$ are associated in the tableau with columns of $\rho_{k2} > 0$, and again are known. Thus, we have $l + 2$ equations in $l + 2$ unknowns $(v_1 \ldots v_l)$, η_1, and η_2. In principle, we may solve for v, η_1, and η_2.*

We now wish to discuss how Step 1 in the algorithm is carried out. At some stage in order to determine the most negative u_{ki} we have the following equations for u_{k1} and u_{k2}:

$$(23) \quad u_{k1} = -p'_1 x_{k1} + x'_{k1} C_{11} \Sigma \rho_{k1} x_{k1} + x'_{k1} C_{12} \Sigma \rho_{k2} x_{k2} + v'_1 A_1 x_{k1} + \eta_1$$

$$(24) \quad u_{k2} = -p'_2 x_{k2} + x'_{k2} C_{22} \Sigma \rho_{k2} x_{k2} + x'_{k2} C_{21} \Sigma \rho_{k1} x_{k1} + v'_1 A_2 x_{k2} + \eta_2$$

According to Step 1 we are to determine that particular u_{ki} which is minimum. This is equivalent to minimizing the expression for u_{ki} over all extreme points $\{x_{ki}\}$. In order to express the problem in a more interpretable fashion we may take the maximization of the negative expression for u_{ki}. Thus, we have

$$(25) \quad \underset{x_1}{\text{Max}} \; p'_1 x_1 - x'_1 C_{11} \Sigma \rho_{k1} x_{k1} - x'_1 C_{12} \Sigma \rho_{k2} x_{k2} - v' A_1 x_1 - \eta_1$$
$$\text{s.t.} \; B_1 x_1 \leqslant b_1$$
$$x_1 \geqslant 0$$

$$(26) \quad \underset{x_2}{\text{Max}} \; p'_2 x_2 - x'_2 C_{22} \Sigma \rho_{k2} x_{k2} - x'_2 C_{21} \Sigma \rho_{k1} x_{k1} - v' A_2 x_2 - \eta_2$$
$$\text{s.t.} \; B_2 x_2 \leqslant b_2$$
$$x_2 \geqslant 0$$

Both maximization problems are linear-programming problems, and therefore the solution is at an extreme point. From these solutions we obtain both the minimum u_{ki} value and its associated extreme point.

In the course of the algorithm we must be able to determine the current basis values of ρ_{ki}, v_i, η_i, and the particular u_{ki} currently designated by

* This point will be discussed below in more detail.

Step 1. In a certain iteration we refer to the u_{ki} designated in the preceding Step 1 as $u_{ki}^{\star}$. Of course, as the algorithm proceeds the particular variable designated as $u_{ki}^{\star}$ will vary.

At any iteration we are either introducing a $\rho_{ki}^{\star}$ variable complementary to $u_{ki}^{\star}$ designated by Step 1 or some u_{ki} variable. If we can show that at any iteration we can determine the tableau elements of the particular incoming column associated with ρ_{ki}, v_i, η_i and $u_{ki}^{\star}$ in the basis, we then will know the values of these basic variables throughout the algorithm.

Consider the system of equations (6), (7), (9), and (12). Associated with each variable is a column of coefficients. However, during the course of the algorithm not all coefficients will be known. The algorithm, as represented by the rules 1–3, can be viewed as a procedure for moving from one basic solution to (6), (7), (9), and (12) to another one via a simplex-type pivot. Each basic solution is successively an improvement in terms of certain criteria. What we wish to know is that, in general, we need only be concerned with a smaller basis matrix – a sub-matrix of the larger basis matrix where all the coefficients are known.

We first consider the case where we are introducing $\rho_{ki}^{\star}$ into the basis. By determining the appropriate tableau elements for $\rho_{ki}^{\star}$ we may determine which variable will leave the basis among the $\rho_{ki} > 0$ and the appropriate $u_{ki}^{\star} < 0$. Let p_{ki} be the column associated with $\rho_{ki}^{\star}$. Let B be the basis matrix where we partition $B = (B^1, B^2)$. B^1 contains the columns of u_{ki} in the basis except $u_{ki}^{\star}$, while B^2 consists of the columns associated with ρ_{ki}, v_i, η_i, and $u_{ki}^{\star}$ in the basis. Thus we have

$$(B^1, B^2) \begin{pmatrix} \lambda_1 \\ \lambda_2 \end{pmatrix} = p_{ki}$$

where $\lambda' = (\lambda_1, \lambda_2)$ is the vector of tableau elements. By permutation of the rows of $(B^1, B^2) = B$ and p_{ki} we write the problem as

$$\begin{pmatrix} B_{11} & B_{12} \\ 0 & B_{22} \end{pmatrix} \begin{pmatrix} \lambda_1 \\ \lambda_2 \end{pmatrix} = \begin{pmatrix} p_{ki1} \\ p_{ki2} \end{pmatrix}$$

where $B_{11} = I$. The dimension of I is equal to the number of columns in B^1. Note also that B_{22} is a square sub-matrix. Next we wish to show that all the coefficients in B_{22} are known. The last $l + 2$ rows of B_{22} correspond to the constraints (6) and (7), and since the columns correspond to 'ρ_{ki}' variables in the basis of the coefficients are known. The remaining rows of B_{22} consist of equations drawn from (9) and (12), where the 'u_{ki}' variable associated with each constraint has been removed from the basis. Therefore the extreme point x_{ki} associated with the complementary variable ρ_{ki} has been determined. This, combined with the fact that the columns are associated with variables in the basis, establishes that all coefficients are known. A similar argument holds for p_{ki2}. The matrix B must be non-singular, since it is obtainable by a series of simplex pivot operations, therefore the matrix B_{22} is also non-singular. The system of equations

$$B_{22} \lambda_2 = p_{ki2}$$

is solvable for $\lambda_2 = B_{22}^{-1} p_{ki2}$. The vector λ_2 contains the needed tableau elements.

With this result we may determine the tableau elements associated with a $\rho_{ki}^{\star}$ which is to come into the basis. If some u_{ki} is to be introduced into the basis according to Step 3, then with a similar argument we may show that the required tableau elements can be generated.

We have shown that the various steps of the algorithm can be carried out even though not all extreme points are known at every step. Each time a new ρ_{ki} variable is brought into the basis, as a result of Step 2, the criterion function increases. Steps 2 and 3, which involve non-standard tableaux, do not decrease the value of the criterion function, and after a finite number of iterations lead back to a standard tableau, where Step 1 is again applied. We then have a series of standard tableaux, each one associated with a higher value of the criterion function. Therefore no standard tableau can ever be repeated. Since the number of extreme points is finite, there can be only a finite number of standard tableaux, and consequently the algorithm is finite.*

A model of organizational decision-making

In recent years a great deal of attention has been given to the study of organization theory, but one important area seems to have received little treatment in the literature. This is the question of the relationship between decision-making and information flow. The design of an efficient decision system for an organization requires the patterning of information flow. The co-ordination and motivation of the decision-makers are significantly dependent on a continually changing stream of information, which may not be automatically available to them. This section will discuss the relationship between decision-making and information in general terms, focusing on the structural and dynamic features in any given system. The following section will develop a specific system and discuss its dynamics in detail.

GENERAL DISCUSSION OF THE MODEL

Abstracting from the particular characteristics of the individuals in an organization, a decision-making system may be described as having three main parts: (i) a set of decision variables; (ii) inter-relationships among the decision variables; (iii) a criterion function depending on values of the decision variables. Thus, the decisions and actions which the organization must carry out are the primary elements of this model.

Any decision has implications for other decision variables in the system.

* For a discussion of these points see C. Van de Panne and A. Whinston.[4]

For example, the decision to produce a thousand units of a new product may imply that existing lines of operation would have to be curtailed for lack of production facilities. Similarly, the decision to increase the length of tne coffee break for one group of workers may necessitate a similar increase for other groups. It may be useful to present an interpretation of the interaction of decision variables in a formal manner.

Let $X = \{X_1\}$ be the set of decision variables. The collection of functions $(\Gamma_1, \ldots \Gamma_m)$ can be considered to represent the interconnexions among the decision variables. Each Γ_i can be viewed as mapping a set of decision variables into some subset, viz. the particular subset of decision variables interconnected by Γ_i. We may construct a matrix to represent this type of information by setting:

$$a_{ij} = 1 \text{ if } x_j \, \varepsilon \, \Gamma_i \, x$$
$$a_{ij} = 0 \text{ otherwise}$$

we thus obtain a matrix composed of ones and zeros.

$$E = \begin{bmatrix} 1 & 0 & 1 & 0 & 0 \\ 0 & 1 & 0 & 0 & 0 \\ 0 & 1 & 0 & 0 & 0 \\ 1 & 0 & 0 & 0 & 0 \end{bmatrix}$$

Note that permuting rows and columns do not affect the information presented in the matrix.

A matrix P_i of zeros and ones is called a permutation matrix if it contains the element 1 in every row and column. A permutation matrix of appropriate dimension, when used to premultiply the matrix E, permutes the rows of E. Correspondingly, post-multiplication of E by a permutation effects a permutation of the columns.

Let P_k, P_e be two permutation matrices. Then the structure represented by E is capable of decentralization if for some P_k and P_e we have

$$P_k E P_e = \begin{bmatrix} M_1 & M_2 \\ M_3 & 0 \\ 0 & M_4 \end{bmatrix}$$

where M_i is a matrix of zeros and ones, and 0 is a matrix of zeros of appropriate dimension.

Let us assume that $\Gamma_1, \ldots \Gamma_k$ are associated with the rows of the matrices $[M_1, M_2]$ and $\Gamma_{k+1}, \ldots \Gamma_m$ the remaining rows of $P_k EP_e$. In an intuitive sense it seems reasonable to consider the relations $\Gamma_1, \ldots \Gamma_k$ as an entire unit. On the other hand $\Gamma_{k+1}, \ldots \Gamma_m$ are relations which involve a subset of the decisions and may permit a special treatment.

We may divide all relations roughly into two types of grouping: (a) a grouping which commonly involves many different variables, and (b) several groupings, each involving only a distinct subset of the variables. Any decision system is likely to have many groupings of type (b), in which each group co-ordinates a particular set of relationships. It would clearly be advantageous to design a decision-making system which takes this structural characteristic into consideration.

An hierarchically structured organization may be designed in which type (*a*) interconnexions designate a central staff co-ordinating group. This group will be responsible for co-ordinating the various type (*a*) relations. Let type (*b*) represent the various divisions. As we have seen, each division is responsible for a group of relations which involve a particular subset of decision variables. If it should be desirable, these analytic procedures could be applied to each unit of type (*b*), discriminating a co-ordinating group and sub-sectors within the divisional unit. In any case, however, the criterion function, as the measure of effectiveness, is applicable to any unit or group of units. It usually involves all the decision variables in the discriminated system.

Having determined the structural properties of an hierarchical system, we now turn to the design of the decision system. Naturally, the decision system will attempt to exploit the structural system that has been evolved.

Decision schemes may be divided into two kinds. The first is a centralized organization decision scheme where ultimate authority for making decisions rests with a central staff group. The second type, where authority for certain decisions rests with divisional managers, may be characterized as decentralized decision schemes.

It is often suggested that the centralized and the decentralized schemes describe mutually exclusive approaches to the organization of authority. Centralized authority, it is thought, requires that all organizational decisions be made by a small group of people whose orders are followed by the rest. Except for very small businesses, this is seldom the case. Realistically, information regarding the requirements of the lower-level units is supplied by them in the form of suggestions as to what actions they think should be taken. The planning process which is the responsibility of the central staff depends on this information. Thus, it is of interest to design a system that facilitates the flow of useful information to top management where final authority rests. As we develop the centralized decision system, we shall see that some decisions may be decentralized while authority is maintained over other decisions. In effect, the operation of a mixed, centralized–decentralized organization will be described.

For the present discussion, we take the organizational structure as given, and define $x_i{}^j(t) = $ the value of *i*th activity variable in the *j*th division at time *t*. The accounting system is assumed to be structured along divisional lines so that each manager may accurately assess the effects of his decision. Central staff communicates to the divisions both a measure of effectiveness relevant to the particular variables in the division and certain costs assigned to the varying level of the variables. Thus we may define

$$\pi^j(x_1^j(t) \ldots x_{i_j}^j(t); t)$$

as the criterion function for the jth division at time t. The criterion function may vary from one decision period to the next as a result of alterations by central management in accounting costs relevant to divisional variables. At each division decision time the current solution

$$\left(x_1^{0j}(t) \ldots x_{i_j}^{0j}(t)\right)$$

for each division is communicated to the central staff. The divisional solution will have the characteristic that, given the criterion function,

$$\pi^j(x_1^j(t) \ldots x_{i_j}^j(t); \, t),$$

the solution is the best attainable under the constraints induced by the divisional relationships. Each manager is asked to specify a tentative proposal which takes into account those factors related to his division, based on information accessible to him.

The central staff receives the vector of proposals $(x_1^{0j}(t) \ldots x_{i_j}^{0j}(t))$ from each division and uses them to determine a co-ordinated central solution. A new tentative solution is obtained by co-ordinating the divisional proposals with the central staff constraints, in terms of the criterion function of the organization. On the bases of the new tentative solution, the central staff alters the divisional criterion function to take into account certain aspects of the central solution. For example, if the central group co-ordinates a general warehouse and the current solution indicates that the warehouse is not used to capacity the central group will lower its charge for storage space to the divisions. On the other hand, if current requests for funds for capital investment exceed funds available the financial charge to divisions will be raised. Thus, by varying the criterion function or, in particular, by altering specific accounting charges, alternate and more profitable suggestions can be obtained. Note that the proposals offered by the divisions provide the information required by the central staff, so that there is no need to inaugurate special inquiries.

A SPECIFIC MODEL

Having described the general organization of a decision-making system, we can proceed to construct a model that will allow us to discuss a specific decision process. We begin by considering a problem of a type that arose earlier:

$$\text{Max}_{x_1, x_2} \; p'_1 x_1 + p'_2 x_2 - \tfrac{1}{2}[x'_1, x'_2] \, C \begin{bmatrix} x_1 \\ x_2 \end{bmatrix}$$

(27) $\qquad A_1 x_1 + A_2 x_2 = b$

(28) $\qquad B_1 x_1 \qquad \leqslant b_1$

(29) $\qquad B_2 x_2 \qquad \leqslant b_2$

$$x_1 \geqslant 0, \, x_2 \geqslant 0$$

Constraints in (27) must be considered interdivisional, since they commonly involve all the variables. Constraints in (28) and (29) include only subsets of the variables and can be considered as divisional constraints.

The algorithm developed earlier in the paper represents the type of decision process we are proposing. Recall that in step one of the algorithm we had to solve the problems of the form

$$\text{Max}_{x_1} \, p'_1 \, x_1 - x'_1 \, C_{11} \, \Sigma_{\rho k_1} \, x_{k_1} - x'_1 C_{12} \, \Sigma_{\rho k_2} \, x_{k_2} - v' A_1 \, x_1 - \eta_1$$

$$\text{s.t. } B_1 \, x_1 \leqslant b_1$$

$$x_1 \geqslant 0$$

and

$$\text{Max}_{x_2} \, p'_2 \, x_2 - x'_2 \, C_{22} \, \Sigma_{\rho k_2} \, x_{k_2} - x'_2 \, C_{21} \, \Sigma_{\rho k_1} \, x_{k_1} - v' A_2 x_2 - \eta_2$$

$$\text{s.t. } B_2 \, x_2 \leqslant b_2$$

$$x_2 \geqslant 0$$

In the present context these may be interpreted as divisional problems and each criterion function may be looked upon as a particular

$$\pi^j \, (x_1^j(t) \ldots x_{i_j}^j(t); \, t)$$

where $j = 1, 2$. Since we have

$$\pi^1(x_1^1(t) \ldots x_{i_1}^1(t); \, t) = p'_1 x_1 - x'_1 \, C_{11} \, \Sigma_{\rho k_1} x_{k_1} - x'_1 \, C_{12} \, \Sigma_{\rho k_2} x_{k_2} - v' A_1 \, x_1 - \eta_1$$

the central staff must communicate to the division the current central staff solution

$$(\Sigma_{\rho k_1} x_{k_1}, \, \Sigma_{\rho k_2} x_{k_2})$$

'prices' $v = (v_1 \ldots v_l)$ and η_1 for each iteration. The $v = (v_1 \ldots v_l)$ correspond to certain per unit accounting charges which the central staff imposes on the divisions. The η_1 represents a fixed charge made to division one. If a division cannot find a profitable solution for given accounting prices v and charges η_1 in terms of its criterion function it makes no proposal. Otherwise it communicates its present solution to central management as a tentative proposal. Given the divisional proposals, steps 2 and 3 in the algorithm formulate the procedure under which the central staff utilizes the proposals to find a new tentative solution. Thus, the algorithm discussed offers a method for developing a decision system in a large centralized organization.

In order to illustrate the ideas developed above, we consider the following example:

$$\text{Max}_{x_1, \, x_2} \, 6x_1 - 2x_1^2 + 2x_1 x_2 - 2x_2^2$$

(30) $x_1 + x_2 \leqslant 2$

(31) $0 \leqslant x_1 \leqslant 1$

(32) $0 \leqslant x_2 \leqslant 1$

The organization we are considering operates two activities at levels x_1 and x_2. There are two divisions where each one is associated with a particular process. Thus, division one is concerned with the optimal level of the variable x_1 and division two with the optimal level of x_2. The constraint (31) represents a limitation on the output of division one and (32) similarly for division two. These are the divisional constraints. The condition (30) is an example of an interdivisional constraint. It could represent, for example, a jointly used production facility of capacity two units.

To initiate the method, let us assume that each division proposes to operate its activities at level zero. Thus, $x_1^1(0) = 0$ $x_1^2(0) = 0$. The problem of the central staff is to co-ordinate the two proposals to maximize the overall criterion function for the firm. Given the initial divisional proposals, the solution of the central staff is

$$\rho_{11} = 1, \ \rho_{12} = 1, \ \eta_1 = 0, \ \eta_2 = 0, \ v = 0$$

This information is transmitted to the divisions and is utilized to formulate problems given in expressions (25) and (26). We have

$$\text{Max } 6x_1$$
$$0 \leqslant x_1 \leqslant 1$$

and

$$\text{Max } 0x_2$$
$$0 \leqslant x_2 \leqslant 1$$

as the two-divisional problems. Division one has a proposal to operate its process at one unit, e.g. $x_2^1(2) = 1$. This has a net profit of six in terms of its own criterion function. Any proposal of division two would have a zero profit so that the central staff will take into account the proposal of division one.

A new problem of the central staff is then solved. It gives a weight of one to the new proposal of division one. We obtain

$$\rho_{21} = 1, \ \rho_{12} = 1, \ \eta_1 = 2, \ \eta_2 = 0, \ v = 0$$

This information is, in turn, transmitted to the divisions and we obtain the two problems:

$$\text{Max } 2x_1 - 2$$
$$0 \leqslant x_1 \leqslant 1$$

and

$$\text{Max } 2x_2$$
$$0 \leqslant x_2 \leqslant 1$$

Note that η_i acts as a memory device. Recall that the central staff combines the current proposal with earlier proposals of the various divisions. However, each division keeps no record of past proposals or the relative merits of past proposals in terms of the profitability of the present proposal. But this is, in fact, the role of the η_i variables. For the present example $\eta_1 = 2$ in the current iteration. This indicates that the proposal $x_1 = 1$, which shows a profit of two units without the fixed charge, should not be introduced.

The proposal of division two, $x_2 = 1$, has a net profit of two units. Thus $x_2^2(3) = 1$ is communicated to the central staff and it is designated x_{22}, the second extreme point of the second division. We obtain as a central staff solution $\rho_{22} = \frac{1}{2}$, $\rho_{21} = 1$, $\rho_{12} = \frac{1}{2}$, $\eta_1 = 3$, $\eta_2 = 0$. This gives us two divisional problems:

$$\text{Max } 2x_1 - 3$$
$$0 \leqslant x_1 \leqslant 1$$

and

$$\text{Max } 0x_2$$
$$0 \leqslant x_2 \leqslant 1$$

Neither division has a profitable proposal to make. Consequently, the decision problem is terminated. Division one is instructed to produce at $x_1 = 1$ and division two at $x_2 = \frac{1}{2}$.

Mixed system

Until now we have been discussing schemes where ultimate authority rests with a central staff group, but to the extent to which decisions are delegated some type of decentralization occurs. In order to present this common practice of delegating some authority, we shall give an illustration in terms of the preceding model. Suppose that there is a central staff constraint reflecting a limitation on capital funds available. Many items involving small expenditures would not be included in central staff constraints. A few items would involve large expenditures, and present additional policy implications. For example, funds for building a new wing of a divisional plant might be considered not only in terms of actual capital expenditure but also in terms of market penetration of a product or other policy considerations.

Let the explicit form of this constraint be

$$\Sigma a_{iz}^j x_{iz}^j \leqslant K_z$$

The variable x_{iz}^j is the expenditure for the ith capital good in the jth division and a_{iz}^j is a dimensionality constant. For each division we may partition the variables into two groups: The first group contains variables for which authority is delegated to the divisions, and the second contains the variables for which ultimate authority rests with the central staff. Call x_{iz1}^j the first set and label the variables in the second class x_{iz2}^j. Define for each division the variable y_z^j by $\Sigma a_{iz1}^j \leqslant y_z^j$. Then we may write the central staff constraint in the form

$$\sum_{i,j} a_{iz2}^j x_{iz2}^j + \sum_j y_z^j \leqslant K_z$$

Under our assumption that the set of variables x_{iz1}^j does not enter into any other central staff constraint we have removed large numbers of variables from the central staff problem and replaced them with one variable. This represents the total investment for the type one variables. Thus, the central staff needs to know only the total investment rather than the many small capital investments that a division is interested in undertaking.

For this mixed centralized–decentralized system we may again formulate a decision system. In this case the divisions propose to the central management a tentative total expenditure which is based on their decisions concerning levels of x_{iz1}^j. The central staff combines the various divisional proposals and decides on an appropriate interest charge for the divisions. This in turn causes the divisions to reconsider their investment plan and supply a new proposal to central management. After several iterations central management communicates a total level of expenditure. On the basis of this figure the divisions commit themselves to specific projects, and the total of divisional expenditures will not exceed the amount authorized by central management. At the same time the divisions supply proposals concerning x_{iz2}^j variables and the decision process concerning centralized variables proceeds as before.

Concluding remarks

We have been assuming the establishment of an organizational system where divisional constraints are relevant only to the decision variables of a particular division. This idea of structural articulation is not always to be found, for complicating interactions may arise. For example, one division claims that another is not providing proper maintenance and is saving on its own by causing excess maintenance costs to be shouldered by the other division. That is, the complaining division argues that its maintenance costs could be reduced if only the alternate user of this production line were somehow made to conduct its own maintenance 'efficiently'. This phenomenon has been discussed in economic theory under the heading of external effects. It is well known that complications of this kind may lead to decisions which are not in the best interests of the company.

Where external effects are present, the structure of the decision-making system should be altered to take them into account. One method puts the constraint which involves variables of both divisions under the jurisdiction of the central staff. This has the disadvantage of increasing the co-ordinating task of the central staff. Another method extends the decision system to accommodate the interactions. To illustrate, let x_i^j be the ith decision variable in the jth division. Assume that x_i^j affects the decisions through some constraint for the kth division. Then both the kth and jth divisions are asked to specify a tentative proposal to the central staff concerning x_i^j, each from its own point of view. The central staff will attempt to accommodate the divergent views as to the proper level of x_i^j by communicating to each division a new criterion function. Both divisions make proposals on the level of a particular variable and the decision procedure progresses as described earlier.*

In general, how viable are the decision schemes we have proposed from the viewpoint of the firm's criterion function? If the divisions act in good faith when they make their proposals to central management, then, in general, under conditions of a convex technology, i.e. one where there are diminishing returns to scale, these types of process do lead to desirable solutions. In the absence of these conditions, divisional proposals may lead a central staff to decide on poor solutions. Another problem may arise when divisional managers, in making their proposals, attempt to 'game' the decision system by trying to anticipate the convergences of their proposals beyond the particular criterion function. The study of such problems leads beyond the framework of this paper, but these difficulties should be kept in mind.†

ACKNOWLEDGEMENTS

I am indebted to Chris Argyris and Menaham Yaari of Yale University and C. Van de Panne at the University of Birmingham (England).

REFERENCES

1 T. Marschak (1959)
2 M. Gordon (1963)
3 A. Whinston (1964)
4 C. Van de Panne & A. Whinston (1964)
5 G. B. Dantzig & P. Wolfe (1961)
6 G. B. Dantzig (1963)
7 G. B. Dantzig (1959)
8 G. Debreu (1959)
9 G. B. Dantzig & P. Wolfe (1960)
10 O. Davis & A. Whinston (1962)

* For further discussions at this point see O. Davis and A. Whinston,[10] and A. Whinston.[3]

† For further elaboration see O. Davis and A. Whinston.[10]

15 · Man–Machine Simulations of Management Systems

The History and Uses of the Logistics Systems Laboratory

MURRAY A. GEISLER

Introduction

In this paper I shall present a brief history and description of the Logistics Systems Laboratory of The RAND Corporation and its research activities. The laboratory has played a central role in the logistics research conducted for the U.S. Air Force. As the next section indicates, the laboratory was developed to fit a much-felt void in the spectrum of research techniques that were needed to study complex logistics systems. The emphasis in creating the laboratory was to secure a greater correspondence between reality and the research model by employing the device of man–machine simulation. It was believed that this striving for verisimilitude would bring the researcher into greater contact with the difficulties of logistics systems study and improvement, and therefore help him to produce valid products of meaningful benefit.

Recent experience with the results of the latest of the laboratory's experiments indicates that even more intervention between research and implementation is desired by the Air Force in its evaluation and acceptance of research. In this instance, a field test of part of the experiment's findings has been proposed and is being undertaken by the Air Force, with technical assistance. This experience does highlight the tremendous problem of making changes in large and complex systems. It does, however, at the same time, provide large opportunities for meaningful research to improve the capabilities of research techniques.

The Logistics Systems Laboratory

The Logistics Systems Laboratory began as a consequence of experiences between the Air Force and RAND in trying to make use of research findings. The problem experienced in such areas as inventory and supply policies and information system design was that the translation of the broad findings of research studies into the detailed procedures required by an operating system

209

raised many important questions for which the previous research provided no guidance. As a consequence, it was not readily apparent to the Air Force how to implement findings, and it was frustrating to RAND to see how little of its research was put to direct use in the Air Force.

This led to a proposal developed jointly by the Air Force and RAND that it would be useful to the development and consideration of research findings by the Air Force if a simulation laboratory were established in which experiments could be conducted that would simulate how the proposed changes to the Air Force logistics system would work. The simulation laboratory idea was partly stimulated by the experiences of the Air Force with the Systems Research Laboratory, in which simulation was used to produce training benefits for the Air Defense Command. It was recognized early that there were significant differences in the goals of the Logistics Systems Laboratory and the Systems Research Laboratory. The latter organization was primarily interested in the human element in an existing air defence system, and it was concerned therefore with a very precise reproduction of the environment and physical conditions in which the air defence ground crews operated. There was a great stress on teaching the crews to follow the prescribed procedures efficiently. In the LSL the simulation of a proposed logistics system was the first occasion that such a system was brought into being, and therefore it was subject to frequent change as it was put together in the laboratory. Also, the Air Force participants' role in the LSL experiments was different from that in the SRL. In the LSL experiments the participants were asked to help to assess the feasibility and realism of the proposed system, as well as to participate as decision-makers in the simulation.

As a consequence of the close relation between the Logistics Systems Laboratory and the Air Force, a Special Air Force Regulation 20-8 was published defining the objectives of LSL and the relations between the Air Force and RAND. The laboratory came into being in October 1956, and in the early years of its operations a staff of Air Force consultants was assigned to the laboratory to help in its experiments. The laboratory also began functioning in the former facilities of the Systems Research Laboratory, but later a new laboratory was constructed.

The initial laboratory staff was recruited from personnel of the Logistics Department and from former members of the Systems Research Laboratory. Thus, the initial staff consisted of psychologists, economists, engineers, and mathematicians. In addition, a clerical staff was recruited to help in the laboratory. Computational and programming assistance was provided.

The LSL held two preparatory experiments in late 1956 and early 1957 called Prologs I and II. These were undertaken to develop a feeling for how logistics systems might be simulated in the laboratory, to develop staff skills and team work, and to mock up potential candidates for the first laboratory problem, called LP-I. Work on LP-I began in early 1957 and ran until the end of 1957. In the autumn of that year early design work began on LP-II, intensive efforts began in early 1958 and continued until late in 1958, when LP-III began to be defined. The main effort on LP-III began in the middle of 1959, and continued until the middle of 1960. In the middle of that year the Air Force created a committee to evaluate LP-II and the simulation technique that had been developed during it for studying weapon systems early in their life cycle. The purpose of this evaluation was to determine whether the LP-II technique should be applied to the Minuteman weapon system. During this period consideration of future LPs was deferred, since a substantial part of the laboratory staff would have had to be involved in helping the Air Force to organize its own laboratory and to use the LP-II technique for the Minuteman weapon system.

When it was decided by the Air Force in late 1960 not to proceed with the Minuteman study, work was begun on LP-IV. That experiment, currently* under way, will not be reported in detail here.

Experiment evolution

Experiments start in a variety of ways. The way that seems to be evolving as the most preferable is to select a pool of accomplished research performed by traditional operations research means, such as a set of new logistics policies or a description of the trade-offs or main variables in a given weapon system, and then to build an experiment to test these policies in a larger system context with a view to designing the detail of the management system for applying the policies in the real world, and then evaluating them in the experiment. Since the research on new policies or system characteristics is done in parts of the RAND Logistics Department other than the laboratory, it is also becoming usual to set up LP teams, consisting of members of the groups making the policy proposals and the laboratory staff, who work together on designing, comparing, running, and analysing the experiment in the laboratory. Sometimes the head of the LP team is drawn from the laboratory and sometimes from outside.

We can identify several stages of a laboratory problem. These can be classified as the design, modelling, mock-up, operations, and analysis phases. These phases have primarily a serial relation to one another, but they also tend to overlap; and, further, the decisions made on a later phase can require some redefinition and change in an earlier phase.

In the design phase the objectives of the experiment are broadly defined. The policies to be tested are identified, the organizations to be simulated are specified, the experimental design is determined, and the general goals and characteristics of the analysis are developed. In a usual LP the design phase may take from six months to a year to be completed.

The modelling phase involves the definition of the environment in mathematical terms for computer simulation, the collection of the necessary data required to simulate the environment, the detailed description of each

* Spring 1964.

simulated organization (including which functions of it will be simulated on the computer and which will be handled by the participants), how it interacts with the other organizations, the information that is available to it, the authority it possesses in decision-making, etc., and how the data to be used by the experimenters for purposes of analysis will be obtained. It also involves the preparation of the resulting computer programmes, the writing of the manuals for the instruction and guidance of the participants and laboratory staff, the coding of the data for use in the computer to produce environmental conditions, and the design and preparation of the formats to be received by the participants as their management reports, and by the analysts as their experiment outputs. In the laboratory this phase has taken from six to eight months.

The mock-up is the first time that the entire experiment is put together. At this time the effort is made to run the computer models and programmes, the reports are given to the participants and the analysts, the laboratory staff is trained in the operations it will perform during the experiment, and the necessary experience is developed to determine whether the laboratory resources assigned to the experiment are sufficient for the tasks required; and estimates are obtained of the computer time, elapsed time, etc., needed to accomplish the various steps in the experiment. The laboratory staff takes the roles of the participants during this mock-up so that they also develop experience in how the participants will have to function during the actual runs. Typically, during each mock-up many useful findings are made which improve the overall structure and operation of the experiment. The mock-up usually requires about a month to run and to make the adjustments needed as a result of the experience thereby gained.

The operations phase represents the actual running of the experiment. Typically, several runs constitute each experiment. The need for efficient experimental designs, continued interest on the part of the participants, etc., suggests that several comparatively short runs should be made in which the conditions are changed from run to run. This usually results in several teams of participants being used. There is an advantage from the standpoint of experimental validity in having several groups of participants because it is very desirable to expose proposed systems to as large a group of Air Force personnel as possible in order to ensure the feasibility and acceptability of the findings on a broad scale.

When each team reports for participation in the experiment it must be given a training course before it enters the experiment proper. In this course the team is acquainted with simulation techniques, and it is taught the elements of the logistics system it will manage. During the course the participants are given specific assignments in the experiment, and consequently some of the training they receive is specialized for the specific position they will fill in the experiment.

In the early experiments the laboratory made very little use of formalized experimental design and more or less adapted its experimental course to the results as they unfolded. This did not yield very sophisticated opportunities for analysis. In the more recent experiments much more attention has been given to the relationship between analysis and experimental design so that the course of each experiment is much more defined during the design phases. This is important from the standpoint of experimental preparations, since the data used for each run must be prepared in advance of the start of the run. Also, this permits a much more systematic scheduling and assignment of personnel, computer time, and participants in the experiment.

The time devoted to the operations phase of an experiment varies, depending on the number of runs required, the extent to which computers are used, and the length of each run. In the past, from four to six months have been used in the operations phase. It should be stressed, however, that the learning which goes on in an experiment is not confined exclusively to the operations or even the analysis phases. A great deal of learning and insight is developed during the design, modelling, and mock-up phases as well. At these stages the need to fit several interrelated policies, organizations, and functions together raises all kinds of relevant questions such as the effect that decisions in one area have on the other areas, the need for separate organizations to share common information and to report to one another, and the need for joint decision-making. It is often necessary in the analysis phase, after the operations phase is over, to return to the operations phase to obtain additional runs so as to fill in gaps in knowledge, to test new hypotheses, or to recheck an unexpected prior result.

The analysis phase really goes on throughout a laboratory experiment. During the design phase the experimental design, the definition of objectives, etc., all contribute to the final analysis. Also, the use of side studies to analyse basic data, to make field tests, to formulate hypotheses from similar models, etc., all contribute analyses to the experiment and outputs that can be issued before the completion of the entire experiment. During the runs, analyses are conducted to ensure that the experiment is under control and that the unfolding results can be reasonably explained in terms of the known factors. Finally, in the post-run period the more comprehensive and conclusive analysis is done. This involves the study of vast amounts of data, the reconsideration of the original hypotheses, the possible formulation of fresh hypotheses derived from analysis of the data, the identification of recommendations to the Air Force, and the assessment of the technique in terms of new developments or advances. The outputs of the experiments are produced in a variety of ways. First, there are the aforementioned side studies of specific topics examined in the early stages of the experiment. Second, there are the learning and experience which the Air Force take away with them from their assignment to the laboratory. Third, there are the information and the impressions given to the large number of Air Force visitors who come to the laboratory during the operations phase to be briefed on the purposes and techniques of the experiment and to see the runs while they are under way. Fourth, there are the briefings on results given at the end of the analysis period to the commands that have helped in the construction and operation of the experiment and to the organizations that have a particular interest in the results. Finally, there are the reports written to present the results formally to the Air Force, which make recommendations and contain the detailed procedures used in the experiments. The experience with past laboratory experiments has been that the details presented in such reports are as interesting and useful to the Air Force as are the more general findings, since the former results do provide more specific and explicit guidance than broad policies. It is far more feasible for the Air Force to understand what should be done to use a given research result if the explicit ways in which it fits into the organized policies, etc., are described.

The laboratory experiments

LP-I

The origin of the first laboratory project (LP-I) and the reasons for creating the Logistics Systems Laboratory had much in common. Supply and data-processing policies had been developed by traditional analytical research; their implementation would involve major changes in Air Force methods of operating a supply system. For example, the notion of centralized record-keeping of inventory data and calculation of inventory levels required the large-scale introduction of electronic computers. Also, these new concepts could require some changes in Air Force logistics organization. Such major implications for the logistics system required considerable review and assessment at top Air Force staff levels before they could be finally adopted. Since such an evaluation would be very difficult to carry out in the real world, it was suggested that the policies and the management system be simulated and studied in the laboratory as part of informing the Air Force further about the usefulness and worth of the proposed policies. Air Force interest in further study of these supply policies led to the selection of the supply system as the subject of LP-I.

The purpose of LP-I can be summarized as follows:

1 To test supply policies, using

(a) selective management,
(b) centralized control of assets,
(c) data processing centres.

2 To test supply policies for high-value items, using

(a) deferred provisioning,
(b) responsive procurement,
(c) responsive repair.

3 To test supply policies for low-cost items, using

(*a*) trade-offs between inventory cost, ordering cost, and depletion costs,

(*b*) automatic reordering,

(*c*) centralized calculation of inventory levels.

4 To design and evaluate a data-processing system for using these supply policies.

To provide a meaningful test of the proposed supply policies, it was deemed necessary to simulate two logistics systems, LS-I and LS-II. In LS-I we represented the supply system then current in the Air Force (*circa* 1956), and in LS-II we put together a logistics system that would function using the newer logistics policies. The intent in the experiment was to give both logistics systems the same support job to do, and then to determine the cost and effectiveness with which each system would do the job.

The LP-I experiment began with a provisioning conference which made initial procurement decisions for the purchase of spare parts, with each supply system following its particular provisioning rules. Then the simulated bases were phased in over time so that at the peak of the programme there were ten bases to be supported by each logistics system, each base holding two squadrons of fifty aircraft. The occurrence of aircraft series changes was also introduced into the experiment to stress the inventory data system and the procurement and distribution rules, since these are relevant problems faced by an inventory system.

A sample of 850 spare parts represented the simulated aircraft, with the sample being heavily represented with high-value parts and higher assemblies rather than with lower-cost parts. Sample parts were chosen to give a representative distribution of low and high failure rate parts, with some bias in favour of the higher failure rates. The simulation used the day as the basic unit of time. Each simulated day, the corresponding operating bases in both logistics systems had identical schedules of aircraft to maintain on alert, to fly, and to assign to periodic maintenance. These operational and maintenance activities led to the occurrence and detection of failures, which in turn led to a demand for parts at the bases.

Each base had a supply warehouse and a field maintenance facility. Unserviceable parts that could be repaired at the base were sent to field maintenance; otherwise, they were sent to the parts repair depot. The base also received supplies from the depot, either automatically in the LS-II system or by explicit requisition in the LS-I system.

There was also an IRAN (Inspection and Repair as Necessary) or aircraft depot repair schedule. An aircraft would be sent periodically to the IRAN depot for overhaul. This led to a demand for spare parts at the IRAN depot. In addition to the simulated factory, as mentioned previously, there was a specialized repair activity (SRA). Parts requiring depot-level repair were sent to the SRA, and then shipped to the depot storage sites after overhaul.

In this way we tried to give each simulated logistics system in LP-I many of the characteristics and thus the appearance of a real-life logistics system, so that the experiment tended to give the proposed logistics policies a reasonably comprehensive test for feasibility as well as a measure of their comparative costs and benefits. Also the application of the policies to the simulated environment required a fairly detailed specification of procedures for carrying out the proposed logistics policies. It was believed that this specification would also help in any subsequent implementation of these policies.

The experiment ran for three simulated years, enough time to permit the study to deal with the complete phase-in of an aircraft type, including one change in series of the aircraft, and to study the operation of the aircraft fleet at peak inventory and flying activity level for about a year. In addition, special alerts were imposed on the aircraft to cause sudden and unexpectedly high stresses of activity and demands for logistics support during the course of the simulated activity.

There were approximately twenty-five Air Force personnel assigned to each logistics system, with base managers primarily coming from the Air Defense and Air Training Commands, and logistics managers for the back-up activities coming from the Air Materiel Command. Each of the Air Force personnel had been selected so that there was close agreement between the jobs they were given in the simulated logistics system and their real-life experience and speciality. Each simulated year took about a month of laboratory time; the entire simulated run of LP-I required slightly over three months to accomplish.

Results of the study were that the LS-II system spent about half as much on the procurement of high-value parts as the LS-I system, but had no more stockouts and AOCPs (aircraft out of commission for lack of parts). In the case of category 2 and 3 parts – that is, the low-cost spares – LS-II spent about as much as LS-I on procurement, but it had less than half as many stockouts and AOCPs. In addition, LS-II required much less support management during the experiment for category 2 and 3 parts as shown by the finding that there were only 15 per cent as many orders and priority requisitions for LS-II and for LS-I. Thus the experiment confirmed the predicted performance of the policies in that the high-value policies produced considerable savings in procurement with no loss in support effectiveness, while the policies for low-cost items produced much greater support effectiveness with no more expenditure on spare parts and a lower expenditure on other support costs.

The main reasons for the superiority of LS-II were that the policies were better tailored to fit the demand uncertainties and that, as a result, LS-II took better account of the total support costs involved in an inventory system. By using more intensive management, the LS-II system was able to secure the savings on the high-value items, and by using better inventory distribution for the low-cost items, it was able to increase support effectiveness, and to reduce the operating costs of inventory management.

LP-I has had considerable influence on the direction of the Air Force supply system. During the floor run many Air Materiel Command groups visited the laboratory. One of these groups was the Advanced Resupply and Logistics System staff who had just begun to design the inventory control system to be used for new missile weapon systems, such as THOR, ATLAS, and TITAN. The men had access to all the information used to create the data-processing centre in LS-II, and to the supply policies used by LS-II. They showed particular interest in the deferred procurement and responsive prediction techniques used, and in the use of automatic reordering for low-cost items. In addition, the laboratory staff included Sacramento Air Materiel Area people, who later put much of LS-II into practice for the F-100 weapon system. Also, AMC used the LS-II category 2 and 3 policies in their development of an inventory system for low-cost items which had been directed by Headquarters, Air Force, and the Department of Defense. The LP-I reports were circulated widely in the Air Force, and we believe these reports helped to stimulate review and revision of AMC supply management.

For RAND, LP-I provided an intensive opportunity to learn how to simulate logistics systems in a laboratory, and a chance to learn what were the strong and weak points of the process. First, the laboratory staff designed and tested the basic simulation technique for creating and operating laboratory experiments of logistics systems. Second, they designed and had built a new simulation laboratory which took advantage of LP-I experience. Third, they became more knowledgeable in the selection of logistic problems for game simulation, in the modelling of simulations so that proper use of man and machine would be made in the experiment, in the selection of runs and the design of analysis of the experiment's outputs, in methods for quality-controlling laboratory inputs, and in the running of the experiments.

LP-II

LP-I was largely concerned with testing, in a more complete system context, a series of separately developed supply and data-processing policies. The environment for the test was well understood, and the major goal was therefore to evaluate the revised policies together, and to determine the ways in which they would interact with each other, particularly through the design and operation of data-processing centres. Also, we did have a control – the existing supply system.

When LP-II began there was much interest in missile operations, but there had been no experience of this novel weapon system. Much effort had been expended on defining the hardware and in considering what would happen to a missile in the environment that could be expected in the day-to-day operation and support of a first-generation missile system like the Atlas or Titan.

The initial purpose in LP-II, then, was to take the available information and data on missile systems and, using past experience on military logistics, see what could be learned about the likely support and operations-support aspects of these new systems. Since there was no real world base to study, RAND and the Air Force decided to assemble in the Logistics Systems Laboratory a simulation of an ICBM squadron which could be manipulated by changing a variety of conditions, these included the assumptions on reliability of the missile system, the resources in terms of manning and equipment assigned to the squadron, the operational requirements specified by higher headquarters, and the management system used by the participants, who represented the managers of the squadron.

A number of questions put to the model follow: what level of alert could be expected for the assumptions used concerning reliability, resources, operational activity, etc.? What amount of utilization did the assigned resources attain? What delays for resources occurred during critical periods? What were the critical and difficult decisions required in the organization? Was the information provided to the managers in the organization adequate? What interactions and problems arose between the various support functions, such as site maintenance, field maintenance, supply, transportation, and the like?

The obvious starting-point in beginning this simulation was the specification of the missile system's hardware, since hardware characteristics greatly shape and dictate the operations and support characteristics of the total system. In order to treat a number of the significant aspects of the support problem, it turned out that hardware needed definition to an appreciably low level of detail. Thus, to construct a failure model that would react to the alternative operations performed on the missile, such as checkouts, simulated and actual count-downs, and keeping the missile at different levels of alert (times from launch), it became necessary to specify the structure of the missile hardware to what we called the support-unit level. At this level there were many parts of the hardware system that were not critical to launching or to holding missiles on alert. These non-critical parts were largely in the facilities portion of the missile system and included such elements as living-quarters for the crew and certain repair, maintenance, and storage facilities.

It took about 1,500 so-called support units to represent the hardware system in the laboratory situation. Typically, the support unit could be considered as a black box or other removable and replaceable component, and it also constituted that part of the missile system to which the diagnostic equipment could isolate malfunctions. These 1,500 support units were distributed approximately 800 to the missile proper, 300 to the ground support equipment, and 400 to the facilities.

Each of these support units required a large amount of data to describe reliability, support, and operational characteristics. These data might be classified into three categories: first, the operations-stress data, which indicate the operations possible with the missile system, and the stresses which are created on each support unit during each fifteen-minute period a particular operation is being performed on the missile system.* Second, the reliability data, which indicate for each type of stress applied to each support unit during a given fifteen-minute period the probability that a malfunction will occur. Third, the logistics data associated with each support unit, which indicate the resources that must be used with each support unit to perform each action required by the missile system, such as diagnosis, checkout, repair, and the like. It required more than 100 elements of data for each of the 1,500 support units to provide data characteristics in these three categories.

With the environment defined, the next step in the design of the simulation was the specification of the management system to be used by the squadron. Since it was not clear at the beginning of the experiment what the management problems would be, and, therefore, what data would assist the managers in solving their problems, it was decided to begin with a very loose and primitive management structure, letting the unfolding experience suggest a more explicit structure for use in later phases of the experiment. Consequently, the first version of the information system was built with hand-drawn forms. The calculations were done by hand or by desk calculator, and the communication of information or data was done very informally.

The experiment thus evolved along two lines: first, the identification of the significant management decisions and the design of the management system for use in the laboratory which would help to carry out the decisions; and, second, the broad analysis of relationships between system effectiveness and cost, which suggested that centralizing of field support to wing level would tend to result in a more efficient use of support resources for achieving a high level of alert. Since the use of a large tactical unit adds to the complexity of the management task, it was important to ensure, to the extent of laboratory test, that the management system could contend with the problems raised by this larger organization.

Therefore, one of the final runs of the experiment tested the evolved management system in conjunction with a missile wing, which had four squadrons of missiles. The test subjected the management activities of the wing to severe operational requirements and even lower reliabilities than seemed likely to occur in the real world.

One of the significant outcomes of this management activity was to obtain a reasonably precise notion of significant decisions confronting the managers. As it turned out, the test provided managers with the opportunity to develop rules that produced more significant gains in alert and efficient resource-use when compared with previously considered and used rules. The experiment also produced reasonable estimates of the alert levels that could be expected from the reliability and operational assumptions used and the resources provided to the system. In addition, laboratory staff found that, because of

---

* Six different stresses were identified: turn-on or turn-off, operating for fifteen minutes, standing for fifteen minutes, raising and lowering, thermal shock, and acceleration during launch.

the improved management system, it was possible for the organization to achieve the previous high alert levels with significantly fewer resources required. That is, the management system permitted assignment of the fewer available resources to tasks in such a way that no increase in queuing for resources occurred. Finally, the outline and even detailed description of the information system provided a guide to the possible installation of such an information system in the real world.

Many of the policies adopted by the Air Force in missile-system management and operations since LP-II reflect the findings of that experiment. First, the squadrons of the first-generation missile force have been becoming progressively larger. This effect is markedly apparent in the Minuteman System, which is now organized into Wings of several squadrons. Second, the inspection and checkout policies with the first-generation system are tending towards moderation, another LP-II finding; that is, there should not be too frequent checkouts nor a complete hands-off policy, but something like a weekly checkout frequency. Third, the management system developed during LP-II is being adopted, to a limited degree in the first-generation missile system, and to a larger degree in early designs of the Minuteman management system. Further, the game-simulation technique is being used within the Strategic Air Command as a means of studying and developing policies for the Minuteman System. Thus, by and large, LP-II has provided the Air Force with many useful results, and we believe it has been well regarded by that organization.

LP-III

A fundamental characteristic of the logistics environment is that requirements made on the system are constantly changing owing to a large and unpredictable set of circumstances and factors. At the same time the resources available for meeting such requirements are also in constant flux owing to the competing demands of the various programmes, unexpected delays in the creation and delivery of resources to the system, changing priorities, and so on.

An essential task of the support system, then, is continually assessing requirements and available resources to determine how they can best be matched to support overall Air Force objectives. Satisfactory accomplishment of this task would seem to require an adaptive and responsive management system instead of reliance on large and expensive inventories in the support system. The former approach seems particularly attractive for the high-value or category I and II-R (moderately priced repairable) spare parts, which include the bulk of expensive repairable spare parts in the Air Force inventory. Consequently, LP-III concentrated on this aspect of support management.

At the start of LP-III there was also considerable interest in the question of whether material management within the Logistics Command should be organized along weapon system (WSM) or inventory class (IM) lines. The laboratory staff postulated that the type of organization used would interact with the goal of attaining a responsive and adaptive management system. They therefore designed an experiment which provided for testing and comparing two management systems which would be oriented towards responsiveness, one built around a WSM organization and the other along IM lines. The performance and cost of these two organizations would then be studied.

As the detailed design of these two management systems emerged and became consistent with the specified objective of the support system, it was found that the management systems for either the IM or WSM cases would be very similar in many essential features. Consequently, the question of these differences in management organization became subordinate considerations in later phases of LP-III.

The emphasis ultimately focused on the following goals: first, the detailed definition of policies and management procedures for assuring that the functions of determining requirements, distribution, repair scheduling, and procurement scheduling would be integrated, and that they would consistently reflect the importance of relative need in the allocation of their limited resources to provide support for the operating activities. Second, the determination of the value and cost of different degrees of responsiveness in the management system, with a view to determining that degree of responsiveness which seems both feasible and desirable. The design of the LP-III simulation and the selection of the runs for the experiment primarily reflected these two purposes, although the WSM and IM organizations were included in each run and their separate results compared.

The underlying environment consisted of two inventory classes and two weapon systems. Each inventory class contained thirty-two category I and category II-R line items that were common to both weapon systems. The thirty-two line items in each inventory class reflected the range of different characteristics that can significantly affect the cost and effectiveness of support, including demand rates, repair times, repair man-hours, procurement lead times, and the accuracy of initial predictions of demand rates. Each weapon system contained nine bases, with Weapon System-I containing six low-precedence and three high-precedence bases, and Weapon System-2 containing six high-precedence and three low-precedence bases.

All line items could be repaired at the specialized repair activity so that they competed for the limited amount of available depot man-hours. Also, making repair decisions interacted with decisions made in distribution and procurement, through the requirements computations.

It was assumed that each experimental run started after the weapon systems were near the end of their phase-in, and then eight months of simulated operation was accomplished in each run. In all, fifteen runs were made using different assumptions. In particular, the runs differed with respect to the amount of available repair capacity, and the amount of responsiveness assumed for the management system.

Analysis of the results obtained in the fifteen runs indicates, first, that both organizational arrangements did about equally well in adjusting to the conditions and stresses occurring during the run. Second, policies and procedures used for allocating available serviceable inventories to the weapon systems, and for allocating available repair capacity to the repair of unserviceable items, worked as desired so that they provided balanced and differential support. Finally, the responsiveness provided to the management system significantly affected the performance attained in supporting the weapon systems. Some indication was obtained of the amount of responsiveness desirable in distribution of repair from a cost-effectiveness standpoint.

Analysis of the elements involved in creating responsiveness in a management system indicates that the first requirement is an effective inventory control system. To significantly increase responsiveness, the second requirement is that the support functions should be properly designed and integrated. It would appear that the management procedures developed in LP-III can provide a highly useful and informative benchmark for the design of such a responsive system.

LP-IV

LP-IV is concerned with the design and analysis of base-maintenance management systems required for 1965–70. Many new ideas have been developed within the past several years, both in the Air Force and RAND, that appear to be very promising for the design of improved base-maintenance management systems.

The environment selected is a B-52 Wing/KC-135 tanker squadron base. These aircraft are given a series of operational training and crew-training flying programmes to meet. These programmes result in a need for maintenance. A key organization in managing the maintenance activity is called maintenance control. This organization schedules the aircraft that are to fly to satisfy the flying programme, and assigns the maintenance resources that are to be used to repair the aircraft and prepare them for flight.

LP-IV has concentrated on the management activities of maintenance control. The experiment has been divided into a series of phases. The first two phases are called B and B + 1, and these have been completed. The main purpose of phase B, which is really a shorthand designation for Benchmark, was to simulate the then-current Air Force management system, so as to ensure that the data derived from the simulation are consistent with real-world experience. To determine this, the B-52 Wing/KC-135 squadron was simulated for a three-week period, and the resulting experience measured in terms of such elements as: sorties accomplished, turnround time of aircraft, man-hours used, aircraft delays, etc. This simulation experience was then compared with actual data collected from real-world B-52/KC-135 bases, and good correspondence was found.

Given a good benchmark, the next phase of the experiment designated as B + 1 was concerned with obtaining and evaluating changes to the current maintenance management system which can be implemented within a comparatively short time, perhaps a year. A number of changes have been tested in B + 1. In particular, they included dispatching rules for assigning maintenance personnel to aircraft requiring service or maintenance. They also included event-control devices to ensure that jobs were started at the appropriate times, and that the required resources would be available. All this emphasis on having the resources available to do the required jobs, and to assign them in a way which minimizes turnround times to increase aircraft availability, has led to more work for ensuring that feasible schedules of aircraft flying and availability can be designed which are consistent with workload and resources. Such scheduling devices have been developed and tested in Phase B + 1.

In addition, much analysis of maintenance data has been done with a view to determining how such analyses can help maintenance management in its scheduling and dispatching activities. This effort has led to the identification of important data for such analyses and to ways of analysing and presenting such data to maintenance management. This work has led to a much better definition and integration of the maintenance data collected at base level, which is important for possible development of an automated base-maintenance data system. It has also suggested ways of making such data more useful to base managers.

A computer simulation of LP-IV has been programmed for an IBM 7090. It has been written in SIMSCRIPT, which is a new programming language designed for simulation applications. The computer model is intended to test a variety of maintenance policies as a prelude to testing promising policies in the laboratory. Some of the policies being studied include shift policies, manning levels, dispatch rules, and priority assignments. By this combining of computer simulation with game simulation, it is hoped to obtain, first, a good statistical basis for selecting from alternative policies through running of the computer simulation, and second, by using the policy on the laboratory floor in the game simulation, it is hoped to see what problems arise in incorporating it in the total management process.

LP-IV has other potential features. It may prove both desirable and feasible to study the designing of a base-maintenance data system which could be implemented by 1970. Presumably, such a data system would be highly automated, and would have procedures that make the data much more readily available for management use, and add flexibility to the whole data-processing operation. Also, little is really known of how managers use data to increase the effectiveness of their decision and control. Some work has been started on designing a so-called reports game. Under present plans, managers

I

will be given certain kinds of report, and, on the basis of these reports, they will make decisions. These decisions will then be played through computer simulation, and the resulting effectiveness obtained by the manager will be used to help to evaluate the benefit of the reports he receives.

Conclusions

The final story on the Logistics Systems Laboratory is still to be written. The experiences with the fourth experiment are still very fresh in the minds of the laboratory staff and the participants. Much has been learned from all the experiments about the possibilities of studying management control processes in a laboratory setting, and of interpreting such lessons for real-world use. We have not yet been able to transfer large segments of such management control systems bodily from the laboratory to the real world. LP-IV offers us much more hope that this might be achieved. However, the duration of LP-IV will undoubtedly be longer than any of the other experiments if this goal is achieved. We also see the continuing development of by-products that were not originally anticipated in the early design of each experiment. These by-products contribute not only specifically to the substance of a given experiment but also to the general methodology of management systems research.

BIBLIOGRAPHY

1 M. A. Geisler (1958)
2 M. A. Geisler & W. A. Steger (1962)
3 M. A. Geisler (1960)
4 W. W. Haythorn (1959b)

5 W. W. Haythorn (1959a)
6 H. W. Nelson & J. W. Petersen (1962)
7 R. M. Rauner (1958)
8 R. M. Rauner & W. A. Steger (1961)

16 · Decision-making in a University System

EDWARD L. BRINK

Introduction

In summing up the International Operational Research Conference at Oxford in 1957, Professor West Churchman made a statement which I believe is appropriate as a beginning to this paper. It was as follows:

'To the second type of paper I have given the title "programmatic". These papers – and I identify two at this Conference, one by Koopman and one by Ackoff – try to outline a job which needs to be done. They point out that there is an area which we have not successfully attacked, and the author feels that unless we do successfully attack it our own status as research workers is weakened – perhaps disastrously weakened. Professor Koopman pointed to a mathematical problem prevalent in many of the discussions here, and Professor Ackoff to a problem which none of us as researchers can deny exists and is important, namely the problem of control.

'There was some worry about the feasibility of getting at a solution of these problems. Should operational researchers be concerned with jobs which need to be done when they themselves have no idea how they are going to be done? There is also the worry, of course, about whether or not the problem is really a serious one. It is interesting to note, however, that at almost every session throughout the week two or three commentators said that they did not think that such-and-such a problem had been emphasised enough. There was certainly not a universal agreement on the problems that need further study, but the discussion shows our self-conscious concern about areas which we feel have not yet been satisfactorily studied. I should like to see in our coming meetings more papers of this sort. The papers must do more than simply say that such-and-such a problem has not been adequately solved; the authors must attempt, as Koopman and Ackoff did, to formulate the area to be investigated as precisely as possible.'

We have done our best to date to attempt to formulate the area of 'decision-making in a complex university'. We must now proceed to 'crack the nut'.

I should like to state now that this paper is in no way the unique result of my effort alone. At the Management Science Center we have been studying the problem of decision-making in a university for about two years. Professor Wroe Alderson and I have been particularly interested because of our exposure to decision-making in the University of Pennsylvania: Professor Alderson while he was chairman of the President's Administrative Committee to study the role of the faculty in decision-making, and myself when I served as Secretary of Senate of the University.

In the course of the paper I should like to discuss briefly, first, the importance of decision-making in the university both as to its own internal operation and as it affects society. I should also like to describe, again briefly, the efforts over quite a few years to separate the 'parts' of my university. Next, I would like to talk about the difficulty of arriving at outputs and units of measurement. Finally, I will present the flow models which we have evolved. In conclusion, I should like to discuss these models as they relate to the previous topics, explain as best I can, and ask your advice, aid, and criticism for our future plans.

American education is receiving a great deal of national and international attention today. The focal point of much of this interest is the role and contribution of the university in our society. Government, business, the general public, and the universities themselves are showing increasing concern with the stature of American higher education, the quality and depth of this resource, and its potential for meeting the increased demands of the future. Soul-searching questions regarding the *basic objectives and plans* of higher education are now transcending more traditional interest in the future availability and financing of university facilities.

Few would question the difficulty of decision-making in the complex and interrelated system which even today's university represents. Not only must the usual problems of financing and logistics be solved but university administrators must also face the far less tangible task of allocating available intellectual resources among major competing activities (teaching, research, scholarly publication, public service), as well as the many programmes which support these basic functions.

The universities of the United States now play a much greater part in our national life than they did twenty or even ten years ago. Their activities will continue to enlarge as a consequence of international competition, increasing sophistication in technology, and the sheer physical demands imposed by the growing number of qualified students. This growth in size, coupled with the expansion of the university's responsibilities to the nation, its students, and its faculty, portend significant future changes in both the structure and content of our educational system. Moreover, influencing this changing environment and adapting to it will require the best of decision-making skills.

At the recent conference on Higher Education for Urban America, Dr Ravitz of Wayne State University warned that a university must avoid 'being all things to all men and stick to doing only those things that it does best'. This is fine, and it would make decision-making simple. However, for an urban university such as ours there are various categories of choice – for example, as follows:

Area of Influence	*Emphasis by Level/ Specialization*	*Area of 'Physical' Responsibility*
Community	Graduate	Community
Regional	Undergraduate	Regional
National	Liberal arts	
International	Specialized	

A choice must be made realistically in each of these areas – unless, of course, you can wall yourself off and say, 'We are an international graduate university dealing only in the humanities.' This is highly unlikely in today's world. The reason that I bring this up is that the choice greatly complicates or simplifies a measurement of the output of a decision model. I hope that this will be brought out when we look at the flow charts.

In all fairness, the efforts of others at the University of Pennsylvania should be briefly noted. Under generous grants from foundations we were able to carry out a five-to-six-year self-examination. This survey, with the help of many of our own and outside visiting faculty members, looked closely at the educational 'parts' of the university and to some extent at the financial and administrative areas. The facts and opinions in their voluminous reports were of great help.

The University of Pennsylvania also played a prominent role in the still current National Science Foundation's Project, which has as its objective 'to devise and test simplified adequate systems of measuring and reporting financial, manpower, facilities, research, and other activities in colleges and universities'.

Both of these studies represented a large amount of data-gathering and preliminary analysis already accomplished.

The Administrative Committee, appointed by President Harnwell, worked for over a year on the problem of faculty participation in the decision-making process. This committee recommended adoption of a new concept of decision-making structure involving the recognition of three separate phases of faculty interests as being those programme-oriented, institution-oriented, and discipline-oriented. The committee also felt that it was vital to focus faculty consideration on plans or broad policy issues rather than on individual current decisions.

If the faculty is asked to react to alternatives at this broad level of structure and function, it is essential that some means should be available for *generating and displaying the probable consequences of alternatives.* A major recommendation, springing from this conviction, was that the university should institute an integrated planning office to explore the possibilities of developing an operational model which could simulate alternative comparisons of organization and courses of action.

In summary, then, there existed at the University of Pennsylvania past and continuing work in this area, extensive quantities of readily available data, and a willingness and desire on the part of the administration and faculty in general, and of the Management Science Center in particular, to pursue the problem and attempt to make a contribution in this area of decision-making.

Discussion of methodology

Now comes the knotty problem, the difficulty of arriving at outputs and at measures of effectiveness and efficiency. A university may be likened to a commercial enterprise. There are inputs, a process of 'manufacture', and outputs. But what are the outputs? As we shall see in the flow charts, some, such as the financial, are relatively easy.

From the methodological point of view, we planned to utilize quantitative techniques which have evolved recently from the areas of management science and systems theory. Specifically, we planned to investigate the potential contribution of value and decision theory to university administration and the means by which the operational characteristics of these tools might be improved. One of the exceedingly difficult gaps to bridge is the development of appropriate 'measures of effectiveness' for a university. That is, what are the operational goals of the system and how can these multiple objectives be reconciled in order to select plans which optimize the 'output' of the system? We believe that some of the recent strides made in value theory provide a good basis for attacking this important and complex problem.

With respect to other methodological considerations, we planned and still do plan to rely heavily on the use of computer simulation in deriving the impact of alternative allocations of resources on the optimization of return functions. These allocation processes would probably involve the use of various mathematical programming models under conditions of uncertainty and interdependence of activities. Our objective will be to construct a computer model powerful enough to serve as a 'miniature university' in which the effects of alternative plans might be simulated.

From a substantive point of view, we have focused on the major decision levels of university administration, studying how decisions are affected by the university's organizational structure and the availability of relevant information. We hope to derive useful insights concerning the relationship of alternative organizational structures to: (*a*) the speed with which problems are recognized, communicated to appropriate decision levels, resolved, and decisions implemented; (*b*) the procedures by which organizational and individual goals are reconciled; and (c) the manner in which appropriate information is gathered and disseminated.

In looking for clues or profitable avenues regarding the objectives of the total system (or sub-system for that matter) we were immediately plunged into the subject of values. There is no reason to go into any discussion of objectives and value theory here.

Leaders in management science have been exploring the relation of their disciplines to value theory from various perspectives. A notable recent contribution was C. West Churchman's *Prediction and Optimal Decision*,[1] in which he seeks the roots of value in the relation of each system to the higher system of which it is a part. Churchman's views are criticized on logical grounds by Nicholas Smith and other management scientists with a background in philosophy. Ackoff projects a behavioural theory of decision-making in which he is less concerned with the roots of value than with the impact of information on values, and hence on the decision-making process. Many other names, such as Nash, Arrow, Schelling, and Rapoport, are associated with special topics such as bargaining, the resolution of conflict, and paradoxes in individual or group value systems.

All of these aspects of the subject are relevant in a systematic attempt to study the decision processes of a university, but a chief concern is the problem of evaluating or measuring university outputs. We must be interested in both financial and academic operations, and hence a range of inputs both monetary and non-monetary.

A very large system such as that in which a university performs its functions for society is inescapably a probabilistic system. Thus, the units of capacity in the system must be related to some set of probabilities concerning their use. Formal decision theory would appear to provide appropriate technical tools for structuring such a system and dealing with the very difficult problem of value with respect to the outputs of the system.

Professor Alderson has suggested that our approach is something like boring a tunnel through a mountain from opposite directions and hoping to meet in the middle. On the one side we start with monetary values and move in the direction of ultimate social values. From the other end we start with the broadest possible conception of the social sciences involved and explore the possibilities of quantification.

But as I have said, value theory must be considered with objectives, as we all know. How can we define the objectives of a university in a 'higher system' and then in its sub-system? At this point it must be realized that the overall objectives of a university are 'fuzzy'. This has been borne out in our case by personal experience. In all fairness it must be realized that the rank order of objectives must be flexible.

When a university is placed in a situation where it must be a 'multi-university' the problem frequently becomes one of agility in planning. Professor Alderson has said that short-range planning is 'as far as I can jump, medium-range as far as I can see, and long-range as far as I can hope'. This is the situation which faces a decision-maker in a university, and the outside decisions (over which he has no control) which, we shall see, force him to alter this order. It would be very nice if we could employ a conventional matrix as follows and relate the conditional probabilities in the matrix to the objectives.

$$Outcomes$$

	O_1	$O_2 \ldots O_m$	
A_1	a_1	a_2	a_m
A_2	a_1	a_2	a_m
.	.	.	.
.	.	.	.
.	.	.	.
.	.	.	.
A_n	a_1	a_2	a_m

Available 'free' actions

This does not mean that the university decision-maker cannot utilize a system. Certainly, the procedure, a practical method, as suggested by Ackoff in *Design of Social Research*,[2] seems applicable at this point. Now, applicable to what? Applicable to the 'systems', and I use the word loosely, that follow.

Development of the model

These systems, as shown in *Figures 1–7*, present four sub-systems and three types of facility culminating in an overall system for the university as a whole. Where the discussion starts is academic, and therefore let us consider *Figure 7* first. It also seems fitting, since it deals with students. The nature of the system itself is self-evident. We have student prospects or prospective students, who may or may not become applicants. If the applicant is accepted by the university, and he in turn accepts the university's acceptance, he becomes an admission; note that in this process the amount of tuition (price tag) plus the nature and availability of scholarships affect the prospective student's application and ultimate acceptance. He, the student, then passes through simultaneous paths of instruction and student life, culminating in graduation. This in turn leads to placement in graduate school, industry, etc. In any event, the graduated student becomes a part of the new alumni body, and in turn passes to old alumni. This latter group is a valuable source of new desirable students. Industrial employers and to some extent graduate schools also feed back to the placement function. Now, if we can turn to *Figure 7* and focus attention only on the system which we have just discussed it will be seen that there are four decisions that must be made. One of these, the student's selection of the university, is outside, and three are inside. For the sake of simplicity in this decision system, the feedback from old alumni to new students has been omitted. However, it can be an important outside decision to the extent that disgruntled alumni may discourage prospective students. Now, as to the decisions within the university. First, the university must constantly evaluate its market position, as it were, versus competition and set a price. There is no doubt that a university such as Pennsylvania

Figure 1

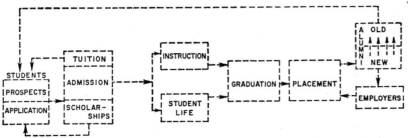

prices a good many prospects out of the market. However, another internal decision on the amount of scholarship and financial aid also must be considered along with this. Finally, the university must decide on the number of students that it will accept. Apart from tuition, the remaining two decisions

Figure 2

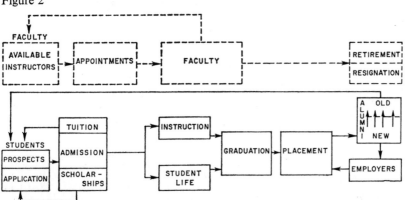

can be quite important. For example, the University of Pennsylvania in 1964 accepted 2,800 students (from 6,800 applicants) in its undergraduate schools, with the expectation that 1,600 would accept. It offered scholarship aid to 1,000 incoming students in the amount of $1,200,000, with the expectation that 600 would accept at an almost proportional cost. Now let us consider the impact of a bad decision in these two areas. At the extreme, if zero accepted, tuition loss would be balanced against scholarship aid, but the total financial loss would reflect itself in the financial system. If all accepted, tuition gain would again go against increased scholarship aid, but would also overtax beyond help 'instruction' and 'student life', resulting in an increased cost to the university for temporary facilities.

It would also result in poorer instruction. It might be noted here that one of our colleagues, Dr John S. de Cani, and I have discussed the use of Markov chains in predicting the transfers from one state to another ending with solid admissions. There are obvious limitations similar to those encountered in consumer acceptance in marketing. The costs of bad decisions can be calculated quite well except for poor instruction. However, the decision-makers seem to be doing fairly well with their own historical and intuitive 'model'. For example, the University of Pennsylvania aiming for a class of 1,600 spread among five schools in different proportions sent out 2,800 acceptances based on five different expectancies (by schools) as to the percentage of acceptance and received 1,640 spread fairly close to the desired proportions. A year or so ago they aimed at 1,800 and received 2,100, a fair error.

Let us turn briefly to *Figure 2*. It is quite clear. The only feedback is the function of existing faculty in seeking new junior members.

Figure 3, which adds a research system, is, I believe, equally clear. Sponsored research comes into being by application from an outside agency as a rule, and unsponsored arises from within.

Figure 3

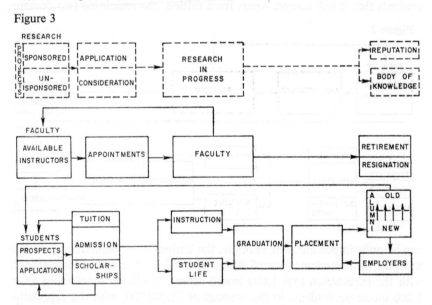

In *Figure 4* the three systems which we have discussed remain and the three types of facility needed are introduced. Here, again, note that for simplicity the feedback in the student loop and faculty loop have been omitted.

Figure 5 finally presents that which many consider to be the most important loop, the financial one. It also is quite simple, although the single box CAPITAL FUNDS naturally has many decision points within it, relative to types of investment, length of investment, etc.

Figure 4

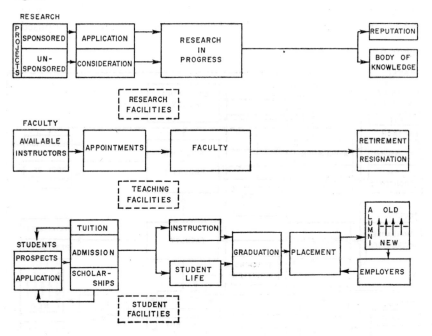

Figure 5

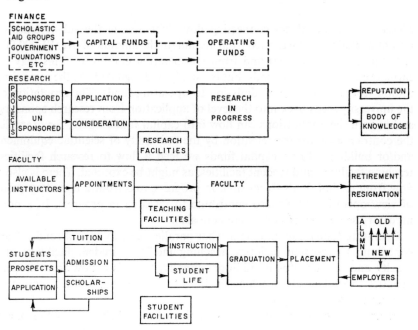

No detailed comment has been made on sub-systems other than the first. The nature and number of decisions involved in each of these sub-systems will become apparent as we look at *Figures 6* and *7*. *Figure 6*, as opposed to

Figure 6

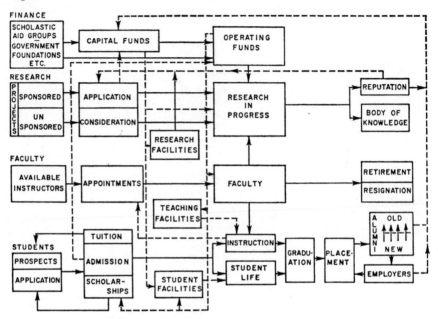

Figure 5, first introduces connecting flow lines among the sub-systems. A flow of capital may be expected from alumni (in the amount of over $1,000,000 last year at Pennsylvania) and from co-operating employers. This may be earmarked for operating funds, but is usually undesignated. At the same time tuition fees will flow from admission to operating funds. The reputation of the university feeds back into the level of application from research sponsors, and in turn the applications can flow into capital funds where, for example, the contract calls for the retention by the university of scientific equipment and/or buildings. From capital funds we feed a flow to research facilities, teaching facilities, and student facilities, as might be expected. There is also a flow from capital funds to research in progress, and from a monetary point of view operating funds also contribute to research in progress. In a non-monetary sense faculty contribute here also.

Operating funds flow in a somewhat parallel path to capital funds. They contribute to research facilities, teaching facilities, student facilities, and faculty and scholarships in addition. Finally, there is a flow from student facilities to student life, teaching facilities to instruction, and instruction to appointments.

Figure 7 shows the completed system plus what we believe to be the logical decision points. These are designated as those which can and usually are made within the university and conversely those outside. There are in this concept of a university decision-making system 25 decision points. Seven are outside and eighteen are inside.

Figure 7

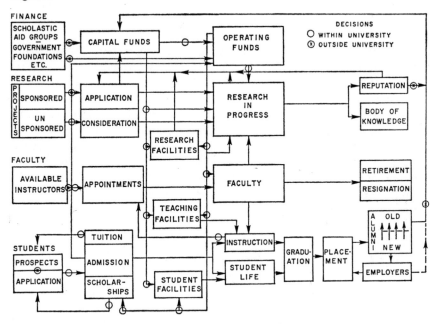

Future work

There is every realization that many of the individual 'boxes' in this system must eventually be 'blown up' to recognize the system within it. For example, INSTRUCTION. At the University of Pennsylvania there are 19 faculties, 19 deans, 4 Vice-Provosts, 2 academic Vice-Presidents, 1 Provost, and the President, not to mention such advisory bodies as the University Council.

Once the systems and decision points have been established, we can examine their utility for analysis. Consider the hypothetical case in which a new course of instruction is being contemplated by one of the faculties of the university. Assume that some new faculty will be needed and some present faculty diverted. Horizontally there are some questions to be answered first. First, there is availability, regardless of cost, then willingness to make appointments by the university as a whole. That is to say that the individual faculty may be convinced of the merits of the potential staff, but the University Appointing Committee may not. Looking ahead, as most good planners do, a dean might question the overall balance of his faculty with respect to retirement, etc. Vertically, of course, we start at operating funds and ask what drain can be expected at research facilities, teaching facilities, and, of course, faculty salaries. At this point it is logical to examine the possibility of outside aid to supplement operating funds. Finally, looking at the existing amount of operating funds as a fixed amount, we can see the other decision points that will be affected by this decision. Some may be quite evident, such as student housing. Others, such as the way research from this programme will enhance reputation and increase the body of knowledge, are difficult. Here is where value theory and objectives which I have mentioned must come into play.

In this connexion, Professor Paul Green and I have been discussing the use of Bayesian decision theory in decisions of this particular type. It seems practical to assume that such a decision as this is very much akin to one of opening a new sales territory or introducing a new product in the market. Perhaps the case of the introduction of a new product is more applicable. In this, as we know, more information becomes available as we pass from laboratory stage to pilot plant, to limited on-trial production, to full-scale market invasion. Unless an educational programme requires a 'go–no go' decision by reason of equipment, etc., this approach seems fruitful. All too often these programmes have been committed when a sequential step-by-step approach might have been used with a constant review of posterior probabilities as to final success.

What is next?

First, we have, I believe, a reasonable framework now for a beginning of computer simulation. It is my personal belief that this can best be accomplished on an analogue or analogue–digital computer. I believe that this is compatible with the nature of the inputs. Second, we expect to use an historical approach and take three or four major decisions that have been made in the university in the past and attempt to fit it into our system. Third, we will contrive to try out operational research tools such as Markov chains and Bayesian decision theory, as mentioned, for example, in specific sub-systems. Finally, we will try to continue boring from the 'social effects side of the mountain' as Professor Alderson has put it – objectives, values, decisions, social effects. This is the lot of a university decision-maker.

REFERENCES AND ADDITIONAL BIBLIOGRAPHY

1 C. W. Churchman (1961)
2 R. L. Ackoff (1957a)

3 I. D. Bross (1953)
4 R. Schlaifer (1959)

17 · Artefacts, Automation, and Human Abilities

ARTHUR A. BROWN

This paper presents a qualitative version of an approach to a theory of automation. The material grew out of a study of what it is that electronic computers might be used for in the various processes that go on in industry and business; those of us who worked on the project found that, although the concepts we use are on the whole commonplace, the pattern I am going to discuss is useful as an organizing principle, and we have not found it in the literature relating to automation.

In brief, what I am going to say is this:

The abilities people use in making something lie along three different axes: (i) the exertion of force or expenditure of power; (ii) stereotyped motion; (iii) reaction to variability. Mechanization means transferring the power function, or the pure motion function, to machines. Automation is the transfer of responsibility for coping with variability. There is a natural language available for discussing variability: it is the language of information theory, as developed and used by communications engineers.

There are three parts to the presentation of the groundwork – first, a dangerously brief sketch of the meaning of information; second, a discussion of the three kinds of ability I have just mentioned; and, third, a discussion of the way in which these abilities are used in manufacture. Although the presentation is qualitative, and one does not need to be a mathematician to follow it, the quantitative theory is applicable; I have not brought information theory into the discussion for the sake of picturesque language alone. In my opinion, the known results of information theory provide at least a fund of stimulating concepts that can be translated almost directly into results in the theory of automation, and suggest ways in which we can get quantitative results.

THE NOTION OF INFORMATION

In its technical sense, as it is used by communications engineers, the word 'information' has a simple, definite, numerical meaning. It denotes a measure

237

of the variability inherent in a probabilistic process; the unit of information is called the bit, and corresponds to the tossing of an unbiased coin. I shall not try to give the full definition, with all the necessary qualifications, but we may note that a process that may have outcomes E_i with corresponding probabilities p_i yields information $H = -\Sigma p_i \log_2 p_i$. If there are N events, all equally likely, $H = \log_2 N$. Information theory deals with the conclusions one can draw by combining this definition with the basic laws of probability. There are a number of good texts for the mathematically trained reader; I know of only one for the layman – J. R. Pierce's *Symbols, Signals, and Noise.*[1] Even this book demands some doggedness on the part of the reader, but I believe anyone who chews his way through it will find it most enjoyable.

The number defined by the above equation is called 'information' because it in some way measures the amount of surprise that we get when drawing from a universe. If the universe contains no uncertainty we know the outcome of a drawing in advance, and get no information from carrying out an experiment. If any possible outcome is as likely as any other, then the uncertainty is as great as it can be, and an experiment somehow seems to convey a large amount of information. The quantity H, as we have defined it, has the value zero when there is no uncertainty in the process, and is at a maximum when all the probabilities are equal. Also, it turns out that the amount of information derived from, or characteristic of, the combination of two independent processes is the sum of the amounts of information contributed by the two separately. This property is all we need for today's discussion – namely that information is a measurable quantity, and that in suitable circumstances amounts of it can be added or subtracted.

I need one further piece of jargon. In the communications field variability that one wants corresponds to a *signal*, and variability that one does not want corresponds to *noise*. I should like to use these two terms in this spirit.

ARTEFACTS AND THE PROCESSING OF INFORMATION

Non-living Nature exhibits great variability, and so, as a message source, has a high information content. If we think of an object as a message, however, we find that some of these messages are much less likely than others. Robinson Crusoe concluded from the evidence of a footprint that one or more humans were on the island with him; shoes, ships, and sealing wax are different in nature from cabbages and kings, but none of these are as humdrum as sand, rocks, water, oceans, and so on.

If we come across a single shoe we must assume that it was not created by the action of non-living forces – the converse is simply much too improbable. As a product of Nature, it has a very high information content, and that content must have been supplied by the forces that shaped it. On this view, the contribution of the creator of the artefact is the information content supplied by him during the creation.

There are two essentially different ways in which this information content is supplied. First, there is the conception, the will, the purpose that lead to the development of a process that makes shoes. Second, and this is the phase that is of interest in dealing with automation, there is the selection of raw materials, collocation of workpiece and tool, and control of the operating forces. Here the creator acts to filter out noise, to read the noise, so to speak, and counteract it. This is as true in the work of a single craftsman as it is in the process of mass manufacture. The information content of the archetype, of the ideal product, is supplied by and transmitted through the process design, through the existence of the physical plant, through the recruitment, training, and organization of the work force. The individual copies of the prototype should vary from one another as little as possible. In this sense we may say that the objective of the maker of an artefact is to remove the noise from Nature, and turn out a wholly informationless result.

There are some aesthetic objections to this view. In some cases the value of a product depends on its uniqueness. Accidental variations in the raw material, a serendipitous preservation of the results of a miscarried action, may enhance the desirability of the product. I do not believe these objections are relevant to the considerations we now have in mind. The great bulk of manufactured articles are meant to conform closely to a design standard; they are meant not to vary. And this is the area of concern when we think of automation in today's world.

The raw materials, the environment, the machines, and the work force itself are all sources of variation (of noise) which from moment to moment they inject into the stream of product. This variation is unwanted. The process must somehow counteract it and eliminate its effect. Thus, the function of the worker is to process information for the purpose of neutralizing it. This is the function that is transferred to machines when automation takes place; this is the function we should study when we want to know what automation can accomplish, how far and fast it will go, and what will be left for humans to do.

At this point we arrive at a fork in the argument. We may either discuss the ways in which information is received and processed in manufacture, whether by humans or by computers, or we may discuss the abilities of humans that now enter into the manufacturing process. Both these paths must be traversed, they are to a great extent independent of each other, and so it is a matter of choice which way we go first.

THE DIMENSIONS OF HUMAN ABILITY

In this discussion of human abilities I omit all reference to interpersonal and social action, as being irrelevant to the technology of automation. I might better, perhaps, borrow a term from science fiction and speak of android abilities. But, since we find people working in factories and do not find androids working in factories, I shall speak of human abilities. These occur in four different categories, or dimensions.

First, the dimension of power. Man is a quarter-horsepower motor with a variety of output mechanisms. As a pure power source, he processes no information at all; he is a device for converting food into work. Classically, he is enslaved, chained, blinded, deafened, perhaps maimed, bound in a treadmill, and set to moving his muscles. His environment is stereotyped and simplified so that he does not need his senses, which he would use only for the purpose of escaping. Although there are several ways in which pure power can be expended, I should like to use the term *treadmill* labour for the whole lot.

Second, there is the dimension of learned reflex behaviour. Man can acquire complex habits that permit him to execute a sequence of precisely, even exquisitely, regulated motions over and over again. This dimension also involves no processing of information. The environment is not observed; the action is all from inside out (once it is learned); only the commands to start and stop are relevant. If my understanding of West Indian mythology is correct the zombie is an entity that can execute any number of reflex patterns on command; he has no will of his own; he goes through the motions without being present. Since this is the behaviour, or ability, that characterizes the stereotyped motions that make up this dimension, I should like to refer to it as *zombie* labour.

Zombie labour may be highly delicate, it may be pleasant to watch or to perform, but it is purely mechanical.

The third dimension of ability is that of interaction with a variable environment. As a highly evolved animal, man senses his environment and moves his body about in it with great skill. He adapts to a shifting set of circumstances, which he perceives by his senses, and counteracts the effects of variability by muscular activity. Versatile bodily control of this type is common to all higher animals. I should like to use a name for this dimension that equates all the bodily skills at the lowest level, rather than the highest, and so I shall refer to work of this kind as *coolie* labour. It represents a very high order of information-processing, and should not be underrated.

The fourth dimension of ability is that of Gestalt formation, pattern recognition, generalization, abstraction. Man is aware of similarities amid differences; he regards two objects, or situations, as the same if they are alike in certain essentials, even though they differ in accidental qualities. Let me call this dimension that of *pattern recognition*.

THE MECHANICAL SUBSTITUTES FOR HUMAN ABILITY

As a pure power source, man is displaceable, and for a long time has been displaced by other sources. Animals, water wheels, windmills, steam engines, internal-combustion engines, generators, motors, pumps, pneumatic devices, hydraulic devices – these are all replacements for man's muscles. Of course, they not only replace the muscle – they greatly increase the power that man can control, and the spatial density of the source. Nevertheless, they merely displace treadmill labour.

Zombie labour is mechanical anyway. It is displaceable by all sorts of programmed devices, such as sets of cams, gears, levers, stops, or tape-controlled electronic devices. Where man is useful, instead of the machine, is where the motion is so complex or devious that most machines would get in their own way; but even here I expect that the ingenuity of the inventor would prevail: a machine can be made to imitate any stereotyped motion.

Coolie labour uses a whole repertory of skills. I mean here to include all forms of bodily response to the environment, all the way from load-bearing to fencing or tennis. It is true that coolie labour is what is normally classified as unskilled, but compared with a machine it is highly skilled. There are three ways in which the coolie skills can be displaced.

First, the information content of the environment can be reduced or removed, so that what was a skilled response becomes a stereotyped motion. For example, material can be moved on rails, conveyor belts, trolleys, and so on; rough ground can be smoothed; obstacles can be pre-located and removed. The environment is reduced to a treadmill, and motors can take over.

Second, computers and servomechanisms can be used to calculate trajectories, to maintain steady courses, speeds, and so on; the helmsman punches a card to indicate the new course for the ship, and the guidance system brings her on the correct heading. By this means, too, the amount of coolie work that one man can do is enormously increased, as with lift trucks, cranes, keyboard-controlled positioning machines, and so on.

Third, modern feedback devices and sensing devices allow the machine to perceive its environment directly and to respond to it in an adaptive way.

Pattern recognition is more difficult to replace; some progress is being made by the modern computer, and certainly more such progress will be made in the near future.

THE PROCESS OF MANUFACTURE

We have now reached the point where we should take a look at the manufacturing process, in order to see what use is made of the human abilities we have just listed. As I noted at the outset of the discussion, we are attempting to generalize the argument so that it applies to any manufacturing process whatever (or almost any), without regard to the specific nature of the materials, the operations, or the product.

I suggest that in carrying out any one operation involved in the creation of an artefact, the operator goes through three distinct steps. These steps may be executed concurrently, and the operator may not perceive them as distinct from each other. They may be separated conceptually, however, and they constitute three different phases of the process, with differing relationships to the human abilities and to the potential for automation.

These steps are:

1 Inspection of the workpiece and the tools, to make sure they are fit for the coming operation.
2 Putting the workpiece and the tool into the proper relative positions.
3 Applying force so that the tool transforms the workpiece.

We may call the first phase the *watchdog*, or monitor, phase; the function involved in the second may be called the *make-ready* function; and the third function we shall call the *operating* function. Any automaton that hopes to displace human labour must be prepared to cope with the information flow that goes along with the execution of these three processes; each process involves its own kind of information; and any specific manufacturing procedure demands its own characteristic amounts of the three processes.

We can describe a manufacturing process as a sequence of steps separated by a transfer process. The transfer takes the output from one step and conveys it to the input area of the next step.

NOISE, INFORMATION, AND THE MANUFACTURING PROCESS

Usually the initial monitoring of the raw material is concentrated in an incoming inspection agency. We may think of this agency as a filter, which has two or more outputs. One output stream consists of rejects; the remainder of the streams consist of filtered (graded, sized, batched, matched) raw materials. To see how the notion of information may bear on this function, suppose we think of an input stream containing on the average one defective item in sixty-four, and otherwise homogeneous. The variability, H, is then determined as

$$H = (63/64) \log_2 (64/63) + (1/64) \log_2 (64/1)$$
$$= 6/64 \text{ bits per item, approximately}$$

After inspection (if the inspection is complete and perfect) there are two streams, one consisting entirely of defective items, and therefore devoid of information; the other consists entirely of good items, and is equally devoid of information. The inspection process has reduced the information content of the input stream by 6/64 bits per item, and has therefore had to be able to process at least this much information. How much more it has processed depends, of course, on the nature of the defects and the method of recognizing them.

There may or may not be some technical information left in the accepted stream; that is, there may be variations from one item to another, within the tolerance limits of the process, but requiring to be sensed at a later state and adjusted for. There may also be positional information; i.e. the output may be sent forward helter-skelter, or it may be packed in a standard position. The transfer process will alter the amount of positional information; it may either increase it or decrease it; and will perhaps inject some technical noise by damaging or contaminating the raw materials.

The work stations take their input from the transfer processes. The input stream at any station is filtered by the monitor, and unfit items are removed. The noise is therefore decreased, or remains constant.

The positional information is sensed in the make-ready phase, and counteracted; i.e. increased or decreased. Normally, we expect it to be decreased, since the workpiece is to be put into a standard position *vis-à-vis* the tool, but the amount of noise permitted is determined by the tolerance limits of the process, and we would therefore have to look at each specific case to determine whether noise is added or subtracted. It is possible that some technical information must be processed in the make-ready phase.

The tool operates on the workpiece, transforming it, and perhaps damaging it or malforming it. The operational phase therefore adds technical noise, and perhaps positional noise, before turning the workpiece over to the next transfer operation.

From time to time pure filters are inserted, in the form of inspection stations and classifying, or grading, stations. These do not transform the workpiece, but change the information content of the material streams, by filtering off noise or creating several streams of lower variability than the input.

THE ABSTRACT PROCESS OF AUTOMATION

We define automation as the shifting of an information-processing function from living to non-living entities; i.e. from men to machines. To determine the extent to which any specific manufacturing process is susceptible to automation, we must look at the information flow that is inherent in the process and see how much can be either eliminated or given over to machines. It is therefore worth while to look at each of the four general functions individually, in order to see what goes on, and perhaps to derive a measure of what it is that the operator contributes.

The *monitor*, or *watchdog*, function demands that the operator has a feeling for what is right, and a sensory apparatus that will activate an alarm when the environment does not match the feeling. Such a feeling corresponds to what psychologists call a Gestalt, a pattern or form that has meaning apart from its elements. In some cases, of course, we may be able to describe the pattern as the logical product of a number of simple elements; in other cases our understanding of the process may be too meagre. In many cases neither the operator nor the industrial engineer is explicitly aware of the extent to which the operator continuously performs a monitoring function; an automaton may be able to replace the other functions of the operator, but fails miserably on the job through being an incompetent watchdog.

The Gestalt in question will be formed as a result of the operator's familiarity with the process. He will understand the nature and purpose of the tool and the workpiece; he will have had experience with errors and accidents. The pattern of expectations that he forms may be quite simple, or it may be highly complicated.

One can eliminate the watchdog function by putting up a series of filters at the source – i.e. purifying the raw materials – and carefully guarding the purity of the stream. For example, although I doubt whether one can build an electro-mechanical leather grader at a social cost competitive with the cost of training the human archetype, I am told that leather graders may disappear from the mass shoe-manufacturing industry because of a change in the raw material. I understand that a recently developed plastic called Corfam is an acceptable substitute for leather, and that it is wholly uniform within the tolerance limits of the industry. If this is true, the grader is no longer needed, because there is nothing to grade.

We can also decrease the noise injected by the work stations and the transfer processes – in other words, we can make the process more reliable, so that it does less damage, and we can avoid jumbling the material while transferring it.

I suggest that the monitor function is the highest expression of human abilities in the manufacturing process, and is probably the least noticed. It is not easy to mechanize.

The *make-ready* function should involve little technical information. The monitor should have inspected the piece; there should remain only the problem of locating the appropriate reference points and moving them into a standard position. If there is technical information to be processed the manufacturing step should be subdivided into two or more steps, so that the operational portion of the make-ready function becomes an operational step in its own right, followed by a negligible transfer and make-ready for the succeeding operation.

The make-ready is mainly a positioning function. The workpiece arrives in a more or less random position (place and orientation) from the input transfer. The make-ready finds it, grasps it, and puts it into position for the work. Finding the workpiece may, of course, involve sensing a non-positional variable; e.g. the instruction may be: 'Find the blue-coated wire and put it around the binding post with the blue cap.' One can build devices that will follow such instructions; but the colouring of the wire and the cap is nonessential; it exists only as a signal for human operators, and the code given a machine might be quite different, perhaps positional.

The positional noise is injected in the preceding work and transfer stages; it can be decreased as well by preventing its injection as by removing it at the make-ready point. It can be removed by barriers, gates, slots, sieves, channels, etc.; it can be prevented by moving the workpiece, during the transfer process, in a standard matrix, or by devices such as vibratory feeders that cause the workpiece to fall naturally into a standard position.

The *operational* function is probably the least demanding of the three, in so far as we are concerned with the conversion of mass manufacturing processes to automatic control. The very existence of mass manufacture depends on having got rid of most of the operational information-processing requirement, through breaking up the process into small steps in which the environment, the materials, and the machines are standardized. Measurement of the information content is reasonably straightforward – if the technology of the process is well understood – and the information handling can be done by servomechanisms, thermostats, relays, and the like.

The *transfer* process does not in general involve information-processing, although some portion of the monitor and make-ready phases might be performed during the movement of material between work stations. In order to have enough flexibility to keep an assembly line, or a sequence of operations, running when one of the steps has been shut down or delayed, there have to be stocks of semi-finished pieces at various inter-station points. The transfer process may have to keep track of the information needed to store and retrieve specific items.

THE HUMAN AND THE AUTOMATON IN MANUFACTURING

We may make up a table to show how the various abilities of the human are used, and what is required of the automaton, in each of the functions we have just been considering.

Table 1 *Comparison of Human and Automaton*

Function	Human Ability	Automatic Mode
Monitor	Pattern recognition; latent alarm system. Requires experience and familiarity.	Multiple sensors; computing programme. Requires analysis of environment. Simplify conditions.
Make-ready	Simple signal system. Coolie labour minimal; primarily zombie type.	Tape-controlled action. Some sensing if too much input noise.
Operate	Simple or complex signals, depending on whether process is understood theoretically. Pattern recognition and coolie labour. Includes filtration.	As in monitoring, plus effector control devices.
Transfer	Coolie labour.	Mechanical systems, tracks, belts, etc.

From what we have said so far, it becomes clear that there are two channels through which automation can flow into new areas. First, the information-handling requirements of some process or other can be reduced to such an extent that existing machines can cope with the remaining variability; for example, the raw material can be thoroughly filtered, or replaced by a uniform raw material. This channel has been open throughout the course of history, and its existence leads many writers on automation to argue that we are witnessing today only the current version of an age-old process.

There is a second channel that has been opened only very recently. The machines of today can in fact process information – i.e. cope with variability – of a kind that their predecessors could in no way have dealt with. The technical barriers to automation are either broken or are wearing very thin; the restraints that prevent inundation are now primarily due to economic factors. They are frictional, rather than impenetrable. They have to do with a higher order of information processing, embodied in the versatility of the human, and needed because of the variability and diversity of demand.

SOME QUESTIONS OF ECONOMICS

Generally speaking, a single plant and the corresponding production force make more than one product. At a minimum the product will appear in a number of versions differing as to size, colour, shape, and so on. A production line must have a certain flexibility to it; it must be able to make one thing now and another tomorrow. The cost of changing must be economically supportable.

It is not the abilities of the labour force at any one time that must be replaced if automation is to take over the plant. It is the complete range of régimes, of modes of operations, that have to be replaced. The automaton, or crew of automatons, must be as easily and cheaply reprogrammed as the worker is.

Consider, for example, an assembler working on a conveyor line in a plant devoted to making electronic equipment. A production rate of 1,200 copies per eight-hour shift is by no means unheard of; this amounts to one completed item each twenty-four seconds. The job of the individual worker is very simple; for instance, he may grasp a wire of a specified colour, slide the free end of it through a slot, twist it with pliers, and solder the junction so made. What he is doing is essentially pure zombie work, pure stereotyped labour. He can be replaced by a machine with no information-processing capacity at all.

In fact, such a machine exists, and is in use at the same plant where the assembler is employed. But the cost of setting up the rather complex working-head of the machine for any one job may be as much as $500. On a lot of 12,000 copies of one chassis the machine will have cost $500 for a ten-day run; the worker will have cost something like $200. On a twenty-five-day run the machine will recover its set-up cost; on even longer runs it may recover its capital cost. But if the plant is devoted to short-run production the machine will never pay off because it lacks cheap versatility.

If a stupid but flexible little machine, controlled by a magnetic-tape program, could be developed to the point where it could replace the many different habit patterns of the worker by a simple change of the controlling program, it might perhaps compete . . . but only with the zombie component of the labour. The monitor function would still remain, and some procedure would have to be set up to guard against the accidents that the work force had formerly prevented.

The versatility must appear in each of the three components of the automaton's function. The monitor machines must have at their disposal as many Gestalten and as much sensory equipment as their human predecessors used; the zombie machines must have as wide a repertoire, and be able to learn new roles, as well and cheaply as the operator they displaced; the coolie machines must find their way in as wide a variety of environments as the operator met. Failing this, the environmental information content must be decreased.

THE COURSE OF AUTOMATION

Perhaps the best way to describe the course of automation is to say that it will flow where it is not resisted, or better, that it will cover the areas of low information content. The unflooded areas will be those that have one or more of the following characteristics, all derived from the single condition that the information-processing requirement is too high to permit machines to take over cheaply. The ways in which it can be too high are the following:

1 The raw material is highly variable.
2 The number of production patterns is high and each is complex (i.e. the plant makes a number of different products, each in relatively small numbers, and each relatively difficult to make).
3 The monitor function is important and complex.
4 The process is not well understood, so that the operational function must be left to the skilled workman. (This applies particularly to new processes.)

Even if a plant is resistant to automation on one or more of the above grounds, it may yet disappear because the product it makes is displaced by one that can be made automatically.

Failing these modes of resistance, a plant would be expected to proceed with automation at a rate corresponding to the investment of new capital. If its product is not viable the plant will go out of business, and in this case automation will have advanced by entering new plants, leaving the old ones behind.

THE KINDS OF WORK THAT WILL SURVIVE

If the thesis I have been putting forward is correct the surviving jobs will be of two kinds:

1 those with high information-processing requirements, and
2 those in which manual dexterity is required and in which the patterns of action change frequently.

What kind of people are needed for work involving high information-handling requirements? They will be people who can perform all the functions, in particular the monitor function. I believe it is important for any nation to discover how to find and train such people; I suspect that the training should begin in the cradle, with the greatest possible development of the child's alertness and understanding of the world around him.

The second kind of work requires a ready ability to learn new motions, to be, as it were, a quick study.

There is a possibility that I have not mentioned, but which I suppose I should, in this connexion. We are still talking about zombie labour, and only requiring that the zombies should be versatile. I understand that some process engineers have developed a technique for controlling the human operator by means of recorded instructions, played through earphones, jointly with visual instructions displayed on a screen. The operator mimics the motions shown on the screen. Whether this mode of participation in the industrial process will survive – if it even exists as a practical mode – I do not know.

SOME POSSIBLE LINES OF RESEARCH

There are three different directions of research, each with its own justification. These are:

1 technical and economic research into process design;
2 research into the training and development of people; and
3 research into the human values derivable from the man–machine relationship.

The first of these lines would begin with a quantitative study of the information content inherent in existing manufacturing processes. I have said that I believe the concepts and results that are typical of information theory are applicable; but I do not say that the application is a mere matter of translation. New definitions have to be laid down, in the spirit of information theory but not in the letter, and these have to be brought into use in connexion with process design.

As to the training and development of people, I can only suggest, very tentatively, that much of what passes for training consists solely of instruction in the zombie component. It would be interesting to know how much more effectiveness is got from a work force trained in the elements of the process, so that the monitor function is alerted and the zombie motions are set in a matrix of personal enterprise. If the categories of human ability that I have listed have any psychological, or psychophysiological, basis perhaps our testing devices could be adapted to measure these aoſ puɐ̈ıןıq 'səɳb descriptions could keep them in the explicit foreground. I must say again, here, that for all I know, this area of research has been completely mined and the results evaluated.

The third line gets us into the field of ethics, perhaps. I suspect that, since man is a product of evolution, evolving under conditions of high information content (supplied by terrain, weather, plants, animals, other men, and his own devices) for millions of years, he is at his best and happiest when processing a high amount of information. On the assumption that work is made for the benefit of the worker, and not vice versa, we might study the question of what processes yield the efficiency we need if we are all to live, and at the same time provide the qualities of life that we must enjoy if our civilization is to be worth while. For centuries we have been turning men into machines, by simplifying and fragmenting the manufacturing process. The recent developments in the theory and practice of information-handling allow us to reverse the process, and to restore the human, enlivening, interesting elements to our daily round of work. The zombie component should tend to disappear, and the coolie component can take on the aspect of partnership with a responsive and friendly robot.

Provided, of course, that we can solve the necessary political, social, and economic problems.

POSTSCRIPT

The terms 'zombie' and 'coolie' have offended a number of readers and are not good for use in further research. I therefore suggest that 'zombie' is replaced by 'mimetic' and 'coolie' by 'myotropic'.

REFERENCE

1 J. R. Pierce (1961)

18 · Experimental Studies of Implementation

PHILBURN RATOOSH

Introduction: the problem of implementation

Every operational research practitioner can give examples from his personal experience of technically successful operational research studies that resulted in no improvement in the client-organization. In the recent paper 'Unsuccessful case studies and why',[1] Russell Ackoff, describing a survey of forty-eight cases in which there were many *unsuccessful cases* but not a single *technical* failure, defines an unsuccessful case as one involving partial or complete failure to implement findings.

The failure to analyse the process that takes place after a report is presented to management shows that what workers in the field refer to humorously as 'OR squared' is not taken very seriously.

The experiments I should like to discuss concern the problem of implementation. Professor C. West Churchman and I have been collaborating on studies in this area for the past few years. I should like to summarize some of our old results and present some new ones in greater detail.

We began with the belief that the problem of implementation is, to use a word in current American use, 'researchable', that is, that questions relating to implementation lie in the domain of experimental management science and that it is foolish in the extreme to rely on clichés such as, 'use language management can understand'. Like many aphorisms, the negations of many of these platitudes are no less plausible than the originals.

We consider implementation to be a class of behaviours designed to increase the likelihood that an organization will accept a research finding that, in the opinion of the research group, constitutes a solution of an operations problem or at least constitutes a policy superior to the one currently in use by the organization. In short, it is a special case of the general problem of the modification of behaviour – a problem central to many other fields such as education, public opinion studies, and psychotherapy, for example. Our studies are attempts experimentally to answer the questions 'What can the

251

research team do to maximize the organization's acceptance of research results?' and 'What is the nature of the resistance to implementation?'

Previous work

A group of five persons were given instructions (see Appendix 1) for operating a business firm. These subjects were usually students of business administration, some of whom had completed courses in operations research. The instructions to subjects described a company that manufactures three products. The instructions also contained a two-year past history of the firm giving prices and sales of each product, price of raw materials, production rates, labour costs, and opportunities for outside investment. In the case of raw materials, there was an explicitly mentioned cost-to-place-an-order. There was also a set-up time and set-up cost for production scheduling. The inventory carrying cost could be ascertained rather easily from the instructions, since the cost of storage involved only taxes, insurance, and opportunity investment cost. All outside investments yielded 0·5 per cent per month; taxes and insurance added up to another 0·5 per cent. Thus, the cost of carrying inventory was 1 per cent of the inventory value.

Consequently, both an optimal purchase policy and optimal production scheduling were based upon an economic lot quantity determination, *provided* that the monthly requirements were known. Past history indicated very clearly that quantity sold is linear with price. This implies that profit is a quadratic function of price and that there is an optimal price for each product. Given the optimal price, it is possible to estimate the consequent monthly requirement and therefore to solve the optimal policies for purchasing and production scheduling. None of this solution was revealed to the subjects, but sufficient information was supplied for them to be able to work through the solution, even with a fairly elementary training in mathematics.

The subjects were told that they must decide for each period (a period corresponding to a month of the firm's operations) the price of each product, the raw material purchases, the production schedule, and the outside investments of liquid capital.

Usually communication among subjects was in writing, and the subjects did not see each other.

One of our subjects was a confederate who was instructed to present the solution in all its aspects to the organization and to get the other subjects to accept it. We anticipated incorrectly that some of the experimental groups would accept the solution, some would not, and we would merely have to study the differences – both the differences in the characteristics of the two kinds of organization and the differences in the mode of presentation used by the successful and unsuccessful confederates.

It turned out that the solution was rarely adopted, and even in those cases in which it was, the adoption appeared to result from a blind yielding to pressure from the confederate. We then modified the experiment by permitting any group that accepted the solution to manufacture a fourth product. (The adoption of the solution led to excess capacity.) The confederate was instructed not to assist in the application of the solution to the fourth product. This gave us a way to distinguish experimentally between *adoption* of the solution and *understanding* it. A group may *adopt* the solution for various reasons, but unless it can use it for the fourth product, we consider that it does not *understand* it.

The reactions we observed to the introduction of the solution were quite interesting. When a group first begins to work together they become familiar with routines, adapt to the interpersonal situation, and develop techniques for handling their anxieties. Even if the organization is not doing well, they feel they are all in it together. Then someone suggests a radical change in every aspect of their activity. This is a threat to all and must be resisted. The subjects then often form a coalition, sometimes obviously, sometimes subtly, against the one who threatens. Often they ignore him. The threat to the subject playing the role of chief executive is most clear, but is only quantitatively different from that to the others. The chief executives reveal in the post-experimental interview that for them to have accepted the solution would have been tantamount to agreeing that someone else, who, presumably, had no more time to study the solution than they, was able to solve a problem they could not. This they were unwilling to do.

Recent studies

Our most recent studies involved some modifications. In some experiments communication among subjects was restricted to a formal language (see Appendix 2). A small penalty was imposed on all deviations from this language. In some there was no confederate, but instead the subjects were told that at the end of each decision period they would be given the policies, decisions, and their consequences of two other companies in the same situations as theirs. One of these made optimal decisions, the other made decisions actually made by a previous experimental group.

The purpose of the formal language was to maximize the problem's rational, objective aspects and to minimize emotional, interpersonal ones. The idea behind presenting other firms' decisions is simple: instead of telling the subjects what to do through a confederate, we would show them what would happen if they make one set of decisions rather than another.

Our results are the outcome of experimental runs of nine groups, and conclusions are necessarily tentative.

The full or partial acceptance of the solution and the number of periods taken to reach acceptance seem not to depend on whether there is a confederate or on whether information is given about other companies. Two groups who had neither an experimental confederate nor other groups' policies reached partial acceptance at about the same time as two with a confederate and two with other firms' reports. However, one group with a confederate *and* other reports reached the full solution. This implies that although presentation of results is not sufficient to assure implementation, presentation together with persistent active support from within the group greatly increases the likelihood of acceptance. Two groups receiving the financial reports did not follow the optimal firm at all, but reported that its reports were too theoretical and complicated.

Two groups made up of students of operational research reached a near-optimal point a little earlier than most of the others. American teaching of the subject, it seems, is not wholly wasted.

In those groups without a confederate the restriction on communications obtained by imposing the formal language increased the likelihood of partial acceptance. The aspect of the language that seemed to accomplish this is the requirement that all assertions must be justified. As can be seen in Appendix 2, statements end with a clause beginning with 'because'. The use of a formal language made no difference in those groups with a confederate, presumably because the confederate by advancing mathematical suggestions tended to force the consideration of rational arguments in the same way as the formal language did.

In only two cases was the fourth product, our means for differentiating acceptance from understanding, adopted. Most groups prefer to bear those ills they have.

Conclusion

Our general assumption has been that the area of implementation of research results is a legitimate part of operational research. More than that, we believe the neglect of such problems renders operational research sterile and ineffectual.

But this widespread neglect is understandable. The background of most workers in the field is largely engineering, the physical sciences, and mathematics. Furthermore, the results and conclusions of the social sciences that can be fruitfully applied to this area are meagre. But this does not account for the lack of interest – an area of ignorance will often present a challenge. It seems to me that there is another reason that problems pertinent to the social sciences attract little interest among most operational research workers. It is intimately related to the reasons that our experimental groups reject the solution. It is that the recognition that something that seems as complicated and uncontrollable as human psychology plays an essential role in operational research would lead to very grave doubts on the part of operational researchers about the potency of their techniques. And these doubts operational research workers are no more willing to entertain than were our chief executives willing to accept a solution when the acceptance would lead to doubts about their own competence.

Appendix 1. General Instructions to Subjects
(*past history of the firm is omitted*)

UNIVERSITY OF CALIFORNIA
Centre for Research in Management Science

Experiment in Decision-making
C. WEST CHURCHMAN AND P. RATOOSH

Instructions:

You are a member of a firm which manufactures three products for use in technical laboratories: a drawing pencil (P), a pen (F), and a ball-point (B). The firm purchases the parts for each of the products and assembles them. The history of the firm's activities for the last two years is attached, together with other relevant information.

At the beginning of each 'monthly' period the firm must make decisions about the next period. These decisions are to be transmitted in the manner indicated below. *The firm should try to maximize its long-range net profit.*

The following decisions *must* be made by the firm at the beginning of each period of its operations:

(*a*) the price of each product, P, F, and B;
(*b*) the amount of each product that is to be produced and the time schedule for the production during the month (a month consists of 20 working days);
(*c*) the number of parts to be purchased from the supplier;
(*d*) investments of available liquid capital outside the firm.

The following decisions *may* be made, at the option of the firm:

(*e*) Request for any relevant information about the firm's operations in addition to what is supplied here. If the information is available it will be supplied by the firm, but at an appropriate cost. If the firm wishes, it may ask for the cost of obtaining a certain kind of information, and it will receive this cost-figure free.
(*f*) Any other decisions relevant to the firm's operations, including dropping a product, or shift, or adding a new product or additional capacity.

IT IS ESSENTIAL THAT NO MEMBER OF THE FIRM COMMUNICATE ABOUT THE FIRM AND ITS OPERATIONS WITH ANYONE ELSE DURING THE RUNNING OF THE FIRM'S OPERATIONS – EXCEPT AS SPECIFIED IN THE INSTRUCTIONS.

The following describes how decisions are made, how information is obtained, and how the members may communicate.

Decisions

The firm has five members, a comptroller, a production manager, a sales manager, a purchasing manager, and a chief executive.

The *comptroller* must decide each period on the amount and kind of outside investment which the firm will make. This decision is to be written on the decision sheet, and an extra copy must be sent to the chief executive.

The *production manager* must decide on a production schedule for the coming
K

period. This decision is to be written on the decision sheet in the manner illustrated below, and extra copies must be sent to the comptroller and the chief executive.

The *sales manager* must decide on the price of each product for the coming period. This decision is to be entered on the decision sheet, and extra copies must be sent to the comptroller and the chief executive.

The *purchasing agent* must decide on the amount of raw material to be purchased for each product. This decision is to be entered on the decision sheet, and extra copies must be sent to the comptroller and the chief executive.

The *chief executive* is responsible for the running of the firm. He may make request for information or for the costs of certain types of information. He does not directly control any of the decisions of the firm at the outset, but he may by message criticize or praise any decisions that have been made. Furthermore, he may, if he wishes, deprive any member of his decision-making powers. If he does so, he must inform the member in advance of the decision time, and he must tell him what functions (if any) he wishes him to perform. Thereafter, the chief executive must make the decision or else designate some other member of the firm to do so. He may assign any duties he wishes to the other firm members. Any member of the firm may make any suggestions he wishes concerning the firm's operations to the chief executive.

Information

In addition to the information contained in these instructions, a financial report will be given to the chief executive each period and to anyone else he designates. Other information may be acquired, sometimes at a cost, on request from the chief executive. No other member of the firm can request information unless the chief executive authorizes him to do so.

Description of Purchasing, Production, and Sales

1 *General.* The production of finished items is very simple. The firm buys the parts for each product from an outside supplier. In its plant it runs one assembly line to assemble the parts. It is advantageous to assemble one product for a period of time, because the assembly line must be shut down for a while (during set-up), before another product is run.

2 *Purchasing.* The prices of the parts which the firm buys are listed on p. 258. If not enough parts are available to meet the production schedule the schedule will be reduced accordingly. All parts purchased during any month are available for production the same month; the excess goes into inventory. Because the supplier must set up to make the parts, he charges a fixed amount for each order placed, as indicated on p. 258. This amount is high, because he must set up special machinery to make the parts.

3 *Assembly Line.* The one assembly line which the firm operates requires eight men and can be operated for three eight-hour shifts per day. There are 20 working days each month, and therefore a maximum of 3 times 8 times 20 = 480 hours available for production each month. All products are made on this line. The wage rate is $2.50 per hour. This means that it costs the firm (in direct labour costs) 8 times $2.50 = $20.00 to run the assembly line one hour; 8 times $20.00 = $160.00 to run it one shift.

4 *Set-ups.* Each time the assembly line is changed to run a different product it is necessary for the crew to take time to 'set-up' for the run. There is no new set-up required when the product was the last one produced in the preceding period.

The company has a contract with an outside firm to do all of the special work required to set up for each product. The outside firm provides the skilled workers necessary to perform certain complex parts of each set-up which the regular crew cannot do. The contract expires at the end of period 15, and it specifies that for every set-up of F the outside firm is paid $180; each set-up of P costs $195; and each set-up of B costs $195.

5 *Production rate.* The maximum rates of production for each product are given on p. 258. These include time out for breakdowns, etc., but not for set-ups. Thus, for example, if the firm decides to run 1,000 times of Product F it must allocate 5 shifts (40 hours) for set-up (as shown on p. 258) plus at least $1,000/15 = 66 \cdot 7$ hours for production; where 15 per hour is the maximum rate of production for Product F.

The assembly line need not be run at the maximum rate. Indeed, the policy in the past has been to run it at a slower rate.

6 *Shifts.* There are three shifts: day, night, and graveyard. But the day, night, or graveyard, shift can be closed down entirely without additional costs. However, if any one is closed down it must be closed down for the entire month at least, and it will cost the firm $10,000 to open the shift again. These factors have, in the past, caused management to run all three shifts at less than capacity.

7 *Shortages.* The production line cannot be run at greater than maximum capacity. Since the assembly line operates twenty-four hours a day at maximum capacity, there is no room for overtime. Orders cannot be backlogged. Consequently, if the firm cannot fulfil its orders it must go outside to purchase the finished items at a cost to the firm indicated on p. 258. Whenever the firm fails to meet the demand for a product, an order for finished items will be placed immediately and the firm's financial status will be changed accordingly.

8 *Sales.* Sales are for cash, and cash generated within a month can be used to pay the month's expenses. Sales requirements can be met by the current month's production.

9 *Inventory.* The inventory value for both raw materials and finished goods is based on the purchase price for parts packages.

Taxes, insurance, and other charges for stored parts amount to $0 \cdot 5$ per cent of the average inventory value. Taxes, insurance, and other charges for finished goods amount to $0 \cdot 5$ per cent of the average inventory value plus $0 \cdot 5$ per cent of the added labour value. The added labour value per unit is calculated as the ratio of the labour cost per hour ($= \$20.00$) and the maximum output per hour (e.g. for $F = 15$ items per hour). (So the added labour value for product F is: $20 = \$1.33$ per unit.)

To simplify the calculation of the finished goods (or parts) average inventory level, assume the inventory at the beginning of the nth month, B_n, consists of the ending inventory from last month, $E_n - 1$, *plus* the total amount of production scheduled (for parts, the total purchases) for the current month, P_n, that is, $B_n = E_n - 1 + P_n$. The ending inventory level, then, is the excess inventory from last month plus the current month's production (for parts, the total purchases) minus the current month's sales, S_n (for parts, the current month's production). That is $E_n = B_n - S_n$. Hence, the average inventory level for the nth period is $(B_n + E_n)/2$.

There is no deterioration of the parts or finished items, no matter how long they are stored.

Be sure to ask the umpire for clarification if any part of this information is not clear to you.

Basic Information on Products

Product F:

Time required for set-up = 5 shifts (40 hours)

Maximum rate of production while the line is running = 15 finished items per hour (including packaging and shipment).

Cost to firm to purchase finished items outside = $20 per item.

Parts purchase price: $5 per package (each package contains all the parts required for one finished item).

Each time a new order is placed, it costs the firm $2,680.

Product P:

Time required for set-up = 2 shifts (16 hours).

Maximum rate of production while the line is running = 180 finished items per hour (including packaging and shipment).

Cost to firm to purchase finished items outside = 65 cents per item.

Parts purchase price: 10 cents per package.

Each time a new order is placed, it costs the firm $215.

Product B:

Time required for set-up = $2\frac{1}{2}$ shifts (20 hours).

Maximum rate of production while line is running = 45 finished items per hour (includes packaging and shipment).

Cost to firm to purchase finished items outside = $3.15 per item.

Parts purchase price: 50 cents per package.

Each time a new order is placed, it costs the firm $880.

Financial Information

The firm does not pay dividends.

The firm may, if it wishes, invest any available cash in a long-term outside investment which pays 0·5 per cent interest per month.

Once an investment is made, it cannot be sold for 20 periods.

The firm may borrow cash up to any amount at 0·5 per cent interest per month. If it runs out of cash it automatically borrows the additional amount needed at an interest rate of 1·0 per cent per month. Any such borrowed amount will be repaid automatically once cash is available.

The amount borrowed should include the *total* amount of money needed each period: if there are loans payable and one expects still to need more money in this period one should borrow the total amount needed (i.e. loans payable + extra borrowing) in order to make use of the lower interest rate for the full amount borrowed.

The decision regarding borrowing and investment is handled in each period by the Comptroller.

Appendix 2. Instructions–Company Communication Channel

1 The company has its own communication channel that can be used *free*.
2 In case you prefer to write your message in your own language, you can do so. In this case, however, you make use of a special communication channel for which the company has to pay $50.00 per message.

Figure 1 *Company Communication Channel*

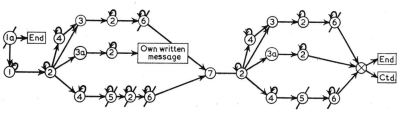

$\bigotimes$ = After having chosen from this column, one can choose another item from the same column and repeat this as many times as desired

$\bigcirc$ = This column may be by-passed

3 When you write a message and you want to make use of the company communication channel you have to observe the following rules:

(*a*) Each message consists of a number of parts or building units, where each unit is selected from a column (columns 1 through 7).

(*b*) The order in which these message-units are selected from columns is not arbitrary, but you have to select a chain from the flow-chart and to follow the order of columns as given by this chain. E.g. you might select message-units from columns 1, 2, 3, 2, 6, 7, 2, 4, 5, 6, End in that order (see flow-chart).

(*c*) You have to follow a chain *completely*, i.e. you have to start with a message-unit selected from column 1 (or 1a) and select from all following columns in a chain until you reach 'End' or 'Continued'.

(*d*) Some columns, however, may be by-passed (see flow-chart).

4 Ad column 1: The unit 'I direct that . . .' may only be used by the chief executive. You may 'cycle' in column 1, i.e. you may choose two or more times from this column, e.g. 'I suggest that you decide that . . .'.

5 Ad column 4: 'not' may be used in connexion with one of the others.

Examples:

'I provide info that prices of F, P, and B have been too low in past, because profit was insufficient'

'I[1] suggest that you direct[1] that financial[2] report[4] is[5] sent to the controller, because the[7] decision[2] of the controller depends[3] on the information[2] in financial report[2].'

6 Channel 3a should only be used when you want to describe a more complex relationship than can be handled by using channel 3.

7 Channel 2 ('because') may only be neglected when use of 'because' makes clearly no sense. E.g.:

'I[1] request info about why number of[2] manhours used has[4] been lower than[5] number of[2] manhours in period[6] 4.'

(1)

I (you) direct	that (chief exec. only)
I (you) decide	,,
I (you) recommend	,,
I (you) suggest	,, (when)
	(what)
I provide info about	(how)
	(why)
I provide info that	

(1a)

	(Name code)	(Number)	(Time)
I check on previous message	....	....	....
I reply to previous message	....	....	....
Please reply to my message	....	....	....
I cancel previous message(s)	....	....	....

(2)

Quantity purchased outside	(F,P,B)	Labour cost	(F,P,B)
,, produced	,,	,, ,, per part	,,
,, sold	,,	,, ,, per hour	,,
,, finished goods	,,	,, ,, per shift	,,
,, raw material	,,		
,, raw mat. purchased	,,	Fin. goods invent. cost	
		Raw mat. invent. cost	
Fin. goods inventory	,,	Restarting shift cost	
Raw mat. inventory	,,	Cost of special communication channel	
Price	,,	Cost of goods purchased outside (per unit)	
Purchase order cost	,,	Fixed cost	
,, ,, ,, per order	,,	Total cost	
,, ,, ,, per part	,,		
Production cost	,,	Profit	
,, ,, per run	,,	Loss	
,, ,, per part	,,	Profit margin	
Set-up cost	,,	Gross return sales (F, P, B)	

Expenses
Loan
Investments
Cash
Number of manhours (used available)
Time
Set-up time

Production time
Production capacity
. . . (number) set-up(s)
. . . (number) shift(s)
Financial report
Decision of . . . (name or subject)
Information . . . (subject)

(3)

(is) independent of
increase(s) with increase in
increase(s) with decrease in

decrease(s) with increase in
decrease(s) with decrease in
depend(s) on

(3a)

varies as follows with

(4)

        'not' optimal
is
are
will be
was
were
has been

have been
may (be)
might (be)
should (be)
not
(may be neglected)

(5)

high
higher than
too high
low
lower than
too low
just right

equal to
(un)changed
(in)sufficient
shut down
. . . (real number with kind of units)
sent to
(may be neglected)

(6)

per period
in period (number)
in future
in past
approximately

linearly
respectively
fully
(may be neglected)

(7)

because

(may be neglected only in case use of
because makes no sense).

REFERENCE

1 R. L. Ackoff (1960)

19 · The Evaluation
of the Effectiveness of Systems
# of Command Support

JOSEPH H. LEWIS

Introduction

There is a subject commonly referred to as command and control. The intent of this paper is to concentrate on operational research in the area of command, as opposed to control.

One way of establishing the distinction between them is to note that at the lower or outer end of command organizations are control systems. The control systems are in the form of feedback loops, capable of manipulating forces in and against environments in accordance with instructions received from the command or management organization. Control systems sense what has happened, measure the appropriate deployment change that is required to continue to comply with instructions, manipulate the forces again accordingly, and so on until new instructions are received.

Command at high levels of military organization, such as the national level, is like management at high levels of economic or political organization. It involves the continuous sensing and prediction of own and opposing actual and potential situations of military significance, the generation of policy guidance, and the making of plans as required, in accordance with overall objectives, to meet the actual or potential situations sensed. It issues policy guidance and instructions (command) to control systems at subordinate levels of organization as necessary to produce deployments intended to further national objectives. For our purposes, command is management.

Command can therefore be said to deal with questions of future and current resource allocations, with respect to organizational objectives, in ambiguous circumstances. It deals with questions of *whether*, such as, whether to make a commitment; if so, whether this one or that one. It answers, or attempts to answer, *what if* questions, such as, what if I do this, what will he do then, and how will that affect me? It is the continuous process of introduction of as much definition as is possible into ambiguous circumstances. It is done by organizations of men arranged in a matrix of hierarchy, procedures, facilities, and equipment in such a way as to approximate an organism, having indefinite life – *as long as* it is capable of evolving commensurate with the changing requirements of its environment, and in response to its own changing objectives, and to the changing guidance impressed upon it from outside.

Search for quantitative evaluation criteria

Now let us try to find some criteria against which to judge performance of command and hence performance of supporting systems. One would suppose that the first question to be answered about an aid to command would be: What is it for? The next question might be: What difference does it make? If we find answers to that, the next question might be: What other ways are there to do it? And finally: What do they cost? But, to begin with, there are not immediately available good and applicable quantitative answers to the first two questions: What is it for? and What difference does it make? Without good answers to these the effectiveness evaluation process is in trouble.

THE SUBSTANCE DEALT WITH

Let us look for ways in which to deal with these two questions. Let us first look for answers in terms of what it is that command or management organizations are supposed to deal with. Presumably we are interested in the performance of command in dealing advantageously with conflict situations. It has been noticed that conflict is a continuum. There is something called the spectrum of conflict. At one end are crises – conflict situations which are largely politically dominated, but which may lead to military commitments. At the other end is the ultimate in conflict, for today anyway, the nuclear holocaust. Somewhere in between are limited engagements or limited wars. It is in this latter area that lie our six thousand years of recorded experience of actual combat between deployed forces. It is the management of this whole spectrum of conflict, it would be supposed, that command support systems are meant to assist with. What are these things like, these management problems?

At the holocaust end of that scale, although we have no such wealth of experience here, one is happy to say, there is, at any given time, a very great deal of agreement as to who the principal enemies may be, the kinds of actions that might be thought desirable in certain circumstances, the sorts of considerations which should help to determine whether and what actions to select in various classes of circumstances. In short, whether the agreements are right or not, they have sponsored a good deal more definition at this end of the spectrum than at the other end. It is also true that nearly all the money that has been spent on command and control in recent years has been spent in response to this problem. This is a tremendously important problem. If this end of the spectrum is ever reached we in the West had better be good at it. But only in quite recent times have much energy and money begun to be spent explicitly on other parts of the spectrum, as opposed to dribbling down from the holocaust end.

At the crisis end of the spectrum are the situations which, with luck, have to be dealt with every day, day in and day out. What is the process of response to emergencies of this kind, that is, the crisis reaction? We do not, of course, have peace. We have continuous conflict at some level or other in the pre-military-commitment period. Although the questions here are politically dominated, it is absolutely essential that there should be strong interplay between the political and military parts of the government establishment to determine what policies are feasible, what commitments can be made, what the consequences of actions may be, which can be supported, and, in general, to deal with the questions of *whether* to make commitments and *what* will happen *if*. There is never enough information at any given time to deal with these questions in a precise, sharply defined manner. This is the most ambiguous context of all. Furthermore, formal, open use cannot be made of line institutions of government. Questions of *whether* must be dealt with in secret, by small numbers of men, trusted by the leader whose responsibility it is to select from among the choices made available to him. This cannot be done in public. Obviously if an enemy knew which alternatives were being considered, or that any alternatives were being considered, he could alter his own course of action accordingly and one's own purposes would be defeated.

One recalls in October 1962 – how the U.S. President had met, in great secret, with a very small handful of men, in the most intimate association, in long meetings, over a period of some days, to formulate the choice available – the *whether* questions; to consider and reconsider them – the *what if* questions; and, finally, to take the first decisions. This group of men became known in the news as 'The Executive Committee of the National Security Council'. Some of the men prominent among those consulted in those truly critical days were not, when one stops to think of it, even in the National Security Council. Some of them clearly were there because of who they were, as *men*, in the President's mind. Only some were there because they represented *institutions* the President wished to employ. Their deliberations were carried on in all the secrecy these circumstances demanded.

Even when a situation moves into the period of actual commitment of military force, although this period would then be dominated by military considerations, there is, again, a strong requirement for interchange between the political and military authorities. Frequently, this can be a strong requirement with respect to the minutest detail of a military act or a proposed one, on even the smallest scale, because of the ever-present possibility of escalation and the requirement which this imposes for precise, firm control at the highest political level.

Again, the sort of 'peace' that can be supported and maintained when the combat phase has terminated is determined in large part by political–

military interaction with respect to courses of action which are feasible. Where can a '38th parallel' make both military and political sense? What military interests in other arenas may be ill supported by actions politically desired in the one at issue, and so on?

Taking into account the breadth of the substance command must deal with in terms of the spectrum of conflict and the unresolvable ambiguity of the circumstances in which command organizations must function, particularly at the crisis end of the spectrum, one must conclude that the 'what's it for' question with respect to aids to command must have widely various answers, and that many of them are not now neatly defined, definable, or predictable.

THE ESSENTIAL NATURE OF THE PROCESS

Let us look for quantitative criteria for finding aids to command in terms of the *process* of command. In studying subjects of this sort it is often useful to invent clichés. They have their uses in conveying information. One that has been useful is this: the study of command is the study of the distribution and exercise of power. It is this to which people react when alterations in the distribution or constraints on the exercise are at issue. This is a far cry from technological magic. It is undoubtedly not an accident that this is also a respectable definition of the study of politics.

There appears to be a law – or another cliché, it seems idle to attempt to distinguish – with respect to power. It is a conservation law. There is a law of the conservation of power, and it appears to be about as good as any of the other conservation laws. If an accretion of power appears in one place it came from somewhere else. It is not new or created. It has flowed, or has been pulled, from one place to another. Reactions to the dynamic nature of power distribution are not a matter of logic, they tend to occur somewhere around the stomach or the liver, and, as is well known, either of these are sources of powerful response.

It follows, also by definition, that any significant change in command capability causes a change in the distribution of power and, consequently, will be resisted – by some. Therefore, to achieve a change requires a study and a solution of motivational problems as well as of the substance of the command problem itself. These are some of the most fundamentally important aspects of this subject, but they do not yield quantitative criteria against which to judge aids to command.

THE DECISION PROCESS

Let us examine the nature of the decision process, the apex, in a way, of the command process, to determine whether it may be a source of the quantitative criteria one would like to find.

It is clearly evident that decisions are made throughout an organization, at every level. One important function of a staff or command organization is to narrow the choices which must be made by the responsible man who makes them. Naturally, in the process they deny him many choices. These are decisions. There are modifications to the information as it passes through an organization, many intentional. That is, information coming in is aggregated with information already there, and must be. Or it is interpreted, whether it should be or not. Therefore the choices offered to the man who takes the decision do not represent just the information coming in about an event of interest. They also represent the context in which it occurs, other things going on in the world, overall interests, other commitments, and so on.

Similarly, at each stage, when a decision is made – or neglected, and therefore made negatively – incoming current information is a trigger, but the information in the *backs* of the heads of all the persons involved, including the highest, also enters into the decision that is made. That information, relevant and irrelevant, has been accumulated over the lifetime of each individual. It would therefore appear that decisions are made not only throughout an organization but also over a long period of time. In any particular instance it may be very hard to determine who made them, when they were made, and upon what they were based. It is therefore not at all obvious in any general sense how to answer in quantitative terms the What is it for? and What difference does it make? questions about aids to command, based upon any idealized view of the decision process.

It seems clear that there are not available valid, precisely defined, quantitative criteria against which to judge performance of command, in terms of the substance it deals with, the nature of the process involved, or the nature of the decision process. It follows that the same must be said of procedures or mechanisms intended to support or improve the performance of command organizations. There are not clear and obvious, quantitative general principles or statements that may be used to indicate where or in what way a new aid to command should be introduced for optimum effect, measured in quantitative terms.

The evolutionary approach

THE BASIS

For these reasons, it would therefore seem that quite intimate knowledge of the inner workings of the particular organization one is attempting to assist with machine aids, or other procedural improvements, would be required. How does one gain that? If a student of operations approaches any organization and says, 'How do you operate? I need to know because I'm to make improvements', he may be handed an organization block diagram, information flow charts if it is a sophisticated place, by-laws, rules and regulations, statements of procedures, telephone books, and he will be told, 'Now, that's how we operate.' If he really *is* a student of operations he will know that the true situation is more likely to be as follows:

At any given instant, in any organization, the formalized or legitimatized structure falls into two categories. Some ways of doing things will be obsolete. Of these, some are unused. People have found ways not to use them. Therefore they do not matter very much. Those that are used work against the interests of the organization.

Of those that are current, the second category, some are irrelevant – because the goals of the organization may be changed rapidly or abruptly from outside by the nature of changes in the environment, or changes in the guidance or constraints imposed upon the organization. These are either useless or work against the interests of the organization. But some are current and relevant, and it is *these* which 'produce the goods' for the organization. It is *these* one wishes to improve.

Any responsible operator in an organization knows these things, although not, perhaps, explicitly, or in these terms. In order to compensate for obsolescence, for irrelevance, he tries to do two things. One is to increase the speed of *evolution* of the organization in the direction of currency and relevancy; to reduce as much as possible those parts of the structure which are obsolete or irrelevant. Since this can never, it seems, be a perfect feedback loop, there is always some lag, in particular in very large, ponderous organizations. The other thing he does is parallel this legitimatized structure with an informal, *sub rosa* structure. These are the backstairs communications channels – the controllers' informal nets, the man who puts the message in the pneumatic tube, having phoned his friend, saying, 'Jack, wake up, this one is important!' Whereupon a pneumatic-tube system suddenly becomes extremely efficient.

By these two means, legitimatized and *sub rosa*, an operator or manager can deal with problems arising at his own level and below. If the student of operations is to perform a useful function he must convince the operators that he must know in detail the informal parts of the structure. He must, in order to do so, gain the confidence of the people with whom he is working, convince them that he has no intention of interfering with informal or *sub rosa* means of making a formalized structure work, that he is all for it. Part of the improvement sought *might* be increased speed of formalizing the informal parts of the structure. But it may not. It may always be better to have informal and *sub rosa* parallel or by-pass channels. These can avoid becoming rigidly specified. They are *ad hoc*, by their very nature, and will not be perpetuated if they are no longer useful. In any case, the operator must be confident that the student of operations is on *his* side in these respects, and the student of operations must avoid simply taking the batch of material which is handed to him and 'improving' everything, across the board. He must distinguish between obsolescence and irrelevance and currency and relevance.

For those problems which arise at levels above a given operator or manager, it sometimes happens that these two ways of operating, the legitimatized and the informal or *sub rosa*, cannot cope to his satisfaction. If he feels sufficiently strongly that the objectives and interests of his organization are not being served or that they are being subverted, the only actions available to him are of a kind that must be categorized as wrong or improper in some sense. Every responsible operator knows this. When he decides that a student of *his* operations is competent and knowledgeable he may therefore become exceedingly uneasy, because discovery of these types of activity can jeopardize his personal career. The student of operations cannot promise to assist in the performance of functions in this category. All he can do, and this can sometimes be quite important, is to help to describe the problem and the processes involved in ways which the operator can transmit upward to his superiors more powerfully, as it is only by effective transmission upward that this class of problem can be solved. But, in any case, the operator must be convinced that the student of operations is not going to jeopardize his, the operator's, whole future, either by inadvertence or on purpose.

The gaining of this degree of confidence is time-consuming, not always successful, and certainly not easy. Unless it is done, however, one can never be certain that a student of operations will have the basis for a responsible determination of the difference between obsolescence and irrelevance and currency and relevance. And it is *this* knowledge which determines the origin and direction of the vector which establishes evolution in a forward direction, in some sense. This knowledge is essential if an organization is to be helped to evolve in a direction which helps it to cope with its changing environment, rather than simply giving it new problems of its own to cope with.

Having developed enough mutual confidence to begin, and having begun to learn the intimate details of how a command organization really works, what use does a student of operations make of operational analysis and evaluation processes? Operational analysis and evaluation are required, in principle, throughout the whole process of command support system development. They are necessary as an adjunct to the process of definition – for the specification of objectives, functional requirements to match, corresponding technical system requirements – for both hardware and software, specification of hardware and software components accordingly, acceptance of system elements, integration into the using command organization, and determination of incremental effectiveness in achieving the stated objectives.

One wishes that it were really as neat as that. In practice, it is far from being so. In the first place, all the processes listed above are going on continuously, simultaneously, throughout the life of any command or management organization. This process never ends unless the organization dies. (This fact makes nonsense of the question, 'How much is so-and-so command system going to cost?')

These are all very old processes, not for the production of something new but for the purposeful evolution of something old. What engages our explicit attention is the pressure of technology which makes it both necessary and possible for command support capabilities to evolve at much higher rates, and in terms and by means not familiar to the operational users and manipulators of command organizations. We operational research people are working on the procedures and mechanisms by which command organizations do what they do. We are not creating command organizations. We are not eliminating, suppressing, or changing the substantive problems they are faced with. We are trying to help the users to guide the continued growth of their organizational capabilities.

In this context, operational analysis, although now commonly accepted as a fairly old activity, takes on a very different colour. The 'operations' referred to in the term 'operational analysis' are all physical processes of some kind. Although it is often extremely difficult to do, it is usually possible to state an objective for these processes, such as, shoot down aircraft at minimum cost in terms of money, load on the communication system, man-power, or some combination of these, under specified conditions, and also to measure performance against that objective, and finally to determine cost. The operations one is concerned with in a command organization are the operations to initiate and control those physical processes. These are *operations* operations. One is not measuring the performance of carrying out an interception and devising better ways to do so. One is attempting to improve the process of deciding: whether or not to do something, whether this is it, whether this is the right time, and the acceptable way, to tell someone else, to initiate, or continue, or modify, the process of carrying out the interception, if there really is or is going to be an enemy to intercept.

That last point is of particular importance. As noted earlier, the business of command or management is to deal with ambiguity. This is in fact an ambiguous world. Some say probabilistic, but it is really less knowable or predictable than that, because only some of the events one would like to bound, or to specify, or to predict are really as predictable as they would be if they were subject to the laws of probability in some known way. To date the only instruments we have for dealing with ambiguity are human senses and brains. All that we can do to assist men in dealing with ambiguity is to give *them* as clear a picture of it as possible.

It will be noticed that the word 'command system' has not been used so far. That is not an oversight. It is intentional. In fact, one ought to quarrel with that use of the word 'system'. It was borrowed, as you probably know, from the weapons system concept developed for a very different purpose, beginning in the late forties and early fifties. The weapons system concept proved to be a fairly powerful tool in controlling and rationalizing the complex processes which must go on concurrently in the crash development, testing, engineering, supply, operational testing, and training associated with the introduction of major new armaments – large numbers of fighting tools – into essentially invariant fighting force organizations. But then this usage was transferred to the development and acquisition of major *control* systems, of which one buys *one* of a kind – and changes the nature of the host control organization for ever. The systems approach became, for a time, a dominant aspect of control philosophy. We are now plagued with the consequences of applying this aspect of control system philosophy to the problems of acquisition of machine aids to *command* organization.

The term 'system' itself implies a degree of definition of inputs, processes, and outputs on a repetitive, reproducible basis, which comprehends only an incoherent fraction of the workings of a command organization. One must therefore approach the problem of producing a clear picture, for *men*, of ambiguity by saying that command *support* systems are systems to which those processes which *are* defined and repetitive, i.e. clerical, can be relegated. They may contain machine aids to free men to act more effectively as staff officers. But the object is the provision of information and the reduction of self-noise.

THE PRACTICE

How, then, does one apply the concepts of operational analysis or evaluation of effectiveness in this context? It is first necessary, as noted earlier, to try to understand the nature of the functions which must be performed to achieve the objectives of the organization. When a student of operations in a command or other management organization starts to do this he soon finds that, although he does not understand or even see a lot of what the organism is doing, certain functions can be identified as producing outputs and having inputs. Sometimes interrelationships can be seen and defined between them and among them, but in general this is more difficult. He will find, for example, that certain functions are so well defined as to processes, as well as input and output, that immediate data-processing assistance can be given. This is probably something to do with an inventory. Another function may contain processes which will clearly benefit from the application of data-processing techniques, but some time would be required in further defining and modelling the processes to allow the useful introduction of machine aids. A third function may be such that, although it appears certain that machine aids would eventually be of use, extensive study and research would be necessary to model the processes adequately for their useful introduction. Still another may be such that it is not obvious whether or when machine aids would ever be of assistance.

In the usual organization these functions are always interrelated by men in some way. The most obvious aspect of this is frequently a colonel or a general sitting in the middle, receiving outputs from these functional boxes and others, perhaps feeding the output from one as an input to another, or perhaps performing some sort of aggregation or cancellation of the outputs he receives for upward or downward transmission, storage, or destruction.

The next step is to begin. By that is meant one begins by helping the people who can be helped today. One continues by helping the people in the second function who can be helped tomorrow, or next week, or next month, or six months from now. One is concurrently studying function number three with an eye to providing assistance there when feasible. It is very important that this study is taking place with the benefit of experience being accumulated on functions one and two as to how these functions are being affected by the introduction of machine aids. One may even learn something about interaction among functions for future reference. Any attempts to assist or replace functions which one cannot see how to define, or, if definable, how to separate in some useful, meaningful way from the general body, are deferred as far as machine aids are concerned and treated as research projects. The question of what an 'ultimate' system would look like, even if one means by that only the automated processes in the headquarters, is begged at the outset as not really being of any interest.

APPLICATION OF QUALITATIVE CRITERIA

The reason this form of attack, as opposed to the 'ultimate system' approach, is so important is that this is the only one it is known how to employ in terms of meaningful criteria. As mentioned earlier, there are not easily available, definitely quantifiable criteria for the measurement of either requirements or performance of command organization. It has therefore been necessary to rely on the most qualitatively important criteria it has been possible to identify. These are relevance, utility, and convenience – all as seen through the eye of the user. For example, a rather clumsy data-processing programme which assists in the performance of a relevant activity, more effectively than it was previously done, is worth far more than the most elegant and sophisticated programme performing an irrelevant function. Relevance is comparatively easy to establish in qualitative terms if one has intimate knowledge of the nature and purposes of the command organization with which one is dealing.

Relevance

Relevance, used in this sense, is a very great driving force towards the employment of the so-called evolutionary process, described above in rather crude terms, as opposed to using the conventional 'systems' approach. The reason is that the goals and purposes, the guidance and constraints, and the energies and forces controlled – which determine what is required of the command organization – are in constant flux. That is the one element of this problem that is constant – flux. Therefore it is inevitable that any form of development which takes a reading at a given instant, then, after a long lead-time, produces an aid to command, will have produced an irrelevancy. Relevance can be established and maintained only by treating development of improved command capabilities as a *continuous* process.

Operational Utility

The notion of operational utility, of course, brings up questions of cost-effectiveness, or at least it ought to. There are two things that have to be said about it. One is that even a qualitative notion of cost-effectiveness is too seldom applied, because people often tend to be sun-blinded when they are offered the capacity to do a very large number of things at very high speed, just because it can be done. The other is that it is extremely difficult to find solid, quantitative criteria for judging cost-effectiveness. For example, the value of time saved is not quantifiable – although it may conceivably mean the difference between catastrophe or safety, or between one catastrophe and another. Also the costs which matter are more likely to be man-power than money. Command support systems, such as information systems, are fed by people not by electronic devices, generally speaking; and it is not unusual to discover that a system designed independently of the user command requires far more people to feed it than the command will ever have. Data-acquisition, after the *first* small improvements in processing have been made, is most frequently the bottleneck. We in operational research are still in the process of determining good ways to assess utility, but we are saved from having to apply such criteria very often by the prior question of relevance.

Operational Convenience

Convenience was mentioned, again from the user's point of view. By this is meant that it is essential to help the user to perform his functions, the ones he desires to perform, rather than to make him change his function to something that is conveniently or elegantly done on a machine. In short, to aim for *operational* efficiency and convenience at the expense of *technical* difficulty and inelegance, if necessary, rather than to accept *operational* constraints and inconvenience for the sake of *technical* efficiency and elegance. Operational research people are still learning how to apply these precepts, but it seems clear that they are the right ones to try to apply.

AN IMPORTANT LIMIT

It is important to stress a point with respect to a controlling element in the rate at which improved command capabilities can be 'grown' by a command organization partnership with a benevolent technology. It is becoming increasingly evident that whenever a small number of technologists approaches a command organization and says, 'Technology is here to help you!' they give work to a very large number of operational members of the user's staff, to perform functions which only they, the users, can perform, in preparation for the application of hard and soft technology. They can be *helped* but cannot be *supplanted*. Therefore, one of the determinants, strong determinants, of the rate at which improved capabilities can be developed is the amount of capital investment, so to speak, in terms of man-power, that the operator himself can make. The application of technology beyond a rate commensurate with his capital investment will almost certainly result in expensive, irrelevant, useless, and inconvenient systems.

Recapitulation and conclusions

This paper concentrates on operational research in the area of command, as opposed to control. Command, for purposes of this discussion, means management. The paper proceeds from that definition to examine the matter of operational research in systems effectiveness evaluation in that context.

The purpose of command or management is to be right. There are no quantifiable criteria for requirements or measures of performance that permit valid, overall cost-effectiveness determinations of means for being right.

A fundamentally important point is: the study of command is the study of the distribution and exercise of power.

Another fundamentally important point is: there is a law of conservation of power. If an accretion of power occurs in one place it came from somewhere else. The flow of power will be resisted by those who are losing it, or think they are.

Organizations, to live, are continuously evolving to match their capabilities to their changing environment, objectives, and guidance. This is a very old process.

Machine aids to command are a form of modification of procedures, and therefore a technical contribution to the evolutionary process.

The improvement of command or management capabilities can be approached usefully only on a step-by-step, function-by-function evolutionary basis, employing the criteria, largely qualitative, of relevance, utility, and convenience – all as seen through the eyes of the user.

The evolutionary approach is difficult. It makes continual living together of operators and technicians essential – acting on each other, performing the dual information-extraction process. It means that operational research in systems effectiveness evaluation is a *continuous* process which is related to organic growth.

Operational research approaches to systems evaluation in the area of command will, for a long time to come, have to continue to concentrate on trying to understand 'What is it for?' and 'What difference does it make?'

ACKNOWLEDGEMENT

This paper is based on a lecture entitled 'Evaluation of Systems Effectiveness', delivered by the author in January 1964 in a series on 'Information Sciences and Command and Control', sponsored by the University of California. It represents what have seemed to the author to be some of the fundamentally important methodological aspects of the problem at the national military level of command operations. It is derived from the work of all members of the command and control activity in the Weapons Systems Evaluation Group of the Department of Defense with which the Institute for Defense Analyses is associated.

20 · Discussion and Commentary

S. L. COOK

We have so far in this part of the book spoken of the present situation of operational research and the social sciences in the study of organizations, the factors which had led to the conference, and the aims in inviting the review and contributed papers. We have attempted to make some linking and integrating comments on the papers themselves and have reported the more important points relating to the content of the papers which came out in the discussions. We now move to the general discussions which took place, in both the small group and plenary sessions, concerning past, present, and possible future collaboration between operational research and social scientists in the organizational field.

General questions about such collaboration are dealt with in various of the papers – those by Bennis, Churchman and Emery, Cooper and Churchill, Charnes and Stedry, Burns, Ratoosh, and Brink. No attempt is made to reproduce their comments here unless they were strongly taken up in the conference discussions.

What kinds of collaboration might be fruitful

It was stressed many times in the discussions at the conference that neither group has any cut-and-dried theories or even research methods which could be handed over in working order to the other group; the common interest was primarily in the problems and subject-matter studied. A certain amount could be gained by intellectual discussion of theories and methods, but the main gains would come from joint study of problems. Just as problems provide the focal point for the interdisciplinary activities of operational research teams and of social science teams, so will they provide the focus for collaboration between operational research and social science.

The scope for joint studies can be divided into the basic and the applied research areas.

BASIC RESEARCH

In the basic research area there is clearly scope for much combined work, as illustrated by many of the papers in this section (Woodward and Eilon, Churchill and Cooper, Charnes and Stedry, Radnor, and Ratoosh). An expansion of descriptive-observational study of exploratory model-building and of laboratory experimental work of the kind illustrated here could clearly be useful, especially if there is continual interaction between the three kinds. Here the operational research approach to modelling complex systems ought to prove valuable.

INTERACTION BETWEEN BASIC AND APPLIED RESEARCH AREAS

An important area for collaborative work is that of interaction between the basic and applied research areas. In the social science field Bennis gives several examples of independent evaluations of applied research programmes (Argyris by Harrison; David by Seashore, Bowers, and others; Bennis and others by Argyris; and so on) which seek to measure the effectiveness of these programmes. This attempt to gain the maximum possible research value from applied studies is clearly commendable. In the case of operational research there should be even greater value, because of the greater volume of work going on in industry, and the present lack of adequate documentation of the work and of its effectiveness. Such reviews might well be conducted by joint social science/operational research teams. Documentation of particular studies could in turn make possible some broad review and analysis of the work as a whole, leading to conclusions of a more general research nature. We could hope to learn more about the effectiveness of different approaches to organizational structure and control, including applications of operational research and social science. (One social science study of this nature in recent years has been that of Northwestern University on the birth and death of operational research groups in industry.)

The help which the growth of applied studies by internal or consulting groups can give to basic organizational research is referred to in the paper by Cooper and Churchill: 'Just as the advent of operational research has produced a more easily tapped field of inquiry in the area of management planning, so may we anticipate a similar revolution in the more subtle activity of management control, in symbiosis with the behavioural sciences.' One might perhaps add that, just as the areas of planning and of control run into one another, so do the applications of operational research and behavioural science in both areas; so that this interaction of basic and applied research is important for operational research and social science working jointly as well as separately.

Certainly the interaction between basic and applied research need not be one way only. The evaluative study of applied research projects by basic research teams as described above might very well lead on to collaboration in the other direction. For example, the applied researchers might attempt to validate, within particular organizations, the models and hypotheses developed by basic research.

APPLIED RESEARCH

There is indeed a large volume of operational research work going on in organizations, both by internal and by consulting groups. There is a smaller volume of social science applied research of the type reported by Bennis. There is as yet little if any joint operational research/social science going on inside organizations. In the history of the development of science much advance has been due to applied research, and this might be expected particularly in the problem-oriented areas of operational research and social science, where to a large extent the live organization is also the laboratory. Thus, collaboration on applied work may have a triple value – it may help to solve the immediate problems more effectively, it may contribute to the development of a generally applicable joint operational research/social science approach to organizational problems, and it may help to develop the basic theories of organizations.

Some of the problem areas which might be tackled collaboratively are explored below.

Areas for collaboration in studies to improve particular organizations

The aspects of organizations of primary concern to operational research and/or social science might be considered under four headings:

A. Values
B. Objectives
C. Systems (formal)
D. Systems (informal)

Organizational values are usually implicit; organizational or management objectives may sometimes be explicit. Values would normally pertain to the whole organization; different parts of an organization may well have different objectives, but they should not be contradictory.

There are normally several formal management control systems in an organization, and they should support rather than contradict one another. There may also be many informal systems, and these should contradict neither one another nor the formal systems. They should, of course, also be in line with the objectives and values of the organization.

In any studies of values, objectives, and/or systems intended to improve organizational effectiveness the following four stages would seem to be essential:

A. Define and understand the present situation.
B. Explore possible new situations.

C. Define the desired situation (or at least the preferred direction in which to move).

D. Assist the change.

Here the word 'situation' may refer to values or objectives or particular control systems.

The four steps are, of course, not necessarily clearly separated in time; the sequence may cycle.

The parts played by social science and operational research in the different stages of such studies will depend on many factors, and will differ according to the level in the organization. The Churchman and Emery paper has a good deal to say about the importance of organizational values and objectives in any studies by operational research and social science in an organization. However, studies of value and objectives are not likely to arise often in particular organizations in their own right; they are more likely to arise out of lower-level studies.

MISUNDERSTANDING, CONFLICT, AND COMMUNICATIONS

At the everyday working level of operational research in industrial organizations many problems arise which might be cleared up by collaboration with social scientists. One of the greatest problems the operational research man meets in the course of his work is that of *misunderstanding* between one part of the management and another. If the social scientist is to cope with this problem he must clearly be given more than a subordinate role within the organization. It may be that misunderstanding is a fundamental component of organizational life and that one objective of the organization should be to cope effectively with it. In a joint study the social scientists might provide the ideas and the operational researcher might attempt to quantify them within the context of the ongoing self-improving organization.

A relevant concept from sociology is the idea of a 'barrier to upward communication'. Studies to remove this barrier and allow latent problems in an organization to be brought to the surface might improve the flow of communication in a way which might be measurable, even if it could not be related quantitatively to overall organizational goals.

Both operational researchers and social scientists have been asked at different times to help to resolve conflicts within an organization. The operational research man will normally do this by a logical analysis and reference to the explicit objectives of the parts of the management concerned. Applied social scientists will be more interested in helping conflicting parties to gain a problem-solving approach to their conflict. It seems that there are basically two forms of conflict within an organization, that between roles or jobs and that between individuals in roles or jobs. It is seldom easy to diagnose in advance what form of conflict exists, and therefore there would appear to be a major advantage in forming joint operational research/social science teams for such conflict studies.

The social scientist, approaching such a problem, tends to subdivide a study of conflict roughly into that: (i) within the individual; (ii) between individuals within small groups; (iii) between groups within companies or organizations; (iv) between networks of organizations; and (v) between organizations and governments, both local and national.

Some conflict can be anticipated, although social scientists cannot yet give a quantitative forecast of the phenomenon. For example, an innovation such as the introduction of new machinery is likely to give rise to conflict within an organization if it will cause small working groups to be broken up. In such situations management frequently assumes that regrouping will gradually take place after the new equipment has been installed and the conflict will disappear, but this may not be so, and the social scientist here can give a better prediction than can the layman.

There is considerable controversy about how much conflict is desirable within an organization. Some regard the ideal as the removal of all sources of conflict, some stress understanding the causes of conflict and living with them, and some see conflict as essential for operational stability. Until this has been understood, studies of conflict within particular organizations are bound to remain empirical, whether carried out by operational researchers or social scientists or both.

The applied social science methods described by Bennis in his paper were unfamiliar not only to the operational researchers at the conference but also to most of the social scientists. They appear to hold great promise as an approach to organizational analysis, improvement, and development that could use the relevant skills of people trained in operational research and in organizationally oriented social science, but they received little attention in the syndicate discussions.

PROBLEM-SOLVING AND SYSTEMS IMPROVEMENT

The social science contribution to an operational research study can very well begin at the very first stage with formulation of the problem. The social scientist may concede that the operational research worker is more skilled at the integrated and articulate presentation of complex ideas, generally made possible by the use of powerful sophisticated mathematical techniques. However, the social scientist has an important and real contribution to make in analysing the roles and obligations in the organizational structure. He may well suggest additional variables which may be considered in the study.

The social scientist can also give great help at the implementation stage. He will not necessarily have greater human relation skills than a good experienced operational research man, but he will have a better understanding of the abilities and motivations of the people who will need to operate the new procedures. He can make an independent assessment of the extent to which ideas and procedures related to findings and changes recommended by an operational research group will be seen by the operating people to follow logical principle and not violate common sense. This is liable to be a wasteful procedure, however, if the social scientist has not already been consulted on the formulation of the problem, since his comments on the proposed solution may well suggest starting again from scratch.

It is, of course, even more naïve to think that the social scientist can be called in to help the operational research team and the management to implement recommendations based on a study in which he has played no part at all. Apart from the likelihood of failure in such an approach, the social scientist's values will not usually allow him to manipulate people to get them to accept 'technocratic' solutions. Most operational research men would have similar values in this respect. For further discussion of values in this context, see, of course, Churchman and Emery in this volume, and also a paper by Bennis on scientific values and human health. [1]

The social scientist certainly might usefully advise the operational research man on how and at what level to present his report to management. This would be based on a knowledge of the political system in the organization.

The conference discussion concentrated rather on the intellectual division of roles between operational research and social science, and tended to refer to the managers or other organization members affected by the study in a somewhat detached manner. Had more 'applied social scientists' been present, no doubt there would have been much more attention to the need for full participation in the study by all people affected, so that 'implementation' ceases to be a separate stage demanding separate treatment. This is a point that is accepted intuitively by most experienced operational research men (it is expressed clearly in the Lewis paper), but there seems a tendency for them (and many social scientists, too) to forget about it in this type of discussion. Collaboration between operational research and social science, particularly on the lines of the methods described by Bennis, might lead to a more explicit understanding of the problems and advantages involved in such participative studies. It might also help to show how better to organize work within the operational research group itself.

DESIGN OF MANAGEMENT SYSTEMS

A recent investigation by Professor Scott [2,3] at Liverpool University has been made into the effects on fifteen firms of the installation of computers as management aids. Detailed results of the study are not yet available, but the main conclusion is that only in one firm was the installation carried out without organizational troubles. The exception was a Swedish firm which employed a behavioural scientist to plan a new organization as part of the total design and engineering of the system.

There seems little doubt that behavioural scientists ought to be seen as an essential part of any management system development team. One of their main concerns should be with the 'influence' component in the system. More broadly, they should be concerned with developing a coherent and consistent philosophy of management roles and structure, based on up-to-date findings of social science, together with the views of the management of the organization and its perceived values and objectives. At the present time such contributions are not likely to be quantitative, although some of the human factors may later become quantifiable for inclusion in an operational research model.

An equally important contribution would concern the relation between the management systems development teams and the rest of the organization. At times of rapid management innovation the relation between line and staff functions is particularly critical. A social scientist well versed in the work of such people as Rensis Likert (*New Patterns of Management*),[4] Burns and Stalker (*The Management of Innovation*),[5] Harold Leavitt, Herbert Simon, and others, could help to change the organization in directions which would make it easier for it to accommodate further change.

The obstacles to collaboration

The closeness with which the subject-matter of operational research and of social science is interwoven in any organizational problem would seem to make the two approaches essentially complementary, and would seem to demand that they should be used in collaboration. However, it does not follow that they can easily be used in this way. In so far as they are both highly exploratory, with little established and undisputed theory as yet, it could even be argued that their explorations should continue separately and not be allowed to interfere with one another. No doubt the right answer is a diverse strategy – 'may a thousand flowers bloom' – but this does not mean we cannot consider a possible change of emphasis from the present pattern. Before doing this, let us consider some of the apparent obstacles to collaboration between operational research men and social scientists, as they were discussed in syndicates and plenary meetings at the conference.

BASIC DIFFERENCES IN INTERESTS AND PHILOSOPHY

A majority view in one syndicate was that operational research and the social sciences just did not mix. They were thought to be entirely different in outlook and quite antipathetic to one another, despite an apparent similarity in the disciplines. This antipathy was considered to arise primarily from the different orientation of the training of the two groups; the operational research scientist's training tends to lead him away from human problems and to concentrate his efforts on material ones; the social scientist, on the other hand, is bound up with people and personalities to the exclusion of the economic and production-type problems.

LACK OF KNOWLEDGE OR UNDERSTANDING OF EACH OTHER'S ACTIVITIES

Channels of communication between operational researchers and social scientists were generally thought to be very inadequate. Hopes were expressed in one syndicate that the channels created by this conference would be kept open. In another 'the discussion was characterized throughout by a considerable gulf of ignorance between operational researchers and social scientists present'. There is little or nothing of the human sciences in the operational research literature, and vice versa.

Some social scientists and some operational researchers who had tried to penetrate each other's literature had not found the experience encouraging. Operational research men complained of long words and long-winded verbal arguments in social science writings; social scientists found many operational research papers too arid, mathematical, and full of implicit assumptions that seemed unjustified.

One result of the lack of mutual understanding was that the operational research man, if he expected any help at all from social science, seemed to expect too much. He did not appreciate that, although a vast body of knowledge was being built up, it was not by any means all relevant or useful, and there were still many gaps. To put it more crudely, the operational research man did not seem to want to take human factors very seriously; if the social scientists could provide pat solutions which could be fitted into operational research studies without much trouble this was all right, but otherwise his attitude seemed to be 'forget it'. Another way in which the operational research man tended to expect too much from the social scientist was in the social skills needed for operational research work. In fact, as several social scientists pointed out, experienced and successful operational research men probably develop social skills quite as good as those of the trained social scientists. The social scientist's contribution here is rather more subtle, and relates to his ability to analyse and understand the political system within which a given problem is being studied.

In one syndicate the question was asked (by a sociologist) whether there were any examples in the history of operational research of the incorporation of concepts developed by social scientists in operational research models and whether these had resulted in a better solution to the operational problem. Some examples were quoted, but it seemed that a written review of such applications and their outcomes could be valuable.

We can generally conclude that much deeper mutual knowledge and understanding are needed if there is to be real collaboration between the two groups, and that lack of satisfactory documentation has been one cause of failure to achieve this end.

DIFFERENCES IN METHOD

Differences of method between the two groups may be due to real differences in aims and subject-matter. To the extent that this is true, exchanges of methods may not be very fruitful. However, each needs to understand, if it does not adopt the methods of, the other.

Measurement is the basis of much operational research work; there is consequently always a strong bias on the part of the operational research worker to work in those areas capable of being measured and to base his arguments on quantitative data. (A more cynical way of putting this point of view was 'operational research people attempt only those problems they can easily solve'.) The social science worker often lacks understanding of the use and power of measurement. This deficiency is often characterized, paradoxically, by an obsession with figures and a 'naïve preoccupation with statistics and statistical methods in order to prove something'. The gulf is great, but it can be overcome by an effort on the social scientist's part to understand the theory of measurement and what it really is. This will help to give him more common ground to work with the operational research scientists.

Another aspect of operational research arising from its strong mathematical background is the tendency, alien to many social scientists, to develop arguments from formal rules and a formal framework. The crudity and lack of quantification in present social models is a barrier to the operational research man; the social scientist tends to be logical but not mathematical. Both groups subscribe to the scientific method, but they interpret it in somewhat different ways. Operational research men consider that this method involves: (*a*) measurement; (*b*) developing and validating a mathematical model; (*c*) predicting from the model. Social scientists substitute the cycle 'observation, hypothesis, refutation'.

Nevertheless, social scientists generally recognize the desirability of quantification and of developing mathematical models to aid this. Undoubtedly operational researchers could help in this area if they could communicate about the general nature of the problem.

STEREOTYPES AS AN OBSTACLE TO REAL UNDERSTANDING

Some social scientists in particular, reading this account, may recognize that on both sides 'stereotypes' of the other group played a considerable part in the discussions. For example, social scientists were regarded as being more concerned with such factors as 'morale', operational research men with productivity; social scientists were naïve about measurement, operational research men about human values and behaviour; social scientists emphasized the relevance of change, operational research men its endpoint; social scientists emphasized basic research, operational research men applied research; and so on. Clearly, these are at best half truths. As Bennis pointed out, there is a wide range of viewpoints and activities within each group, probably wider than the differences between them. In the case of almost all the stereotype statements above, some social scientists and some operational research men could be found for whom the truth would be the exact reverse of the formulation. The difficulty is to discuss the problem in so many dimensions at once, and some degree of oversimplification seems essential.

There were indeed two opposing undercurrents in the discussion: the weaker current tried to achieve unity at the outset by emphasizing similarities and common purposes, and to resist the polarization into two groups and the concentration on differences. This was perhaps the more sophisticated approach. Much the stronger current, however, was concerned with clarifying the initial position of the two groups and particularly with exploring and understanding the differences; discussion was lively, and certainly at times the two groups found themselves attacking and defending professional positions, which inevitably exaggerated the polarization and led to oversimplification and stereotyping.

The question arises whether these oversimplifications are helpful or harmful. It seems likely to this observer at least that they played a valuable part at the conference in enabling members of the two groups to get to grips with and to explore one another's basic beliefs and approaches. At the end of the conference most members probably realized the extent to which they *were* oversimplifications and had some feel for the greater subtlety of the true situation; but it is likely that they will require a good deal more examination, discussion, and debate before they can be finally set aside.

If discussion in terms of stereotypes helps towards understanding in the early stages it must also be true that if the stereotypes 'stick' they will block really effective co-operation. The next stage must therefore be to go beyond them. This will be done not by further abstract discussion, which, as Bennis said, is of limited benefit, but by interdisciplinary collaboration on real problems, with adequate documentation. To achieve this collaboration in full measure, the participation of applied social scientists or 'social engineers' in the team, to help all members to forget their professional boundaries and achieve a problem-solving approach, may be particularly necessary. While the operational research man prides himself on his ability to operate in an interdisciplinary team in which the whole is greater than the parts, he cannot lightly refuse such skilled help in this difficult area, especially when social scientists are to be part of the team.

THE 'MIXED TEAM' CONCEPT – IN PRINCIPLE AND IN PRACTICE

There was some feeling that the mixed team concept in the operational research approach, originally one of its great strengths, had degenerated into a rather exclusive club, basically for physical scientists and mathematicians but allowing entry to others occasionally if they fulfilled strict requirements. This concept was thought, on the one hand, to discourage operational research men from collaborating with social scientists as separate groups, since the operational researchers took the view that if there was to be collaboration it would be best for the social scientists to join the operational research mixed team. On the other hand, the social scientist feels he is asked to deny his birthright and become highly competent in a number of alien fields before he can operate in such a group as an equal.

In fact, the fundamental idea of mixed teams in operational research has not really changed since operational research began; but it is clear that the nature of the mix should vary according to the general nature of the problems being tackled, and in the majority of industrial operational research teams in the last ten years there has been a very great concentration on problems suitable for teams composed primarily of mathematicians and physical scientists. Moreover, these teams have become more intensively skilled and knowledgeable about the quantitative techniques which have been developed under the name 'operational research'. This increased professionalization over a narrower range of the total problem area has been highly productive within that range, but it has the compensating disadvantage that from the broader point of view it has become more a specialized discipline than an inter-disciplinary approach. There is now a very real ambiguity over the question of whether the term 'operational research' describes this particular specialized discipline or the original broader approach. If the former, then a new colla-borative grouping between this operational research discipline and the social scientists is needed for joint studies. If the latter, then we must restore the full original meaning to the mixed team, and the only qualification we can ask for from the social scientist wishing to join the team is that he be a good social scientist.

But even if this were done, there would still remain some possible diffi-culties in assimilating social scientists in the operational research group. It can reasonably be said that the physical scientists, economists, and even mathe-maticians joining an operational research group cease to act primarily as physical scientists, economists, and mathematicians once they are in the group. The philosophy of the mixed team, as generally accepted up to now, in operational research, requires all members to become operational research men, that is to study the whole problem collaboratively. They may contribute approaches to the problem derived from their own disciplines, but they contribute these collectively. They are equally happy to tackle any opera-tional problem that comes along.

By contrast, the social scientist joining an operational research group is probably doing so as a dedicated professional social scientist wishing to use his training as fully as possible on social science problems. He will probably want to concentrate on these and spend the minimum time considering the more 'mechanistic' parts of the problem, especially where these are complex.

It is clear that we may have to recognize that in collaborative operational research/social science studies in organizations, the social scientist is there primarily because of his extensive knowledge and skills in the social science area. If he can learn the language of the other members of the team to some extent, all well and good, but it should not, perhaps, be a requirement. He would then be more like the manager or technical specialist who joins an operational research team for the duration of a given project because of his special knowledge in the area, rather than a permanent member of an operational research group that tackles any of the problems that may arise.

This approach would reduce the problem to an organizational one – where should the social scientist sit in the organization so that he is available for working with operational research on appropriate projects when they arrive?

Another difficulty put forward concerning the use of social scientists in operational research groups, or for that matter operational research men in social science teams, was the professional career structure. It was thought that periods spent in this way might set back a man's career in his own field. It seems likely, however, that this is rather a symptom of the more fundamental difficulties mentioned above. As it becomes recognized that collaboration between the two fields is valuable, so will experience across both fields be regarded as exceptionally useful and the men's careers will benefit rather than suffer. Even the holding of this conference is likely to increase the value attached by both professional groups to such experience.

A good professional umbrella under which operational research and social science can collaborate in the field of organization at the present time is that loosely termed the 'management sciences'. This can cover all the types of activity of operational research and social science in organizations and also of the university research groups variously called management research, business studies, industrial administration, organizational science, and so on. A management sciences group can, as a whole, adopt the mixed team principle of operational research and can at the same time contain an operational research component in the more narrow sense of the term as described above. In this sense the management science grouping is broader than operational research in that it includes basic disciplines working in their own right as well as in interdisciplinary studies; but it is narrower in the sense that it is usually regarded as being confined to the management of organizations and not concerned, for example, with problems of community planning, regional and national and international politics, military systems, and so on.

Nevertheless, the development of the broadly based mixed team concept of operational research is still being pursued as an area of study in its own right in a number of environments, for example at the University of Pennsylvania, and at the Institute for Operational Research in London. These offer an alternative environment for collaborative work that should be 'professionally respectable' for both operational researchers and social scientists, whether this respectability is sought after or not. The approach is likely to differ somewhat from the 'management science' grouping as described above – for example, there will be a more conscious attempt to develop generally applicable methods of collaborative problem-solving – and thus the two are complementary.

The question of who should take the lead in developing studies involving both operational research and social science in particular environments will still remain. It could very well be that, in basic research, the social scientists should take the initiative and invite operational researchers to join them and help to develop, for example, more quantitative approaches to social theory. On the other hand, operational research groups strongly established inside organizations should perhaps try to provide a base from which behavioural problems could be studied. The approaches should be matched to the situation; any reasonable approach should work if the major obstacles already referred to can be overcome.

SHORTAGE OF 'SOCIAL ENGINEERS' TO DEVELOP APPLIED SOCIAL SCIENCE

Although both operational research and social science are very much concerned with application to the real world, it seems true that operational research is much more developed on the application side and social science on the basic research side. A greater concentration of social science on applications and of operational research on theory development would undoubtedly make collaboration easier. The growing academic activity in operational research should soon help in this direction; it is not clear whether the apparent lack of applied social science in organizations, in the United Kingdom at any rate, will as quickly be remedied. It appears that quite a number of people with first degrees in social science subjects do work in organizations in various functions such as personnel, administration, and so on, but the number of these who could be regarded as doing applied research in any sense, and as having any feeling of involvement with the development of social science, is probably few outside such bodies as the Tavistock Institute of Human Relations. For example, a management educationist felt that there seemed to be no 'social engineers' in industrial organizations equivalent to the operational research scientists.

The development of such larger applied social science research activities in organizations, either through internal groups or through some form of consulting, would undoubtedly make it easier to organize some collaborative applied work with operational research. It might be desirable for the social science profession to encourage more of its members to go into applied work in this way, as well as to persuade organizations themselves to sponsor such work. It was also suggested, however, that operational research scientists should take the trouble to seek out the social scientists working in their own organizations – even if not engaged on anything like applied research – and discuss with them possible forms of collaborative study.

Really effective collaborative studies in organizations will also require the emergence of senior investigators capable of bridging a number of disciplines in reasonable depth – something akin to the 'project engineer'. Such men would need to have the respect of the social-scientist and the operational research members of their teams. No doubt such men will gradually be developed through the increase in collaboration in applied research and perhaps also through collaborative basic research activities at universities.

L

SPONSORSHIP OF APPLIED SOCIAL SCIENCE STUDIES

Even if social scientists are available, there are some difficulties in getting adequate sponsorship for applied social science research in organizations.

First, there is the question of cost. In the early years of an internal operational research group, for example, there is pressure on the group to show an economic return in the fairly short term. This favours the more mechanistic type of study in which human factors, in any complex or analytical sense, can be ignored. Even in management consulting groups which employ some social scientists as well as operational research men, it seems that they are often used separately rather than together. Cost is again a reason given for this: consultative jobs are often of short duration, and apparently it has often proved impracticable to form interdisciplinary teams because of the time required to break down barriers; relatively homogeneous teams have been reluctantly accepted as the only practical solution.

One suggested remedy is that those engaged on large research programmes should pioneer the breaking down of methodological barriers, so that the use of mixed social science/operational research teams for problem-solving will become easier and less expensive.

An equally important factor discouraging management from sponsoring behavioural studies is the fear of what will be discovered 'wriggling under the stones'. Undoubtedly, incompetent social science work in an organization could be most damaging to it; even competent work might prove disturbing if it were found, for example, that the values of the social scientists clashed with those of the managers. But much of this fear is due to management's own lack of understanding of the social science field.

For similar reasons, managements may feel happier to sponsor social science studies by external consultants (academic or commercial) rather than from an internal group. This makes it easier to cut off the study if it is thought to be going wrong, and to insulate the researchers from the other members of the organization. (Bennis discusses this point quite fully.)

Undoubtedly, this very real problem raises some obstacles to full collaboration. The normal operational research group maintains its effectiveness by a full and free exchange of information and experience on projects within the group, while maintaining proper confidence on such matters outside the group. Many behavioural studies might be expected to disclose facts that ought not to be discussed so freely even inside the group. An operational research group tends to be larger and less intimate than a social science group, or at least less accustomed to handling exceptionally confidential matters *as a group*. Some degree of separation may perhaps be necessary, whether the social scientists work as part of the operational research group, as a parallel internal group, or as consultants from outside. All this will be less difficult where the organization as a whole has accepted the principle of free and open discussion of its problems – this no doubt will depend on the amount of influence social scientists have had already in the organization.

Although this aspect needs careful handling, there seems no reason why it should prevent close collaboration between social science and operational research in organization at the senior level, and at working levels on all appropriate studies.

OBSTACLES TO COLLABORATION – A SUMMING UP

These, then, are some of the obstacles to greater collaboration between operational research and social science, especially in the applied field. They can be overcome, and considerable enthusiasm and optimism developed as the conference went on. However, to avoid complacency and to illustrate the ambivalent attitudes in at least this first session of the conference, we might quote the concluding remarks of the reporters of two of the syndicates:

'As the end of the time allocated for discussion approached, the syndicate appeared to be groping for some conciliatory formula by which to assure itself that the differences between the two ideologies were more apparent than real, that there was a "real need" for the two specialities to work closer together, and that, while respecting differences in the other's approach and techniques, both were in agreement fundamentally in their perceptions of the priorities of problem-solving. It was difficult, however, to avoid the impression that the syndicate dispersed in the spirit of an uneasy and un-conclusive truce dictated more by the expiry of the time-limit than by any deeply felt conviction that the two groups had much to offer one another.'

But in another syndicate:

'The outstanding idea which emerged from the syndicate was that these two professions need each other's skills if they are to help to solve the problems of industry and society and that co-operation on the job is the only practical way in which to meet those needs.'

Conclusions and recommendations

There seems little doubt that social science and operational research do need to work closer together in many areas of basic and applied research in organizations. There is little doubt also that a lot more mutual contact and exploration will be needed before it will become very clear how best they can collaborate. We consider here some ways in which the two professions, the universities, the research foundations, and the managers of organizations can encourage movement in this direction.

The Two Professions can help, first, by setting out to create an atmosphere in which collaborative work is not only respectable but is also seen as valuable pioneering. This would help in many ways. Those junior members of each profession who felt some interest in the overlapping area would be encouraged to spend a year or two 'on the other side' to gain experience. There could be a greater interchange of subject-matter, at least at the appreciation level in post-graduate courses for the two professions. Most important, there would be an incentive for some creative leaders in each field to move into the other and develop new approaches.

Second, the two professions should improve communications all round. There should be much more documentation of applied work in language suitable for both professions. Operational research particularly should seek out more papers on social science subjects, and vice versa. There should be more joint professional meetings, for which very careful preparation would be needed. These should aim to link basic with applied research as well as operational research with social science.

The Main Operational Research Groups should set out where possible to do a proportion of collaborative work involving social scientists. In particular, they should invite the outstanding creative men in the field to join them in their effort. One way might be to offer senior research fellowships; such fellows might be invited to carry out a behavioural study of the work and effectiveness of the operational research group in its organization, as well as to lead a joint team on a combined behavioural/operational research problem in the organization. Another way would be for the operational research groups to seek out projects in which they could work with staff from personnel or industrial relations having social science qualifications. Any such work should be documented with great care and comprehensiveness.

The Universities can help greatly by expanding collaborative basic research. Departments of business administration or centres for management research provide one obvious focal point for such studies, being well oriented to the problems requiring joint collaboration if less so to the development of joint methodology. Joint work should also be developed by the broader academic operational research groups where the aim is to develop problem-solving methods in the widest interdisciplinary sense. In universities where the less broad, more mathematical/engineering type of operational research group exists side by side with a behavioural science group, there is a lot to be said for the establishment of a third group of equal standing between the two to pioneer collaborative work, borrowing its staff from the other two groups.

All these proposals imply some deliberate slowing down of the rate of progress in the two separate professions and particularly in operational research. We should acknowledge that the desire for quick results from operational research has sometimes lead to defects which can be remedied only by bringing in the social scientists. The immediate spectacular pay-off may sometimes have to be sacrificed in the interests of a deeper understanding of the problem as a whole.

Clearly this cannot be applied universally; indeed, there are many areas where the operational research worker must strive for even faster results in order to keep pace with management's requirements. If the majority of projects cannot be slowed down for this reason, then there needs to be an increase in longer-range projects of a collaborative nature.

The suggestion of slowing down in both basic and applied research areas implies, in turn, problems of cost and sponsorship. In applied research, in so far as the outcome expected is an improvement to the particular organization, the extra cost ought to be met by the organization itself. If, however, there is not a very good and clearly seen chance that the study will in the long run repay the cost for the organization the cost ought to be met from basic research funds in some way. This brings us to the more general question of the contribution of the government agencies and research foundations towards research in and for organizations.

Research Foundations and Agencies. A good deal of the research reported in the contributed papers in this session is financed by research grants from government organizations or private foundations. In each case, however, the project is a fairly specific and self-contained piece of basic research. It would seem that we need similar financial support on a considerable scale for several other types of study, particularly those which would harness the research value in the large volume of applied research going on in different organizations. The search for material for this conference and book revealed a serious lack of documentation of industrial operational research. Apart from one inquiry by Ackoff, there is no evidence of any independent attempt to evaluate completed operational research studies, their implementation and results. One major study well worth undertaking immediately would be a joint evaluation of the work of operational research and social science in industry in, say, the past ten years, with an analysis of the methods used, the results obtained, and the relative effectiveness of different approaches. Such a study would provide a better basis for communication between operational researchers and social scientists working in industry and between both of them and industrial management. It would also provide a starting-point for more detailed collaborative programmes. Another type of basic research investment that could be extremely valuable would be the well-endowed establishment of applied research in each of two or three major organizations, in which the immediate aim is long-term benefit to the particular organization, but in which it is recognized that the main outcome is to be the general advancement of the field for the benefit of all. It might be reasonable for such an effort to be financed half from the organization itself and half from outside basic research funds. The demand for useful results for a real organization would provide the practical discipline, and the basic research responsibility would ensure that the maximum research value would be obtained from the work. If we recognize that many of the main advances in this kind of work must come from applied research in particular organizations, then we are surely bound to seek some such arrangement. Otherwise, the community at large depends on the generosity and long-range thinking of the managements of these organizations, not only to sponsor good applied research in the first place but also to cause much time and effort to be devoted to documenting it and extracting the basic research value. Those who have worked in industrial organizations know at first hand just how small is the percentage of this kind of work which is salvaged for the outside world.

This suggests in fact a further possible immediate basic research study; a look at all current programmes of basic management research, in relation to the study already mentioned of applied work going on in organizations, leading to recommendations for new forms of collaborative research which would link parts of the basic and applied research activities.

Managers, Other Professions, and Consultants. The theme of this book is operational research and the social sciences, and we have therefore concentrated on the interaction of these two groups doing research on and in organizations. This does not imply that the two groups have an exclusive interest in the way organizations are to develop. There are very many other professional groups which have an interest in such developments, if not from the research point of view at least from the development or operation viewpoint. To attempt to list them all here, let alone to discuss them, would be inappropriate. However, we must make a brief mention of the managers, and particularly the senior managers, in organizations. These are the men who indirectly support our basic research, directly sponsor applied research studies, decide whether to use the results of basic research, and decide whether to accept the recommendations of applied studies.

No one could read the collected papers given in this session – particularly those by Bennis, Churchman and Emery, Charnes and Stedry, Burns, and Ratoosh – without realizing how vital it is that the leaders in line management should take a very close interest in the work in this field. In any organization where there may be a social science group and an operational research group both dedicated to the task of improving the effectiveness of the organization in the broadest sense, it is clearly quite essential that there should be a continuous meeting of minds over principles and objectives – means and ends – between the groups concerned and the top management of the organization or the parts of the organization being studied at any time. Further, there would appear to be considerable benefits from a joint achievement of this close contact, because the interactions between these basic approaches – as so well described by Churchman and Emery – are likely to be at least as important as the results of the separate approaches themselves.

In spite of the efforts of the professional management organizations, many senior managers do not feel they have much time to spend on discussing or developing abstractions or broad concepts of management. Some of those that do may not think of bringing in to such discussions their operational research men, who are often regarded as somewhat narrow specialists, or even their social scientists (if they have any), who are probably regarded as rather woolly but well-meaning advisers on industrial relations. It may be that the initiative in this area needs to come from some of our most senior and experienced social science consultants – men respected in the basic research field and carrying sufficient independent status to persuade top management groups to start up this kind of discussion. Certainly, if this happens, the internal operational researchers and social scientists ought to welcome it as a breakthrough and co-operate in every possible way.

REFERENCES

1 W. G. Bennis (1962)
2 R. Scott (1962)
3 R. Scott (1965)

4 R. Likert (1961)
5 T. Burns & G. M. Stalker (1961)

Part III
Social Effects of Policies and their Measurement

SPONSOR: R. T. EDDISON

21 · Introduction and Commentary

R. T. EDDISON

The session on which this section is based was planned to concentrate on discussion. The authors were specially asked to write provocative documents which would provide ingredients for discussion rather than polished papers for publication; and they were told that no time would be allowed for them to present their papers. The session would start straight away in a series of discussion groups, each of which would be given a subject for discussion arising out of the material provided in the authors' papers. It is obvious that a prerequisite of success for such a plan was that a substantial number of the delegates should have read the papers before the session meetings. The need for this was demonstrated by an audience survey at one of the groups, in which only four out of sixty delegates admitted to more than a passing acquaintance with cost–benefit analysis. The authors were therefore asked to make their papers crisp and readable as well as provocative.

The authors' papers are published here, and the reader can see how well they played their part in this plan. Unfortunately, however, some delay in producing the material meant that delegates had very little time to sift and read. It was therefore found necessary to replan the session at the last moment, and it was decided to have only two discussion groups and to give them subjects of very wide generality. This explains the final character of this section.

Nevertheless, the two discussion groups did in fact provide lively meetings with discussion led by authors. But with only two groups to report on two rather innocuous subjects, there was little scope for argument at the plenary session, which was, however, enlivened by a brilliant short dissertation by the Chairman, Monsieur Lesourne. Considering the difficulties, the experiment of introducing topics for discussion rather than starting with the potted presentation of papers can be judged to have been remarkably successful.

The topics for the parallel discussion sessions were:
1 What are the conceptual and mensural limitations in cost–benefit analysis?
2 Can cost–benefit analysis aid acceptable public decision-making?

297

At the first of these sessions it seemed fairly clear that members were more worried about mensural limitations than conceptual ones. Even the inevitable suggestion that the title 'cost–benefit analysis' should be replaced by some other such as 'n-dimensional accounting' showed preoccupation with the mechanics of the subject rather than its objects. It is, of course, absolutely proper that anyone trying to sell new ideas should make quite sure that he has a valid article to sell before he sets about doing so. None the less, it is as true for marketing ideas as for marketing any other product that a technically perfect article which nobody will buy is of merely academic interest. If cost–benefit analysis is anything it is an effort to balance the pressures of narrow economic forces over the broad social field. It will get nowhere without broad social understanding. How many Ministers or Members of Parliament, let alone constituents, faced with a proposal for major social change would be persuaded by the argument that 'our n-dimensional accountants tell us that it must be so'?

The point was made that cost–benefit analysis is interested in choice, i.e. in the ranking of alternatives in sectors of the economy where allocation of resources is not decided in the market. It is impossible to operate in the context of the theoretically infinite number of possible alternatives between which to choose. The first problem is therefore to limit the number of alternatives, and this applies not only to the alternative practical outcomes but also to alternative bases of assessment; for example, as mentioned by Foster, there is a very large number of possible value systems – all democratic. It seemed to be accepted that in all these matters a decision function is required, first, to limit the alternatives and, second, to order the remaining ones rather than to attempt a cardinal evaluation of them.

There was considerable discussion on the problem of measuring preferences. No important variant was suggested on the standard principles of observing people's actual behaviour when faced with a choice and of asking their opinion about what they would do if . . . The hazards of assessing preferences between alternatives in relation to completely new projects where there is no existing behaviour to observe and where opinions must be purely imaginative were touched on but not resolved. They were also dealt with at the second discussion session. As a special case, the problem of measuring effectiveness of military systems was mentioned. The traffic problems described in Goldberg's paper provided specific examples; thus, in determining an assignment curve between underground and bus travel, it had been established that mass transport values showed a direct relationship linear with time, charges, and some comfort indices. But the assignment curve and generalized value function being dependent upon the population of users and the comfort of each different means of transport, a single assignment curve for all means was not feasible. The problem was still being studied.

Pruzan emphasized the difference between dealing with major step changes and with marginal changes. With major changes the transformation of one factor cannot be treated independently of the values of the other factors. There was considerable interest in his idea of an adaptive decision function, which led on to a general discussion of whether people behave rationally and whether in fact utility functions can be measured at all. A suggestion that Pruzan's views conflicted with Von Neumann's utility theorem was apparently settled out of court.

In the session discussing whether cost–benefit analysis can aid acceptable public decision-making, the emphasis of the discussion not unexpectedly lay on the mutual contributions which the social scientist and the operational research worker could make to the use of cost–benefit analysis for making better and more acceptable decisions in the public sector.

Lichfield, in opening the discussion, suggested three lines along which the group might approach an answer to the question. In the first instance a consideration of public decision-making reveals that it is unsatisfactory and badly needs constructive assistance: the public sector is increasing in most countries, and it is desirable that the people should see why certain decisions are made, if only to achieve more satisfactory public relations between public bodies and citizens. Second, the process of decision-making in the public sector, i.e. the political process, is distinct from the analysis of the costs and benefits of those decisions. Third, proper cost–benefit analysis can improve decision-making in a number of ways: it can force the consideration of alternatives and a more detailed analysis of objectives; it can direct decision-makers to think in terms of systems and so avoid the temptation to consider segments only. Since decisions in the public sector are not just efficiency decisions but are concerned also with the distribution of effects, it is difficult without cost–benefit analysis to discover the weight assigned to each group interest when decisions are reached. Cost–benefit analysis therefore exposes the value preferences of the decision-maker. Light can be thrown on political decisions by means of 'after the event' evaluation using cost–benefit, and can reveal that the cost of achieving some 'sacred cow' has been very great.

The point was made that public bodies already take into account the considerations to which the cost–benefit analyst draws attention and that they would welcome techniques that will improve the quantification of these values. As Mrs Thygesen emphasized, cost–benefit analysis should take into account all measureable consequences of the project.

Another speaker suggested that the imposition of the most rational decisions would be an undemocratic practice; but the distinction drawn between the analysis of the consequences of possible decisions and the decision process itself answers this objection to the use of the technique. Furthermore, it was mentioned that the questions the cost-analyst deals with are ones concerned with means not ends.

Public bodies are under instruction to act under certain constraints, and by implication they are not free to consider certain matters in their decision-making. Cost–benefit analysis encourages them to think in a wider context and to weigh a greater variety of factors before reaching conclusions. Town planners are perhaps the only people who try to find solutions in the total public interest. The technique will help public decision-makers really to act in the public interest, because at present public bodies tend to think only in terms of the public interest of the groups they serve.

A speaker suggested that the social scientist could contribute information to the analyst on what peoples' needs were. The social scientist could also help by throwing light on the level at which decisions on matters of public interest are actually made and the effects of various political forms on the decision-making process. Equally, cost–benefit analysis could clarify their goals for social scientists working with large organizations.

How one can determine the preferences of people in areas that they have not yet experienced was the next topic discussed. One solution suggested was to determine their preferences in related areas and then to extrapolate. Another solution to this difficulty was that the social scientist should simulate the novel experiences in the laboratory and then allow samples of the population to go through these experiences; as a result, it was thought, their preference ranking would be more reliable. One speaker suggested that forcing people to rank experiences which they had not actually experienced was not satisfactory; what cost–benefit analysts really needed to do their job were well-verified theories of human nature.

An objection similar to that which considers the technique undemocratic was raised, namely, that it replaces the party system and the private property system.

Lichfield, in answer to an earlier question, said cost–benefit analysis could help in the evaluation of various judicial procedures. The social scientist, he claimed, could be particularly helpful in determining preferences and in the devising of simulation techniques, as someone had suggested; cost–benefit analysis could show whether the ends chosen were realistic in relation to resources. Public bodies should calculate not only the financial returns to them of their activities but also their effects on the wider environment.

Another speaker suggested that the concentration of the discussion on the use of the technique for the weighing of the costs and benefits of alternative courses of action led to the neglect of another important use of the technique; namely, the direction of decision-makers towards the consideration of alternatives they had not perhaps previously considered. Reference was made to the two-way flow of communication between the analyst and the decision-makers. In one direction, communication would refer to the consequences of certain decisions and, presumably, to the possibility of considering alternative decisions including even those not originally put to the analyst; in the reverse direction information would be revealed on preferences and the compatibility between courses of action and their preference orderings.

The discussion can be summed up as follows:

1 Social science could assist by using simulation techniques to determine preferences when attempting to define social benefit in the case of particular projects.

2 The joint contribution by social scientists and operational researchers through cost–benefit analysis would have significant effects both on the decision-making process in public agencies and on the acceptability to the public of such decisions. The terms of reference of public agencies are frequently believed to preclude these agencies from considering the effects of their decisions on the wider environment. The suggestion was made that the public agencies should employ groups to investigate these wider effects by means of cost–benefit analysis.

3 The operational research contribution in the public sector decision-making process could have the effect of forcing the planners to consider the best selection from a large number of possible alternatives, and so would offer not only cost alternatives but also real choices to the public.

4 The distinction clearly emerged between, on the one hand, the act of decision in the public sector and, on the other, the need for the rational analysis of the alternatives from which choice could be made. It was felt that, regardless of the basis on which the decision itself is made, the use of cost–benefit analysis to identify alternatives has an intrinsic value.

In summing up the plenary session, Lesourne spoke of the need for understanding the meaning of information criteria. There was a danger of using cost–benefit analysis without knowing the meaning of the criteria and without understanding the limitations of the method. It was vital, for example, that research should be done on the relationship between social welfare functions and practical criteria such as present value analysis and the minimization of cost in money or time. Present value analysis could omit problems of uncertainty; and how, for example, did one treat the value of human life in minimizing cost? Such matters as these were a vital part of the social welfare function. Again, it was essential that complete micro-economic models be used to ensure that nothing is counted twice and that nothing is forgotten. Lesourne showed on a theoretical model how many hypotheses are necessary to give a meaning from the collective point of view, to the use, as indicator, of the profit of a given firm. Examples of complete models were quoted from studies in France into the oil industry, town development costs, waterways, health policies.

Research on criteria must start both from theory and from practical problems. Research teams must therefore include theoretical economists, but they must be linked with others; for example, engineers, architects, mathematicians, computer specialists, psychologists.

Lesourne saw cost–benefit analysis as a language rather than a calculus. It compelled people to formalize their thinking and was a valuable training for managers. In particular, it helped in selecting criteria, defining policy, and measuring and quantifying important variables. On the other hand, it had weaknesses; in particular, it had not, hitherto at least, paid attention to system stability or to the possibility of adaptation to change.

The discussions throughout this session showed that the problems faced by the cost–benefit analysts are very much the same as those so familiar in operational research. It could, of course, be that this was because the majority of the delegates were operational research people, and they used this session as a platform for raising their own pet hobby-horses. However, the reason undoubtedly goes much deeper than that. Earlier in this report it was remarked that participants at this session appeared more worried about mensural limitations of the subject than about conceptual ones; and this is not surprising, for clearly there are no conceptual limitations except in terms of what is practicable. Cost–benefit analysis has the objective of bringing into the balance all the ramifications of outcomes resulting from a decision or set of decisions. In other words, it sets out to look at total systems, just as does operational research. That it does so in specific areas – usually of public policy where many of the benefits accrue to people or bodies other than the decision-maker and where, moreover, such benefits are often more in the form of vaguely defined social welfare rather than hard cash – does not distinguish it from operational research.

In treating total systems there is perpetual conflict between the desire for ease of manipulation – by breaking down the problem into parts which are small and self-contained – and the risk that such parts may be so constrained that their solution merely produces sub-optima which are irrelevant to the total problem; above all, attempts to analyse problems into every ultimate component element and to study each separately can only lead to disaster. The second task is to establish meaningful measures of those components of the problem which it is necessary to measure.

The suggestion that cost–benefit analysis differs from economics in that the latter is interested in allocating scarce resources between competing ends so as to maximize profits, seems of doubtful validity. Pigou in *Economics of Welfare*[1] surely gives an excellent description of cost–benefit analysis. The main object of economic study, he says, is to help social improvement, and economic welfare may be defined roughly as that part of welfare that can be brought into relation with the measuring rod of money; economic causes that affect economic welfare in one way may affect total welfare in a different way.

Marginal social net product is defined by Pigou as the total net product of physical things or objective services due to the marginal increment of resources in any given use or place, no matter to whom any part of this product may accrue. The marginal increment due to some continuous type of project may, of course, be small; but the idea applies with generality to the significant changes of discontinuous types of projects. What higher aim can cost–benefit analysis seek?

To the writer, a more intriguing problem is the extent to which it is valid to apply cost–benefit analysis in any way to determine priorities for capital investment in circumstances in which some investment problems are being assessed by normal accounting methods. Unless all investments are assessed on the same basis, there seems serious risk of the priorities being put in the wrong order. Economic assessment of the proposed Victoria Tube line had consistently shown that such a line would not be profitable on normal accounting methods because the shillings taken from travellers using the line could never be expected to cover the operating costs. Cost–benefit analysis, on the other hand, showed that such a line would increase the total social welfare sufficiently to cover the costs; but one of the most important benefits arose to people who would never themselves use the new line but who would gain from the relief of congestion on existing lines from which the Victoria line travellers would be removed. It was a jest of fate to arrange for the Government to sanction the building of the Victoria line – using the evidence of this cost–benefit analysis – at almost the same moment that British Railways announced the closure of many of their existing lines – using rigid calculations that the lines did not individually take enough revenue in tickets to cover their own operating costs. Some evidence has since been adduced to suggest that cost–benefit analysis applied to some, at least, of the railway lines would have shown them to provide more in terms of social welfare than will the Victoria line. One is left with an uneasy suspicion that almost any investment in the public sector could be shown to yield some social benefit in excess of its economic cost; certainly the number that would do so must be very great indeed. It is surely vital that if the cost–benefit approach is to be used for the assessment of any such projects it should be used for all; otherwise the ranking of alternative investments will be seriously distorted.

Ways in which social scientists can contribute to the undertaking of cost–benefit studies were very clear in the discussions. The possibility that they could make particularly valuable contributions also to the presentation and implementation of the results was less in evidence. One of the problems of the present day is the extent to which individuals suffer loss or deprivation of one kind or another in the implementation of necessary schemes of social welfare. As a result, the promotion of such schemes frequently provokes battles of legal attrition which achieve little but expense and delay. What are the real reasons for objections in these cases and what are the motives of the objectors? Could cost–benefit analysis, openly presented, reduce this social problem and make planning decisions more readily acceptable while still democratic? These are questions which were largely left unanswered and could well merit study.

The lesson of this session in relation to the main theme of the conference must therefore be this. Cost–benefit analysis (and equally operational research) applied to problems involving human behaviour cannot expect to succeed unless it includes as members of the study team people who have insights into behavioural models; equally such people will not contribute their full capacity to the studies unless they identify themselves with the team, lose their professional identity, and immerse themselves in the total situation within which the behavioural model is applicable. In short, the skills of social science are an essential weapon in the armoury of operational research.

REFERENCE

1 A. C. Pigou (1920)

22 · Social Welfare Functions in Cost-Benefit Analysis

C. D. FOSTER

Income distribution in cost–benefit analysis

INTRODUCTION

Recently there has been rapidly growing interest in the use of cost–benefit analysis to make public expenditure more efficient. This has been associated, on the one hand, with an obvious need to use economic techniques to control the vast amounts spent on such things as defence, water-resource development, and transport, and on the other hand, with the final collapse of the aprioristic approach to welfare economics brought about by Little,[1] Samuelson,[2] Graaff,[3] and Braybrooke and Lindblom.[4] It is also relevant that cost–benefit analysis has been first and most developed in the United States, as one would expect because of the scale of public expenditure, the tradition of business efficiency, the relative lack of secrecy about the details of government operations, and the superiority and size of the economics profession there. Because of the general American belief in the value of free enterprise, government agencies using or supervising the use of cost–benefit analysis have used it to simulate the market economy. This has meant: (*a*) its use has been generally confined to situations where it is not *possible* for the market economy to work (rather than where on other grounds it might be felt not *desirable* for it to do so);* (*b*) where used, it has meant that they have tried to work out what would happen *if* the market economy did work. In principle, they have opted for what is described below as the Pigovian social welfare function.

---

* See the literature defining the scope of public expenditure, where the emphasis is always on public replacing private expenditure only where the market economy cannot work or would be markedly inefficient: e.g. Samuelson,[5] Colm,[6] Margolis.[7,8] That there is this negative attitude towards the inclusion of costs and benefits which would not normally be considered in the market economy is shown by the negative attitude of government agencies towards the treatment of secondary benefits. See Margolis.[8,p.284]

305

DEFINITION OF THE PIGOVIAN SOCIAL WELFARE FUNCTION

By a decision (or social welfare) function I mean one which, besides obeying the laws of logic, specifies what are to be accounted (i) the costs and (ii) the benefits relevant to the class of decisions it is intended to determine. (iii) It must also state what weight is to be given to the various costs and benefits listed under (i) and (ii). The best-known decision function is, of course, profit maximization where (i) are the financial outgoings, (ii) the financial receipts consequent on the decision, and (iii) every pound is given the same weight in reaching a decision. The one most generally found in cost–benefit analysis can be called the Pigovian social welfare function where (i), (ii) are stated to be all benefits and costs to whomsoever they accrue. As with profit maximization, (iii), every pound is given the same weight to whomsoever it accrues, whenever it accrues.* The Pigovian function, or 'dollar democracy' – as it has been called, since it gives an equal 'vote' to each dollar in coming to a decision – has even been enshrined, almost word for word, in an important law, the Congress Flood Control Act of 1936, which lays it down as the basis for project evaluation.

INCOME DISTRIBUTION IMPLICATIONS OF THE PIGOVIAN FUNCTION

Except in one respect, use of the Pigovian function implies acceptance of the income distribution that follows from its use. If one alternative will confer great benefits on a maharajah while another benefits large numbers of peasants, the logic of the Pigovian approach implies that one selects whichever has the higher present value irrespective of income distribution effects.

The exception is that there is usually thought to be a choice left open when there is a divergence between private and social benefits and costs.† Such divergences exist only because of imperfections in the market mechanism which mean that social costs cannot be recouped or social costs paid for. To take the stronger example first, suppose a project is justified if social benefits and costs are admitted but not otherwise. This implies a financial loss, and subsidization. The weaker case that often escapes notice is when the investment pays, but less than would be the case if financial criteria alone had been the basis for selection. Who is to stand the difference? Whatever the method chosen – price discrimination, voluntary levies, subventions from taxation, or

---

* It is reasonable to call this 'Pigovian' because the proposition that values should be represented by market prices, and that in that way the social welfare function should have cardinal properties, does broadly represent his position. (9, especially part 2) He does, however, discuss the possibility of modifying condition (iii) in the interest of a non-neutral rate of time preference. He also implies the possibility of modifying it to allow for diminishing marginal utility of income.

† It would in principle be possible to subordinate the problem of financing under the Pigovian function by selecting the method which was expected to maximize the Pigovian function.

some other – it will have effects on the distribution of income. This income distribution problem has been widely discussed in the literature.*

DECISION FUNCTIONS INCORPORATING OTHER INCOME-DISTRIBUTION CRITERIA

But to return to the more general problem: where the question is whether income distribution effects are to influence the choice of alternative rather than merely to arise as a problem of financing an alternative already chosen. Most writers on cost–benefit analysis have recognized that the income distribution that results from the use of the Pigovian function has no *a priori* validity; and that it is possible and sometimes politically desirable to modify the function so as to bias project selection in favour of some other income distribution.†

Marglin has pointed out that it is possible to incorporate income distribution effects into the decision-making process in three ways:‡

1 By assigning greater or less weights to some classes of benefits and costs. A decision function designed to bias decisions towards redistributing income to farmers might, for example, give *twice* the weight to benefits and costs accruing to them. A different kind of example would be a function which gave extra weight to, say, accident costs (and benefits) to whomsoever they accrued. Such a modification of the Pigovian condition (iii) would be workable if specific. The only extra data needed would be on the proportion of costs and benefits which fell into the categories of different weight.

Two income redistribution arguments in particular have a long history in economic literature. One is that a different weight should be given to the interests of future generations from that allotted to those of the present. It is often argued that we should be altruistic – giving greater weight to benefits and costs in the future. The simplest way of giving expression to this value judgement is to use some positive rate of time preference in cost–benefit calculations.§ Or, conversely, that we should give less weight to the future than to the present because our heirs will be richer than we are. The principle of

---

* There is an excellent discussion in Krutilla and Eckstein.[10, pp. 199–264] See also Beesley and Foster.[11]

† E.g. Renshaw,[12, Appx. A] Krutilla and Eckstein,[10, p.89] McKean,[13, pp.127–33] Hirshleifer *et al.*[14, pp. 75–7] Maass *et al.*[15, pp. 62–86]

‡ In Maass *et al.*[15, pp.62–86] The earliest general discussion of the first method is perhaps by Meade.[16, ch. 5, especially pp. 69, 70]

§ In a present value calculation one is normally discounting the future by some social opportunity cost rate, reflecting the return on alternative opportunities for investment. Say this rate is x per cent and the time preference rate selected is $+y$ per cent. The one discounts by $x - y$ per cent. If the rate of time preference is negative, then by $x + y$ per cent. However, there is no reason why time preference need be expressed in terms of a compound rate. It may be felt that the right shape is one reflected in a change in y over the life-time of the investment. See Feldstein.[17, pp.114,122] In the past the notion of time preference has been used – for example by Pigou[9, pp. 24–8] – to mean something other than a device for achieving a different distribution of income over time. Sen[18, sec.1] clarifies the conceptual difficulties.

diminishing marginal utility of income states that the richer someone is, the less he will value an increment to his wealth. Given economic growth, it implies giving less weight to benefits and costs of the future. The simplest way of expressing this is as a negative rate of time preference.

In a more general application the principle of diminishing marginal utility of income has a long history.* Most frequently it has been used as an argument for progressive taxation, but Pigou himself† conducts his argument in such a way as to suggest there might be a case for weighting any decision in the interests of greater equalization of income. Certainly the idea that one might use a decision function to redistribute income towards the poor man has become a commonplace of the literature, but how does one express diminishing marginal utility in such a way that it can be translated into a decision function? Though many people would agree generally with the proposition that the marginal utility of a pound declines as income or wealth increases, there is no consensus about the rate at which it declines. (Indeed, many would argue there are ranges of income over which the marginal utility of income increases.)

2 Marglin's second method is to maximize the net benefits of a favoured group or kind, with or without an efficiency constraint, in the interest of income redistribution. An example would be a decision function which laid down that the alternative should be chosen which maximized the net benefits to a stated minority – say old-age pensioners. The constraint might be that the total cost of the scheme should not be more than £x million or that it should break even financially. The disadvantage of this method follows from its logical form: there is no way of weighting the interest of the favoured group against that of other groups or the rest of society, once the constraint, if any, is satisfied. It is formally equivalent to an *absolute principle* in ethics which requires that one should do something, whatever the circumstances – or cost – (subject to any given constraint). And this is the kind of difficulty that this approach might cause. Suppose the decision function relates to a programme of public works and lays down, subject to some efficiency constraint, that the selected programme is to maximize net benefits to some class of people designated the 'poor'. Either the 'poor' are defined in such a way as to become a null class when all income rises above a certain amount (or the class does not become null, but its population changes because income is defined relatively). Or a certain class of people are favoured, in which case the function will go on maximizing their interests long after they have ceased in any real sense to be the 'poor'. Although it is always possible to avoid the last crudity by definition of the function, yet the fundamental limitation always exists in some form: that the interests of the 'poor', however defined, are not weighted against other interests.

3 Marglin's third method would maximize the Pigovian function subject to an income distribution constraint. An example would be maximization of

---

* See D. Hume.[19, sect. iii, pt. ii]   † Pigou.[9, pp. 89–97, 705–67]

the function subject to the constraint that no one should lose more than £*x* as a result of the decision. Or to give a transport example, the closure of unremunerative railways should be decided using the Pigovian function – taking all social costs and benefits that are practicable into account – subject to a constraint such as that all affected should still have access to some form of public transport. Just as the disadvantage of method 2 was that the income distribution function was to be maximized, perhaps subject to a constraint, whatever the cost, this method implies that the constraint is to be maintained whatever the cost. The danger of either procedure is that the function is persisted in without examination of the cost, resulting in waste – that is, the achievement of the income distribution effect at a cost, which if recognized, would be judged too great.

DEFENDING THE USE OF THE PIGOVIAN FUNCTION

But recommendations to use anything but the pure Pigovian social welfare function are conspicuous by their rarity. Writers on cost–benefit analysis have commonly used three defences of the ubiquity of the Pigovian function. (*a*) That the redistributive effects of any particular investment project are trivial and can therefore be ignored. 'Many persons would agree that the differential impact of alternative investments on the distribution of wealth is not a matter of great moment,' McKean writes.* (*b*) That any redistribution that society wants can be achieved through the budget.† (*c*) That by and large society approves of the income distribution achieved by the market mechanism and that the Pigovian SWF is society's choice. The evidence is that it adopts that SWF wherever possible.‡

The first argument – that the income distribution effects are trivial – must often be powerful, but can be weak. A programme of small changes such as British Railways' proposals to close some hundreds of miles of unremunerative branch lines, mostly in country areas, will have considerable impact in redistributing income away from country-dwellers as a class.§

The second argument – that redistribution can be effected through the budget – has force as a description of the method society uses to redistribute income.¶

* McKean.[13, p.132] The most detailed defence of adopting the Pigovian function is Krutilla's.[20] But he would seem to have fallen into an old trap. He puts forward the various defences, with some of their limitations, but ends by contrasting it with Marglin's method 1, which he calls 'frankly ascientific'. But they are no more or less ascientific than the Pigovian function itself. See also Fisher.[21]

† E.g. Hirshleifer *et al.*[14, pp. 75–7]

‡ E.g. Fisher,[21] Hirshleifer *et al.*,[14, pp. 75–7] McKean.[13, pp. 127–33]

§ British Railways Board.[22]

¶ It can also be argued that redistribution through the budget is not always administratively possible. Marglin.[15, p.63] Or one can turn an argument used by Buchanan and Tullock,[23, ch.6] Buchanan and Stubblebine,[24] and Turvey[25] on its head. This is that it is often impossible to compensate exactly through taxation for social costs and benefits. Conversely, one can argue the difficulty of distributing social costs and benefits through taxation in conformity with a given income distribution.

But as will be argued in the next section, its force is less real than apparent. The third argument – that the kind of income distribution achieved by the play of the market, subject to any redistribution achieved through the budget, is *in fact* socially acceptable – may seem the most plausible of all. One can only counter by flat denial that the existing distribution of income is generally agreed to be the best possible, or by producing evidence that this is not in fact a consensus or even a majority view.*

But one does not get evidence of the kind which might seem most promising. It is probably not the case that any SWF redistributing income by methods 1, 2, or 3 has been written into instructions to cost–benefit analysis, certainly not in the way the Pigovian SWF was written into the 1936 Flood Control Act. However, if we look at a different kind of evidence implied in legislation and other political policy-making – there is evidence of intention to achieve income distribution effects other than those implied by the Pigovian SWF, and by other means than the budget.

Political decision functions

POLITICAL DECISION-MAKING

That there is a problem of deciding what decision functions political decisions represent can be shown by an example. The opponents of British Railways' proposals to close down railways have frequently argued that the railways have used financial criteria when they ought to have considered the social costs (and presumably benefits) of closure. But would the opponents be satisfied by cost–benefit analysis on the basis of the Pigovian SWF? This would presumably take account of such benefits and costs as changes in congestion, in the cost of providing road services, in job opportunities, in the utilization of social overhead through migration, and in the subsidy bill paid to farmers and others through migration. But 'dollar democracy' would still be the yardstick. This probably would not satisfy many opponents who seem to be thinking, however nebulously, in terms of some other SWF. The Minister of Transport has the final say whether a closure recommended by the British Railways Board and the Transport Users Consultative Committee shall go through. When he states that he took all important social considerations into account, what does he mean – in terms of some approximation to a social welfare function?† It is likely we shall never know whether he has in mind an ideal which is formally equivalent to the Pigovian or some other function, but if we did know, cost–benefit analysis could be used to clarify the issues. Furthermore, the use of cost–benefit analysis is not just to find the best means of serving clear political ends. As many writers have pointed out, the interaction between ends and means is complicated in practice.‡ It is only in trying to reach a decision between alternatives that it is usually necessary

---

* Cf. Little,[1, p.114] Marglin in Maass *et al.*[15, p.63]
† Rt. Hon. Ernest Marples, M.P.[26] (then Minister of Transport).
‡ Myrdal.[27]

to come to a fairly precise notion of what the objectives of policy are. It is in the context of particular decisions that such ambiguous objectives as equality, full employment, security come to have more definite meaning. Similarly, it is only by trying to examine the consequences of achieving multiple objectives that incompatibilities are discovered. When a phrase like 'social factors' is used in such a context as that of railway closure it is not just a question of trying to discover what was in the official mind and give expression to that. It is also useful to put forward examples of social welfare functions operating in relevant decision situations, and to ask whether they at all conform to the notions forming in the official mind. The first question to ask in the particular case of railway closure is plainly whether it is a Pigovian SWF that is wanted or one with different income distribution consequences.

But at this point it is necessary to face up to arguments that in fact political decision-making seeks to maximize ends utterly different from those implied by the Pigovian function. The general failure to get cost–benefit analysis accepted by Congress is perhaps indirect evidence of this. In spite of lip-service to the Pigovian function as an approximation to the free market ideal, political decisions are determined by various practices lumped together as 'log-rolling'.* In particular, two rationalizations of political decision-making, formally equivalent to SWF, can be analysed, to make it possible to show the difference between them and the Pigovian function.†

VOTE MAXIMIZATION

One theory‡ is that political decision-making aims to maximize votes so as to stay in power. On certain restrictive assumptions this hypothesis would imply that the ruling party would have a programme which appealed to the majority, because if, even on one plank, it favoured a minority opinion, the opposition could steal its clothes, cleave to the majority in all things, and win power. Of course this analysis is grossly oversimplified, neglecting as it does party loyalty, the value of the party image, and the work of pressure groups *inter alia*. But it does indicate one of the salient facts about the policy of a government aiming to stay in power: a tendency for the majority to get its way. (In a more realistic analysis allowance must be made for other factors. Principally they affect the intensity of people's electoral loyalty. The chief concern of a vote-maximizing government would be to attract floating voters without losing too many supposedly intra-marginal voters. Downs's basic proposition is that it will direct public spending until the marginal vote gain equals the marginal vote loss.§) Should the cost–benefit analyst ever be asked to appraise

---

* That this is not necessarily to be taken as pejorative is insisted on by A. Bentley, *The Process of Government*, quoted by Buchanan and Tullock.[23, p.349]

† For a discussion on the relationship between political and economic decision making, see Dahl and Lindblom [28] *passim*.

‡ Downs.[29, passim] See also Peacock and Wiseman,[30, pp.12–4] Peacock in Peacock and Robertson.[31, p.3]

§ Downs.[29, pp.51–74]

a decision such as that to close down an unremunerative branch railway line on this basis, he certainly could do so. The decision function would be: (i) Benefits are defined to be votes gained. (ii) Costs are votes lost. (iii) Every vote is to count the same. But the problem would not be as simple as it might first appear. Even confining the problem to the vote-catching aspects of public expenditure, any additional revenue earned by a chosen alternative can be used to finance vote-catching public expenditure or tax remission elsewhere. Similarly, any additional costs curtail the Government's ability to win votes elsewhere. (In general, the proposition is that removing the drain on the public purse caused by subsidising unremunerative railway lines would make it possible to spend elsewhere, or remit taxation, in a way which would be more to the public's liking as measured by the votes they would cost). But of course this is not all. There will be other benefits and costs of the decision which will affect votes cast. And as Buchanan and Tullock have pointed out, the analysis would be complicated by the behaviour of minorities who could combine and 'trade' votes with each other. To use their example, if there are a hundred farmers, each with a hole in the road by his farm, there is no majority for repairing any hole first or indeed any hole in a society where the hundred farmers are in a minority. But if the farmers club together they may be able to do deals with other minority interests, each promising their votes to support the other.* Allowing for collusion between minorities, the general tendency of such a decision function would be inevitably, as Downs says, to redistribute income (benefits) from the rich. There is indeed empirical evidence that this is so. Lipset has pointed out that even right-wing governments have to move 'leftwards' because of their need for majority support.† (This does not mean that a vote-maximizing government would tend towards equalization of income. It would only redistribute from the rich while the rich remained a minority and the poor the majority. As soon as the poor became a minority – as perhaps today in the United States and Britain – the tendency would stop. In such a society one would expect the distribution to be heavily skewed – almost vertical at the upper end, but with a long tail towards the lower. The most important check on the expropriation of the rich would be the same argument that Bentham used against equality of income.‡ A higher rate of economic growth is possible if there is some inequality of income because of the incentive to saving and entrepreneurship.)

Although the vote-maximizing hypothesis does point up one of the salient features of democratic decision-making – the fact, for example, that railway lines are less likely to be closed in a marginal constituency than in one wholly committed to either party – it has two serious defects as an explanation of political decision-making. (*a*) It assumes a rationality both on the part of the vote-maximizing government and the self-interested elector which is hard to square with the facts.§ (*b*) As Dahl has shown, all voting systems apparently

* Buchanan and Tullock.(23, p.135H)   † Lipset.(32, p.281)
‡ Cf. Baumgardt.(33)   § Dahl,(34, pp.48–50) Simon.(35)

give equal weight to everyone *irrespective of strength of preference* on any issue.* Buchanan and Tullock, as we have seen, have made the suggestion that a system of trading could develop by which minorities 'sold' their votes on some issues (where they had low intensity) in exchange for votes on issues where their strength of preference was great. In such a way a voting-system would become a perfect analogue of the price-system – able to reflect strengths of preference. Quite apart from any other objection anyone might have, the fact is that this would require a highly developed market in votes – and exchange of information – which simply does not exist. But, on the other hand, to describe political decision-making as if intensities did not exert an influence is to ignore an important source of influence: the pressure groups which undoubtedly do affect decisions. And what is a pressure group but an organization of interests to exert more influence than the sum of their votes would? So the vote-maximizing hypothesis has limited explanatory value. Nevertheless, it could have normative significance and might figure in instructions to cost–benefit analysis. However, it is obvious that it would not; and the mere fact that there is not enough cynicism in politics for this to happen is itself a further indication of its limited explanatory value.

MAJORITY RULE

The other political decision function which has been analysed, particularly by Dahl,† is majority rule. Dahl uses the term populist democracy to describe a function which chooses between alternatives on the basis of the highest vote, subject to the constraint of political equality defined as one (adult) person, one vote. The difference between this and the Downs model is primarily that Downs was concerned with the actions of the Government to maintain its majority, while this is concerned with translating the votes of the majority into legislative and other policy decisions. This is more obviously prescriptive, rather than descriptive, since everyone knows that in practice there is not populist democracy. There are some obvious points to be made about it as an objective. It, too, would imply a redistribution away from the rich and other minority interests. Minority opinions would have zero effect unless they could coalesce with other minorities and become a majority. A different kind of problem is posed by geography. If one is thinking normatively decisions will depend on the population chosen, whose majority is to be decisive. To take the example of the unremunerative railway line, it would plainly make a difference if all national voters counted, or only the relevant local authority voters, or if a poll was taken of those whose interests were *affected* by the decision.‡

But the more fundamental objections are the same as to vote maximization. Were cost–benefit analysts given the comparatively easy task of conducting a referendum on such issues as railway closures, these would be decisions which would ignore efficiency and strength of preference. It is Marglin type 2

* Dahl.[34, pp.48–50]   † Dahl.[34, passim]   ‡ Dahl.[34, p.53]

with no efficiency constraint. Yet democracy has to, and in some sense wants to, take account of opportunity costs. And it is arguable that it wants to take some notice of strength of preference. As Dahl concludes, the 'final objection to populistic democracy is that it postulates only two goals to be maximized – political equality and popular sovereignty. Yet no one, except perhaps a fanatic, wishes to maximize two goals at the expense of all others.'* He offers another definition of democracy: 'Whenever policy choices are perceived to exist, the alternative selected and enforced as governmental policy is the alternative most preferred by members.'† The idea is that such a decision function would allow people to put their strengths of preference into the scales, but as Dahl admits, 'to make the first of these operational we must either ignore the problem of different intensities of preference among individuals or find ourselves so deep in a morass of obstacles to observation and comparison' that it would be impossible. And this is where those who have pursued the matter so far leave it. The difficulty of measuring strength or preference is well known. Many political scientists glance at the price mechanism, pointing out that, unlike political decision-making, it does reflect strength of preference. But the insuperable problem is, of course, that while it allows for strength of preference and opportunity costs, it does not allow for political equality. While the majority rule allows for political equality, it does not allow for strength of preference or opportunity cost.

Cost–benefit analysis can have a role in combining the advantages of each. In the next section I will develop a decision function which allows for equality, intensity, and cost – and which could have operational significance. There is a mine of great richness here, since cost–benefit analysis could make many decision functions significant – to protect minority interests *inter alia* – but it will be most useful in this preliminary article to go into one alone in some detail.

The democratic strength of preference function

DEMOCRATIC STRENGTH OF PREFERENCE SOCIAL WELFARE FUNCTION

The bare bones of the proposed function are straightforward. We assume that as far as conditions (i) and (ii) are concerned it is a Pigovian function: all costs and benefits are to be accounted to whomsoever they accrue. (This is made to simplify the argument, though both in practice and from principle there may be good reasons for limiting the scope of those to whom the accounted costs and benefits accrue.)‡

The critical condition is the third: (iii) all social benefits and costs – that is, all benefits and costs other than the financial receipts and outgoings of the scheme in question§ – are to be scaled down or up by the ratio of their income per head to the population mean (depending on whether theirs is

---

* Dahl.[34, p.50]   † Dahl.[34, p.64]
‡ This problem is discussed in Foster.[36, esp. 9.2]
§ This is an assumption. There are, of course, other possibilities.

above or below the population mean). We may imagine our case of an unremunerative railway line again. Suppose national income per head is £500, but the average income of those who stand to lose from closure is £250, then *condition* (iii) would imply that benefits and costs accruing to these should be given *double* weight; if £100, then *five* times the weight; if £1,000, then *half* the weight. It is easy to see in what kind of circumstances a closure which was allowed by the standard Pigovian function would be disallowed by this *democratic strength of preference function*. The basic principle is: give everyone potential equal weight in decision-making by compensating for differences in income, and yet allow weight to differences in strength of preference. So that, for example, someone who was prepared to pay £5 a week to keep the line out of an income of £1,000 would be reckoned as if he valued it as £130 a year. Someone who would only pay £1 out of an income of £500 or 10s. out of an income of £250 would be reckoned as if he valued it at £52 a year. Thus, it would be possible to combine something like the ideal of political equality enshrined in the democratic principle with Dahl's definition of democracy: 'Whenever policy choices are perceived to exist, the alternative selected and enforced as governmental policy, is the alternative *most preferred* by members.' And it also permits the costs to be incorporated in the same decision function. (This is discussed further below.)

Lest there should be misunderstanding, I am not proposing that this decision function should take over as a universal rule – that cost–benefit analysts should transfer allegiance from 'economics' to 'politics'. My aims are limited to (*a*) showing that there is an affinity between 'economic' and some 'political' decision functions; (*b*) suggesting that there are political decision functions which can be elucidated by the same techniques of cost–benefit analysis as have been used in water resource allocation, transport, etc.; (*c*) suggesting that there are perhaps some common, but loose, uses of 'social cost' and 'social benefit' which are more in sympathy with the kind of value judgements underlying the use of this function than the Pigovian. In particular, it might be socially acceptable for analysing such problems involving 'hardship' as the closure of unremunerative railway lines (though no doubt there are those who would want more weight to be given to hardship than is implied by this criterion).

There are problems of interpreting this decision function. Four are particularly important, and these are discussed in the following four sections.

DEFINITION OF EQUALITY

The description of the function given above proceeded as if everyone's preferences were to be weighted by his income. But one might want to modify this.

1 By simulating more closely the usual democratic process and, so to speak, excluding minors and some others from the vote. But the old theory that heads of family *represent* minors and women in casting their vote would have more meaning in this context – since the value placed by any member of the family on *x* would be taken into account before weighting by the family

income. (So that if one member valued the railway line at £a, another at £b, the family valuation would be £a plus £b irrespective of which members of the family set the value, and whether it was set by them or for them.) Nevertheless, who is to be given a 'vote' in this process must be a political decision.

2 So far we have spoken as if the members of the family were to have their preferences summed and then adjusted as the total family income scaled up or down to the average income. But the notion of political equality can have another sense – particularly because there is no correlation between size of family and of income. Instead, we might take the mean income as weighted by the size of the average family. Let us suppose it is *three* persons, and again the mean income £500. Then the valuation for purposes of calculation, of a five-person family earning £600 a year in aggregate and valuing our unremunerative railway line at £125 a year to them, would be:

$$£125 \times \frac{5}{3} \times \frac{500}{600} = £174 \text{ approximately}$$

Again there is no *a priori* reason for preferring one interpretation of democracy. (There may be other exclusions of people from the 'family' for the purpose of calculation, e.g. permanent invalids in state homes or hospitals and criminals.)

3 There are also alternative definitions of mean income per head or per family. (i) The first problem arises over time. Presumably the sensible procedure is to take a view and predict the likely rise in mean income per head or per family over the life of the investment (or other decision). (ii) The virtue of taking *national* income per head, or per family, as the yardstick, is that it has a certain intuitive appeal. It means assessing the poor or the old-age pensioners as if they were as well off as the average man. There may be three sorts of reason for using another yardstick. The first is discussed in the next subsection. The second is that on occasions one may – perhaps when it is a local decision or the finance is local – wish to use the local mean income per head. (Because of our scanty knowledge of regional incomes, this would hardly be practicable at present.) The effect would be that there would be no tendency towards equality between regions. The third point raises a host of other value judgements. It might be decided that old-age pensioners, invalids, and even perhaps the structurally unemployed should be assessed as if they had the mean income (or perhaps the mean income of their kind of person, employed, in the prime of life), but that other inequalities – as for example between people with different jobs – should be ignored, on the ground that these cannot be represented as hardship but as reflections of lack of ability. If the decision function were modified in this direction it would become a compromise between an 'economic' and a 'political' one.

FINANCING PROBLEMS

If a democratic strength of preference function is used in which costs are given the same weight as income-adjusted benefits this makes some concession to 'efficiency', since it is only if there is a surplus of net benefits, so defined, over costs that positive present values will be yielded at the discount rate employed. Yet the use of this criterion will imply financing problems in the sense of subsection 1 above. There will be more of a financial loss or less of a financial surplus than there would be using the equivalent Pigovian function. To take the extreme case, if the democratic strength of preference function were used for all public expenditure decisions there would be a heavy deficit to be financed by taxation. This is no more than to say that this decision function, like vote maximization and majority rule, would have a redistributive effect. Although the decision to subsidize certain classes in this way would have to be a political one, there are two techniques which could be used. A budget constraint could be imposed. This is a standard technique of cost–benefit analysis.* Or the weight given to net benefits could be scaled down by a factor, with the same effect.

INCOME ELASTICITY

So far we have argued as if the scaling up or down to the mean income per head should take no account of income elasticity of demand. This is plausible. It can be argued that we are not trying to discover what x would spend if he had the mean income of y, but just to weight his actual choices by that income. For example, it might be the case that a rich man living in the catchment area of an unremunerative railway line spends less than a poorer man on rail travel; his income elasticity for rail travel would have the opposite effect from that intended. On the other hand, it can be argued that if an old-age pensioner in that catchment area had the mean income he would spend more than the average income-earner on using the railway line – because he probably could not drive a car. Therefore his income elasticity of demand for rail travel would be high. And it might be argued that it is this one would want to allow for. This would imply considerable problems of measurement. On what basis of observation or conjecture would one establish the income elasticity? Yet another suggestion is that one should look for the income elasticity of demand for transport as a whole; but this very obviously raises difficulties of commodity classifications. There is no right answer to the problem of choosing an appropriate definition of elasticity of income. The problem needs much fuller discussion.

PROBLEMS OF MEASUREMENT

The additional information required to make the democratic strength of preference function operationally meaningful would depend on the answers given to the problems raised above. But it should be remembered that one does not necessarily need perfect information. A useful decision function might be constructed which used nothing more than the census information giving proportions in each social class in the relevant local authority areas (or

* See P. O. Steiner.[37]

enumeration groups) and relating these to income levels. Although there are notorious difficulties in getting an exact measure of income by these means, we must be careful what we are comparing our imperfect function with. Despite its faults, it might be more illuminating and politically or socially acceptable in certain circumstances than the Pigovian function. It might be possible to refine it in certain instances by collecting social class information about those directly affected by the decision instead of the area in general. It might even be possible to get some direct information about incomes, though this would run into difficulties on the score of privacy.

One would measure benefits and costs before scaling in any of the usual ways: by asking what people would be prepared to pay, or preferably, using indirect evidence of the willingness to pay by observing choices they actually make. A last point. It is very common at present to use average values in estimating certain classes of costs and benefits, e.g. in the valuation of time. This is because we can do no better. But in so far as these values are meant to be national averages, one could rationalize their use by appeal to some decision function as the democratic strength of preference function: a valuation of these benefits as if those who receive them place on them the valuation of those with the mean income per head.

REFERENCES

1 I. M. D. Little (1950)
2 P. A. Samuelson (1950)
3 J. de V. Graaff (1957)
4 D. Braybrooke & C. D. Lindblom (1962)
5 P. A. Samuelson (1954)
6 G. Colm (1956)
7 J. Margolis (1955)
8 J. Margolis (1957)
9 A. C. Pigou (1920)
10 J. V. Krutilla & O. Eckstein (1958)
11 M. E. Beesley & C. D. Foster (1965)
12 E. F. Renshaw (1957)
13 R. N. McKean (1958)
14 J. Hirshleifer, J. C. De Haven & J. W. Millman (1960)
15 A. Maass, M. M. Hufschmidt, R. Dorfman, H. A. Thomas, S. A. Marglin & G. M. Fair (1962)
16 J. E. Meade (1954)
17 M. S. Feldstein (1964)
18 A. K. Sen (1951)
19 D. Hume (1957)
20 J. V. Krutilla (1961)
21 F. M. Fisher (1956)
22 British Railways Board (1963)
23 J. M. Buchanan & G. Tullock (1962)
24 J. M. Buchanan & W. C. Stubblebine (1962)
25 R. Turvey (1963)
26 E. Marples (1964)
27 G. Myrdal (1958)
28 R. A. Dahl & C. E. Lindblom (1953)
29 A. Downs (1957)
30 A. T. Peacock & J. Wiseman (1961)
31 A. T. Peacock & D. J. Robertson (1963)
32 S. M. Lipset (1959)
33 D. Baumgardt (1952)
34 R. A. Dahl (1956)
35 H. A. Simon (1947)
36 C. D. Foster (1963)
37 P. O. Steiner (1959)

23 · Is Cost–Benefit Analysis Consistent with the Maximization of Expected Utility?

PETER MARK PRUZAN

Introduction

This paper is an extension of work carried out by Dr J. T. Ross Jackson and myself.[1]

The operational research worker is often confronted with the problem of recommending a course of action which will optimize a utility function expressing the preferences of the decision-makers responsible for a system. Optimizing a system thus compels the operational research worker to consider the objectives associated with components of the system, objectives which may be in apparent conflict with each other, and which may be expressed in different units. Furthermore, even the sub-systems may be characterized by multi-goal objectives, and thus by measures of performance which are expressed in different units. For example, in determining the relative desirability of road investments, a decision-maker may be motivated by considerations of damage due to accidents, time-savings for commercial and private vehicles, personal injuries, travel comfort, maintenance and traffic control costs, capital outlay, and very likely many more.

Cost–benefit analysis is frequently employed to aid decision-making in such situations by reducing a multi-goal-system problem to a problem of choosing that alternative course of action whose possible outcomes, transformed into cost–benefit units, maximize the decision-maker's expected utility. *If* such a reduction of a multi-goal system to a single goal system can be achieved by transforming all performance measures into equivalent cost–benefit units, and *if* some function of the resulting expected transformed costs and benefits is an adequate measure of the expected utility of the various alternatives, then cost–benefit analysis can determine the best alternative consistent with the goal of maximizing the decision-maker's expected utility.

However, we cannot always reduce multi-goal systems to single-goal systems by the conversion of all performance measures into one measure if we are to act consistently with the maximization of expected utility. Furthermore,

M   319

even if such transformations can be found as are consistent with the maximization of the expected utility, a function of the accumulated expected transformed costs and benefits will seldom provide a measure of the expected utility associated with each alternative; if it does, the decision-maker's utility space has certain very special characteristics which most decision-makers would not be willing to accept as representative of their goals.

The nature of the decision-making problem in a multi-goal system

We introduce the notion of a vector $(x_1, x_2, \ldots x_m)$ as representing the state of a system, where each element of the vector represents some measure of a particular state variable, x_i, $i = 1, 2, \ldots m$. We assume that with each state there can be associated a unique value, or utility, $v = u(x_1, x_2, \ldots x_m)$ and that a change in any of the state variables can result in a change in utility to the 'individual' whose $(m + 1)$-dimensional utility space, $(x_1, x_2, \ldots x_m, v)$, is in question. 'Individual' here might refer to a single person, or perhaps to a group of people involved in the decision, such as the managers of the various sub-systems belonging to the overall system to be optimized.

We assume that when a decision-maker must choose between several available courses of action, and a set of state variables is considered as representing the outcome of a course of action, he will choose that action which maximizes his expected utility. That is, if the jth course of action, c_j, yields an outcome state $(x_1, x_2, \ldots x_m)$ with probability $dF_j(x_1, x_2, \ldots x_m)$ the decision-maker acts so as to maximize

$$\iint \ldots \int_{R_m} u(x_1, x_2, \ldots x_m) dF_j(x_1, x_2, \ldots x_m) \text{ over all } j = 1, 2, \ldots n,$$

where R_m is an m-dimensional metric space. Only under certain conditions will cost–benefit analysis be consistent with the maximization of expected utility.

We will begin by considering the simple case of only two relevant state variables, and extend the results to m variables at a later stage. We introduce the following notions which occur frequently throughout the development.

(a) (x_0, y_0) represents the initial state of the system.
(b) The courses of action available are $c_1, c_2, \ldots c_j, \ldots c_n$.
(c) To the jth course of action there is associated a joint probability density function $dF_j(x, y)$ which gives the probability that a course of action c_j will have the result that the state changes from (x_0, y_0) to (x, y). That is, $dF_j(x, y) = Pr\{(x, y)|(x_0, y_0), c_j\}$.
(d) To each state (x, y) there can be assigned a relative value or utility $v = u(x, y)$. To define the scale of v, we assign some arbitrary value to the

present state (x_0, y_0) and some other arbitrary value to another state, say (x_1, y_1).

(e) We will consider the following three spaces (see *Figure 1*): vy space, vx space, yx space.

Figure 1

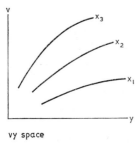

vy space   vx space

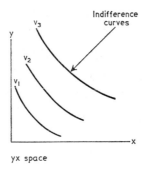

yx space

(f) It is assumed that for any of these surfaces, we can develop the unique inverse function of $v = u(x, y)$

(i) $y = Y(x, v)$ (ii) $x = X(y, v)$.

(g) We define the term 'vertically parallel' in the following way:

(i) In vy space: V.P. $vy \rightarrow \dfrac{\partial v}{\partial y} = h_1(y)$

(ii) In vx space: V.P. $vx \rightarrow \dfrac{\partial v}{\partial x} = h_2(x)$

(iii) In yx space: V.P. $yx \rightarrow \dfrac{\partial v}{\partial x} = h_3(x)$

That is, two parametric curves are V.P. if the envelopes of their tangents have equal slopes. For example, in yx space the indifference curves are vertically parallel if they are as shown in *Figure 2*:

Figure 2

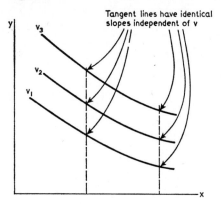

Horizontal parallelism is an identical notion in the horizontal direction. That is,

$$\text{V.P. } vy \rightarrow \text{H.P. } yv$$
$$\text{V.P. } vx \rightarrow \text{H.P. } xv$$
$$\text{V.P. } yx \rightarrow \text{H.P. } xy$$

(h) We define a trade-off function ξ as follows (see *Figure 3*): Given any α, define $\xi = Y(x - \alpha, v) - Y(x, v) = f(\alpha, x, v)$, where α and ξ can be either positive or negative. Clearly, if $\alpha = 0$, then $\xi = 0$ and $f(0, x, v) = 0$.

Figure 3

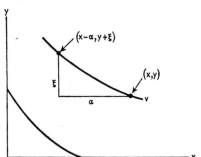

Associated with the notion of the trade-off function ξ is the notion of sliding along a particular indifference curve from a state (x, y) to a new state $(x - \alpha, y + \xi)$. The trade-off function then tells us how many additional units of y the decision-maker requires in order to remain on a particular indifference curve if he is to give up α units of x.

We define a special form of trade-off function, the 'complete trade-off function', as $\xi_c = f(x - x_0, x, v) = g(x_0, x, v)$. This function specifies the amount ξ_c of y which the decision-maker requires to keep him on the same indifference curve if we take $\alpha = x - x_0$, that is, if we are to slide from the state (x, y) to the state $(x_0, y + \xi_c)$.

Clearly, when $x = x_0$, $g(x_0, x, v) = 0$. (See *Figure 4*.)

Figure 4

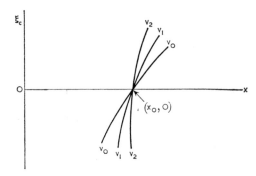

(*i*) We define a 'utility line' to be a particular cut through the initial state (x_0, y_0). The utility line $u(x_0, y)$ represents the intersection of the utility surface $u(x, y)$ and the plane $x = x_0$. Similarly, the utility line $u(x, y_0)$ represents the line formed by the intersection of the utility surface $u(x, y)$ with the plane $y = y_0$.

Necessary and sufficient conditions for cost–benefit analysis to be consistent with the maximization of expected utility

THE USE OF TRANSFORMS TO REDUCE ALL MEASURES OF PERFORM-
ANCE TO COST–BENEFIT UNITS

If the functional form of the utility surface were known over the entire range of possible outcome states (x, y) the computation and selection of the optimal course of action would be routine. To obtain this surface $v = u(x, y)$, the decision-maker would be required to specify a relative value to each possible outcome state. Ideally, the operational research worker might attempt to help the decision-maker to construct such a surface through a series of questions constructed so as to elicit his value structure. For example, he might help the decision-maker to generate his indifference curves by judiciously choosing intervals of x and y and then forming iso-value curves via some sort of best-fit procedure.

However, the construction of the utility surface would require the decision-maker to place himself in many hypothetical outcome states of which he may have had little or no past experience. The conception of such states could be quite difficult for him. It would seem to be a logical statement that the further an outcome state (x, y) is from his initial state (x_0, y_0), the less certain would he be of its relative value; within a certain domain of outcome states near (x_0, y_0), we might expect his estimates to reflect his true relative values fairly well.

The difficulty is that, as yet, there does not exist a proven methodology for generating a utility space, even within a well-defined region of the initial state (x_0, y_0). However, extensive work has been done in the area of generating 'utility lines' for operational problems.[2] We shall show that under certain conditions the utility lines can be used to generate the entire utility surface. In such situations the transforms used to express all measures of performance in cost–benefit units will be identical with the complete trade-off functions ξ_c and the transformation process will be consistent with the maximization of expected utility. Before obtaining these results, it will be necessary to develop a series of theorems. Owing to space considerations, the proofs of all theorems have been omitted from this paper.

Theorem I. A necessary and sufficient condition for the complete trade-off function $\xi_c = g(x_0, x, v)$ to be of the form $\xi_c = h(x_0, x)$ independent of v, is:

$$u(x, y) = u[x_0, y + h(x_0, x)]$$

where $u(x_0, y)$ is the utility line for outcome y.

Corollary I

$$\xi_c = h(x_0, x) \Rightarrow \begin{cases} (1) \text{ V.P. } yx \\ (2) \text{ H.P. } vy \end{cases}$$

Theorem II. If $u(x, y)$ is such that the indifference curves are vertically parallel, then there exists a unique transform between the units of the state variable x and the units of the state variable y, independent of y, and given by

$$\xi_c = h(x_0, x)$$

or equivalently

$$\text{V.P. } yx \Rightarrow \xi_c = h(x_0, x)$$

Interpretation of Theorems I and II: If we are willing to make the assumption of vertically parallel indifference curves, then we can transform any outcome state (x, y) to a state $(x_0, y + \xi_c)$ having the same value (i.e. lying on the same indifference curve) but in a plane such that we know the utility line $u(x_0, y)$. We can then generate the entire utility space, which will be of the form

$$u(x, y) = u(x_0, y + h(x_0, x))$$

Conversely, if we postulate that we can transform the units of state variable x into the units of state variable y by a transform function $\xi_c = h(x_0, x)$ we are implying that the utility surface is of a special form, namely, having the properties of V.P. yx and H.P. vy. In other words, a necessary and sufficient condition for transforming units of x into units of y, so that we act in accord with the goal of maximizing expected utility, is that the indifference curves shall be vertically parallel.

The implications of the existence of such a transform, which does not depend on the state variable y, is that the state variable x is important to the decision-maker only because it can be converted directly into units of state variable y. If the importance of x is dependent on the level of y, or if, as will be shown later, the decision-maker does implicitly or explicitly value x with respect to other state variables in the system, then the indifference curves cannot be V.P. yx and the unique transform of x into units of y cannot be made.

Illustration. Suppose that the decision-maker is a highway commission analysing various proposals for improving traffic control on an existing road which, owing to its inadequate capacity and many intersections, often causes traffic delays during rush hours. We define

x = time-savings for private vehicles (in hours per year)
y = traffic control costs (in dollars per year)

Then the existence of a complete trade-off function ξ_c (same for all levels of y) implies that the time-savings are of importance only in so far as they can be considered as costs. In many cases this could be true, particularly in a region not too far removed from (x_0, y_0). If, however, the value the commission assigns to an increase in time-savings is dependent upon the level of traffic control costs (perhaps owing to possible political reactions), or if it values an increase in time-savings because it affects the expected number of personal injuries or travel comfort, or because it may bring more traffic to an economically depressed region, or if it bears some relationship to any other component of what we might abstractly refer to as the commission's entire value space, then the indifference curves will not be parallel and no such transformation will exist. This is not to say that there is no relation between time-savings and traffic control. In fact, if sufficient data are available such a relationship can often be established statistically.[3] The importance of the foregoing theorems is that such a relationship is equivalent to ξ_c only when the indifference curves are vertically parallel.

Interpretation of parallelism in m-dimensional value space

In general, we may consider a decision-maker as having a value space consisting of state variables $x_1, x_2, \ldots x_m, y$, where y is used to signify some important measure, usually in units of money (e.g. profits, costs, etc.). We can extend Theorem I to the case of m dimensions as follows:

Theorem III. A necessary and sufficient condition for the existence of a set of complete trade-off functions (or transform functions)

$$\xi_{jc} = Y(x_1, \ldots x_{j0}, \ldots x_m, v) - Y(x_1, \ldots x_j, \ldots x_m, v) =$$
$$h_j(x_{j0}, x_j), j = 1,2, \ldots m,$$

is:
$$v = u(x_1, \ldots x_m, y) = u\left(x_{10}, \ldots x_{m0}, y + \sum_{j=1}^{m} h_j(x_{j0}, x_j)\right)$$

where x_{j0} is the initial value of state variable $x_j, j = 1,2, \ldots m$, and $u(x_{10}, \ldots x_{m0}, y)$ is the utility line for y developed for all other state variables held at their initial values. Similarly, by analogy to the earlier corollary and theorem in three-dimensional $(x, y, u(xy))$ space, we state the following:

Corollary I

$$\xi_{jc} = h_j(x_{j0}, x_j), j = 1, \ldots m \Rightarrow \begin{cases} (1) \text{ V.P. } yx_j, j = 1, \ldots m \\ (2) \text{ H.P. } vy \end{cases}$$

Theorem IV

$$\text{V.P. } yx_i \Rightarrow \xi_{ic} = h_i(x_{i0}, x_i), i = 1,2, \ldots m$$

Summary of Theorems I–IV

We have now developed the necessary theoretical concepts to generate the entire $(m + 2)$-dimensional $(x_1, \ldots x_m, y, v)$ utility space under the assumption of V.P. yx_i, which enables us to transform each outcome state variable into equivalent units of state variable y (usually measured in units of money). The method of generation is simply to replace y in its utility line function by

$$y + \sum_{i=1}^{m} h_i(x_{i0}, x_i)$$

The expected utility of the jth course of action is thus

$$E(v) = \iint_{R_{m+1}} \cdots \int u\left(x_{10}, \ldots, x_{m0}, y + \sum_{i=1}^{m} h_i(x_{i0}, x_i)\right) dF_j(x_1, \ldots x_m, y)$$

In other words, a necessary and sufficient condition for being able to transform each outcome state variable into its equivalent cost–benefit units so that this phase of cost–benefit analysis is consistent with the criterion of choosing that alternative which maximizes expected utility is that the utility space should have the property V.P. yx_i.

TOTAL EXPECTED UTILITY OF AN ALTERNATIVE AS THE SUM OF INDEPENDENT CONTRIBUTIONS

The usual procedure in cost–benefit analysis, after the transformation of the various performance measures into cost–benefit units, is the determination of the relative desirability of alternatives. It is usually assumed that the contribution of each transformed performance measure is described by a function which is independent of the levels of all other measures. The simplest example of such a method is the use of constant weights to represent the relative contribution of each transformed measure. This is the form of linear value functions such as are used in linear-programming problems (where the transforms are constants often considered to be prices and costs, and the weights representing the relative contribution of each transformed measure are unity) and in return on investment calculations (where the total time-adjusted net cash flow is the measure of utility and where the total expected transformed cash flows for each time period are time-adjusted, with the time-adjustment factors for each period being the weights). In order to discuss the necessary and sufficient conditions for such a procedure to be consistent with the goal of choosing the alternative which maximizes expected utility, we introduce the notion of vertical parallelism in the vx_i space, $i = 1, 2, \ldots m$ (see *Figure 5*).

Figure 5

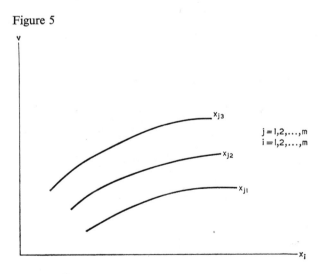

V.P. $vx_i \Rightarrow \dfrac{\partial v}{\partial x_i} = c_i(x_i)$, where $c_i(x_i)$ is a function of x_i only.

Since this must hold for all values of the state variables, it holds for the case when all other state variables take on the initial conditions. Thus

$$c_i(x_i) = \frac{\partial}{\partial x_i} u(x_{10}, \ldots x_i, \ldots x_{m0})$$

where $u(x_{10}, \ldots x_i, \ldots x_{m0})$ is the utility line for x_i generated with the decision-maker's other state variables held constant at their initial values.

Theorem V. A necessary and sufficient condition for V.P. vx_i, $i = 1, 2, \ldots m$, is that the utility surface shall be

$$u(x_1, \ldots x_m) = v_0 + \sum_{i=1}^{m} M_i(x_i)$$

where $M_i(x_i)$ is the marginal utility of x_i and is given by

$$M_i(x_i) = u(x_{10}, \ldots x_i, \ldots x_{m0}) - v_0$$

$$i = 1, 2, \ldots m, \quad v_0 = u(x_{10}, \ldots x_{m0})$$

Comments on Theorem V. The V.P. vx_i condition might be described as a 'separability' or 'independence' condition where the value contributed by each state variable depends in no way upon the levels of other state variables. It is difficult to conceive of such a relation holding over the entire utility space. However, it may give a good approximation within a decision domain near the initial state $(x_{10}, \ldots x_{m0})$. If we assume the V.P. vx_i condition, then the calculation of expected utility is greatly simplified, for we no longer require joint probability density functions, as with V.P. yx_i conditions, but need only the marginal probability density functions $dF_i(x_i)$. That is, for a given course of action

$$E(v) = v_0 + \iint \ldots \int_{R_m} \sum_{i=1}^{m} M_i(x_i) dF_i(x_1, \ldots x_m)$$

$$= v_0 + \sum_{i=1}^{m} \int_{R_i} M_i(x_i) dF_i(x_i)$$

The implications of the 'independence' assumption when the contributions are functions of transformed performance measures

It is interesting to note the effect of assuming vertical parallelism in both yx space and vx space, or, equivalently, assuming both the one-to-one transformation functions and the 'independence' of state variables. It turns out that both assumptions combined imply a linear utility curve in y.

In fact, an even weaker condition, namely V.P. vy, when combined with V.P. yx_i, $i = 1, \ldots m$ implies V.P. vx_i, hence 'independence'. Therefore V.P. yx_i and V.P. vy combined imply a linear utility curve in y.

Theorem VI. The combined properties of V.P. yx_i, $i = 1,2, \ldots m$ and V.P. vy are necessary and sufficient for a utility surface to be of the form

$$v = v_0 + k_1(y - y_0) + k_1 \sum_{i=1}^{m} h_i(x_{i0}, x_i)$$

where k_1 is a constant and $h_i(x_{i0}, x_i)$ is the complete trade-off function for x_i implied by V.P. yx_i.

Corollary I. The combined properties of V.P. yx_i, $i = 1,2, \ldots m$, and V.P. vy are necessary and sufficient for 'independence' as defined by V.P. vx_i, $i = 1,2, \ldots m$.

Corollary II. Under combined properties of Theorem VI, the utility v is just the sum of initial state value v_0, and the marginal utilities of y and of x_i, which in this case are identical with the complete trade-off functions ξ_{ic}, $i = 1,2, \ldots m$.

Comments on Theorem VI. From the point of view of value theory, applying the assumptions of Theorem VI results in a degeneracy. Under the assumptions of this theorem, if we for the moment assume that y represents profit, then we maximize expected utility by maximizing expected profit, taking into account that we transform all other state variables into their equivalent profit. This is the same as saying that we assume that the decision-maker's utility line for profit is linear. Since in typical cost–benefit analyses, performance measures are transformed into equivalent monetary units, and then functions of expectations of the transformed measures are added to obtain the relative utility of the alternative considered, an implicit assumption in such analyses therefore is that the decision-maker's utility for money (cost–benefit) is linear! Certainly in many situations where cost–benefit analysis is employed the operational research worker and the decision-maker would not be willing to accept this assumption. If they use cost–benefit analysis in such situations they implicitly make this assumption, and thus act in opposition to the goal of choosing that alternative which maximises expected utility.

CONCLUSION

We can now formally state, in terms of the definitions given on p. 321, the implicit assumptions we are making about the nature of the utility space when we follow the standard procedures of cost–benefit analysis; namely, we assume vertical parallelism of all indifference curves, vertical parallelism in all vx_i spaces, and horizontal and vertical parallelism (hence linearity) in vy space. If these assumptions are not justified, then cost–benefit analysis is inconsistent with the goal of maximizing the decision-maker's expected utility.

An illustration of the relevance of the preceding theorems to practical decision-making

The following illustration is based upon an investment analysis of an expressway north of Copenhagen, Denmark.[4,5] Let $a(n)$ be the expected income from time n to $n + 1$ which results from an investment, and let $b(n)$ be the corresponding expected costs, with $a(n) - b(n)$ a non-decreasing function of n. Let C be the total capital outlay during the construction period of length T time units, r be the desired social rate of return, and $F(t)$ the total net present value of the project evaluated at time 0 if construction starts at time t and thus is completed at time $t + T$. Then,

$$F(t) = \sum_{n=t+T+1}^{\infty} \frac{a(n) - b(n)}{(1 + r)^n} - \frac{C}{(1 + r)^{t+T}}$$

and thus

$$F(t) - F(t + 1) = \frac{a(t + T + 1) - b(t + T + 1) - rC}{(1 + r)^{t+T+1}}$$

It can be shown that if $F(t) - F(t + 1) < 0$, then the project should not be undertaken, while if $F(t) - F(t + 1) \geq 0$, then the investment is desirable. By this method a decision as to the desirability of an investment can be made without having to forecast the effects of the investment farther than $t + T + 1$ time units into the future.

The problem arises how to take non-economic consequences into consideration when determining $a(n)$ and $b(n)$. In their paper[4] the authors considered, aside from the capital outlay, C, the following costs and benefits:

Public maintenance, tariff control (money units)
Private maintenance savings (money units)
Damage due to accidents (money units)
Time-savings for commercial vehicles (money units)
Petrol consumption (money units)
Time-savings for private vehicles (hours)
Decrease in personal injuries (fatal injuries, severe injuries, slight injuries)
Increased travel comfort (no specifically defined units)

Figures for those performance measures with monetary units were available; not available were the value of a private car hour, the value of a decrease in injuries and deaths, the value per trip of added comfort of travelling on the expressway. We may now refer to the theorems and observations of the previous section of this paper and conclude the following:

(a) If it were assumed that the non-monetary performance measures could be transformed into monetary units by simply multiplying these measures by constants having the units kroner per hour saved, kroner per personal injury, kroner per added comfort of travelling on the expressway, then the implicit assumption would be that there exists vertical parallelism in yx_i space; that is, the complete trade-off functions are of the form

$$\xi_{jc} = h_j(x_{j0}, x_j), j = 1, \ldots, m$$

(b) If these transforms were assumed to exist, then since $F(t)$ and $F(t + 1)$ the measures of the relative desirability of starting construction at times t and $t + 1$ are sums of the functions of the transformed measures, with each function independent of the level of all other measures, the functions being the time-adjustment factors $1/(1 + r)^n$, according to Theorem V an implicit assumption underlying the analysis would be that there exists vertical parallelism in vx_i spaces, $i = 1, \ldots m$. Furthermore, and more easy to grasp, it is seen from Theorem VI that an implicit assumption would be that the decision-maker's utility line for money is linear. (Presumably the decision-maker is a commission attempting to describe the utility space of the overall economy through their choice of factors to consider as costs and benefits, and the weights they would assign to these factors.) It is doubtful whether, when considering questions of the public welfare, particularly when subject to budgetary and political constraints and interactions, the decision-makers would agree to the hypothesis that their utility line for money is linear. Yet, were they to carry out a cost–benefit analysis like that described above, this would be an implicit assumption. Thus, cost–benefit analysis could lead to results which would be inconsistent with the desire to maximize the public welfare.

It should be noted that in the paper discussed the authors did not attempt to transform the non-monetary units into monetary units, and no attempt was made to determine such nebulous concepts as the value of human life or the value of increased comfort. Rather it was intended to develop a computational scheme which could decrease the length of the horizon to be considered. According to the authors, 'the method does not provide an answer to the more fundamental objection that measurements in money terms inadequately reflect the true benefits and costs of public investments'.[4] From Theorems I–IV such measurements in money terms will adequately reflect the true benefits and costs only if there exists vertical parallelism in yx_i space, $i = 1, \ldots m$.

A suggested procedure for determining whether the assumptions of transforms and independence of utilities are consistent with decision-making designed to maximize expected utility

The motivation behind this section is to show how, using the theorems presented earlier, the operational research worker may determine whether the usual assumptions underlying cost–benefit analysis are appropriate if it is desired to maximize expected utility.

In the discussion that follows, we restrict ourselves to the case where the decision-maker's value space is assumed to be adequately described by two state variables, x and y, and the corresponding surface $v = (x, y)$.*

By considering only two state variables, the presentation is simplified and we can take advantage of graphic demonstrations. Many of the results can be extended into a general n-dimensional state space, but this is beyond the scope of this section.

The assumption is made that it is difficult for the decision-maker to describe his feeling about relative values, trade-offs, etc., when he is removed from his present state, described by x_0, y_0, and $v_0 = u(x_0, y_0)$. Therefore, we attempt to develop a procedure for eliciting information about the actual utility space by continually allowing the decision-maker to refer to at least one of x_0, y_0, or v_0.

(i) DETERMINE THE APPROPRIATENESS OF AN ASSUMPTION OF THE EXISTENCE OF TRANSFORMS

It is clear from the theorems that if there exists V.P. yx, then there exists a unique complete trade-off function which can be used to translate units of x into units of y, independent of the actual magnitude of the state variable y (or y into units of x in the case of the V.P. xy).

Thus, if such transformations are considered as proper the value space describable by $x, y, u(x, y)$ can be equally described by $x, y', u(x_0, y')$, where $y' = y + h(x_0, x)$, which is far easier to generate than the former space. This becomes all the more true when the number of state variables increases. The following steps are suggested to determine the appropriateness of the assumption of parallelism in yx space, and thus the appropriateness of the existence of the transforms:

(a) Generate the indifference curve v_0 which passes through (x_0, y_0). This can be done by presenting the decision-maker with a series of different states

Figure 6

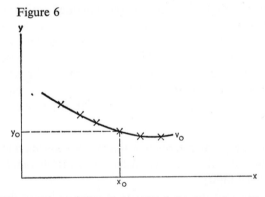

* To select relevant state variables, the partial derivatives of v with respect to these variables must be different from zero. That is, if x, y and $u(x, y)$ are sufficient to describe the value space over some reasonable decision domain, the decision-maker considers that

$$\frac{\partial u}{\partial z}(x, y, z) = 0$$

for any other state variable z.

of x and asking him to select the corresponding states of y which would permit him to be indifferent between remaining at (x_0, y_0), a state having the same value, v_0, to him (see *Figure 6*).

(b) Hold x at x_0 and generate $u(x_0, y)$ by some suitable method. Assume a value for v_0, say v_0 equals 100, and assume a value for some other state (x_0, y_1), say v_1 equals 200. This is sufficient uniquely to define a scale of relative values for the utility line $u(x_0, y)$ (see *Figure 7*).

Figure 7

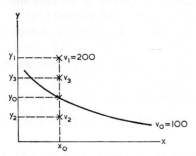
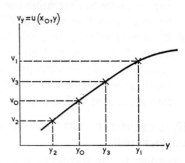

(c) Holding y at y_0, determine the states (x, y_0) which correspond to the same relative value as the points (x_0, y_1), (x_0, y_2). . . . . These points can be

Figure 8

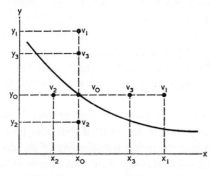

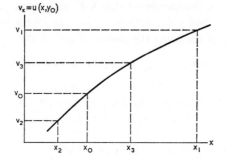

obtained by asking the decision-maker what value of x_1 he would require to be indifferent between being at the state (x_0, y_1) and the state (x_1, y_0), etc. This permits determination of $u(x_1, y_0)$, etc., and thus $v_x = u(x, y_0)$ (see *Figure 8*).

(d) Check for parallelism in yx space. This can be done by sliding the indifference curve for v_0 upward and downward and seeing how well it passes through iso-value points. If it passes through these points reasonably well we can assume V.P. yx. (Similarly, we check for H.P. yx — V.P. xy.) In order to determine the 'goodness of fit' various procedures might be used, including the 'eyeball' method, or more sophisticated tests.

(e) If yx parallelism exists, this implies that there exists a unique complete trade-off function, and all that is required for decision-making that is consistent with the objective of maximizing expected utility exists in the form of the complete trade-off function ξ_c, the joint probability distribution associated with a course of action, and the utility line $v_y = u(x_0, y)$.

(ii) DETERMINE THE APPROPRIATENESS OF THE INDEPENDENCE ASSUMPTION

According to the theorems, if there exists V.P. vx, then the assumption of independence of utilities is justified. The following steps are suggested to determine the appropriateness of this assumption:

(f) From (i) we have developed both $u(x_0, y)$ and $u(x, y_0)$, the so-called utility lines. Furthermore, these curves are appropriately scaled with respect to each other via steps (b, c). We now develop an analytic expression for each of these curves, perhaps in terms of polynomials, etc.

(g) Assuming the property of independence, we then derive the mathematical form of the indifference curve with v equal v_0. That is, we solve analytically or numerically for the values of x and y which will be such that $v_x + v_y$ equal v_0.

(h) Compare this plot of y versus x with that graph of y versus x obtained in step a (see *Figure 6*). It will be recalled that that plot of the indifference curve v_0 was obtained via direct questioning of the decision-maker.

(i) If, on the basis of some statistical or other form of test procedure, it is concluded that the agreement between these curves is sufficient to allow the assumption of independence (i.e. V.P. vx_i), then, given the marginal distribution of x and y for action c_N, we can immediately calculate the expected utility of choosing the course of action as

$$E(v) = \int_{R_x} v_x dF_N(x) + \int_{R_y} v_y dG_N(y)$$

where R_x and R_y represent the decision domains for x and y and where $dF_N(x)$ and $dG_N(y)$ represent the marginal density functions of x and y respectively with the Nth course of action, c_N, and where v_x and v_y are the utility lines established from steps b and c.

(iii) DETERMINE THE APPROPRIATENESS OF THE ASSUMPTION THAT
THERE EXIST TRANSFORMS AND THAT THE UTILITIES ARE 'IN-
DEPENDENT' OR 'SEPARABLE'

The assumption that there exist transforms and that the total expected utility can be determined as the sum of 'separable' functions of the resulting expected transformed costs and benefits is justified, according to Theorem VI, if, and only if, the decision-maker's utility line for money is linear. Thus, if the cost–benefit analysis uses both these assumptions we may be able to determine the appropriateness of the analysis without following steps (i) and (ii). We may forgo the checks as to whether each of the individual assumptions hold, and check whether both hold simultaneously by determining whether the decision-maker's utility line for money is linear. Since extensive work has been done in the area of generating utility lines, we will not discuss here a procedure for validating or invalidating the proposition that both assumptions are justified.

(iv) IF NEITHER THE ASSUMPTION OF TRANSFORMATIONS NOR THE
ASSUMPTION OF INDEPENDENCE IS ACCEPTABLE

If neither of the assumptions appears at first to be acceptable by the test criteria, then the usual assumptions required for cost–benefit analysis will be inconsistent with the goal of maximizing expected utility, owing to the nature of the utility space. In such situations the decision-maker and the operational research worker must generate the value space $v = u(x, y)$, either by placing the decision-maker in a large number of hypothetical situations (i.e. states) and then attempting to assign relative values to each such state or else by modifying the surface that would be generated under either assumption until it is acceptable to the decision-maker.

REFERENCES

1 P. M. Pruzan & J. T. R. Jackson (1963)
2 R. L. Ackoff (1962b) Chapter 3
3 R. L. Ackoff (1962b), pp. 78–80
4 A. Jensen & I. Thygesen (1963)
5 I. Thygesen, this volume, pp. 357–64

24 · Cost–Benefit Analysis in Town Planning

Possibilities and Problems

NATHANIEL LICHFIELD

Role of cost–benefit analysis in planning

'Economics is the science which studies human behaviour as a relationship between ends and scarce means which have alternative uses.'[1] The economist is therefore concerned to devise methods of analysis for indicating that course of action among alternatives, including the situation where one course is to do nothing at all, which will make the best use of scarce resources in the sense of deriving the maximum social welfare from them. This is the purpose of cost–benefit analysis. The term can be equated with operational research or systems analysis, in that all seek 'to estimate the cost of sacrifice and the gains or achievement that each course of action implies'.[2] While it can be applied to any proposed action which involves inputs and outputs, including in the home or private sector of the economy, the term tends to be restricted to the analysis for investment in the public sector, where particular problems arise. For example, the benefits are not often exchanged in the market, and therefore their valuation must be based on other than market prices, and the rate of return on the investment, even where calculable, cannot be equated with market returns. Therefore some methodology must be devised if choice is to be based on an evaluation of comparative costs and benefits of alternatives.

From a slow start in the field of U.S. water resource investment,[3] there have been of recent years rapid advances in attempts at application to an ever-widening field, including highways, transportation, defence, education, public health, municipal services, urban renewal, and regional resource development.[4] The writer takes the view that the analysis can be adapted with profit in the field of town and regional planning.[5]

The logic of applying cost–benefit analysis in the field of public investment is fairly apparent, for a public agency should be just as concerned as a private agency in 'efficiency', using this term to indicate that use of resources which shows the optimum return of benefits for the cost of resources which are employed. But the logic is perhaps not so apparent in town and regional planning, and some justification is therefore called for. In brief, the argument is this. In any geographical area where economic and social forces are producing change a host of independent agencies, both private and public, will make decisions to invest in housing, factories, roads, shops, open space, civic buildings, etc. Even if each individual decision were of itself efficient in the sense used above, experience has shown that the consequences, in the form, shape, appearance, functioning, and general efficiency of our towns and settlements, leave much to be desired. Some form of town and regional planning is thus necessary. In economic terms the shortcomings can be ascribed to the inadequacies of the land market which, it can be shown, cannot work sufficiently smoothly, works hardly at all in the public sector, and, above all, takes account only of private and not social costs and benefits.[6] Thus, the object of the planning is to remedy the market inadequacies by setting out a framework within which the individual decisions can be influenced so that the resultant whole is 'superior' in form, shape, etc., to what would otherwise have occurred. This 'supra-investment framework' is the town or regional plan. But while the need for the planning is accepted, and techniques of planning are now reaching some maturity, there is no accepted method for evaluating a plan to ensure that it produces a better use of resources than the unfettered combination of individual decisions, or to show which of two plans is the superior in this respect. Now, although the planning agency is not producing a direct service for consumption or production, just because the plan is a supra-investment framework, cost–benefit analysis is an appropriate and relevant methodology, if suitably adapted, for aiding rational decisions on alternative plans.

Three case studies

To demonstrate the contribution of cost–benefit analysis in this situation, reference is now made to three published case studies. These do not cover the whole content of a town or regional plan, but only restricted redevelopment projects within it. The aim is to devise the methodology of analysis which can then be extended to the plan as a whole. Actual problems were studied, and the conclusions that were reached show that the decision-makers would be in a better position to make their judgement with the analysis than without it.

STUDY NO. 1. ALTERNATIVE TRAFFIC PROPOSALS FOR A TOWN CENTRE[7]

The first study applies the analysis to road-traffic proposals, but it is of interest in this connexion because it widens the application of conventional highway cost–benefit analysis in the direction of the fuller analysis required in planning. To this end it measures as benefits not simply the savings to motorists (in operating costs, time, accidents), but instead the quality of the layout both for its use by motorists (accessibility) and for its potential impact on the environment. This combined quality is expressed in a portmanteau index of 'environmental accessibility', which was measured by a points system with suggested weightings for a predetermined check-list of performance standards.

The study relates to three alternative plans for the centre of the small town of Newbury, England. To test the expected traffic conditions in the year 2010, various possible layouts were designed, of which three were selected for comparative study. In the first, A, only modest road proposals were made which would not cater for all the traffic need. In the second, B, and third, C, full traffic needs were met, but by minimum redevelopment in B and partial redevelopment in C. The schemes, therefore, involved varying costs for road and redevelopment and varying benefits in terms of vehicle accessibility and impact on the environment.

The costs were measured in pounds sterling and the benefits by the 'environmental accessibility' index. Although costs and benefits were not in common terms, it was possible to compare the schemes by a ratio of benefit to cost, and of incremental benefit to cost, and to draw conclusions as to which gave the best value (in terms of environmental accessibility) for money cost. This use of the analysis made it possible to draw conclusions on three alternative schemes where there were three competing variables.

STUDY NO. 2. PRESERVATION OR DEMOLITION OF A HISTORIC BUILD-ING [8]

In this study the analysis is applied to an ubiquitous problem in town planning, in which the benefit, the preservation of a historic building, is very elusive of measurement.

The Old Mint is the popular name for a former United States Branch Mint within the Central Business District of San Francisco, California. Built in 1869–74 in connexion with the Californian gold- and silver-mining boom, its mint operations ceased in 1937. It has earned fame and the right to preservation not only for its historic associations but also for being a fine representative of the Federal Group Revival style of the period. But it was none the less threatened with demolition, for its original use having disappeared, there is no appropriate alternative contemporary use, and it occupies a potentially valuable site in a central location. The ubiquitous problem thus arose: should this building be preserved for its historic/architectural associations, by reconditioning for use by a Government Department and access to the public, or be demolished for its site value? While this problem often involves buildings in private ownership, and thus a balance of public and private interest, in this case the Federal Government was the owner and had to decide between its two responsibilities: to current and future generations as custodian of the national heritage and as a property owner on behalf of the national taxpayer.

Taking the latter object first, conventional real-estate analysis showed that the Federal Government as owner, and therefore the taxpayer, would benefit financially from demolition rather than retention to the extent of $2,200,000. This clearly posed the question: was the value of the Old Mint in the American heritage worth $2,200,000 to the American taxpayers? Such a question sharpened the issue, but still left the Government with a very difficult, if not uncommon kind of, value judgement.

Cost–benefit analysis helped in this instance by tracing through the difference in costs and benefits, from the alternative courses of action, which would fall on sections of the community in addition to the national heritage and national taxpayer. These other sections were the government department which would use the Old Mint if retained, occupiers of the new building on the site if it were demolished, nearby business proprietors, nearby and more remote property owners, the city's municipal revenues and costs, and the city economy generally. From an analysis of all these costs and benefits it became clear that, while the federal taxpayer would lose financially by retention, the wider community would have a net economic advantage, which could be obtained with a smaller investment of real resources. The Federal Government's decision in the public interest clearly lay therefore in the direction of retention.

STUDY NO. 3. VALUE OF AN URBAN PARK TO THE COMMUNITY[9]

The third study tackled a similar problem to the second, for it dealt with another kind of asset in which the value is elusive of measurement – a city park. But the problem was more complex, for three reasons. The asset was not already owned by a public agency, but had to be created through redevelopment; the park was part of a larger scheme for redevelopment; and three alternatives were involved.

The Golden Gateway Urban Renewal Project comprised 45 acres of downtown San Francisco, near the financial–administrative centre. As designed in 1959, the plan included a 3-acre park to be provided by the city, in addition to commercial and residential and urban freeway proposals. But, some thought, the park would be too expensive: about $2,700,000 in initial costs and $50,000 per annum to maintain, without benefit of any direct tax revenue. A much clearer course for the city was either to redevelop the park instead for offices, for which a demand existed, and so earn a greater net rental and tax income; or to leave the 3-acre site in its current blighted condition, and so save redevelopment costs and retain tax income. The question thus arose: was the benefit to the city from the park worth the extra cost?

Cost–benefit analysis helped in this instance in the following way. It traced through the repercussions of costs and benefits of the alternatives on to the various sections of the community in addition to the city (as provider of the park) and the immediate beneficiaries of the park – i.e. through organized use, unorganized use, and general amenity enhancement. These sections included the Federal Government Redevelopment Agency and Municipal Railway, who were also concerned with the redevelopment, landowners and occupiers who would be displaced, landowners on the site, developers and occupiers of the new buildings in the project, city municipal revenues and expenses. This number of parties and the need to consider three alternatives concurrently made the problem somewhat complex, and only a rigorous form of analysis permitted of its clarification.

From this analysis of the wider costs and benefits falling on the community and the incidence, it was seen that the comparative net costs of providing the park were smaller and the net benefits greater than appeared when considering only the position of the city and the park users. This would make easier a decision in favour of the park.

Some problems in application

These studies, if not their over-brief summary, have brought out some of the technical problems to be surmounted before cost–benefit analysis can be used with ease and confidence in town and regional planning. The problems fall into two classes: those common to the use of the analysis generally, and those particular to the application in this particular field. Each class is considered in turn.

GENERAL PROBLEMS OF METHODOLOGY

Some of the main problems are:

1 *Measurement of benefits.* Whereas on the cost side it is rarely difficult to measure the value of the input of resources, on the benefit side it is rarely easy to value the output. This arises not just because the product so rarely has a market price, which is the main *raison d'être* for the analysis, but also because, in its absence, no standardized method of measurement can be found for publicly provided services, and several different approaches seem required.[10]

2 *Prices.* Where a method of measurement seeks to simulate or estimate market prices, there often arises the difficulty of forecasting the effect of the supply of the service in question on the current or historical price level simply because the supply is so often in comparatively large quantities (e.g. irrigation in a desert area).[11]

3 *Discount rate.* Since the timing of the investment or yield of benefit in alternative projects is often not the same, it is necessary to discount to present worth to make a true comparison. But in the absence of market data, the appropriate rate of discount needs to be selected by the analyst, and this has given rise to many excursions into theory.[12]

4 *With and without.* The true product of an investment is not necessarily what it yields, but the difference between the yield 'with and without' the investment. For example, benefits from savings in road accidents resulting from a new road should exclude benefits which will be simply due to higher standards of vehicle-driving. This necessitates forecasts and projections of what would occur in the 'without' situation, which are often more difficult than the estimate of the yield from the investment itself.

5 *Criteria for choice*. The object of the analysis is to compare the relation between input and output. The comparison requires adoption of a criterion (such as ratio of benefits to costs), and it has been shown that of the apparently possible criteria, each might give a different ranking of projects, particularly when there is also introduced the consideration of constraints on any of the input resources in question. The adoption of the correct criterion is therefore vital.[13]

6 *Social choice*. Where a public body provides the goods or service in question out of the rates and taxes, it does not have the benefit of guidance from individual consumer demand as to what should be produced. It must therefore exercise 'social choice' on behalf of the public, frame objectives on behalf of the public, and make decisions which achieve them. While this is necessary even where cost–benefit analysis is not used as an aid to choice, the use of the analysis stimulates rational social choice, and this is a very difficult art indeed.[14]

METHODOLOGY PROBLEMS PARTICULAR TO TOWN AND REGIONAL PLANNING

In cost–benefit analysis applied to town and regional planning there are not only the general problems just indicated but also particular complexities that stem from the nature of the process described earlier. Some of these are:[15]

7 *Total costs and total benefits*. Since the plan provides a framework for the services from all private and public investment, all costs and benefits to the community and not only those arising from the production of a particular service must be considered. To exemplify, the impact of a new road on the users of lands and buildings adjoining the road must be reckoned with as well as the direct service of the road to motorists.

8 *Systems not projects*. Since the plan covers a defined geographical area and looks, say, twenty to thirty years ahead, it is necessary to consider all projects within that area and over that period of time. The plan thus becomes a series of interdependent projects, in space and time, and, moreover, of projects which may be as varied as schools, shopping, and housing. These should not be considered in isolation, but as a system.[16]

9 *Non-measurables are always present*. Since the total costs and benefits must be considered, and many are as yet unmeasurable, it is inevitable that many items, particularly benefits, can be expressed only in qualitative and not quantitative terms. Since any omission of the qualitative items would distort the analysis, the conclusions cannot be as definite as when all costs and benefits are measured, and particularly in money terms.

10 *Equity as well as efficiency*. A planning decision must have regard not only to efficiency but also to equity, that is incidence of costs and benefits. The

analysis must therefore consider not only real costs and benefits, that is resources that are used and wealth created, but also shifts in costs and benefits, such as losses in land value which are compensated by gains elsewhere.

11 *Interdependence of planning areas.* In general, planning areas are sub-units of a larger area, such as the town in a region, the region in a country, the country in a continent. Thus, costs incurred or benefits derived in one area could be at the expense of other areas, as where a new shopping centre in town X will reduce the utilization of an existing shopping centre in town Y. Furthermore, people in their use of services do not pay tidy regard to planning areas, which are chosen often enough for administrative conveniences. It follows that the judgement on a particular analysis could well be different depending upon the definition of area from which the decision-makers are viewing the problem.

Limitations on usefulness of cost–benefit analysis

There is thus some considerable distance to go before cost–benefit analysis can be used in everyday practice in town and country planning. But even were this stage reached now, there are some who would doubt its usefulness in any form. In conclusion, three of their major arguments will now be mentioned, with critical comment.

1 First come those who fear the limitations implied in the term 'economic' when applied to an analysis to guide decisions in a field which embraces more than the economic – that is social, spiritual, aesthetic, etc, considerations. The fears are of two kinds. First, why should the analysis be economic and not, say, sociological or architectural? And, second, is not the term 'economic' too narrow, in implying a concern only with those costs and benefits which can be measured in money terms, and sometimes even more narrowly in market prices?

On the first point, the reply would be that whatever else there is in planning, a very large element is the provision of the supra-investment framework mentioned earlier, and this, having to do with scarce resources, requires an economic-type analysis. This does not answer all questions, so that other types of analysis would be required in addition.[17] On the second point, I would agree that to confine the analysis to what can currently be encompassed within 'the measuring rod of money' is to invite continuing scepticism on the contribution from economics. The content and objectives of town and regional planning demand that a certain range of considerations should be brought in to the balance sheet of decision, and they must be brought in even though currently non-measurable. This view is strengthened by the conviction that great advances in measurement will yet be made, and there is no difficulty about applying economic reasoning to costs and benefits which have no money content at all. A good cost–

benefit case study can be made on the best use of leisure time on a Sunday afternoon, where the competing ends are sleep, gardening, a walk in the country, or tea with an aunt.

2 But even among the economists who see no difficulty in this last point, there are some who see economics only as a positive and not as a normative science, and who doubt whether economists can define welfare criteria that of themselves can be used to decide whether certain courses of action are desirable for society. The theory behind these competing views lies in the complex controversies on welfare economics which in modern times have raged since the thirties and are still unresolved.

But even if economics cannot define the appropriate function, so that the value judgements by the decision-makers are still necessary, the usefulness of the cost–benefit analysis itself is not undermined, for it is an analysis designed to assist in the value judgement itself. This was the view of Krutilla,[18] following a review of welfare economics literature in its bearing on cost–benefit analysis. His conclusion was that since the alternative to offering recommendations to government is 'not to retire into inactivity but rather to reach decisions in the absence of analysis, we may take some comfort from the belief that thinking systematically about problems and basing decisions on such analysis are likely to produce consequences superior to those that would result from purely random behaviour'.

3 Coming to the third category of doubters, even those who are prepared to recommend government intervention in the public interest might doubt the potential of cost–benefit analysis, in that they think that decisions by government are based not so much on the rational evaluation of costs and benefits as on other processes.[19] For example, decisions might be based on the political process, that is one which is in accord with a particular political philosophy, or perhaps which will do most to ensure the return to power of the ruling party at the next election. Or they might reflect the competing weights of current pressure groups, so that the compromise solution emerges which is likely to arouse the minimum opposition. Or they might be idealists, being influenced not so much by the public's own evaluation of the benefits likely to arise from a decision as by the government's view on how people ought to value the benefits. In all these examples it is hardly necessary, so the argument would run, to have a rational rigorous analysis, for the decision will not be rational in this sense, and the analysis could be an embarrassment for decisions taken on other grounds.

This source of doubt is the more difficult to quell, since it stems from the certain knowledge that governments do not act rationally any more than individuals do, and may never do so. But if greater rationality rather than less is the aim, and surely it must be in a world which will never be free from scarce resources, then analysis has its role whatever the model of decision-making that is pursued. At the worst it will help to improve those innumerable lower-level decisions which are made free from politics or from pressure groups, and in which rationality is thus clearly acceptable. At the best it will, even by *post hoc* illumination of what the decision should have been, limit the freedom of those in power to take decisions which clearly diverge from the public interest.

'You can fool some of the people some of the time . . .'

REFERENCES

1 L. Robbins (1935), p. 16
2 R. N. McKean (1963)
3 O. Eckstein (1958)
4 H. Mohring & M. Harwitz (1962)
   M. Clawson (1959)
   B. Weisbrod (1961)
   C. J. Hitch & R. N. McKean (1960)
   C. P. Wibberley (1959)
   C. D. Foster (1963)
   C. D. Foster & M. E. Beesley (1963)
   J. Vaizey (1962)
   A. T. Peacock & D. J. Robertson (1963)
   O. Eckstein (1961)
   R. N. McKean (1958)
   H. G. Schaller (1963)
5 N. Lichfield (1956)
   N. Lichfield (1959)
   N. Lichfield (1960)
   N. Lichfield (1964)

6 N. Lichfield Undated, pp. 101–5
7 Ministry of Transport (1963), appendix 2
8 N. Lichfield (1962), pp. 13–19
9 N. Lichfield (1962), pp. 20 et seq.
10 C. W. Churchman & P. Ratoosh (1959)
11 R. N. McKean (1958), pp. 168–82
12 O. Eckstein (1958), pp. 81–104, for example
13 R. N. McKean (1958), pp. 103–27
14 J. Rothenberg (1961)
15 N. Lichfield (1960)
16 T. Kuhn (1962), pp. 92–123
17 N. Lichfield (1964)
18 J. V. Krutilla (1961)
   T. W. Hutchinson (1964)
19 M. Meyerson & E. C. Banfield (1955)

25 · A Comparison of
Transport Plans for a Linear City

S. GOLDBERG

Introduction

Cost–benefit analysis has been applied to transport problems with the main purpose of comparing alternative plans for a single mode of transport. However, planning in big cities is primarily concerned with a sound allocation of investments between individual and mass transport. Even if we assume that every urban dweller has a car and would like to use it rather than any other means of transport, the scarcity of space in city centres imposes physical restraints upon such free use of individually owned vehicles. It entails increasing costs of operation which cause a shift in the demand for various transport facilities. Furthermore, the choice that rests upon public authorities is not only determined by transport needs.

Decisions are too complex to be made on a purely rational basis. Simplified models, however, can greatly clarify the problem. Such a model is presented here. As in any first attempt, its scope and usefulness are limited by numerous assumptions. Before reviewing those limiting hypotheses that are specific to the model, we shall restate the more general limitations which are implied in the underlying theory.

Theoretical basis

The model involves the comparison of several transport plans, defined by the capacity of roads and railways and by the amount of parking spaces provided at selected locations. It appears to be similar to the comparison of various urban schemes, with which Lesourne [1] has dealt.

From the economic point of view, each scheme is described by three sets of variables, which determine:

1 The distribution of population (location, density, activity rate, economic status, . . .).
2 The distribution of employment.
3 The transport system.

An overall optimality function is then introduced, which applies to the whole population of the city. Since it is unknown, a first set of general assumptions is needed to determine its variations:

A price system can be defined and individuals maximize their utility function under such price system.
The time and revenue which every individual can spend are limited.
It is also convenient to assume that the initial distribution of revenues is optimal.

Calculations are greatly eased if a second set of assumptions is introduced:

Preferences of individuals are not directly related to the location of their dwellings.
The various schemes to be compared do not affect the size of dwellings.
Profits to all enterprises – and more specifically to the transport industry – are optimal in the initial stage.
The balance of foreign trade remains unchanged, in the initial price system.

The variation of the overall optimality function dU for a marginal change is then expressed as the sum of:

1 The variation of income accruing to transport enterprises (including parking authorities) at constant fares.
2 The variation of operating costs to transport enterprises.
3 The total value of time saved by people using mass transport in the initial scheme.
4 The total time and money saved by individuals using a private car in the initial scheme.
5 Investments required to realize the change of scheme.
6 The variation of fuel tax collected by the State, owing to changing road traffic.

The variation of the optimality function in a structural change can be estimated by assuming that all functions involved are linear. If only transport fares vary from one scheme to the next – other prices, tax, and time value remaining constant – the estimate is quite similar to the expression found for a marginal change: in terms 1, 3, and 4 initial fares and traffic volumes are replaced by average values.

If changes take place over a long period of time so that most of the economic parameters cannot be taken as constant, more restrictive assumptions must be added to enable an approximate calculation of ΔU.

Specific hypotheses of the model

Improvements or extensions of transport networks do not only modify travelling habits. They also bring about a shift in the locational pattern of population and employment. Such a shift may even be promoted by public authorities in connexion with a stated transport policy. At this stage we shall not concern ourselves with such after-effects of a transport plan, although they may become in the long range the leading criteria for decision.

More precisely, it will be assumed that the first two sets of variables (population and employment) defining the urban scheme are not altered by changes in the transport network. The area required for this network is not explicitly limited. However, since we have assumed that population and employment distributions are not disturbed by changes in the transport system, it is required that residential units displaced by a widening of roads or tracks are rebuilt in the immediate vicinity. In other words, the scarcity of land does not impose a physical constraint, but is reflected in the price of land.

All transport facilities are assumed to be built simultaneously, and the time needed for their building is supposedly short enough to be disregarded. Under such conditions two plans can be compared if we are able to predict how people will use the transport facilities.

Trips made in a city interact in too many ways to enable a simple evaluation of traffic pattern changes. As a first step, the following simplifications have been introduced:

The city is quasi-linear. It is defined as an angular sector. Places of work are concentrated at the summit of the angle. The population is distributed in the sector with varying densities.

Transport routes connect the centre of employment to residential areas. They include a motorway with controlled access, and a suburban railway line. Both facilities are located along the bisector. Parking is provided near the stations and near the heart of the city. All characteristics of the transport network are allowed to vary.

Since the capacity of the transport networks is determined mainly by the volume of home-to-work trips, only such trips are considered.

All movements are thus reduced to trips from and to the centre of town, i.e. the summit of the angle. The schedule of arrivals at the centre is also given. Finally, for a given set of transport and parking facilities, what the model has to do is to determine the traffic pattern, knowing the general characteristics of users' behaviour. The total travel time and costs, the required transport capacities, and the corresponding building and operating costs can then be calculated. The estimate of the variation of the optimality function follows.

The traffic model

At the start, characteristics of the motorway are given, i.e. the number of lanes at each abscissa and the location of exits. The location of railway stations is also given. The capacity of the line is assumed to meet the final demand and is determined at the end of traffic computations. What is needed for a start is to know that the railway capacity is not a limiting factor. At each station parking spaces can be provided to meet the local demand. Near the centre of the city, parking capacity and operating characteristics can vary.

Traffic volumes on the motorway are calculated by an iterative process under the following conditions:

The road has continuous characteristics. There is no crossing, no curve, no traffic light.

Vehicles cannot pass each other.

The traffic density is high enough for the following relation to hold: flow = density × speed.

Such conditions prevail at peak hours. The motorway is divided into short sections whose characteristics (geometry and traffic) remain constant along the section during any given time unit. Thus, within a time unit the speed of vehicles is a linearly decreasing function of the traffic flow at the end of the section nearer to the centre of town. Time units and road sections are short enough to correctly approximate our hypothesis of continuity.

At each step of the iterative process the number of road-users entering the motorway is given at every entrance. It is compared with the number of commuters who will choose to drive to work, according to traffic conditions prevailing at that time.

The process will be described in the simple case where commuters can leave the motorway only at the terminal near the centre of the city (in other words, they are not given the choice of using combined means of transport). Computations are more elaborate without this restriction, but the principle is not different.

Traffic flows at the terminal are deduced from the working schedule of commuters, assuming they will not choose to arrive early at work. Travel times and flows entering at each entrance of the motorway are then deduced as follows:

The traffic volume at the terminal determines the speed and the travel time up to the first entrance. In its turn, this time determines the percentage and the number of commuters served by this entrance that would drive to work. Hence the traffic between the first and the second entrance follows.

The same method applies from any entrance to the next.

The total flow entering all entrances must equal the exit flow at the terminal.

More generally the flow must be zero at the border of the city. The terminal flow is corrected after each iteration until this condition is met with sufficient precision. It can be shown that the process is convergent if the choice of commuters is represented by an assignment function which is necessarily a monotonically decreasing function of traffic volumes on each section. The assignment curve which has been adopted expresses the percentage of road-users as a function of the difference of generalized costs to users (monetary costs, value of time, and comfort) between road and rail.

One of the items taken into account is the cost of the last part of the trip to work, between the terminal and the place of work. Among other things it depends on how the parking is to be filled. The simplest case is obtained when all spaces are assigned in advance and when the speed near the centre is a function of the traffic volume at the terminal of the motorway. A more interesting case would make allowance for parking spaces available to anybody who could find them after a searching time increasing as the number of free spaces decreases. The corresponding model is more elaborate and the computer programme is not yet ready. It will give the number of users of each means of transport, the entrance flow at each parking area, the flow at each entrance of the motorway, and the traffic volume on each section of the motorway.

These results enable the estimation of the difference of the overall optimality function between two transport plans. An optimal plan can then be approached through a sequence of systematic comparisons. The following sequence is given as an example:

1 The characteristics of the motorway are given. Parking at the centre is unlimited. The maximum number of parking spaces needed is determined.
2 Same motorway; parking spaces at the centre are less than the maximum required. Their number is kept decreasing until the optimality function reaches a relative maximum or until the traffic on the motorway would justify a reduction in the number of lanes.
3 A new sequence is started for various road capacities.

Numerical data

The computing programme should allow the following data to vary:

The number and type of parking spaces available at the centre or near the stations.
The road and rail capacities.
Operating speeds and the spacing of stations or road entrances.
Costs and fares.

The first computations make use of data pertaining to the Parisian Metropolitan Area. The city is an angular sector ($\beta = 24°$), 20·25 km long, with a population of 480,000. The densely populated stretch along the bisector is 800 m wide, except near the centre, where a high density is uniformly distributed. Farther from the centre, densities decrease as the distance increases. The number of commuters using some means of transport is 50,000.

Two transport plans have been compared:

1 Railway line all the way from the centre; stations 1·5 km apart.
Motorway all the way: 2 × 2 lanes. Entrances 0·5 km apart.

N

2 Railway line as before.

Motorway: 2 × 3 lanes. Entrances 1·5 km apart except near the centre (5·25 km), where they are 0·5 km apart.

Costs and average speeds are recent data collected in Paris. The relation between speed and traffic volume on the motorway has been chosen after American studies. The speed decreases from 70 km/h for a volume per lane of 1,000 veh/h to 30 km/h for 2,000 veh/h per lane.

The most difficult data to determine relate to the assignment curve between different modes of transport. Here again, they stem from studies made at the Institut d'Aménagement et d'Urbanisme de la Région Parisienne about the behaviour of commuters in the Paris area. One study was made in 1963. It made use of data collected in 1961 by the French railway company from its suburban customers. Several questions pertained to the means of transport used by these customers to travel from the railway terminal to their places of work. The main choice lies between bus and underground. The influence of the following factors of choice has been measured:

Monetary cost
Difference of travel time
Number of underground transfers
Interval between buses

In order to compare these factors, a common scale has been set up: two situations are considered equivalent if the percentage of bus-users is the same. The survey reached 6·5 per cent of workers commuting from the suburbs to Paris. More than 70,000 answers were received. It was found that:

1 A 1-hour increase of travel time equals an additional travel cost of 2·90 Frs. (the hourly wages of commuters average 5·50 Frs.).
2 The unit value of time spent in transfers is twice the unit value of time spent in travelling: an underground transfer requires about 4 minutes. Users choose as if they really had spent 8 minutes.
3 The theoretical average waiting time in bus queues is half the interval between buses if the capacity is sufficient. Users react as if it were three times longer (irregular spacing of buses, queues, discomfort).

Through such relations a generalized cost or time differential between bus and underground can be evaluated and used as a single factor of choice.

Another study deals with the choice between individual and mass transport. It is based upon a sample of the 1962 population census (part of the census was devoted to home-to-work trips. The corresponding questions were similar to those usually asked in traffic surveys). The sample pertains to two groups of suburban and four groups of Parisian census blocks. The study reveals the influence of parking difficulties and variations of time value in relation to the socio-economic status and the total length of the trip. Assignment curves look like the curve found in the preceding study. However, their parameters are related to factors which are not all taken into account by generalized travel costs. Therefore, since assignment curves relate the choice of commuters to these costs, there is a specific curve for each pair of travel modes, and trips combining several means of transport raise difficulties that are not yet solved.

If curves are used for predicting future choices the value of the various parameters must be modified (for example, the value of time). It is usually difficult to appreciate the extent of such modifications. It is thus essential to know how sensitive the curves are to varying parameters.

Appendix. The Traffic Model

The problem to be solved is stated as follows:

Underlying hypotheses are

1 Home-to-work traffic flow is continuous and independent of other kinds of traffic.
2 It is similar to the flow of a continuous fluid.
3 Speed is a decreasing function of traffic density.
4 Each individual knows when he must arrive at his workplace and organizes his trip so that he reaches this place just on time.
5 The number of individuals served by each entrance to the motorway is known.
6 The assignment curve between road and railway is given.

We must determine the terminal flow (near the centre of town) $Q_s(t)$ so that the traffic $Q_0(t)$ before the first entrance (near the outskirts of the city) shall be zero.

The motorway is divided into short sections s.

Speed on each section is a linearly decreasing function of the flow at the end of the section nearer to the centre of town.

The continuous function $Q_s(t)$ is replaced by a sequence of constant values. This means that the traffic flow can be represented by independent clusters of vehicles.

Let Q_s, ρ_s be the flow and density of traffic on section s, whose length is L_s

  N_i the number of cars in cluster i
  T_i the time of arrival of cluster i
  ξ_{is} the travel time of cluster i on section s
  θ_{is} the time when cluster i enters section s
  ϕ_{is} the flow at the entrance leading to section s (it may be 0, if no car enters the motorway at this point at time θ_{is} or if there is no entrance at the far end of section s)
  $u_s(t)$ the speed on s at time t
  β_{is} the number of commuters owning a car who are served by entrance s and must arrive at the terminal at T_i
  $\alpha[D(t)]$ the assignment curve, $D(t)$ is the cost differential between road-users and train-users, when the travel time by car is t.

Hypotheses 2 and 3 are expressed by the relations:

$$Q_s(t) = \rho_s(t)\, u_s(t)$$
$$u_s(t) = f_s[\rho_s(t)] = K_s[1 - bQ_s(t)]$$

K_s is related to the geometry of the road on section s.

θ_{is} is then:
$$\int_{\theta_{i,s}}^{\theta_{i,s+1}} u_s(t)\, dt = L_s$$

Travel time:
$$\xi_{is} = \theta_{i,s+1} - \theta_{is}$$

The percentage of commuters choosing to drive is:

$$\alpha_{is} = \alpha[D(T_i - \theta_{is})]$$

The entrance flow $\phi_{is} = \alpha_{is}\,\beta_{is}$, and therefore the recurring relation holds:

$$Q_{s-1} = Q_s - \phi_s$$

Starting from Q_s, Q_0 can be evaluated. It should be zero.

ITERATIVE PROCESS

When commuters' choice is described by an assignment curve, we shall prove that the iterative process has one and only one solution.

Let us assume there are only two clusters of N_1 and N_2 cars arriving at times 1 and 2. Let $\sum_s \phi_{is} = \psi_1$ be the sum of flows entering the motorway at all entrances and arriving at time 1. $\psi_1 = \psi_1(N_1, N_2) \dots$ *

By definition:

$$N_1 = \psi_1(N_1, N_2) \tag{1}$$
$$N_2 = \psi_1(N_1, N_2) \tag{2}$$

If N_1 or N_2 decreases, speed on each section increases and so does the flow entering every section. Functions ψ are monotonically decreasing functions of N_i. Solutions $N_1(N_2)$ and $N_2(N_1)$ of equations (1) and (2) are also decreasing. If $\bar{N}_1$ and $\bar{N}_2$ are minimum terminal flows (they are zero if no commuter is compelled to use a car), let:

$$N^\star_1 = \psi_1(N^\star_1, \bar{N}_2) \qquad\qquad \bar{N}_1 = \psi_1(\bar{N}_1, N^\star_2)$$
$$N^{\star\star}_2 = \psi_2(\bar{N}_1, N^{\star\star}_2) \qquad\qquad \bar{N}_2 = \psi_2(N^{\star\star}_1, \bar{N}_2)$$

Since $\bar{N}_2$ is the minimum of N_2,

$$\psi_2(N^\star_1, \bar{N}_2) \geqslant \bar{N}_2 = \psi_2(N^{\star\star}_1, \bar{N}_2)$$

It follows that
$$N^\star_1 \leqslant N^{\star\star}_1 \tag{3}$$

In the same manner
$$\psi_1(\bar{N}_1, N^{\star\star}_2) \geqslant \bar{N}_1 = \psi_1(\bar{N}_1, N^\star_2)$$

and
$$N^{\star\star}_2 \leqslant N^\star_2 \tag{4}$$

Thus, if (3) and (4) are not equalities, curves $N_2(N_1)$ and $N_1(N_2)$ intersect in only one point. If (3) and (4) are both equalities N_1 and N_2 is the solution.

The iteration process is developed in the same manner. The curve $\psi_1(N_1)$ is first

* Actually, in our example $\psi_1 = \psi_1(N_1)$.

determined. The equilibrium value $N^\star_1$ is calculated. Then $\psi_2(N^\star_1, N_2)$ and $N^\star_2$ are evaluated.

More generally, knowing $N^\star_1, N^\star_2, \ldots N^\star_{k-1}$, the curve $\psi_k(N^\star_1, \ldots N^\star_{k-1}, N_k)$ is determined as well as $N^\star_k$.

ACKNOWLEDGEMENT

The research presented here is a joint project of I.A.U.R.P. and the Ministry of Public Works (Department of Economic Affairs), in co-operation with S.E.M.A.

REFERENCE

1 J. Lesourne (1964)

26 · Long-term Planning and Timing the Implementation of Transport Investments

INGE THYGESEN

Introduction

In recent years cost–benefit analysis has become increasingly popular in the evaluation of public transport investments. It supplies a logical theoretical framework for deciding when, how, and to what extent the demand for transport facilities is to be met using the optimality criterion of maximal total net present utility under a budgetary constraint in the planning period.

Theoretically the approach has several weak points, but important advances have been made recently, especially within the following areas:

Effects of budget restrictions.[1,2]
Substitution of a dynamic instead of a static viewpoint.[1]
Methods of evaluating the utility to an individual of each type of consequence [3,4] and combinations thereof.[5]

The problems of aggregating individual utilities [6] and of determining the social rate of return [7] have proved rather intractable.

Problems in the application of cost–benefit analysis

To put the method into practice one must evaluate the consequences to citizens of meeting their demand in several alternative ways. So far this has been done by making the following two critical assumptions:

First, that the consequences of implementing one particular project are unaffected by the decisions taken with respect to other projects under consideration, *the independence assumption.*
Second, that the consequences of implementing each individual project are known for certain within the planning horizon, *the certainty assumption.*

In principle, the consequences of implementing a project extend from the start of construction into infinity, but in practice one usually takes into account only the period from the opening of the new facility to the end of the planning horizon (traditionally twenty years). Even within this limitation, the certainty assumption is obviously illusory. The same holds for the independence assumption, as will be apparent in the remarks below. In the discussion of the latter it will, however, be useful to distinguish short-term and long-term effects according to whether the structure of the area (city or region) served by the new facility changes or not. A new transport facility will *eo ipso* induce such changes.

In *the short run* the problems of measuring the effects are primarily of a practical nature in the sense that they can be overcome by collecting data and by studying the experience with similar projects. This is not meant to belittle the task. It is particularly important to ensure that the approximations which must necessarily be used do not introduce important systematic errors. Unfortunately this appears to have been the case in past studies of the profitability of urban highways. The most striking illustration is found in Los Angeles. Though calculations show high user benefits of new expressways, the individual driver is faced with an increasing number of traffic breakdowns, an acute shortage of parking facilities, and higher taxes to finance underground railways.

A recent paper by Beesley, Blackburn, and Foster [8] has analysed the causes of such inconsistencies. They demonstrate that the traditional disregard of the indirect effects produces a considerable upward bias in the estimates of the rate of return on urban highways. There is a tendency to estimate the average user benefit as the savings of time and costs to existing road traffic. A major improvement of the transport system, however, sets into motion an adjustment process not only within but also between all parts of the system. In the case of a new urban highway, motoring becomes relatively more convenient, and this in turn induces some people to shift their demand from mass to individual transport.

When a new equilibrium is reached the benefits of using the improved road network will be smaller than they appeared at first. The constructed example from London given by Beesley, Blackburn, and Foster suggests that the difference is likely to be considerable. In practice, a satisfactory analysis of the full short-term effects of a transport facility [9] meets with formidable difficulties: it requires information about the marginal costs of all competing modes of transport and the direct and the substitution elasticities of demand for these services.

In *the long run* the effects of a project become much harder to evaluate. In addition to the stochastic variations possible structural changes in society introduce uncertainty. The widely used extrapolation of past trends is basically inappropriate. Land use and the demand for transport corresponding thereto will have changed as a result of the economic development of the region, changing preferences, and public policy. Of course, the influences do not run in one direction only; in the long run all these phenomena are interdependent.

The major short-run effect of improving the transport system was substitution between different modes, as total demand for transport can be considered rather inelastic in the short run. In the long run the total elasticity of demand must be substantial. The location of industry is influenced by new transport facilities, and these at the same time offer to individuals a greater freedom in choosing their residences.

This feedback from the transport system to land use grows in importance with the size of the project, and it can only be disregarded in the evaluation of very limited improvements. However, even the most ambitious studies, such as 'The Chicago Area Transportation Study',[10] have so far neglected it. In this and similar studies future land use is hypothesized on the basis of fairly vague motives of city planning. It is, furthermore, assumed that past economic growth trends may be extrapolated and that preferences remain unchanged; the method is then to determine a transport system conducive to the fulfilment of these projections. This is in itself a formidable assignment, but one is entitled to question whether city and regional planning do as yet offer a sufficiently firm base on which to build such an elaborate analysis.

Apart from the particular projects under consideration, the actions of the public authorities have an impact on the structure of the region through other investments, zoning, regulations, and pricing of public services, etc. The effects of minor projects are especially sensitive to such other influences.

All these problems can be referred to the unsatisfactory assumption of independence. A partial cost–benefit-analysis should not be applied to situations where interdependences exist. An exception is the special kind of dependence created by budgetary restrictions, which only involves computational complications.[1,2] On the whole, it must be concluded that the problems in the application of cost–benefit analysis are of a fundamental rather than an empirical nature.

The interdependence of public decisions

Since no aspect of public policy can be looked upon in isolation in the long run, one ought in principle to regard all public efforts as part of one huge project designed to maximize social welfare. But this way of posing the problem offers little guidance. In reality decision-making is delegated to a large number of central and local government agencies, each with limited functions. The question is, however, whether this necessary administrative decentralization pays due regard to the desirability of a reasonable degree of independence in the sense that the needs looked after by one agency are reasonably unaffected by administrative decisions taken elsewhere.

As far as *transport* is concerned, the answer is clearly no. There are no doubt compelling arguments in favour of delegating the administration of local traffic to local authorities, provided that agreement can be reached on the principle of financing such activities.[1] But there is no justification for delegating the administration and planning of each mode of transport to separate agencies. After all, their task is to meet the same basic demand; that for transporting persons and goods.

Owing to the long life of transport facilities, long-term planning imposes itself. The only satisfactory procedure is to make a total assessment of the combined possibilities of all modes of transport and thereby determine the optimal way of allocating any given amount of traffic. In the end costs will have to be confronted with the benefits accruing to users, i.e. with the demand for transport.

The success of such a long-term plan depends on a series of current decisions with regard to pricing and quality of service ensuring that each mode of transport carries the optimal amount of traffic. This requires pricing in accordance with costs. The fact that this is not at present politically feasible provides no excuse for not carrying out the computations suggested. Only by doing so, can the implications of any departure from optimality involved in existing pricing policies be assessed. The computations are indispensable in an analysis of changes in pricing policies.

Evaluating the total future demand and assigning it to different modes of transport according to costs would be a major step forward. But even conceived in this broad fashion, the demand for transport can hardly be studied in isolation. Transport is not demanded for its own sake. It derives from the interacting preferences of consumers and producers with regard to residence and location of economic activity. The extent to which these preferences can find expression depends crucially not only on the rate of economic progress in society but also on public policy concerning land use, i.e. on city and regional planning. Obviously all these factors are interdependent: without effective city and regional planning economic growth is retarded, while a slowdown of economic activity delays implementation of even the best plans.

City and regional planning by a total cost–benefit analysis

Planning is, of course, feasible only if one is prepared to disregard some of the complications involved. Generally it appears reasonable to base city and regional planning on the assumption of a given rate of economic growth.

In designing *a long-term plan* for a city, for example, by means of a *total* cost–benefit analysis the analogy to the analytical framework of operational research seems helpful. It involves the specification of an effectiveness function expressing quantitatively the aggregated preferences of the inhabitants with respect to present and future city structure. Furthermore, one must formulate mathematically a dynamic model of the city including all important interdependent factors. In principle, the formulation of a model makes it possible to compute the effects of any conceivable policy. All predictable bottlenecks, such as the limited availabilities of capital and man-power, must be formalized as mathematical restrictions to the problem. On the basis of the effectiveness function one may subsequently select the optimal feasible policy to be pursued in planning the city. The task of determining the relative weights of the different objectives entering the effectiveness function may prove impossible. In that case one is confined to illustrating the effects of a limited number of feasible alternatives, leaving the ultimate choice to the political process.

There is much theoretical and empirical research to be done before the operational research approach can be put into operation. In particular, it is imperative to gather more information regarding the preferences of the citizens with respect to the city structure – as measured by their collective willingness to forgo other consumption in order to obtain the further benefits of the city plan. Regardless of the number of empirical studies that may be undertaken to clarify these issues, a considerable degree of uncertainty will necessarily remain. But at least the operational research approach has the advantage of focusing attention on what is at present the weakest element in the process of city planning: the formulation of objectives.

The model can only be crude; its assumptions are restrictive, its results subject to error. However, the risk of these inadequacies must be preferred to the certainty of non-optimality inherent in the traditional partial approach, which in accordance with the institutional set-up systematically disregards interdependencies on the demand side. Finally, the risk involved in applying the approach suggested can be limited by effective short-term planning and by frequent revisions of the long-term plan.

The purpose of *short-term planning* is to elaborate in detail the decisions taken in the long-term plan and to integrate into its framework a number of minor investments of a supplementary nature. Since the main lines of action are given by the long-term plan, the risk involved in delegating the authority for short-term decisions to a number of semi-autonomous agencies is considerably reduced. The advantage of preserving some degree of autonomy is to ensure that administrative experience is brought fully into play.

In the case of *transport investments* the long-term plan specifies the major projects within each mode of transport and gives an outline of their location, capacity, and timing. On this basis it may be justifiable to decide by traditional cost–benefit analysis on when and how each individual project is to be implemented. There is, however, a considerable danger of misallocation involved even in this procedure. The model can give only an imprecise account of the reaction of citizens to public policy decisions and other influences. In addition, the assumptions regarding economic and social development on which the whole long-term plan is based may not be fulfilled; while the nature and direction of change is often foreseeable, this is not the case with respect to the speed of change. It is accordingly essential to review the *timing of the projects* at regular intervals in the light of the most recent information about economic and social trends.

Timing the implementation of a long-term plan

This can often be done by a particularly simple type of cost–benefit analysis, which requires only short-term forecasts of the consequences of constructing the facility in the subsequent period. The method [1,11] selects the optimal time to start the construction, subject to the assumption that the net benefits of the project are non-decreasing with time, and independent of the time that has elapsed since the facility came into use. This will usually be true in the case of transport facilities. As the cost and benefits of the project considered can be assessed only approximately anyway, it does not have to be specified in great detail.

Let $b(n)$ be the net benefit of the investment from time n to time $n + 1$, C the total capital outlay during the construction period (T units of time) accumulated at the end of construction, r the social rate of return, and $F(t)$ the total net present value of the project evaluated at time 0, if construction starts at time t and thus is completed at time $t + T$. Then

$$F(t) = \sum_{n=t+T+1}^{\infty} \frac{b(n)}{(1+r)^n} - \frac{C}{(1+r)^{t+T}}$$

$$F(t+1) = \sum_{n=t+T+2}^{\infty} \frac{b(n)}{(1+r)^n} - \frac{C}{(1+r)^{t+T+1}}$$

and the advantage from starting construction at time t instead of waiting one time period becomes

$$F(t) - F(t+1) = \frac{b(t+T+1) - rC}{(1+r)^{t+T+1}}$$

The optimal time t_0 to start construction must satisfy the inequalities:

$$F(t_0 + 1) - F(t_0) \leqslant 0 \leqslant F(t_0) - F(t_0 - 1)$$

or

$$\frac{b(t_0 + T)}{C} \leqslant r \leqslant \frac{b(t_0 + T + 1)}{C}$$

Because of the assumption that $b(n)$ is a non-decreasing function of time n, the above-mentioned condition is in fact sufficient to secure that one is justified in carrying out the project at the optimal time t_0, since

$$F(t_0) = \sum_{n=t_0+T+1}^{\infty} \frac{b(n)}{(1+r)^n} - \frac{C}{(1+r)^{t_0+T}}$$

$$\geqslant rC \sum_{n=t_0+T+1}^{\infty} \frac{1}{(1+r)^n} - \frac{C}{(1+r)^{t_0+T}} = 0$$

To select the projects to be started in the next time interval (from t to $t + 1$) is now a simple matter, requiring only estimates of the 'immediate return' $\dfrac{b(t+T+1)}{C}$ of each project under consideration. All projects showing an 'immediate return' no smaller than the social rate of return ought to be carried out. If, however, the budget of the agency for the coming time interval does not allow it to follow this rule, the short-term optimal policy is to choose projects within the budget restriction that show the highest 'immediate return'. In this way the direct and immediate opportunity cost is minimized. But the indirect and long-term effects of the postponement of projects will not enter into the choice. The optimality of the long-term plan is thereby disturbed. In the formulation of the long-term plan it is therefore important not to choose a social rate of return so low that the implementation of the plan will repeatedly be impeded.

Naturally, this method of determining the timing of the implementation rests on the same basic assumption of independence and certainty as any other partial cost–benefit analysis. These assumptions, however, appear somewhat less unreasonable now that the analysis is confined to the short-run benefits, $b(t + T + 1)$. If the projects are not too narrowly delimited – e.g. by looking at a motorway without taking into consideration the access and terminal facilities – interdependencies are likely to be of minor importance in the short run when only a small number will be carried out. As mentioned above, one must take care in including indirect effects to such an extent that no systematic error is committed. Adaptive forecasting [12] is highly suitable in predicting the development of traffic, since one can legitimately assume that observed trends will persist in the short run ($T + 1$ time units). One may hope that experience will eventually reveal reliable standard relationships between the volume of traffic and the benefits accruing from the more common type of minor investment.

This would open up possibilities for extensive use of electronic data-processing for short-term planning.

The choice between alternative designs requires a cost–benefit analysis of the usual type. The long-term benefits of each alternative will have to be assessed on the basis of the long-term plan, while observed trends up to the moment of choice can be drawn upon in estimating the short-run effects. It will therefore be advantageous to postpone the decision until the timing method shows that the time for implementing the project is approaching.

On the other hand, it must be admitted that the process of adjusting and complementing the long-run plan through short-run plans also entails risks. One may depart from the framework of the long-run plan despite the continued optimality of the latter; unforeseen budgetary restrictions may force the planners into this type of situation, but errors may also easily arise simply because the less comprehensive short-term approach is misleading. Or the planners may be unduly restrained by long-run targets – in particular as regards capacity – which are not in fact optimal. By regular revisions of the long-term plan, e.g. at five-year intervals, the inoptimalities can be kept within manageable bounds.

REFERENCES

1 S. A. Marglin (1963a)
2 H. M. Weingartner (1963)
3 R. L. Ackoff (1963a)
4 H. Maass *et al.* (1962)
5 P. M. Pruzan & J. T. R. Jackson (1963)
6 K. J. Arrow (1951)
7 S. A. Marglin (1963b)
8 M. E. Beesley, A. J. Blackburn & C. D. Foster (1963)
9 C. D. Foster & M. E. Beesley (1963)
10 Chicago Area Transportation Study (1959–62)
11 A. Jensen & I. Thygesen (1963)
12 M. Nerlove & S. Wage (1964)

Part IV
Conflict Resolution and Control

SPONSOR: ERIC L. TRIST

27 · *Introduction*

ERIC L. TRIST

During the last ten years the study of conflict has emerged as a major focus of interdisciplinary research. Patently, this represents a recognition on the part of the scientific community that the arrival of a developed thermo-nuclear military technology has ruled out major war as a method of 'solving' international conflicts on any calculation that can be deemed rational. This has created a new situation which has brought a new level of uncertainty to the world, since, whatever intended rationality one may ascribe to oneself or to others, the doubt remains that somehow runaway processes may gather momentum and the whole situation swing out of control. Nor is escalation into major war the only process through which events may now somehow get out of control, though, of course, it is by far the most immediately threatening. Farther ahead lie more insidious dangers from over-population and environmental pollution.

Psycho-analysis has shown that every human individual is beset with primitive unconscious phantasies of killing everyone, devouring everyone, and poisoning everyone. The echoes of these phantasies are variously represented in the cultural material of all societies. Our inherent destructive tendencies are intense, but formidable also are our constructive capabilities, and in most individuals in most societies the constructive forces come to predominate as socialization takes place through growing up in the ordinary family. But there are exceptions, and for reasons that combine genetic and ontogenetic factors in ways that remain obscure, a certain number of individuals in any generation become dominated by their destructive drives, resulting in the extremes of mental illness or anti-social behaviour. Anxieties about our destructive tendencies also make all of us prone to some degree to project them on to others and, by so ridding ourselves of them, win the advantage of remaining in a more comfortable personal state. Especially convenient for such purposes are people more distant from our immediate circle, out-groups of various kinds being the repositories of choice, who then, however, become correspondingly threatening. Nothing in all this has changed appreciably in human history until this century, when our accumulated technical advances have provided the means of realizing our destructive urges in the external world on a scale which now endangers the species as well as the individual, minority groups, or particular nation states. Our last chance of learning from what may happen when the destructive forces temporarily gain control in a technologically advanced society has been afforded in our experience of the rise and consequences of Nazi Germany. Next time the technology will be so advanced that there will be no further chance of learning.

Fortunately, the capability of the human being for learning is very great. Learning more than anything else distinguishes us from other species. Learning is both cognitive and emotional, and learning processes are social as well as personal. Very early, experimental psychology showed that as learning develops means may become ends, so that whole sets of new – and more civilized – objects can become the goals of basic drives. Psychobiologically, we have the plasticity to learn our way out of our present dilemma and reach a new level of conflict regulation. This endowment gives us the necessary but not the sufficient conditions.

To attain these entails a lot of hard work – in the intellectual sense of problem identification and problem-solving and in the emotional sense of 'working through' to a more mature level of toleration and acceptance. Improved cognitive maps reduce anxiety by offering a wider range of behavioural alternatives. We draw special attention to this point, since the increased complexity of the contemporary human situation can only too easily lead to an increase in regressive behaviour, because the level of uncertainty becomes too great to be met by established modes of learned behaviour. Cognitive search must not only continue but also be accelerated. This places a high priority on bringing together new conceptual models derived from the mathematical sciences and empirical studies of human behaviour. And this makes the field of conflict resolution and control a 'natural' for collaboration between operational research and the social sciences. Indeed, it may be said already to have established itself as such.

As the field has opened up it has become apparent how much insight may be gained from the comparison of conflicts of all kinds and at all levels. The papers chosen for this section illustrate this trend and also the conceptual interpenetration and empirical enrichment of operational research and the social sciences made possible when their traditions are joined to develop a mutually relevant field.

28 · Laboratory Studies
of Conflict and Co-operation

ANATOL RAPOPORT

Introduction

Controlled experiment has been the traditional tool in obtaining reliable knowledge, especially when several strands of knowledge could be fitted into a recognizable pattern. Such patterns are called theories. Controlled experiments enable the investigator to put circumscribed portions of theories (hypotheses) to a test and so, by introducing modifications whenever necessary, to mould the theories into a semblance of reality.

The limitations of the method of controlled experiment are due to the fact that the relevance of contrived laboratory situations to the phenomena supposedly represented by them is by no means guaranteed. This is especially true in behavioural science. Human beings participating in experiments usually know that they are doing so. By its very nature, an experiment is a short-lived situation, usually quite remote from the everyday experience of the participants. It is a moot question how much of the important aspects of the subject's psyche can be tapped in a laboratory experiment. Moreover, if the subject knows that his personality is under scrutiny, he may behave in ways other than usual because of conscious or unconscious attempts to appear as he defines himself instead of as he is.

This essential dilemma of experimental behavioural science pervades all laboratory approaches. The more controlled and therefore contrived the experimental situation, the more it is usually divorced from real-life contexts. The more it resembles real life, the less precise the observables become.

The dilatation of a pupil is precisely measurable in centimetres, but the relation between pupil size and psychic state is not a clear-cut one-to-one relation. Jealousy or trust, on the other hand, although admitted by most to be 'real' psychological states, elude precise description and lend themselves even less to manipulation under controlled conditions.

The crux of the problem, then, is to design an experimental situation in which genuine psychological variables or parameters are determinants of behaviour and, at the same time, the results of the experiments can be stated in sufficiently precise terms to admit of a rigorous theory.

Psychologists of the behaviourist persuasion emphasize primarily the second principle, sometimes at the expense of the first. The protocols of their experiments are, as a rule, sequences of events labelled as 'stimuli' and of other events, associated with the former, called 'responses'. The development of a theory follows the outline presented in textbooks as the 'scientific method'. That is, regularities in the correspondence between stimuli and responses are noted, hypotheses are offered to account for the regularities, frequently in quantitative form, deductions are drawn from the hypotheses in terms of predictive statements related to future experiments, which are then designed to test the hypotheses.

With the growth of mathematical sophistication among psychologists, particularly statistical sophistication, this method has led to the construction of quite fruitful theories. For example, the application of stochastic models to rote learning has revitalized learning theory and has given it a direction at a time when the vast accumulation of data in this area by the earlier generations of experimental psychologists was beginning to look like an untidy heap and when theories of learning were proliferating in several unrelated directions.

Let us see how this came about. We shall pursue an analogy in another field in order to show the general applicability of the method. Suppose someone wished to follow the method outlined above in an investigation of the behaviour of falling bodies. Suppose he conceived the idea (as it was conceived by Galileo in his day) of relating the distance travelled by a falling body down an inclined plane to the time elapsed. The results would be described by Galileo's formula

$$s = at^2 \tag{1}$$

where s is the distance travelled, t is time elapsed, and a is a constant of proportionality. The formula relates s and t but says nothing about a except that it is a constant. However, a physical interpretation of a can be derived from formula (1), namely, one-half of the acceleration suffered by the body. Once this is done, the question naturally suggests itself: on what does acceleration depend? Further investigations will yield the results (also obtained by Galileo) that the acceleration is not dependent on the mass of the falling body, nor on the material from which it is made, but that it does depend on the angle of inclination of the inclined plane. Now the focus of attention shifts. Acceleration is no longer considered a constant or a 'free parameter' (the role it plays in a particular experimental setting), but becomes instead a variable to be related to another variable, namely to the angle of inclination of the plane. The next stage is the discovery of the relationship

$$a = \tfrac{1}{2}g \sin \alpha \tag{2}$$

where α is the angle of inclination and g a new constant, the acceleration of gravity. This new constant is independent of the angle of inclination, but subsequent investigations will reveal that it does depend on the distance from the centre of the earth. Once the relation between g and the distance to the centre of the earth is discovered, a new constant is revealed, namely, K, the universal gravitational constant.

In short, the method proceeds by uncovering quantities which are constant under a given set of conditions. They are quantities which stay put as other quantities (the variables under investigation) change. These *relatively* constant quantities, called *parameters*, suggest further systematic developments of the theory by raising questions about what the parameters, in turn, depend on.

Let us return to the theory of rote learning. In any learning experiment one observes systematic changes in the pattern of responses. In the simplest case there may be two possible responses, 'right' and 'wrong', the former rewarded, the latter punished. In the process of learning the right responses become more frequent at the expense of the wrong responses. One could therefore represent the protocol by a formula, where the independent variable would be time, while the dependent variable would be the frequency of correct responses. Once such a formula is put down, the constants could be read off as parameters and questions could be raised concerning the dependence of the parameters on the experimental conditions, for example, the magnitudes of rewards and punishments, etc. The parameters would then be assigned psychological meanings, e.g. in terms of motivations, and quantitative analysis would be joined to a psychological theory.

In principle, then, the method of experimental physics could be replicated in a psychological context. However, certain technical difficulties arise immediately. We mentioned 'frequency of correct response' and 'time' as the variables to be related. However, while 'time' can be unambiguously measured at a given moment (say by the total number of responses elapsed), 'frequency' can be measured only over a considerable stretch of time. If we do this we get not an 'instantaneous' frequency but an average frequency over a stretch of time. But this frequency changes with time (for this is what learning means). Therefore our model leads to a dilemma: if we take the stretch of time long enough to get an accurate estimate of frequency, we may lose sight of the progressive change of this frequency; if we take the stretch of time short, the statistical fluctuations of frequency become so large as to make our estimates meaningless. Thus, the ubiquitous Uncertainty Principle appears in one of its guises.

These difficulties were overcome by the so-called stochastic theories of rote learning, in which not frequencies but probabilities of responses are the essential variables. Probabilities are not directly observable. They are only inferrable in terms of observed frequencies. We have already seen that we cannot take long stretches of time in which to estimate frequencies accurately. Can we take large populations of subjects in order to do so? It is clear that this can be done only if we have a population of 'identical' subjects, i.e. a population in which every individual obeys the same learning law. But even in a population of 'identical' subjects, a learning protocol will not necessarily be replicated by each individual. To see this, consider a sequence of coin tosses repeated many times. Although the coin is the same (obeys the same probabilistic law), the sequences of heads and tails may be different in each repetition. However, the *statistics* of the process will be replicated. That is to say, the proportion of heads, the distribution of lengths of runs of consecutive heads and tails, etc., will be the same in each sequence of tosses of the same coin provided the sequences are long enough.

Stochastic theories of learning, therefore, concentrate on the statistics of learning protocols. These statistics are derivable from the fundamental mathematical model, which states how probabilities of response change depending on the outcomes of the responses. In the simplest case, of one rewarded and one punished response, the model has the following form:

$p'(t + 1) = \alpha p(t) + (1 - \alpha)\lambda$, if the response is rewarded.

$p'(t + 1) = \beta p(t) + (1 - \beta)\mu$, if the response is punished (3)

Here $p(t)$ is the probability of one of the responses at time t [the other has accordingly probability $(1 - p)$], while α, λ, β, and μ are four parameters, presumably constant for a given individual in a given experimental situation.

We note first that the parameters lend themselves to a psychological interpretation. Thus, α represents the effectiveness of the reward in enhancing the probability of the response in question, while β represents the corresponding effectiveness of the punishment. The parameters λ and μ represent the degree of fixation of the response respectively if only rewards or only punishments were to be applied.

At this point two problems present themselves. The first is the problem of estimating the parameters in a given experimental situation for a given subject. This problem is one of statistical inference, and can be attacked by standard methods. The methods will yield definitive results if the underlying model is sufficiently realistic, that is, if individuals in a given situation *are* characterized by sets of parameters of the sort described. But even if this is not so, the model may still represent the situation up to a point. It can then be interpreted as an 'as if' model. It is 'as if' individuals were characterized by sets of corresponding parameters and so behave in ways which can be described in terms of models of this sort. If we keep in mind that every theory is in the last analysis an 'as if' model we see that the ultimate 'realism' of the model ought not to become a methodological issue.

Once the parameters have been estimated and interpreted in psychological terms, the next problem is to discover their dependence on factors hitherto kept constant. As in the case of falling bodies, the parameters now become the variables, and the theory moves on to the next stage of investigation.

To summarize, the link between rigorous methods of investigation and psychological content was established when variables appropriate to be-

havioural situations were discovered. These variables are primarily probabilities – both probabilities of responses and probabilities of reinforcements.
The latter are, of course, related to the probabilities of responses, because the
nature of the reinforcement depends, in general, on what response is given.
But also the *same* response (or rather responses classified as 'the same') may
be associated with a *probability* of reinforcement, as in the case of a random
environment (which can be simulated by the experimenter), where the same
response can be sometimes reinforced and sometimes not. Such situations
are also subsumed under stochastic models of learning.*

In what follows, we shall describe experiments which can be also interpreted as learning experiments. The main difference between these experiments and the classical rote learning experiments is in the circumstance that
now the outcomes of responses will be determined not by a single presumably
interested subject (interested in the sense of distinguishing between rewards
and punishments) and a neutral Nature (neutral in the sense that her responses are fixed by prearranged probabilities) but by two interested subjects,
each of whom receives rewards and punishments associated with the outcomes.

Prisoner's dilemma

The conditions of the experiment are simple. At regular intervals the subjects
must make a choice between two acts, to which we shall refer as C and D
respectively. Accordingly, four combinations of choices are possible, CC,
CD, DC, and DD. Depending on which combination obtains, the two
subjects, to whom we shall refer as player 1 and player 2, receive pay-offs,
which may be positive or negative.

The situation is readily recognizable as a two-person game. The structure
of the game is representable by a 2×2 matrix, each of whose 'boxes' represents an outcome and contains two entries, the respective pay-offs to the
two players, as shown in Matrix 1.

MATRIX 1

	C	D
C	R_1, R_2	S_1, T_2
D	T_1, S_2	P_1, P_2

If the game is symmetrical, i.e. if the pay-offs are independent of the way
the two players are labelled, we must have $R_1 = R_2$; $S_1 = S_2$; $T_1 = T_2$;
$P_1 = P_2$. If the game is zero-sum, i.e. if what one player wins, the other must
lose, we must have $R_1 + R_2 = S_1 + T_2 = S_2 + T_1 = P_1 + P_2 = 0$. Obviously, a game of this sort can be both symmetrical and zero-sum only if

* For a classification of various types of situations, see R. R. Bush and F. Mosteller.[1]

$R_1 = R_2 = 0$; $P_1 = P_2 = 0$. The games we used in the experiments to be described are symmetrical but not zero-sum. Specifically, in all cases the games were characterized by the inequality $T_i > R_i > P_i > S_i (i = 1, 2)$. An example is shown in Matrix 2.

MATRIX 2

	C	D
C	1, 1	−2, 2
D	2, −2	−1, −1

The interesting feature of the game shown in Matrix 2 is in the circumstance that the individual interest of each player conflicts with the collective interest of both players. Note that it is in the interest of player 1 to choose D *no matter what player 2 chooses*. Should player 2 choose C, player 1 gains 2 with D, as against only 1 with C; should player 2 choose D, player 1 loses only 1 with D, as against a loss of 2 with C. Since the game is symmetrical, the same reasoning applies to player 2. Consequently, it is in the interest of each separately to choose D. But clearly it is in the interest of both collectively to choose C, because if the outcome is CC both gain 1, while if the outcome is DD both lose 1. Such games are now known in the literature as Prisoner's Dilemma (so nicknamed after an anecdote originally told to illustrate the game).

If the players were able to analyse the situation together one could expect that they would come to an agreement to choose C, which is in the collective interest of both. If such an agreement were enforceable, either by a rule of the game or by an inclination to keep agreements, the dilemma inherent in the game would disappear. But it does not disappear if the two players cannot communicate, and consequently cannot come to an explicit agreement. Under these conditions the game becomes psychologically interesting, for one cannot answer *a priori* the question of what the players will do. There are powerful arguments for choosing D (presented above) and also powerful arguments for choosing C, since DD is bad for both players. Arguments leading to contradictory conclusions are expected to introduce internal conflict, and so lend psychological interest to the situation.

To be sure, internal conflict may be present also in an ordinary rote learning situation, in which rewards and punishments are probabilistic rather than determined.

Note, however, that the internal conflicts concomitant to the game just described carry overtones related characteristically to human relations, which is not ordinarily the case in learning experiments. For the choice between C and D is not a guess of 'what is likely to happen', as is the case when one takes a chance on what 'Nature' is likely to do. Rather the choice involves questions like 'Can I trust the other player, and does he trust me?'

For, as we have seen, D is the prudent choice, dictated by a conviction that the other player will follow his individual advantage, which is to choose D; while C is the trusting choice, dictated by a conviction that the other player is equally trusting. Moreover, even if one is convinced that the other will choose C, one's own choice of C is associated with *resisting a temptation*, since a choice of D while the other chooses C is more advantageous than the choice of C.

Even more psychological richness is added when one attempts to describe what happens in a long sequence of plays of the game by the two subjects. For the entire mechanism of learning comes into play, the learning being related not to the discovery of 'right' or 'wrong' responses (there is no perfectly rationalizable 'right' or 'wrong' way to play this game) but rather to the interactions between the two players. The dynamics of this interaction is the central core of the corresponding theory. As we shall see, conflict and conflict resolution form the content of this core, so that we are justified to some extent in viewing the method as a tool which enables us to forge the next link between 'scientific' psychology (the science which relies on hard quantifiable data and replicable experiments) and 'interesting' psychology (a body of insights into the workings of the human psyche).

The experiments

In our experiments the subjects were recruited first from the male student population at the University of Michigan, later from the female population. We shall first describe the results of experiments with male subjects. The subjects were paired off in a random fashion and asked to play one of the non-zero-sum games of the type determined by the inequality $T > R > P > S$. The seven games used are shown in Matrices 3–9.

The games were played under a variety of experimental conditions, of which we shall here describe only one. In this condition each pair of subjects played one of the seven games 300 times in succession. Ten pairs played each of the games, 70 pairs in all. After each play (i.e. simultaneous choice of C or D) the outcome was announced to the subjects, but the subjects were not allowed to communicate with each other (did not, in fact, see each other). The pay-offs were in money, 1 mill (0·1c) per point, the winnings or losses to be added or subtracted from the subjects' pay for participating in the experiment.

An examination of the seven game matrices reveals that they can be grouped into three sets of three games each, Game III being a member of all three sets. In the set containing Games III, VI, and I, the parameters S, T, and P are kept constant, while R increases from 1 to 5 to 9. In the set containing Games IV, III, and V, R and P are kept constant, while the magnitude of both S and T increases from 2 to 10 to 50. In the set containing Games III, VII, and II, R S, and T are kept constant while the magnitude of P increases

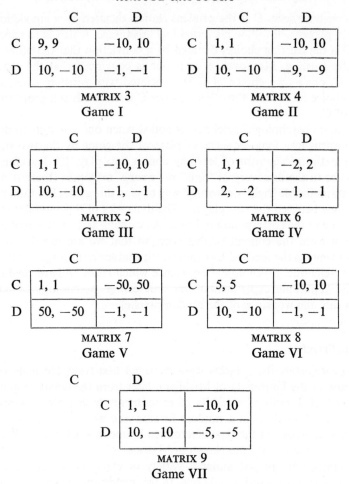

MATRICES 3–9: *The seven Prisoner's Dilemma Games discussed in this paper*

from 1 to 5 to 9. Let us see what these parameters mean in the context of the game.

R is clearly a reward accruing to the two players for co-operating, for this is what they do when they both choose C. *T* stands for the temptation to defect, for this is what the player gets if he chooses D, while the other tried to co-operate by choosing C. *S* stands for 'sucker's pay-off' to indicate that the trusting player (who chose C) was betrayed. Finally, *P* is the punishment which both get when both defect and the outcome is DD.

In view of the meaning of the parameters, we would expect that in the three games III, VI, and I the frequency of co-operative choices would be successively greater in the same order, since other pay-offs are kept the same, while the reward for co-operation increases from 1 to 5 to 9 units.

Figure 1   *Comparison of Frequencies of Co-operative Response in Seven Prisoner's Dilemma Games*

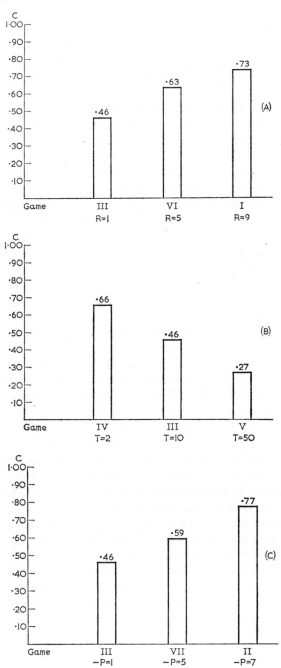

Similarly, we would expect the frequency of co-operative choices in Games IV, III, and V to decrease in that order, because in these games it is the temptation which increases.

Finally, we would expect the frequency of co-operative choices to increase successively in Games III, VII, and II, because here it is the punishment for non-co-operation which increases.

The results of our experiments fully corroborate the hypotheses, as shown in *Figure 1*.

The hypotheses we have just tested are hardly more than common-sense guesses, and the fact that they are corroborated does not teach us much about the situation that we would not have guessed on *a priori* grounds. It is, to be sure, gratifying to see that the pay-offs determine the choice biases in the expected direction, showing that the subjects' motivations can be affected by experimental manipulation. However, there is much more in the data which a psychological theory ought to explain, which cannot be done on common-sense grounds. Compare, for example, games IV and VI. The *R* pay-offs in Game VI are five times those of Game IV. This should make for pressure towards co-operation. However, the *T* pay-offs in Game VI are also five times those of Game IV, and that should create a pressure for defection. Which pressure is the stronger? Examining the frequencies of the C choices, we suspect that the pressure for defection is stronger, since C has the value of 66·2 per cent in Game IV and only 63·5 per cent in Game VI.* However, without a theoretical explanation, this finding remains a purely empirical one, hence unrelated to other findings.

Next compare Games VI and VII and Games I and II. In each pair the roles of reward and punishment are interchanged. In Games I and VI co-operation is rewarded by 9 and 5 respectively, while defection is punished by 1. In Games II and VII co-operation is rewarded by 1, while defection is punished by 9 and 5 respectively. Which is more effective in eliciting co-operation, reward for co-operation or punishment for non-co-operation? Comparing the C frequencies, we see that they are greater in Game II than in Game I, indicating that perhaps punishment is more effective. However, comparing Games VI and VII, we find that C is greater in Game VI, indicating the opposite. How can this result be explained?

Further, the frequency of co-operative choices is not the only variable to be extracted from the data. We can observe, for example, the frequencies of all four categories of responses, CC, CD, DC, and DD. We can observe the time courses of these frequencies. We can observe the correlations between the co-operative responses of one player and those of the other player paired with him. We can ask whether a tendency of one player to co-operate elicits the same tendency in the other or, on the contrary, elicits a tendency to defect and so to take advantage of the large T pay-offs. We can ask how long each

---

* The significance of this difference is, of course, open to question. However, the result has been replicated in several conditions.

of the categories of responses is likely to persist. For example, suppose the players have succeeded in establishing a collusion, i.e. a tacit agreement (which must be tacit, because there is no opportunity to communicate) to choose CC. How long is this tacit agreement likely to last? (Recall that the temptation to defect is constantly operating on both subjects and the realization that it is operating on the other makes it more persistent.) Suppose, on the contrary, that neither subject trusts the other, so that they persist in the DD response. Each is reluctant to play C under these circumstances, because it is costly to be the only co-operator. Attempts to initiate co-operation punish the initiator and reward the defector, hence do not encourage reciprocation and are subsequently inhibited. On the other hand, the DD state is punishing to both. How long is a DD run likely to last?

Finally, consider the runs of unilaterally co-operative responses, where one player is trying to induce the other to co-operate and is taking a beating in the process. We have nicknamed such sequences 'martyr runs'. In addition to the question how long martyr runs are likely to last, we can also ask whether they are more likely to end in a success or in a failure. A martyr run ends in a success if the defector switches his response to a co-operative one. It ends in a failure if the martyr gives up co-operating and switches from C to D. Simultaneous switches can, of course, also occur, where the erstwhile co-operator becomes a defector just as the erstwhile defector becomes converted to co-operation.

The object of a theory, as we have said, is to explain as many of the observed patterns of responses as possible. A mathematical model achieves this aim if from the few postulates which constitute the model many conclusions can be derived mathematically, which conclusions are quantitative statements related to the questions to be answered by the theory. Such a model serves a dual purpose. First, it provides a parsimonious explanation if its assumptions are few and the conclusions corroborated by observations are many. This function of models is generally well understood. However, there is also a second function which can be served by the model even if the first is not. The parameters of the equations of the model, when interpreted in terms of the situation modelled, become the *concepts* of the theory. At times these concepts would not have occurred to an investigator preoccupied with the content of the events under investigation. But they do occur naturally once a mathematical model of these events is formulated. The model so formulated may not be an accurate one, but it helps in bringing out what may prove to be very important concepts in terms of which the phenomenon is described. We shall return to this point below when we talk about the so-called *conditional propensities* upon which some mathematical models of Prisoner's Dilemma are constructed.

Before we discuss the mathematical models proposed as bases of a theory to explain the patterns of behaviour observed in Prisoner's Dilemma, let us list some of the empirical results which the model ought to explain.

We have already listed the C frequencies in the seven games. The rank order of the seven games, as played by male students, according to the frequency of co-operative choices is as follows:

$$II-I-IV-VI-VII-III-V \tag{4}$$

If we examine the time course of C we see the following prevailing pattern. On the first play the overall frequency of co-operative choices in all the seven games is 53 per cent. (The seven games are not very well differentiated initially.) On the second play the frequency of co-operative choices falls to 48 per cent. It keeps dropping for several plays thereafter. The trend is shown in *Figure 2*, where each ordinate is the running average of C taken over successive (overlapping) fifteen-play blocks.

Figure 2   *The Average Frequency of Co-operative Responses Initially Decreases*

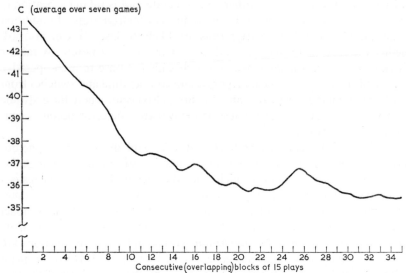

C (average over seven games)

Consecutive (overlapping) blocks of 15 plays

As can be seen, the trend continues for at least thirty plays. Thereafter there is a recovery. *Figure 3* shows the values of C averaged over successive, non-overlapping 50-play blocks in each of the six blocks (300 plays).

As we see, the gross trend is towards increasing co-operation.

We might conclude from these gross observations that at first the players learn to distrust each other, which puts them more frequently into the punishing DD state, after which the trend is reversed and they learn progressively to trust each other, as evidenced by increasing frequency of C. The matter, however, is more complex. The asymptotic steady state value of C, which is about 70 per cent, represents the average among the 70 pairs of subjects used in the experiment. This is not the modal value, however. Indeed, the distribution of 50-play blocks classified by the fraction of double-co-operative choices they contain is strongly bi-modal. This is shown in *Figure 4*,

Figure 3   *The Gross Trend is an Increase of Co-operative Response Frequency over 300 Successive Plays*

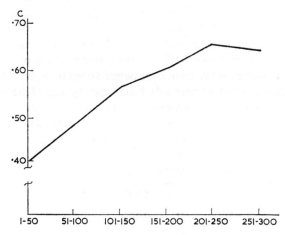

Figure 4   *Horizontal: Fraction of CC Responses in a Block of 50 Plays*
Vertical: Fraction of 50-play Blocks Corresponding to each Fraction of CC Responses

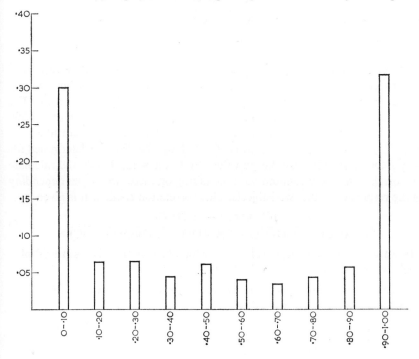

which makes it apparent that 50-play blocks are either predominantly co-operative or predominantly non-co-operative. The same is true of the player pairs. Their patterns of choices tend towards the extremes – either locking in on the CC response towards the end of the experimental session or on the DD response. The number of pairs locking in on the CC response is about three to four times the number locking in on the DD response.

Closely related to the 'lock-in' effect is the positive correlation between the frequencies of co-operative responses of paired subjects. *Table 1* shows these correlations, each over the ten pairs of subjects playing each of the seven games.

Table 1   *The product-moment correlations of the relative frequency of co-operative choice across the paired subjects in each of the seven games (ten pairs playing each game)*

Game $\rho C_1 C_2$	
I	0·997
II	0·995
III	0·982
IV	0·983
V	0·962
VI	0·921
VII	0·911

The correlations answer the question of whether co-operative responses tend to elicit co-operative responses, and vice versa, or whether, on the contrary, co-operative responses tend to elicit defecting responses. The former is the case. Moreover, there is evidence that in the course of the 300 play sessions the paired subjects tend to become more and more like each other. This can be observed in terms of correlation coefficients determined for each of the 50-play blocks. Assign value 1 to C and value 0 to D, and calculate the correlation of the random variable taking on these two values depending on the responses of the two subjects. This correlation coefficient is given by

$$\rho_0 = \frac{(CC)(DD) - (CD)(DC)}{\sqrt{(CC + CD)(CC + DC)(DD + CD)(DD + DC)}} \tag{5}$$

If we calculate the mean value of ρ_0 for each of the successive 50-play blocks we get the trend shown in *Table 2*.

Table 2   *The gross trend is an increase of correlation between the simultaneous responses of paired players*

50 play Block	1	2	3	4	5	6
ρ_0	0·15	0·34	0·46	0·55	0·64	0·61

The trend is unmistakably in the direction of greater positive correlation. We turn to the distribution of the lengths of runs. Consider three types of process, namely:

1 A process that can terminate at any given moment with the same probability. An example of such a process is the 'life' of a radioactive atom.
2 A process that terminates with the greater probability the longer it lasts. An example of this sort of process is human life.
3 A process that is the less likely to terminate the longer it lasts. Examples of this process are frequently given as durations of marriages, lengths of stay in a mental hospital, durations of employment, etc.

The fraction of the processes not yet terminated, plotted against time can be represented by an equation of the following type

$$P(t) = e^{-f(t)} \tag{6}$$

where $f(t)$ is a non-negative function of t and $P(t)$ is the fraction of processes not yet terminated. Clearly, $f(o) = 0$, since $P(o) = 1$. It is easily shown that for processes of type 1 the second derivative of $f(t)$ vanishes, i.e. $f(t)$ is linear with t; for processes of type 2 $f''(t) > 0$; and for processes of type 3, $f''(t) < 0$.

The distribution of all the runs taken from our data consisting of CC responses is definitely of type 3. The same is true of the distribution of the DD runs. From this one could draw the not implausible conclusion that both kinds of runs are self-enhancing: the longer they last, the longer they are likely to keep lasting. This is in line with our conjecture that trust breeds trust and distrust breeds distrust. Unfortunately the conclusion is not warranted without further evidence, because the convex upward character of $f(t)$ implied by its negative second derivative may be due to a 'natural selection effect', to be presently described.

The seemingly self-enhancing process which we observe in the distribution of CC and DD runs characterizes many real-life processes. For example, the duration of strikes in the United States and also the durations of wars for the past 150 years are known to be described by a type 3 process. It turns out, however, that distributions of this sort are compatible with the hypothesis that any given strike can end at any given moment with equal probability, i.e. for any given strike the probability that it will have lasted at least t days can very well be described by

$$P(t) = e^{-kt}$$

where k is a constant, i.e. quite analogously to the situation of radioactive decay, provided only that the parameter k is *itself* distributed throughout the 'population' of strikes. This sort of distribution would imply that strikes are of varying 'severity'. This, in turn, means that the more mild strikes are

O

settled first, which leaves the more severe strikes still unsettled. Hence the rate of settlement of strikes *decreases* as the duration of the still unsettled strikes increases. This, rather than the self-enhancing character of the duration of individual strikes, may underlie the type 3 process. This is the effect which we have called the 'natural selection effect': the more 'viable' processes are selected for, and so the rate of termination decreases.

Our situation is analogous. We have lumped all of the CC runs to determine the distribution of their durations. This was done in the interest of statistical stability. The larger the population whose statistics are estimated, the more reliable are the estimates. However, in lumping all the runs from all the subjects and all the seven games, we have obtained a mixed population. Suppose now that, for any given pair, a CC run is equally likely to terminate at any given time. If the propensity for ending such a run (i.e. the propensity for yielding to the temptation to defect) is not the same in every pair we can assume that those CC runs terminate first which stem from pairs where the propensity to defect from CC is greatest. This leaves the unterminated CC runs, belonging to the more steadfast pairs. Consequently, it appears as if the longer a CC run lasts, the longer it is likely to last. An entirely analogous argument applies to the DD runs.

The foregoing was meant to demonstrate that the distributions of lengths of runs which we obtain, although seemingly pointing towards self-enhancing processes, are nevertheless consistent with the null hypothesis, namely that any given run is equally likely to end at any moment. This does not mean, of course, that the null hypothesis is proved. In order to have good reasons to accept or to reject the null hypothesis, a finer statistical analysis is required, which we shall not pursue here. Suffice it to say that subsequent analysis has led us to the conclusion that the CC runs are indeed self-enhancing, i.e. the players tend to trust each other the more, the more times they have both played CC consecutively. The similar question regarding DD runs, however, remains open. There is no conclusive evidence that at least the male subjects tend to persist in the DD response, the more surely the more consecutive DD's have been played. If the self-enhancing character of DD runs is finally discorroborated the pronounced lock-in effect on DD is to be traced to other causes, such as the 'natural selection effect' described above.

The 'martyr runs' show a picture altogether different from the CC and DD runs. These are typically of short duration, usually not more than three or four in a row. Nevertheless, very long martyr runs occur now and then. The longest one we have seen was 72 plays long, a remarkable example of persistence of 'forgiveness' (since a martyr run is essentially equivalent to returning good for evil). Still this long run is only about one-seventh of the length prescribed in the New Testament which is 539 (7×77).

The martyr runs end in failures (i.e. the martyr turns to defection without having converted the defector) about $2\frac{1}{2}$ times more frequently than in successes. This is not a bad score, since in the course of a 300-play session several martyr runs may be attempted, and so the eventual success of one of them is not unlikely.

Mathematical models

Let us now examine some possible mathematical models of the process consisting of repeated Prisoner's Dilemma plays. Following the lead of stochastic learning theory, we shall concern ourselves with probabilities of responses. In particular, C is itself a probability of a response (the co-operative), and D is its complement.

We may conceive of two broad classes of model, (i) where certain probabilities of response are constant, and (ii) where probabilities of responses are adjustable in accordance with some learning law.

Some of these models we can reject immediately. For example, we cannot suppose that the probability of responding co-operatively is constant for a given individual, for if we did, we could not explain the time trends of this probability, nor the high correlations between members of randomly matched pairs.

We can also reject the model according to which the probability of responding co-operatively is adjusted independently by each player so as to maximize his expected gain. For suppose such to be the case. Then on any particular play, the probability of every joint response is the product of the probabilities of the component responses, i.e. $CC = C_1 C_2$; $CD = C_1 D_2$, etc. Then the expected gain of player 1 will be given by

$$G_1 = C_1 C_2 R + C_1 D_2 S + D_1 C_2 T + D_1 D_2 P \tag{7}$$

and of player 2 by

$$G_2 = C_1 C_2 R + D_1 C_2 S + C_1 D_2 T + D_1 D_2 P \tag{8}$$

Assuming that each player adjusts his own C_1, we differentiate expression (7) partially with respect to C_1 and (8) partially with respect to C_2. Since $D_1 = 1 - C_1$, $D_2 = 1 - C_2$, the result is

$$\frac{\partial G_1}{C_1} = C_2(R - T) + D_2(S - P) \tag{9}$$

$$\frac{\partial G_2}{C_2} = C_1(R - T) + D_1(S - P) \tag{10}$$

But in view of the inequalities $T > R > P > S$, the expressions on the left are always negative. Hence individual adjustment of C_i to maximize expected gain will always drive the two players towards complete non-co-operation, to which the 'strategic' analysis of the game also leads. Since human players do not usually end up in DD (at least not the population under discussion), we must also reject this model as inadequate.

Among the models with constant probabilities, one is particularly instructive. This is the so-called Markov model. We define the following *propensities* for co-operation in terms of certain conditional probabilities:

1 *x:* the probability of responding co-operatively, given that the last response was co-operative by both players.

2 *y:* the probability of responding co-operatively, given that the last response of the subject in question was co-operative, while the last response of the other player was defecting.

3 *z:* the probability of responding co-operatively, given that the last response of the subject in question was defecting, while the last response of the other player was co-operative.

4 *w:* the probability of responding co-operatively given that the last response was defecting by both players.

Let us now see what these propensities may mean psychologically. We note that x is a measure of the degree to which the players stick to the CC response. In a way, therefore, x is a measure of 'trustworthiness', since a large value of x means that a subject is not likely to betray the established mutual trust.

Next, y is a measure of the degree to which a player sticks with the C response in spite of the other's failure to reciprocate, hence, in a way, a measure of 'forgiveness' or of steadfastness in attempts to induce co-operation in a defector.

Further, z is a measure of the degree to which a player shifts from D to C in response to the other's unilateral co-operation, hence, in a way, a measure of 'responsiveness' or of 'repentance'.

Finally, w is a measure of the degree to which a player tends to *initiate* co-operation when neither co-operates, hence, in a way, a measure of 'trust'.

Consider now the two players as a system which at any specified time can be in one of four possible states, CC, CD, DC, and DD. The propensities x, y, z, and w determine the transition probabilities of the system from state to state. For example, the probability that the system passes from CC to CD is given by $x_1(1 - x_2)$, where the subscripts refer to the two subjects. This is so, because the transition in question was occasioned by the fact that player 1 stuck to C following a CC (the probability of which is x_1), while player 2 did not (the probability of which is $1 - x_2$). The probabilities are multiplied to give the probability of the joint event, because in the absence of communication the two events must be considered independent. Similarly, the transition CD to DC has probability $(1 - y_1)z_2$, and so on for all the 16 transition probabilities. We now have a Markov chain, as described in the system of equation (11). The primed quantities on the left denote the probabilities of the corresponding states of the plays following a given play.

$$CC' = CC\, x_1\, x_2 + CD\, y_1\, z_2 + DC\, z_1\, y_2 + DD\, w_1\, w_2$$
$$CD' = CC\, x_1(1 - x_2) + CD\, y_1(1 - z_2) + DC\, z_1(1 - y_2) +$$
$$DD\, w_1(1 - w_2) \quad (11)$$

$$DC' = CC(1 - x_1)x_2 + CD(1 - y_1)z_2 + DC(1 - z_1)y_2 + DD(1 - w_1)w_2$$
$$DD' = CC(1 - x_1)(1 - x_2) + CD(1 - y_1)(1 - z_2) + DC(1 - z_1)(1 - y_2)$$
$$+ DD(1 - w_1)(1 - w_2)$$

If the initial distribution of the four states is known, equations (11) determine the distribution for all future times. It would be easy to test this model if we had a population of 'identical' subjects, all characterized by the same propensities x, y, z, and w. This cannot, of course, be expected from a human population. Still it is instructive to know to what extent our data can be described assuming a *hypothetical* population of identical subjects. From our data we know that the values of CC, CD, DC, and DD approach a constant value towards the end of the 300 plays, when averaged over the entire population of games and subjects. Equations (11) also predict an ultimate steady-state distribution for the four states, which can be obtained by setting $(CC)' = (CC)$, $(CD)' = (CD)$, etc. Therefore if our model is valid the observed steady-state values ought to be equal to the steady state values predicted by equations (11), when the proper values are substituted for x, y, z, and w. But these can be estimated directly from the data, namely from the

Figure 5 *Predicted and observed Time Courses for CC*

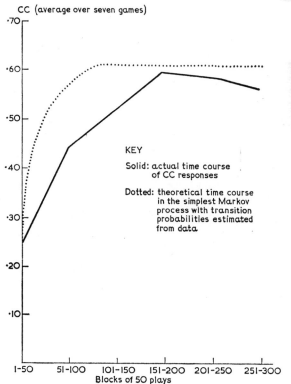

CC (average over seven games)

KEY

Solid: actual time course of CC responses

Dotted: theoretical time course in the simplest Markov process with transition probabilities estimated from data

Blocks of 50 plays

last 100 plays when the frequencies of the four responses have already reached steady-state values. We know that the steady-state values will coincide with those predicted by x, y, z, and w estimated from the steady-state portion of the curve, because these values make the Markov equations for the steady-state identities. To test the validity of the model we must inquire also whether the time courses of the four types of response are predicted by the same values of x, y, z, and w. The comparison between the predicted and the observed time courses for CC is shown in *Figure 5*. Regardless of how accurately the initial frequency of CC was estimated, we see that the discrepancy is considerable, since at any rate the steady state should have been reached before the 100th play, whereas in our experiment the steady state is not reached until about the 200th play.

The value of a mathematical model is revealed in its failure as frequently as in its success. The simple Markov chain (as our model is called) evidently fails to account for the time courses of the response categories. We are now in a position to pursue our investigation further to see just where and how the model fails.

Three sources of failure immediately suggest themselves. One, which has already been mentioned, is the dubious assumption of a population of 'identical' players. As a rule, any characteristic varies in a population, and we have no reason to expect that x, y, z, and w are exceptions. If we wish to correct this error we must devise methods of estimating these parameters for individuals, or at least for pairs instead of for the whole population. But there are also other possible sources of errors. For example, there may be more than just four relevant states of the system. The probability of a co-operative response may depend not only on the outcome of the last response but also on outcomes of previous responses. However, as long as the number of responses on which this probability depends is fixed, the model can still be represented by a Markov chain of the same sort, albeit with a larger number of states.

An interesting special case is a Markov chain with 'absorbing' states. These states have the property that once they are entered they cannot be left, i.e. the transition probabilities out of these states are all zero. Such models have been used with some success in certain learning situations and in situations involving a conflict within a subject between a tendency to yield to social pressure and a tendency to stand firm.[2] Absorbing states in the latter context were postulated to represent a subject's decision to do one or the other, i.e. to 'resolve the conflict'.

In Prisoner's Dilemma the same interpretation applies. It may happen that one or both of the subjects make a decision henceforth to co-operate or henceforth not to co-operate, regardless of what happens. This is the case of the perfect 'lock in'. To be sure, we can never observe this decision directly, because even long uninterrupted runs do not necessarily mean that they would go on for ever. However, we can assume that these decisions happen with certain probabilities (i.e. the probabilities of transition into the absorbing states) and see how well the resulting Markov chains describe our data.

Another class of models departs from the simple Markov chains in the sense that the transition probabilities are no longer considered to be constant. For example, the propensities x, y, z, and w can be considered as probabilities of classes of responses as in stochastic learning theory. These probabilities are constantly changing as a result of learning, and the problem now is to estimate the learning parameters. Here it is appropriate to point out that in the case of two interacting players, the estimation problem is incomparably more difficult than in the case of a single individual in the simplest learning situation. There, we recall, ordinarily four parameters must be estimated, α, β, λ, and μ. If the same model is extended to two interacting individuals, as in Prisoner's Dilemma, there are $4^4 = 256$ parameters to estimate, a herculean and, essentially, thankless job; for even supposing the 256 parameters are accurately estimated for one pair and the behaviour is thereby accounted for, there is little point in developing a theory of the simplest conceivable mixed-motive situation (which is, after all, our objective) on the basis of 256 determinants of behaviour.

In order to construct a tractable theory, we must look for the simplest model from which we can nevertheless gain some insight into the situation. We shall describe just one such model, not with a view to describing our data accurately by means of it but with a view to deriving a possibly important principle governing situations of the sort represented by Prisoner's Dilemma.

We shall suppose that individuals are not characterized by fixed values of x, y, z, and w, but that they *adjust* these values in the direction of increasing their expected gain. Whether this is actually done and, if so, how, will not be our concern. We are not seeking a realistic model, only a heuristic one. The meaning of a heuristic model will, I hope, become clear from what follows.

To simplify matters still further, we shall suppose that three of the propensities, namely, y, z, and w, are fixed and only one, namely x, is 'adjusted'.

Since each of the players adjusts his x independently of the other, we shall assign these values independently: x_1 will characterize player 1 and x_2 player 2. Moreover, to fix ideas, we shall suppose that $y = z = 0$; $w = 1$ for both players. In terms of their behaviour this means the following: Whenever a player is the only co-operator, he immediately shifts to D (since $y = 0$). Whenever a player is the only defector he plays D again (since $z = 0$). Whenever both have defected both shift to C (since $w = 1$).

These players, it appears, are governed by the simplest type of psychology; when in three of the four states they do the same thing if the pay-off is positive and shift to the other response if the pay-off is negative. If they followed this principle also in the remaining state, when CC obtains, i.e. if x were equal to 1 for both, the model would become trivial. For then, as is easily seen, the players would lock in on the CC response after at most two plays and would for ever stay with it.*

Human players are not as fortunate as the two simpletons just described. Very few pairs succeed in locking in on CC from the very start and sticking to it. However, as we have said, x is variable. This means that our 'simpletons' have just one unfortunate human trait: they yield to temptation to defect when in CC (so as to get a bigger gain in T). The question before us is what will happen if each player tries to adjust his x so as to maximize the expected pay-off.

To calculate the expected pay-offs we must solve the Markov equations for the steady state, setting $y = z = 0$ and $w = 1$, in terms of x_1 and x_2. The solution is as follows:

$$CC = \frac{1}{2 + x_1 + x_2 - 3x_1 x_2}$$

$$CD = \frac{x_1(1 - x_2)}{2 + x_1 + x_2 - 3x_1 x_2}$$

$$DC = \frac{x_2(1 - x_1)}{2 + x_1 + x_2 - 3x_1 x_2}$$

$$DD = \frac{1 - x_1 x_2}{2 + x_1 + x_2 - 3x_1 x_2}$$

(12)

We further confine ourselves to games in which $S = -T$, as is the case with the games we have used. Then the expected gains become for the players 1 and 2 respectively:

$$G_1 = \frac{R + T(x_2 - x_1) + P(1 - x_1 x_2)}{2 + x_1 + x_2 - 3x_1 x_2}$$

$$G_2 = \frac{R + T(x_1 - x_2) + P(1 - x_1 x_2)}{2 + x_1 + x_2 - 3x_1 x_2}$$

(13)

To maximize these expected gains, each player differentiates the corresponding expressions with respect to the variable he controls and sets the derivative equal to zero.

Solving the resulting pair of equations for x_1 and x_2, we get the equilibrium point at which the expected gains of both players are stationary, namely

$$x_1 = x_2 = x^\star = \frac{2T - P - 3R + \sqrt{28T^2 + 9R^2 - 3P^2 + 2RP}}{2(3T - P)}$$

(14)

We must not conclude, however, that the players will settle with these values of x_1 and x_2. In order for this to happen, the equilibrium must be stable. In other words, small departures from the equilibrium in either direction must give rise to 'restoring forces' tending to bring the variables back to the equi-

---

* If they happen to start in CC, they stay with it; if in DD, both shift to CC and stay there; if in CD or DC, the next state is DD, followed by CC.

librium. It is easily seen, however, that the equilibrium at $x^\star$ is unstable. The slightest deviation in the positive direction makes both $\dfrac{\partial G_1}{\partial x_1}$ and $\dfrac{\partial G_2}{\partial x_2}$ positive, which enhances the deviation in the same direction, driving x_1 and x_2 upward. The slightest deviation in the negative direction has the opposite effect. Hence we see that $x^\star$ is not the steady-state value of x_1 and x_2 but rather a point on the 'watershed divide'. In other words, values of x on either side of this divide will tend to move away from it, not towards it. It follows that the larger the magnitude of $x^\star$, the more *difficult* it is for the players to achieve full co-operation, because the higher must their x's be *in the first place* to get on the 'right side' of the watershed.

Thus, the model just described predicts the rank order of our games, according to the frequency of co-operative responses to be expected. The smaller the magnitude of $x^\star$ the more co-operation we ought to expect in the game.

Let us now substitute the pay-offs of our seven games into R, T, and P given by equation (14). We obtain the following results:

Table 3

Game	$x^\star$
I	0·855
II	0·987
III	1·11
IV	0·913
V	1·20
VI	0·984
VII	1·03

This model predicts, therefore, that in Games III, V, and VII, x is driven towards zero, since the 'watershed' is beyond the possible range of $x^\star$. However, even with $x = 0$, $C > 0$, since in the final state the progression will be an alternating sequence of CC and DD (since $w = 1$). There will also be C responses before x reaches zero, about which we can say nothing without knowing the *time course* of x, which is determined by the dynamics of the process, not considered in this model.

At any rate, it seems reasonable to predict the rank order of the seven games as corresponding to increasing magnitudes of $x^\star$. This results in the following rank order, according to expected frequency of co-operative choices: I, IV, VI, II, VII, III, V. The only discrepancy is the low rank of Game II, which ranks first in our experiment (cf. (4) on page 380).

The reason for the low rank of II seems clear. The 'sobering' effect of its large punishment ($P = -9$) is not felt when $w = 1$, because in this case each DD is immediately followed by CC. When we change the value of w to 0·25, which is close to its value estimated from the data, the rank of Game II goes up and, in fact surpasses that of I, as it does in the experiment.

It seems, then, that by adjusting x, y, z, and w properly we can fit our model to the observations. However, this does not mean that the model 'explains' the experimental findings. We feel that a mathematical model ought to be designed not to finish an investigation but to start it. This is what was meant by the heuristic nature of the model: its purpose was not to explain or to predict the data so much as to teach us something of the principles underlying the situation. The principle just derived was one of *instability*.

There are strong indications that instability is a principle feature of situations like Prisoner's Dilemma.* Trust breeds trust; mistrust breeds mistrust. There is a certain *threshold* of trust (represented by x^* in our model). If the threshold is passed, trust increases, and with it co-operation. If the players' trust (or, more appropriately, trustworthiness in this case) falls short of the threshold the situation deteriorates.

It turns out that the same situation obtains in the more involved stochastic learning models, which were mentioned but not developed in this paper.

Population profiles

There is another sense in which the mathematical models proposed here are heuristic, namely, in the sense that they single out variables or parameters, which become interesting in their own right, regardless of whether the models ever get to the stage of being put to a test. Consider, for example, the propensities x, y, z, and w. They were singled out for attention, because they are components of the transition probabilities of a Markov chain and of more involved models. The Markov chain failed as a model of Prisoner's Dilemma, and the more involved models have not yet been tested. But we need not wait until we are in a position to test the models. We can examine the propensities x, y, z, and w, as they appear in the data, because they are in themselves interesting indices of behaviour.

We shall estimate these propensities in a gross manner, namely by averaging their values in each of the seven games. The values of x, y, z, and w will then constitute a 'profile' of the population – indices of the population's 'trustworthiness', 'forgiveness', 'repentance', and 'trust'. It is instructive to compare the magnitudes of these indices within a population and the magnitudes of each of the indices across populations. The values of x, y, z, and w in each of the seven games are shown in *Table 4*. The values of $1 - z$ and $1 - w$ are also shown, because the magnitudes of these variables are suggestive, as we shall see.

We note that x is consistently the highest of the propensities and w is the

---

* Compare the basic instability of arms races in the mathematical model of this process developed by Lewis F. Richardson.[3]

lowest. In terms of our psychological interpretation, we could say that our population is characterized by high 'trustworthiness' and by low 'trust'.

Table 4 *The values of the propensities x, y, z, and w observed in the population of male students*

Game	x	y	z	$1 - z$	w	$1 - w$
I	0·919	0·445	0·446	0·554	0·300	0·700
II	0·930	0·417	0·533	0·467	0·318	0·682
III	0·832	0·336	0·343	0·657	0·151	0·849
IV	0·906	0·417	0·397	0·603	0·182	0·818
V	0·705	0·288	0·247	0·753	0·050	0·950
VI	0·852	0·435	0·390	0·610	0·210	0·790
VII	0·792	0·446	0·335	0·665	0·200	0·800

Next, compare x, y, $1 - z$, and $1 - w$. Each of these four parameters represents a propensity to try *to remain in the same state*. For example, x is the tendency to repeat C (after a CC); $1 - w$ is the tendency to repeat D (after a DD); $1 - z$ is the tendency of player 1 to repeat D after DC or of player 2 to repeat D after CD, etc. We might suppose that these repetition propensities would be related to the associated pay-offs, namely x to R, $1 - w$ to P, $1 - z$ to T, and y to S. The basic inequality satisfied by the pay-offs of Prisoner's Dilemma is $T > R > P > S$. On this basis, we might expect $1 - z > x > 1 - w > y$. Let us see how the observed rank orders compare with those expected from the pay-offs.

In Game I we get $x > 1 - w > 1 - z > y$. Here $1 - z$ was 'demoted' from first to third rank. In Game II the same rank order is observed as in Game I. In Game III $1 - w > x > 1 - z > y$, that is $1 - z$ was demoted and $1 - w$ promoted. In Game IV the rank order is the same as in I and II. In Game V $1 - w > 1 - z > z > y$, which is accounted for by the promotion of $1 - w$. In Game VI the rank order is the same as in Games I, II, and IV. In Game VII $1 - w > x > 1 - z > y$, again accountable by the promotion of $1 - w$ and the demotion of $1 - z$.

We conclude that all the departures from the rank order prescribed by the pay-offs are explained either by a demotion of $1 - z$ (in Games I, II, IV, VI) or by a promotion of $1 - w$ (in Game V) or by both (in Games III, VII).

Psychologically, the demotion of $1 - z$ (i.e. the promotion of z) means that subjects respond more co-operatively to the other's co-operative response than is accounted for by the relative magnitudes of the pay-offs. This is true in the four games where the co-operation is highest (I, II, IV, VI). The promotion of $1 - w$ means that the subjects persist in DD more than is accounted for by the relative magnitudes of the pay-offs. This is observed in the game with the smallest C, namely Game V. Note that the two effects, the demotion of $1 - z$ and the promotion of $1 - w$ are opposite: the former indicates a greater tendency towards co-operation, the latter a greater tendency towards persistent non-co-operation. In the two games intermediate between I, II, IV, and VI, on the one hand, and V, on the other, both effects are operating.

Presently we shall pursue this analysis with respect to another population of subjects.

In our discussion of mathematical models we called attention to the importance of the constants (the parameters) of the model as the 'carriers' of the theoretical concepts embodied in or generated by the model. In our search for a mathematical model appropriate for Prisoner's Dilemma we have not yet found such a set of constants. The frequencies of co-operative responses are certainly not adequate to serve in this capacity, for these frequencies are not typically constant throughout a session, and, moreover, the changes in C_1 and C_2 are strongly correlated (cf. *Table I*), indicating that the variables are subjected to strong interaction effects. It would be desirable to find variables which characterize a given individual or a given game or the condition under which the game is played but are 'immune' to interaction effects.

When in our Markov-chain model the conditional propensities x, y, z, and w were singled out, we hoped that they would satisfy both these criteria. It did not turn out so, although they satisfied the criteria better than C_1 and C_2. Our data yield evidence that the time variation of the conditional propensities is not nearly as great as that of C. Nor are the conditional propensities of one player as strongly correlated with those of the player paired with him as are the corresponding Cs. Indeed, while x_1 and x_2 are still considerably correlated, the correlation between w_1 and w_2 is weak, while the y's and z's show no discernible correlation across pairs of players. Thus, we may consider the conditional propensities as 'way stations' to parameters which, we hope, will eventually be found to satisfy the conditions mentioned above.

Rather than continue the search for the fundamental parameters, we shall be, for the time being, satisfied with these conditional probabilities, estimated for the population playing each of the seven games, as a basis of comparison with other populations. Clearly the conditional propensities will give us more information in such comparisons than the single measure C – the overall amount of co-operation achieved. Suppose, for example, one population shows more co-operative responses than another. Examination of propensities will reveal whether this difference is due to the fact that the first population shows more steadfastness in sticking to CC (greater x), or more persistence in unilateral co-operation (greater y), or more responsiveness to the other's co-operative choices (greater z), or a greater tendency to get out of the DD trap (greater w).

It may also happen that two populations show the same C but entirely different profiles in the conditional propensities.

In what follows we shall compare the performance in Prisoner's Dilemma of the 70 male students, which we have just discussed, with that of 70 female students, playing the same seven games under the same conditions.

Table 5 shows the comparison between the C's. Clearly, the men show a higher level of co-operation than the women.

Table 5 *Comparison of frequencies of co-operative choices (per cent) between men and women*

Game	Men	Women
I	73·4	34·4
II	77·4	26·5
III	45·8	27·7
IV	66·2	48·2
V	26·8	10·8
VI	63·5	54·6
VII	59·4	30·3

Table 6 shows the conditional propensities of women, analogous to those of men shown in *Table 4*. We note that women have smaller x in every one of the seven games, smaller y in four games, smaller z in all seven games, and

Table 6 *The values of the propensities x, y, z, and w observed in the population of female students*

Game	x	y	z	$1 - z$	w	$1 - w$
I	0·791	0·442	0·290	0·710	0·184	0·816
II	0·717	0·340	0·258	0·742	0·185	0·815
III	0·735	0·378	0·243	0·757	0·074	0·926
IV	0·868	0·429	0·326	0·674	0·185	0·815
V	0·590	0·291	0·233	0·767	0·055	0·945
VI	0·845	0·376	0·180	0·820	0·236	0·764
VII	0·792	0·352	0·260	0·740	0·175	0·825

smaller w in four games. Thus, the smaller amount of co-operation shown by the women must be attributed to the lower values of their 'trustworthiness' parameter (x) and their 'response to the other's co-operation' parameter, or the 'repentance' parameter (z). The differences in the 'forgiveness' parameters are probably not significant. Indeed, the mean values of y are exactly equal in men and women. The mean value of w in women is 0·150 compared to 0·202 in men. This difference is probably significant, but we are not sure.

Let us now examine the rank orders of the propensities in women. Comparing the persistence propensities in women, we have the following results:

Table 7

Game	Rank Order	Obtained from $1 - z > x > 1 - w > y$ by
I	$1 - w > x > 1 - z > y$	Demoting $1 - z$, promoting $1 - w$
II	$1 - w > 1 - z > x > y$	Promoting $1 - w$
III	$1 - w > 1 - z > x > y$	Promoting $1 - w$
IV	$x > 1 - w > 1 - z > y$	Demoting $1 - z$
V	$1 - w > 1 - z > x > y$	Promoting $1 - w$
VI	$x > 1 - z > 1 - w > y$	Demoting $1 - z$
VII	$1 - w > x > 1 - z > y$	Demoting $1 - z$, promoting $1 - w$

As we have noted, 'demoting $1 - z$' can be ascribed to co-operative tendencies, while 'promoting $1 - w$' can be ascribed to non-co-operative tendencies in excess of those which can be accounted for by the relative magnitudes of the pay-offs.

While in men the co-operative tendency so defined is seen in four games, in women this tendency is seen to operate in only two (IV and VI), which, incidentally, are the two games where the women co-operated most. While in men the non-co-operative tendency was seen in only one game (V), in women it was seen in three (II, III, and V), in which least co-operation was observed. In both men and women the mixed tendencies were seen in the two remaining games.

In this way the gross result (women co-operated less than men in Prisoner's Dilemma) can be subjected to a finer analysis, which focuses on some possibly important psychological differences. It appears, from the results of our experiments and from the analysis of the results, that it is possible to combine psychological richness with rigorous methods of observation and analysis. In the opinion of this writer the combination is best accomplished not by introducing psychological intricacies into the experiment from the start but rather by finding experiments which are in themselves extremely simple but which at the same time provide opportunities for deriving psychological richness from an intricate analysis of the data. Mixed-motive games like Prisoner's Dilemma (there are many others with very different strategic structures) can serve as an especially useful tool in such investigation.

ACKNOWLEDGEMENT

The experiments reported in this paper are part of research work supported by the National Institutes of Health, United States Public Health Service, Grants M-4238-01, M-4238-02, M-4238-03, M-4238-04, at the Mental Health Research Institute, University of Michigan.

REFERENCES

1 R. R. Bush & F. Mosteller (1955) 3 L. F. Richardson (1960)
2 B. P. Cohen (1963)

29 · A Threshold Method for Utility Estimation and Resolution of Conflict

CHARLES D. FLAGLE

Introduction

Operational research studies in the health services have led naturally to the consideration of medical decisions in screening, diagnosis, and therapy. These problems at the heart of the medical care process are reflected everywhere in the planning and organization of facilities and services.

As operations analysts, our awareness of these matters has been brought about by the existence of disagreement or conflict within health services over policies with respect to screening, diagnosis, and therapeutic programmes. Such conflicts usually occur in programmes for highly prevalent diseases for which large demands are made on limited resources and for which diagnostic procedures lack both sensitivity and specificity. Lack of sensitivity implies the inability of a diagnostic procedure to identify all positive cases, introducing the danger of not providing treatment when needed. Lack of specificity implies some false positive indications, consequently some unnecessary demand on resources if the indicated action is taken. The implications of the lack of precision in diagnostic and screening procedures are discussed by Kurlander et al[1,2]. The nature of the resulting conflict is treated by Scheff[3]. Blumberg[4] presents the problem of screening for diabetes in terms of probabilities and costs involved in treatment and failure to treat.

A constantly recurring decision problem for physicians is either to choose a therapeutic procedure, costly in terms of medical resources, in the face of uncertainties in the evidence of a disease, or to run the risk of withholding therapy, with consequences which may be very costly in terms of the patient's life, contagion in the community, or damage to the reputation of the physician or health service involved. The problem has its counterpart in many areas of life, notably those involving expenditure for protection against possible disaster.

Many medical decision problems lend themselves to expression, if not yet solution, in terms of formal statistical decision processes. The quantitative

399

problems in direct application are twofold: first, the determination of the probabilities relating symptoms to disease, and, second, the estimation of value measures, utilities, or losses associated with therapeutic actions.

Many statistics now available on the precision of diagnostic procedures are not useful because probabilities and subjective values are confounded. The clinician or pathologist is sometimes influenced in his interpretation by the magnitude of the cost elements present in treatment. The development of data-processing systems gives great promise for widespread availability of the necessary statistics for decision, and much work is being done in correlating symptom complexes and diseases. However, the statistics alone are not sufficient for decision, and their availability only serves to bring into focus our weakness in handling the value problem.

In early efforts to estimate entries in the loss matrix for a public health problem, cast as a game against nature, Flagle and Lechat [5] met with a group of physicians with experience in public health administration. These physicians immediately asked for a definition of their role. Were they involved in an individual patient–doctor relationship, responsible at the moment for the well-being of one person? Or were they in a position of medical administration, responsible for allocation of resources for the community at large? It is not surprising that the values placed upon outcomes differed in these traditionally different roles; nor does difference itself imply conflict. It is only when difference is great enough to cause decision-makers in different roles to espouse different courses of action that we are concerned. Thus, it is with an interest in resolution of conflict that we approach the formal treatment of the problem of medical diagnosis and therapy.

Our efforts to estimate disutilities, losses, or costs directly or to apply standard gamble techniques to measure them, particularly the loss associated with the potentially dire consequences of not providing therapy when needed, have not been successful. Sessions with clinicians and public health physicians have produced a consistent set of objections in addition to those previously noted; the terms 'utility', 'cost', and 'gamble' are objectionable in our context. The bare use of a single probability associated with outcomes obscures the subtleties of the influence of prevalence of disease, prevalence of symptoms, or precision of diagnostic procedures. The standard gamble, in its conciseness, loses verisimilitude for our purpose, even if we make it more acceptable semantically. We have sought some modification of the experimental situation and are currently working with the format of decision theory itself as a means for eliciting some quantitative value expressions from people accustomed to the real decision situation.

The example below presents first a description of one experimental situation and follows with the decision-theoretic representation of the experiment. The particular clinical situation has been chosen because it lends itself more readily than most others examined to expression in familiar decision-theory terminology. It should be kept in mind that our motivation here is not to attempt to demonstrate the general usefulness of existing decision models for medical purposes but to deal with the problem of measuring subjective utility.

An experiment in utility estimation

Consider the position of a physician, the subject of our experiment, treating an ill child who displays a general malaise, loss of appetite, unexplained fever, a heart murmur, and some recent history of lacerations. In about 30 per cent of the cases in which these symptoms are noted the disease, sub-acute bacterial endocarditis,* is present, and it is fatal if not treated quickly. Treatment is relatively costly: about six weeks of hospital care are required with continuous heavy doses of penicillin.

There is one more set of tests that can be made, at very little cost. For the purpose of experiment we will let the precision of this set of tests vary, beginning with the assumption that it is completely sensitive and specific: i.e. it neither fails to indicate the disease if present nor does it indicate it if it is not. Were such a test available, the choice of treatment would be simple; a positive reading results in admission to hospital, a negative reading leads to a search for some other explanation.

In reality, a totally sensitive test is not available and the ultimate decision must be made with the knowledge that the disease may be present, even though a negative reading results. For our purpose we will regard the sensitivity of the test as a variable, to see how it affects decision. If human nature holds here as in other things a very small probability of a false negative, say that of being involved in an aeroplane crash or an accident, would probably not lead us to act. But suppose the probability of false negative indication reaches some typical statistician's α level, say, 0·05. The chances of the child's having the disease, even though the last test showed negative, is 5 in 100.

In an early experiment our physician subject stated with little deliberation that in these circumstances he would treat the patient. With a drop in sensitivity to 0·95 we had already passed the threshold of a change to a conservative decision of admission to hospital on the basis of symptoms alone. Note that such a policy would treat inappropriately 70 per cent of patients with the particular symptom complex. Subsequent discussions developed the opinion that only with a series of carefully timed blood cultures would the policy adopted under certainty be acceptable. The sensitivity of the tests should apparently be in the neighbourhood of 0·98 at the threshold of acceptability of a negative test as a basis for deferment of treatment.

The incidence of sub-acute bacterial endocarditis is low; we do not touch significantly here on the complicating problem of waste of resources through inappropriate hospital treatment. However, enough quantitative information has been gathered from the case to permit us to deal formally with some value aspects of the decisions involved in it.

* Present knowledge of this percentage and subsequent probabilities is not precise. Values are assumed within realistic ranges and stated for the experiment.

An analytic expression of the diagnostic and therapeutic problem

The substance of the foregoing can be expressed in the form of a game against Nature. (In fact, as presented, it could be stated as a standard gamble, but the decision-theory format permits a wider generalization.) Following the nomenclature of Chernoff and Moses,[6] the elements of the problem are the following:

States of Nature

θ_1 — Sub-acute bacterial endocarditis (SBE)

θ_2 — Not sub-acute bacterial endocarditis

A priori probability, for the set of patients displaying the stated symptoms

$$P\{\theta_1\}\ 0\cdot3$$
$$P\{\theta_2\}\ 0\cdot7$$

Sensitivity and specificity of the final diagnostic procedure where X_1 and X_2 are respectively positive and negative indications of θ_1 and θ_2.

Sensitivity $P\{X_1/\theta_1\}$ probability of a true positive indication

$P\{X_2/\theta_1\}$ probability of a false negative indication

$P\{X_1/\theta_2\}$ probability of a false positive indication

Specificity $P\{X_2/\theta_2\}$ probability of a true negative indication

Actions

a_1 – admit to hospital and treat for SBE

a_2 – not treat for SBE, but continue diagnosis.

Strategies

$$S_1: \begin{matrix} X_1 \longrightarrow a_1 \\ X_2 \longrightarrow a_2 \end{matrix} \qquad S_3: \begin{matrix} X_1 \longrightarrow a_2 \\ X_2 \longrightarrow a_2 \end{matrix}$$

$$S_2: \begin{matrix} X_1 \longrightarrow a_1 \\ X_2 \longrightarrow a_1 \end{matrix} \qquad S_4: \begin{matrix} X_1 \longrightarrow a_2 \\ X_2 \longrightarrow a_1 \end{matrix}$$

Each of the four strategies has a special significance. S_1 is appropriate for decision under certainty of diagnosis, otherwise its choice indicates faith in diagnosis. S_2 is a safe, or conservative strategy, since it rules out possibility of incurring the high loss Q. S_3 is a 'head in the sand' policy, ignoring the danger of Q. S_4 is just perverse; it takes actions opposite to those indicated by the diagnosis.

Loss Matrix – $L(a/\theta)$, where c represents the cost of hospital treatment and Q, the high cost of failure to treat when necessary, is the unknown. The cost of not treating when not necessary is taken as 0.

	θ_1	θ_2
a_1	c	c
a_2	Q	0

Given a number to represent Q, and a set of $P\{X/\theta\}$, the optimal strategy could be determined according to several criteria. Our plan here is to begin with an optimal strategy under certainty, and through manipulation of variables to determine Q when a Bayes strategy is the criterion.* The decision under certainty, i.e. for complete precision of diagnosis, can be represented graphically as in *Figure 1*, where the $L(\theta, s)$ are the expected losses given by the relationship,

$$L(\theta, S) = \sum_a \sum_X L\{a/\theta\} \cdot P\{X/\theta\} \cdot P\{a/X\}$$

where $P\{a/X\}$ is 1 when strategy s calls for a/X; otherwise $\{Pa/X\} = 0$.

Figure 1   *Plot of $L(\theta, S)$ for all Strategies when $P\{X_1/\theta_1\} = 1$ and $P\{X_2/\theta 2\} = 1$*

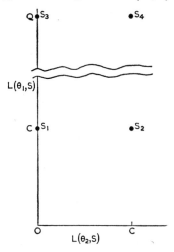

The effect of reducing sensitivity and specificity of the diagnostic test is to move the point representing S_1 upwards and to the right with the following co-ordinates in *Figure 2*:

$$L(S_1, \theta_1) = P\{X_1/\theta_1\}c + P\{X_2/\theta_1\}Q$$
$$L(S_1, \theta_2) = P\{X_1/\theta_2\}c + P\{X_2/\theta_2\}0$$

Note that points representing S_2 and S_3 are unaffected, while S_4 becomes less costly.

When, with diminishing sensitivity and specificity, the point representing S_1 reaches the loss line supporting S_2, we have reached a threshold of optimality of S_2, in that both are Bayes strategies minimizing expected loss. Note that in the experimental situation we have not had to discuss losses at all, just vary probabilities to find the threshold of acceptability of a new strategy.

* The acceptance of Bayes strategy as the criterion cannot be taken for granted. Under certainty, the same strategy, S_1, satisfies both Bayes and minimax criteria. At the hint of uncertainty some subjects (parents not physicians) have shifted immediately to S_2.

Once determined, the threshold fixes the geometry of the convex set. The geometric definition of indifference between strategies is that the line connecting the two equally optimal strategies must be a segment of the constant loss line supporting the two points on the convex set representing the strategies. It is a simple matter then to determine what the value of Q, noted as $Q^\star$,

Figure 2   *Plot of $L(\theta, S)$ in the Convex Set when $P\{X_1/\theta_1\} < 1$, $P\{X_2/\theta_2\} < 1$, and S_1 and S_2 are Simultaneously Optimal*

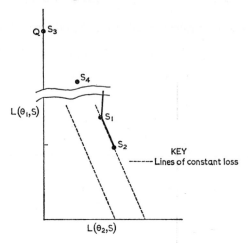

would have to be to satisfy this condition. Noting that the slope of the family of constant-loss lines is $-P(\theta_2)/P(\theta_1)$, an equation of slopes follows from *Figure 2*.

$$-\frac{L(\theta_1, S_1) - L(\theta_1, S_2)}{L(\theta_2, S_2) - L(\theta_2, S_1)} = -\frac{P\{X_1/\theta_1\}c + P\{X_2/\theta_1\}Q^\star - c}{c - P\{X_1/\theta_2\}c} = -\frac{P(\theta_2)}{P(\theta_1)}$$

from which

$$Q^\star = \frac{c}{P\{X_2/\theta_1\}}\left[\frac{P(\theta_2)}{P(\theta_1)} \cdot P\{X_2/\theta_2\} + P\{X_2/\theta_1\}\right]$$

Note that $Q^\star$ is expressed in terms of c. Either Q or c, or their ratio, might be unknown in a particular situation. The main point in the utility estimation procedure is that $Q^\star$ is a threshold value of Q, above and below which strategies S_2 and S_1, respectively, are optimal.

Resolution of conflict

We could say that internal conflict in the case just given exists if some of the decision-makers involved place the loss of failure to treat a positive case, relative to the cost of treatment, above, and some below the threshold $Q^\star$. The case of the child with symptoms of SBE does not provide a clear-cut example of such conflict. Because of the rarity of the disease and its symptoms, one does not place a high opportunity cost on choice of a safe or conservative policy. However, in a disease covered by a large public health programme, in competition with others for restricted resources, such conflicts do exist. The utility in question is often not Q, the value of life, but c, the resource cost of therapy. In general, the physician facing an individual patient is less likely to place as high an opportunity cost on the care of false positives as does the administrator who knows first hand what service is denied to others thereby. On the other hand, the physician may include in Q a subjective component related to his concern over failure to treat false negatives, when subsequent events show treatment to have been required.

A conflict over choice of strategy is represented in *Figure 3*, which is derived from the earlier example. In words, decision-maker A has placed a much higher cost on treatment than has B, although, as drawn, both place the same high loss, Q, on not providing treatment when it is needed.

Figure 3   *A Convex Set of Decision-makers A and B*

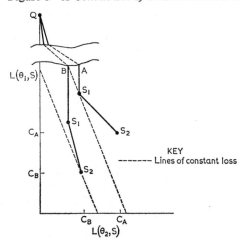

Some of the traditional notions of resolution of conflict are helpful for further discussion. The standard reference here is Mary Parker Follett, whose essay, 'Constructive Conflict[7] listed three means of conflict resolution: dominance, compromise, and integration. The meaning of the first two is self-evident; the third is essentially a study of the elements of the conflict to determine what changes in the environment are needed to satisfy both parties to the conflict. Another form of integration takes place when the conflict causes a change or reconciliation in values. Opportunity for all three of Follett's methods of resolution can be seen in our example.

Dominance of the conflict occurs when one party has the authority to choose his optimal strategy, and does so. In medical problems involving a doctor–patient relationship the physician has the authority for hospital admission and treatment.

Compromise may be made by mixing strategies, choosing what is optimal for A some of the time; what is optimal for B on other occasions.

Integration through environmental change may be brought about in several ways. Improvement of diagnostic procedures can make S_1 optimal for both A and B. Similarly, a change in the *a priori* probability $P(\theta_1)$, will, within limits, let S_1 or S_2 be simultaneously optimal for A and B. If A's higher cost of treatment is explained by opportunity cost an increase in available facilities and services will diminish the opportunity cost so that A's set in *Figure 3* approaches B's.

Integration through conciliation of values is made not by changing the physical environment but by changing the way in which both the issue and the environment are seen by the conflicting parties. In our example pictured in *Figure 3* it was suggested that the conflict lay in differing views of the magnitude of the opportunity cost contained in the total cost of hospital treatment, based in turn on different knowledge of alternative needs for the facilities. Conciliation may result from a sharing of the knowledge or opinions which determine the opportunity cost for each of the conflicting parties. This form of resolution of conflict is embodied in Alfred North Whitehead's notion of 'concrescence', a growing together of disparate components of a system into a new unity of existence.*

Mary Follett, who was, incidentally, at Newnham College, Cambridge, for a time while Whitehead was teaching mathematics at Trinity College, expresses the idea in the following way:†

'One of the most important reasons for bringing the desires of each side to a place where they can be clearly examined and valued is that evaluation often leads to *revaluation*. We progress by a revaluation of desire, but usually we do not stop to examine a desire until another is disputing the right of way with it. Watch the evolution of your desires from childhood, through youth, etc. The baby has many infantile desires which are not compatible with his wish for approbation; therefore he revalues his desires. We see this all through our life. We want to do so-and-so, but we do not estimate how much this really means to us until it comes into conflict with another desire. Revaluation is the flower of comparison.

'This conception of the revaluation of desire it is necessary to keep in the foreground of our thinking in dealing with conflict, for neither side ever 'gives in' really, it is hopeless to expect it, but there often comes a moment when there is a simultaneous revaluation of interests on both sides and unity precipitates itself. . . . Integration is often more a spontaneous flowing together of desire than one might think from what I have said; the revaluing of interests on both sides may lead the interests to fit into each other, so that all find some place in the final solution.'

* See Victor Lowe.[8]					† See ref. 7, pp. 38–39.

The idea of a threshold of some probability or of some utility beyond which a new strategy becomes optimal (or acceptable) is inherent in both forms of integration of conflict. The geometrical representation of the decision process may be used to determine threshold probabilities in much the same way as an unknown entry in the loss matrix was determined in the first section of this paper. The sensitivity of optimal solutions to variations in utilities and probabilities is of importance in this regard. Methods for sensitivity analysis have been suggested by Bovey [9] and Walton. [10] In these references, as well as in the specific example in this paper, some quantities may range widely between thresholds, while small changes in others are sufficient to call for a new strategy.

Conclusions

It may appear that the discussion of resolution of conflict has negated the earlier sections of the paper on measurement of utilities. If losses and values, utilities and disutilities, are subject to change in the process of resolution of conflict, what is the point in attempting to measure them? There are two answers to the question.

First, if we accept that quantitative measures of utility are ephemeral as well as elusive, they should be used while fresh, in an active decision situation. That is why I have chosen to treat together the topic of utility estimation and resolution of conflict. It is hoped that the attempt to estimate utilities in a realistic conflict situation can lead not only to integration of the conflict but also to consistent and stable utility measures.

The second argument for attempting to measure utilities is that it must be done to realize in application the potentials of the formal decision processes that constitute much of the body of technique associated with operational research. However, dealing with utilities, which are by nature subjective and individualistic, is a problem in psychometrics rather than statistics. What appears to be called forth is a co-operative, interdisciplinary effort on the part of social scientists, operations analysts, and those responsible for important social decisions – an effort to deal effectively with value concepts – to 'burst through current abstractions', borrowing again from Whitehead, who embedded those words in his warning, 'A civilization which cannot burst through its current abstractions is doomed to sterility after a very limited period of progress.'

REFERENCES

1 A. B. Kurlander, E. H. Hill & P. E. Enterline (1955)
2 A. B. Kurlander, A. P. Iskrant & M. E. Kent (1954)
3 T. J. Scheff (1963)
4 M. S. Blumberg (1957)
5 C. D. Flagle & M. F. Lechat (1963)
6 H. Chernoff & L. Moses (1959)
7 H. C. Metcalf & L. Urwick (1940)
8 V. Lowe (1962), pp. 24–5
9 R. L. Bovey (1964)
10 W. W. Walton (1964)

30 · Theory of Conflict in Lateral Organizational Relationships

RICHARD E. WALTON

Introduction

This paper is drawn from a joint study of lateral relations by J. M. Dutton and R. E. Walton. This study has been made possible, in part, through the support of Purdue Research Foundation and the research assistance of Mr H. G. Fitch.

Organizations have vertical and lateral relations. Organization theorists have generally focused on the superior–subordinate relations. This paper presents a theory of lateral relationships.

If not systematically understood, the interdepartmental behaviour patterns we have in mind are nevertheless familiar ones. In illustration, we quote production and sales managers in a relationship marked by conflict and tension.

Production Manager: Some demands made by sales are wholly out of reason. Salesmen bring in an armload of small orders and expect us to run them efficiently. We have to trade cost for time. . . . Small orders are costly to schedule and run in the plant.

You have to fight for everything you get from the other area.

Sales Manager: The production manager is not customer-oriented on quality and service. He tends to focus on why the customer is wrong. He is too negative on this. There are too many reasons why he cannot do something and too few reasons why he can. We in sales are in the best position to decide who gets orders when. We know customer needs. They don't look at it that way in production.

The production manager won't take these errors as production errors. I don't take them as sales errors. As a result they get ridden up to the general sales manager and general production manager.

I don't try to understand their problems. They don't try to understand mine. I know that things would go better if we had better understanding.

But relations are often collaborative and harmonious. A production manager comments on the working relationship between two departments otherwise comparable in organizational function to the one referred to above.

We encounter no padding or hedging on the delivery dates given to us by sales. We take their dates in good faith. We have done a good service job for sales. There is an atmosphere of mutual confidence. We do make errors but we can be frank about these. We work with the sales service manager to determine whether the customer can wait.

Discussion below emphasizes three facets of organizational phenomena – lateral relations, joint decision-making, and conflict versus collaboration. Why are these important foci for organizational study?

Foci for organizational study

(a) *Why study lateral relationships?* The literature on organizations reflects a preoccupation with vertical relations – problems of leadership, authority, and control. This attention has been matched by a relative neglect of lateral or horizontal relations. Many useful concepts have been developed for different patterns of superior–subordinate relationships – such as directive versus permissive leadership and Theory X versus Theory Y patterns. Progress has been made in refining these concepts and finding operational measures of these patterns. No comparable progress has occurred in conceptualizing or measuring lateral relations. We attempt this task – advancing later in the discussion what we believe is an important distinction between 'integrative' and 'distributive' lateral relationships.

Research and theory have contributed to our understanding of the factors which influence the leadership pattern adopted – but we know little about why particular styles of interaction in lateral relations are adopted. Studies have explored the internal dynamics of a leadership pattern, but to a much lesser extent the subtleties of co-ordinative interactions between peers. The organizational literature suggests what are the consequences of one leadership pattern versus another, but not the implications of one pattern of lateral relations versus another.

To note an exception, line–staff relations have been given much attention in the management literature, but it has been of a speculative nature with little attempt to theorize about this lateral relationship or subject it to systematic research. Very recently, the general trend has changed and more systematic attention is being given to lateral relationships between units, for example by Dalton,[1] Landsberger,[2] and Strauss.[3,4]

(b) *Why study joint decision-making?* The critical or pay-off activity in lateral relations among managers is co-ordinative decision-making. Specialization within organizations creates a corresponding need for co-ordination. When top management break down the total task into units with such responsibilities as producing the product and selling it, they create the need for co-ordination between these units in several important respects. Functional interdependence in an industrial firm can involve timing and rate of transaction of product or paperwork (scheduling); specification of material state (product designing and quality control); supply of goods and services (servicing); allocation of resources (budget or pricing).

Sometimes the co-ordination in these areas is accomplished or enforced by a common superior, but more often the organization relies upon the members of the related units to assume at least some responsibility for this co-ordination. In many cases only the departmental members themselves have the information required for co-ordination. Hence, the importance of lateral relations in achieving co-ordination, a point elaborated later.

The tendency for management to adopt leadership styles providing for greater delegation, more subordinate participation, more autonomy – these trends have made lateral relationships increasingly important. The individual effectiveness of the manager and of the organization as a whole both depend more and more on the manager's skill in structuring appropriate lateral relations. Different patterns of lateral relationships are appropriate in different organizational contexts, depending generally upon the competitiveness induced by the formal reward system and other structural factors. But along what dimension is it useful to distinguish types of joint decision-making and lateral relationship? We differentiate lateral relationships primarily in terms of the amount of conflict they manifest.

(c) *Why study conflict?* By conflict one can mean opposition processes in any of several forms – competition, status rivalry, bargaining, sabotage, verbal abuse, etc. Collaboration involves processes of an opposite nature. Conflict may be exhilarating or debilitating; it may lead to innovation or conservatism; conflict may lead to more individual self-expression or more conformity; it may result in better organizational performance or worse. The beliefs we as individuals hold about the consequences of conflict are frequently determined by our particular personal needs, rather than through systematic research. We have either a personal liking or dislike for conflict versus harmony. Probably the most widely held current view, held variously by psychiatrists, human relations experts, clergy, and philosophers, is that co-operation is relatively good and that conflict is relatively bad. There have been, however, a few attempts to identify the 'functional' value of conflict for society.[5,6]

In order to develop scientific answers to the causes and consequences of conflict we need to be precise – we need to specify particular social processes and study them in specific contexts. We turn now to a more specific statement of these organizational processes and contexts.

Dimensions of a lateral relationship

BASIC ORGANIZATIONAL MECHANISMS

Managers at the middle layer of the organization make decisions which regulate the rate of flow of orders into the system and the flow of products through the system. These decisions influence the quality of the output and specify the rate at which funds are expended on the inputs into the system, and so forth. This monitoring of selling prices, quantity of production, quality of production, cost mix, etc., involves decisions which vitally affect more than one sub-unit of the system.

Who makes these decisions? More generally, how are the parts of the total task kept in proper alignment with each other so that the combined performance of the many sub-tasks constitutes performance of the larger task? Two mechanisms essential to organization assist in achieving this condition. The first, the performance-reward system, is intended to provide organizational members with the basic direction and rationale for their own participation and performance. By performance-reward system we mean the combination of (a) specifications of preferred performance, (b) devices for monitoring and evaluating performance, (c) rewards and penalties for performance. Essentially, the measurements and rewards are designed with the intention of achieving congruence between the motivational structure of the organization's members and the task requirements of the organization. This important function – which we shall not explore further – is accomplished through the vertical linkages within the organization (i.e. superior–subordinate relations).

The second mechanism which brings sub-tasks into proper alignment with each other is the co-ordination system. A specified goal and the motivation to perform are not adequate conditions for appropriate performance; one must know what actions in a given circumstance will enable one to reach the goal. The specifications for performance at middle-management levels are rarely set forth in great detail. They are merely general guidelines. Co-ordination will involve communication between the parts responsible for the sub-tasks to the extent that the vertical specifications do not lay out a complete routine programme for middle-management behaviour and thereby also provide the co-ordinative mechanism. Appropriate performance in one part of such an interdependent system is contingent upon knowledge of performance in other parts, and often requires joint decisions regarding future performance in the respective parts.

The co-ordination system is thus a regulative mechanism which keeps the parts 'on stream', controlling the flow of work-in-process in terms of the sequence of operations, the quality and quantity of the output, etc. This network involves a type of linkage between points different from the hierarchical linkage described above. Information paths connect points and accommodate the flow of data regarding the state of the world, preferences regarding future courses of action, and decisions regarding future operations upon either the environment or the work-in-process.

The aspect of this regulative mechanism we wish to stress here is that the co-ordinating function is performed at the points in the total work process affected – it is seldom a central unitary mechanism. The co-ordination system we differentiate from the performance–reward system is the main horizontal linkage of an instrumental character at the middle layer of the organization.

The co-ordinative function, however, is performed in the context of a complex horizontal relationship – an empirical reality often ignored by operational researchers in the field and by social scientists interested in the theory of the firm. We abstract and treat several aspects of the general pattern of relatedness between the two units: the amount of conflict in the joint decision process, certain structural characteristics of the relationship, and certain attitudes towards the other unit.

THE JOINT DECISION PROCESS

Co-ordination is achieved by decision-making and performance activities. The joint decision-making activity is comprised of several steps, as defined by March and Simon: [7]

1 Identification of mutual problem or need for a joint decision.
2 Search for alternative solutions.
3 Search for consequences of alternative solutions.
4 Preference ordering of solutions, and selecting 'optimal' or 'satisfactory' solutions.

Of first-order importance is the type of joint decision process which the parties employ – the way in which they make co-ordinative decisions. We distinguish between a bargaining type and a problem-solving type of decision-making process. In bargaining, the orientation of the parties is 'How much will I gain or lose, and how much will the other man gain or lose?' The problem-solving process occurs when the parties explore problems for solutions which will involve maximum gain to both parties considered together.

Bargaining and problem-solving seldom appear as pure processes. Co-operative aspects of the situation blunt bargaining, and competitive forces can enter into and modify problem-solving. Probably all real-world relationships are composed of moderated processes or some mixtures of the two processes. Even the poker game has co-operative aspects – several people have agreed to spend time in each other's company and abide by common rules. Similarly, the integretative task of completing a jigsaw puzzle often has its competitive aspects – competitiveness about who finds the most pieces or places the last one. The question becomes one of the *extent* to which a particular decision process approximates these opposite modes. Thus, we need a way of conceiving of the continuum bounded by these types. Measures of information exchanged will enable us to take this step.

At the heart of these two opposite concepts of decision-making is the information-processing activity. How much information do the departments share with each other at every stage in arriving at decisions; and how much consideration do they give to information about the other's problems? In the problem-solving process maximum use is made of voluntary, open, accurate discussion of an area which affects both groups; and both participants attempt to avoid consequences that would present new difficulties for either person. Just the opposite is involved in the bargaining process. Each participant attempts to gain maximum information from the other, but to make minimum disclosures himself; in fact, he often tries to manipulate and persuade the other. And he examines the implications of actions for possible unfavourable consequences for himself, but does not concern himself with the consequences for the other. Essentially, the problem-solving process is exploratory and problem-centred; the bargaining process is defensive and issue-centred. The problem-solving process is a form of collaboration, the bargaining process is a form of conflict. Thus, our first aspect of conflict in a working relationship is the amount of information sharing in the joint decision-making process.

More formal definitions for the two concepts would be: a *problem-solving decision process* is joint decision activity that involves full sharing between the units of all mental processes at every stage of the decision process. A *bargaining decision process* is joint decision activity that involves only sharing of one unit's preferred solution or some overstatement of it. We speak of decision processes as involving more or less bargain-type behaviour, depending on how little or how much decision information and criteria are shared.

STRUCTURAL DIMENSIONS OF THE LATERAL RELATIONSHIP

The interdependence of the two units requires interaction, especially in a decision-making setting. We chose to confine our definition of the joint decision process to amounts of information exchanged and the way the information was weighted in making a decision. But there are other aspects to co-ordinative decision-making activity and to the relationship in general.

Co-ordinative decision-making and implementation activity can involve differing types of interaction structure. We shall define several structural dimensions of joint decision-making:

1 The structure can be more or less *intensive*; that is, it can involve more or less frequent interactions between representatives of the two units.
2 The co-ordinative decision structure can be more or less *extensive*; that is, it can involve a greater or smaller number of interacting persons from the two units.
3 It can be more or less *jurisdictional* regarding the inter-unit relations; that is, it can place a greater or smaller number of proscriptions on the behaviour of its participants and other members of the unit.

4 The co-ordinative decision structure can incorporate a more or less *flexible rule structure*; that is, rules can be more or less formal, more or less strictly applied, more or less static.

5 The co-ordinative decision structure can be more or less *flexible in its manifest form* or organization; that is, it can allow for more or less change in practices, procedures, and organization.

6 The co-ordinative decision structure can be more or less *self-contained*; relying to a greater or lesser extent on influence from sources outside the inter-unit relation.

These dimensions do not exhaust the possible distinctions which one can make in the form of a joint decision structure. However, each of the variables identified is believed to have some relationship to decision process (actual information exchange).

ATTITUDINAL DIMENSIONS OF THE RELATIONSHIP

In addition to decision process and structure, we are interested in the affective nature of the relationship. The relationship between participants can be differentiated along several dimensions involving *positive* or *negative affect*. The relationship can involve feelings of greater or lesser friendliness towards members of the other unit; cohesiveness or feelings of identity (versus differentiation) with the other unit or its members; respect for members of the other group; trust towards members of the other unit.

Theory of the dynamics of lateral relationships

The joint decision process can be entered into in a mutually facilitating (problem-solving) or mutually hindering (bargaining) way. One party can hinder the other by limiting the flow of relevant information or distorting information. What are the correlates of conflict of this type? What are the implications of this conflict for the other aspects of the relationship between the two units – their patterns of interaction, the formality of their joint decision rules, their attitudes towards each other? When can decision process, structure, and attitudes be said to be congruent? Why? How does one influence or reinforce the other?

Figure 1 presents a model showing the theoretical relationships which exist between different broad aspects of the working relationships between the two units. Each of the boxes – process, structure, and attitude – represents a panel of variables. The arrows connecting them imply a causal sequence, solid lines for primary influences and dotted lines for feedback effects. We shall attempt to set forth the rationale and assumptions underlying the hypo-theses, and review the experimental literature which supports the hypo-theses. For some propositions there appear to be few or no relevant research findings. In other cases there is an abundance of evidence bearing on the

P

RICHARD E. WALTON

Figure 1   *Model of Factors in the Lateral Relationship*

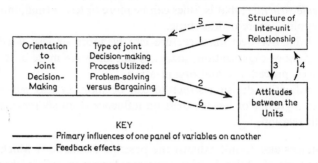

proposition, and the question becomes whether the conclusions reached in those studies also hold for real organizational relationships.

ORIENTATION TO JOINT DECISION-MAKING

The analysis starts with the orientation of the units to the decision situation. Does a participant perceive the situation as requiring that he should optimize the particular sub-function of the organization for which he has direct responsibility? Or, on the other hand, does he perceive the situation as requiring that he should optimize the combined functions represented by the two units? These orientations, of course, are stated in the extreme, and the question is actually one of emphasis.

We do not explore in this paper why they adopt a particular orientation initially. We only note that it is influenced by certain conditions which are given for the participant or which originate outside the two-unit system, such as pay-off, task demands, human and technical limitations, informational limitations, and personalities of the principal participants to decision-

Figure 2   *General Model of Determinants, Dynamics, and Consequences of Conflict in the Lateral Relationship*

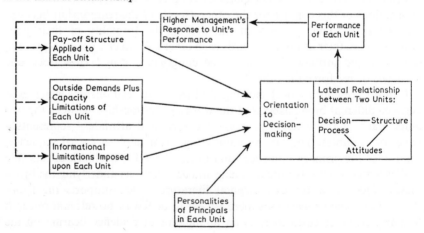

making. Likewise we merely note that the relationship in the two-unit system has certain performance outputs relevant to the larger organization, which in turn makes regulative or adaptive responses. A simplified model of conflict incorporating these variables is diagrammed in *Figure 2*. A systematic theory of the antecedents and consequences of lateral conflict is to be treated elsewhere, along with the findings of a comparative study of six manufacturing plants. The project just referred to also provides an empirical test of most of the propositions about the internal characteristics of a lateral relationship set forth below. At any rate, we assume the following tendency in the decision process involving interdependent units: *The more that the participants adopt a sub-optimizing orientation to the joint decision situation, the more limited will be the exchange of information leading to a decision; similarly, in qualitative terms, the more distorted will be the information exchanged.* In other words, sub-optimizing orientations tend to be accompanied by competitive bargaining rather than by co-operative problem-solving processes.

COMPETITIVENESS IN DECISION PROCESS INFLUENCES INTER-UNIT
STRUCTURE

In *Figure 1* Arrow 1 indicates that the joint decision process which is employed by the two groups influences the structural characteristics of the relationship which develops between the parties. For example, we expect problem-solving to be accompanied by a high rate of interdepartmental interaction; many persons entering into these interactions; few limitations regarding the type of contact a person may have with the other department; infrequent appeals to higher officials; decision rules which are informal, loosely interpreted, and constantly changing; considerable experimentation in decision procedures and organization. The bargaining process would be accompanied by a structure with opposite characteristics.

These hypotheses are based on the assumption that the structural forms are adopted because they promote a particular decision process being utilized by one or both of the parties. The reasoning is that a choice of a certain type of information exchange leads to preferences for certain types of interaction pattern and decision rule and that these preferences are acted upon. The reasoning underlying these particular hypotheses and some supporting evidence are set forth in a study of the negotiation process.[8] A limited number of experimental studies also bear on these hypotheses, which are elaborated below.

(*a*) Our measure of collaboration in the decision process is essentially the amount of accurate information exchanged. A chief function of interactions is to exchange information. Hence, our first proposition is *that a decision structure for bargaining* will *provide for fewer interactions than a structure for problem-solving.* This conclusion is clearly justified if one focuses on the amount of *accurate* information exchanged. It is not a necessary assumption if one focuses on the question of total amount. One can conceive of a high volume of inaccurate communications in a bargaining process which is accommodated by a frequent interaction pattern. The latter point does not, however, lead to the opposite hypothesis; it only weakens the previously stated tendency. Therefore, the net tendency will be for fewer interactions in a competitive process.

This proposition is generally supported by experimental studies. Grossack [9] found that subjects who perceived a co-operative reward structure engaged in more instrumental interactions; they both received and sent more communications containing information and opinions. Altman and McGinnies [10] found that those subjects favourably disposed towards the communication content (which would be true in a collaborative process) showed a greater degree of discussion activity and spontaneity than did subjects who were antagonistic or neutral towards the communication.

We have treated the lesser amount of information exchanged and the fewer communications which occur in a bargaining process as being under the conscious control of the sender. Other psychological consequences of a competitive orientation may add to the tendency cited. Deutsch [11] found that competitive subjects experienced more difficulty in communicating, as both senders and receivers. There were fewer common appraisals of the meaning of a communication in competitive groups than in co-operative groups. The difficulty experienced in attempts to communicate could be expected to lead to fewer interactions.

(b) The second proposition: *a bargaining process will tend to involve less extensive contact between the units*; i.e. fewer persons from each unit will be part of the joint decision structure. This is assumed to be deliberate and tactical to the competitive process – channelling communications to the other unit through one person from the unit is a way of increasing control of the information which reaches members of the other unit. Control may be exercised either to minimize the amount of information sent or systematically to bias the information. If too many persons are allowed to participate it is more difficult to keep their story straight. This point is consistent with bargaining theory, but has not been tested experimentally.

(c) Similarly, the third proposition is that *a unit involved in a bargaining process will attempt to limit the contacts which can be initiated by members of the other unit*. We expect proscriptions and prescriptions applied to members of the other unit, such as who may contact the first unit, what types of contact are allowed, and what procedures must be followed. Again, these would be deliberate and tactical for the control of information which reaches the other unit. There would be less reason for such control in a co-operative decision process.

(d) The fourth proposition is that *bargaining will lead to the development of a structure in which outside authorities play a larger role*. A competitive decision process makes relatively greater use of coercion (versus persuasion) than does a co-operative process. Assuming the outside authorities are agents with coercive capacities, we would expect competitive units to make more frequent attempts to utilize this source of power. This pattern is complicated or obscured when the outside authorities are also contacted because they possess information relevant to the decision process not otherwise available to the unit. Anecdotal evidence bearing on this proposition are the observations that children in conflict are more likely to involve parents and that competitive sports require referees.

(*e*) *The decision rules which are developed to handle mutual problems in a bargaining as contrasted with a problem-solving decision process will tend to be more formal, more strictly applied, and less frequently changed.* This fifth proposition is based on the assumption that in a competitive situation (where one might be taken advantage of) one will attempt to gain certainty and security through more rigid procedures.

(*f*) *Where the decision process is of the bargaining type, there will tend to be less experimentation in decision practices, procedures, and organization.* This proposition is similar to the one above. A departure from the familiar *status quo* contains uncertainty and potential problems – from which a disadvantaged unit might not be able to retreat in a competitive situation. (See also Stendler, Damrin, and Haines,[12] and Sherif and Sherif.[13])

COMPETITIVENESS IN DECISION PROCESS INFLUENCES INTER-UNIT ATTITUDES

Arrow 2 indicates that the decision process also influences the affective character of the relationship. The general proposition is that *the conflictful decision process, bargaining, leads to negative affect; and the co-operative problem-solving leads to positive affect.* There are two aspects of bargaining that contribute to the development of negative affect. First is the very presumption of differentiated interests which underlies the competitive process. Second are the activities required by the process, such as withholding or distortion of information and persistent disagreement over decision criteria.

Those who enter into the decision process with a co-operative orientation tend to indicate more feelings of cohesiveness between the two units, presumably because each perceives the other unit as mediating his own unit's goal achievement. A content analysis of communications in the Grossack study [9] revealed that subjects who perceived a co-operative reward structure showed cohesive behaviour (speaking of the group as a whole, using words: group, we, us, others, etc.) significantly more frequently than did competitive subjects. Levy [14] also found that co-operative groups evidenced greater attraction to the group than did competitive groups. Stendler, Damrin, and Haines [12] studied children painting murals under co-operative and competitive reward conditions. In the condition where all could receive a reward if they met established standards, in contrast with the condition where only the best painter received a reward, the frequency of positive responses always exceeded the negative responses. Deutsch [15] found that subjects who were given a competitive motivational orientation in an experimental game were less trusting of the other players.

In the experiments cited in the paragraph above the significant fact which contributed to negative attitudes towards others was the knowledge of perception of goal conflict. However, the manner by which the parties must pursue their respective goals may generate still more negative affect. Depending upon the nature and degree of task interdependence between the units, there will be more or less frequent occasions when the activity of one unit tends to interfere with the achievement of the other unit. For example, in the competitive decision process the withholding or distorting of information by one person is likely to lead to distrust on the part of the other.

Certain experiments suggest this effect of competitive activities on attitudes. In Deutsch's contrast study of groups with either competitive or co-operative reward structures, [11] observers' ratings indicated that members of co-operative groups were more friendly towards each other than were members of competitive groups. Also, the functioning of the co-operative groups tended to involve more encouraging and rewarding remarks – this can be taken both as evidence of more positive affect and as an activity which would lead to further positive affect. There was a stronger tendency to personalize the relationship in co-operative groups, indicated by the shorter time in which members of co-operative groups learned one another's last names. At the end of the experiment members of co-operative groups tended to rate themselves as being more friendly towards one another than did members of competitive groups, but not at a statistically significant level. This weak tendency to generalize the effect was attributed by Deutsch to the fact that the experimental sessions were not especially prominent in the lives of the subjects.

Other experimental findings: French [16] found that disagreement on how to solve group problems led to lowered group cohesiveness. Gottheil [17] found that co-operative modes of behaviour produced more favourable sociometric distribution in the group. 'It has been shown that individuals became more accepting of the group and perceived this group in a more favourable light after having performed a co-operative task.'

These attitudes are the psychological consequences of the type of decision process. We will note later where attitudes are fostered for more deliberate tactical reasons.

STRUCTURAL VARIABLES INFLUENCE ATTITUDES

Arrow 3 indicates that attitudes are also affected by certain structural variables. Briefly, more frequent and more extensive interaction patterns, more freedom regarding intergroup contacts, more flexible and informal decision rules, more flexible organizational procedures, and less frequent recourse to use of outside influences – all these tend to result in more favourable attitudes in the working relationship.

(*a*) The first proposition assumed by arrow 3 – that *frequent interaction leads to positive sentiments* – is one that has often been advanced. However, the relationship probably does not hold if the parties do not have some preferences – likes, dislikes, values – in common. The more salient are differences in preferences (such as undeniable goal conflict in the joint decision process), the more likely are frequently required interactions to lead to strong negative affect.

Homans [18] states that the proposition that interaction leads to favourable attitudes is probably most potent when the communicating persons are approximate social equals and do not hold sharply differentiated jobs. This proposition has further been modified by Blake, [19] who stated that the drive towards interaction will be strongest when both positive- and negative-feeling states are present and less strong in neutral-feeling states.

(*b*) The second proposition in this section is that *a structure which requires more extensive contacts between the units will tend indirectly to create positive attitudes*. More points of contact between the two units lead to less differentiation in the joint structure. Also more points in the other's organization through which one unit may gain information lead to a more realistic perception of the other, presumably resulting in fewer negative stereotypes and more trust.

That such multiple primary relations result in more positive affect in working relationships between units has been argued by Janis and Katz [20] and others. However, H. Kelman [21] has reviewed some of the research findings regarding the effectiveness of cross-cultural contacts and identified certain conditions which increase the likelihood that the contacts will lead to positive attitudes: the contacts are between persons of equal status, they are not frustrating or otherwise unsatisfying, they do not involve patronizing behaviour.

(*c*) The structure may involve relatively many or few prescriptions and proscriptions governing these contacts. This is not a measure of how frequent or extensive is the interaction pattern, rather how rigidly it is prescribed in terms of who may be contacted and for what purposes. *A high degree of freedom in initiating contact tends to result in more favourable attitudes*. We assume that a person from one unit will tend to contact a member of the other unit when that interaction will yield the initiator some benefit, and not to make contacts which yield him no benefit. Thus, in our third proposition relating structure and attitudes, we reason that the person with freedom to initiate contacts at his discretion tends to engage in rewarding interactions, and thus tends to develop favourable attitudes towards the other.

The hypothesis is based on other assumptions or reasoning. If one is prevented from interacting with another unit at one's own discretion, one can gain less relevant information about the other's motives or activities; as a further consequence, one is denied a basis for building up one's trust in the other and one's stereotypical views of the other are less likely to be challenged. Also, if there is less spontaneity allowed in initiating the interaction the interaction is less likely to lead to friendliness.

Loomis [22] found that subjects allowed to communicate with each other were more likely to perceive trust than those not allowed to communicate. This probability increased with the level of comprehensiveness of the written communication.

(*d*) and (*e*) *More flexibility in the decision rules leads to more favourable attitudes between the units. More flexibility and experimentation in the organizational procedures and practices affecting joint decision-making results in favourable attitudes.* These two additional hypotheses have in common with hypothesis (*c*) the idea of flexibility and informability in some aspect of their relationship. We assume that the flexibility and informality in interaction promote positive feelings. Moreno [23] found that highly spontaneous interactions in a group received more favourable sociometric choices.

(*f*) The sixth proposition represented by arrow 3: *a decision structure which involves less frequent use of requests by one or the other unit for the intervention of persons outside the two-unit system will lead to more favourable attitudes between the two units.* We expect these results because the pattern implies that the two units are more exclusively interdependent; and hence there are more reasons for identifying themselves with the two-unit system as a whole. Also, the opposite pattern of appealing to third parties is likely to lead to distrust, especially if one party is not always warned in advance of the other's appeals.

ATTITUDES INFLUENCE STRUCTURAL VARIABLES

Although we believe that the dominant sequence of influence is represented by the arrows discussed above (solid lines), we also expect influence to operate in the opposite direction. The dotted arrows, 4–6 are feedback patterns, invariably of a reinforcement nature. We treat these as three general propositions, although some of the separate processes are analysed and elaborated in the discussion below. These reinforcement sequences are essential for our explanation of the difficulty of changing patterns of relationships.

Arrow 4 indicates that attitudes act back on the structure of the relations. For example, feelings of hostility towards the other unit would encourage members of the first unit to avoid extensive contact with the other and to avoid frequent interaction. Newcomb [24] states that an initially hostile attitude tends to perpetuate itself because it leads to a breakdown of communication. Even the nature of a particular interaction sequence will be affected by the attitudes: Cervin [25] found that change in group attitude from opposition to co-operation tended to result in significantly different response latency and participation (length of speech/length of silence) by the initiator of a story creation with two role-playing assistants. Negative feelings of low trust and hostility would be likely to lead to structuring the decision situation in particular, and the relationship in general, in more formal and rigid ways.

STRUCTURAL FACTORS INFLUENCE THE DECISION PROCESS
ADOPTED

Following this reverse direction of influence through structure and back to decision process (arrow 5), we can see that minimum and formal contact ensures that information will not be adequate to promote the occurrence of co-operative decision-making, even if it were otherwise preferred. Gibb [26] found that creating a more formal group structure and setting led to a reduction in the number of ideas proposed by the group, hence to a less frequent exchange of task-relevant information.

Experimental evidence on this point is provided by Loomis's study utilizing a two-person, non-co-operative game. Loomis [22] found that persons allowed to communicate before the game tended to perceive trust and make co-operative game choices to a larger extent than persons not allowed to communicate before the game.

ATTITUDES INFLUENCE THE DECISION PROCESS ADOPTED

Arrow 6 indicates that inter-group attitudes directly affect the orientation the parties have towards the decision process, apart from the structures in which it occurs. If a person feels friendly towards another person, he is more likely to behave co-operatively in the decision process. Philip,[27] working with children, found that 'stranger' pairs preferred to compete, while 'friend' pairs preferred to co-operate. Under conditions of hostility and low trust, persons will adopt competitive behaviour strategies in the decision process. For example, one adopts decision patterns which involve furnishing another with less information and less accurate information when one dislikes or distrusts the other. In addition to the logic inherent in not sharing vital information with a person one doesn't trust, there are two other reasons for the tendency cited here.

The first reason is that negative attitudes lead to perceptual distortions, which in turn lead to competitive decision-making. Recall that the decision process involves identifying problems or issues, searching for alternative solutions and their consequences, and choosing between solutions. The decision process tends to move through these phases. If at any point in the process one or both of the units perceive substantial disagreement between them they will tend to shift the decision process towards its more competitive form. Hence the importance of perception as a mediating psychological process between attitudes and behaviour in the joint decision process.

Several studies support the idea that attitudes can influence decision process via perceptual distortions. An experiment by Exline [28] led to the conclusion that members of congenial groups are more accurate than members of un-congenial groups in perceiving task-oriented behaviour, but not social behaviour (Hare [29, Chapter 10]). Gibb and Gorman [30] found more errors in perception and a higher incidence of defensive behaviour in the attitudinally polarized group. Blake and Mouton [31] found that under competitive inter-group conditions a person did not recognize points of similarity between proposals by different groups. Harvey, [32] studying antagonistic and friendly pairs of small groups, found that while the presence of a friendly group did not affect perceptions, the presence of an antagonistic group increased the positive correlation between ingroup status and discrepancy in judgements.

Pertinent again is the study by Loomis, [22] which utilized a two-person game incorporating co-operative and non-co-operative choices for each person. Loomis found that a perception of trust by the other person, based on a prior written communication, tended to lead to co-operative game choices, while a perception of distrust by the other person of self led to non-co-operative game choices.

Mellinger, [33] in a field study, found that if a person was motivated to communicate with another person about a mutually important issue, and if this person distrusted the person with whom he was motivated to communi-cate he would communicate in such a way as to conceal information about his own attitudes towards the issue. The findings also suggested that simply communicating with another person about an issue may be sufficient to increase accuracy in perceiving existing agreement, but not sufficient to in-crease accuracy in perceiving existing disagreement.

Negative attitudes result in more competitive behaviours in the decision process for a second basic reason. Strong negative affect often leads one unit to interfere with the other unit's activities, just to frustrate the latter's goal achievement. The parties tend to lose sight of their own positive goals and assume that 'whatever hurts them must be good for us'.

The relationship between orientation to the decision process and inter-personal or inter-group attitudes has been shown to be a close one. We can cite further direct reciprocal effects. For example, by adopting a bargaining orientation and cautiously disclosing a minimum of information to the other, one communicates a lack of trust; the other is likely to reciprocate with low trust towards the first person. If negative attitudes originate apart from the decision process they can nevertheless be expected to impinge upon it. However, this particular direction of initial influence is less typical. We agree with Bernard [34] that 'Hostile stereotypes are more likely to be the result of conflict than its cause'.

THE RECIPROCAL AND GENERALIZED NATURE OF LATERAL
RELATIONSHIPS

Our first proposition here is that *the two units will adopt similar approaches to the decision process*. Mutually facilitating and mutually hindering patterns of joint decision-making are stable. If one unit entered into the process in a facilitating way and the other in a hindering way the pattern would be unstable. We assume that the pay-off structure is mixed, so that for either unit at least some potential gains exist via both approaches – an increase in the joint welfare via a co-operative approach, and gains for the initiating unit with corresponding losses for the other via a competitive approach. Thus, one unit would be temporarily exploited by the other. However, unless the exploited unit had reason to expect the other to change to a facilitating pattern, it would in self-defence be forced to revise its orientation to the decision-making activity.

Our reasoning here is similar to that of Rapoport.[35] Therefore, his experimental findings may be cited as supporting evidence for this proposition. A learning mechanism would explain the tendency for a person to abandon a facilitating orientation when the other has a hindering one. The reverse is not necessarily true: there is little cost associated with the *status quo* for the person pursuing the hindering strategy when the other is facilitating him. Thus, it is apparent that more conscious and co-ordinated effort by the partner is required if the pattern is to move in the direction of being more facilitating.

Mediating process other than learning theory helps to explain why there is a tendency for the orientation towards decision-making to converge towards similarity: feelings towards the other are associated with decision orientation and feelings tend to be reciprocated (Snoek[36]). Moreover, the structure between the units is defined as common property.

A similar reasoning is involved in developing a second proposition that *there will tend to be a similar orientation to all joint decision areas*. Many of the same persons from each unit are involved in the different decision areas. The degree of trust they hold for the other is likely to be general, not specific to one area of common concern. Similarly, the structure for making decisions is likely to be common to the decision activity for each area of concern.

Thus, where two departments have several areas of interdependence, there will be a tendency for them to use the same decision pattern in all areas. That is, one can refer to *the* pattern of joint decision-making of a particular pair of departments.

Integrative and distributive lateral relationships

To the extent that our propositions enumerated above are valid in organizational settings and confirmed by research findings (and preliminary results from the comparative study of six plants appear to support most of them), we are justified in advancing concepts which identify the divergent syndromes of behaviour. These complex concepts of 'integrative' and 'distributive' are constructed by combining several specific dimensions of lateral relationships.

A *distributive relationship* has the following components:

1 A bargaining form of decision-making where information is carefully rationed and deliberately distorted.

2 A structure of interaction which is rigid, formal, and circumscribed.
3 Negative attitudes towards the other unit.

The opposite, a collaborative form of lateral relationship, is an *integrative relationship* which we postulate to have the following components:

1 A problem-solving form of joint decision-making in which accurate information is freely exchanged.
2 A flexible, informal, and open pattern of inter-unit interaction.
3 Positive sentiments between the two units.

REFERENCES

1 M. Dalton (1959)
2 H. A. Landsberger (1961)
3 G. Strauss (1962)
4 G. Strauss (1964)
5 L. Coser (1956)
6 R. C. North, H. E. Koch & D. A. Zinnes (1960)
7 J. G. March, H. A. Simon & H. Guetzkow (1958), pp. 363–4, 380, 414
8 R. E. Walton & R. B. McKersie (1965)
9 M. M. Grossack (1954)
10 I. Altman & E. McGinnies (1960)
11 M. Deutsch (1949)
12 C. Stendler, D. Damrin & A. Haines (1951)
13 M. Sherif & C. N. Sherif (1953)
14 B. I. Levy (1954)
15 M. Deutsch (1960)
16 J. R. P. French (1941)
17 E. Gottheil (1955)
18 G. C. Homans (1950)
19 R. R. Blake (1953)
20 I. L. Janis & D. Katz (1959)
21 H. C. Kelman (1962)
22 J. L. Loomis (1959)
23 J. L. Moreno (1953)
24 T. M. Newcomb (1947)
25 V. Cervin (1955)
26 C. A. Gibb (1951)
27 A. J. Philip (1940)
28 R. V. Exline (1957)
29 A. P. Hare (1962)
30 C. A. Gibb & A. Gorman (1954)
31 R. R. Blake & J. S. Mouton (1962a)
32 O. J. Harvey (1956)
33 G. D. Mellinger (1956)
34 J. Bernard (1950)
35 A. Rapoport, this volume, pp. 369–97
36 J. D. Snoek (1962)

31 · Structural Conflicts within Organizations

RUSSELL L. ACKOFF

Introduction

This paper has three parts. In the first I attempt to provide operational definitions and measures of conflict, co-operation, exploitation, and competition. This effort has three purposes:

1 To provide definitions of these concepts that reduce ambiguity in both their common usage and uncommon usages in social science and operational research;
2 To indicate how behavioural variables might be defined and measured so as to facilitate their more effective use in operational research and, perhaps, in social science; and
3 To produce definitions and measures in a form that has heuristic value; that is, that suggests factual, legal, and theoretical hypotheses about related phenomena, that suggests ways of testing such hypotheses, and that suggests ways of affecting the phenomena.

In the second part a classification of ways of affecting conflict is derived from the definition of conflict and is compared with the classification provided by Rapoport.[1,2]

The material in the first two parts of the paper has been treated in greater detail in Ackoff,[3] but this source is not very accessible to social scientists and to many operational researchers, particularly outside the United States.

In the third part of the paper I consider a type of conflict that arises within organizations, a type that arises out of the structure of the organization. I discuss ways of measuring and affecting such conflict and the roles of social scientists and operational researchers in affecting it.

Definition of concepts

In order to define co-operation and conflict certain other concepts are needed. In the formulation provided here the central notion is that of a 'purposeful state' of an individual or group. In earlier works [3,4,5,6] I have used this same starting-point for developing the concepts involved in communication theory and decision theory. It should be no surprise that theories of co-operation–conflict, communication, and decision-making can rest on a common conceptual foundation. This should help in the development of a general theory which covers all of these phenomena.

Let

I = a decision-maker, individual or group.

C_i = a course of action, $i = 1, 2, \ldots m$.

O_j = an outcome, $j = 1, 2, \ldots n$: a consequence of a course of action in an environment.

N = the environment: the set of variables other than the decision-maker and the courses of action which can affect the outcomes.

It will be convenient to treat the courses of action and outcomes as though they formed exclusive and exhaustive sets; that is, only one course of action can be selected at a time and one must be selected, and one, but only one, outcome must occur. Given any two or more elements (courses of action or outcomes), they can be formed into an exclusive and exhaustive set by means of the Boolean expansion. For example, if we have two outcomes which are not exclusive and exhaustive, o_1 and o_2, they can be formed into the following set of four exclusive and exhaustive outcomes:

$$O_1 = o_1 \text{ and } o_2$$
$$O_2 = o_1 \text{ and not } o_2$$
$$O_3 = \text{not } o_1 \text{ but } o_2$$
$$O_4 = \text{neither } o_1 \text{ nor } o_2$$

Three measures are required to characterize a 'choice situation':

$P_i = P(C_i|I, N)$ = the probability that decision-maker I will select course of action C_i in environment N.

$E_{ij} = P(O_j|I, C_i, N)$ = the probability that outcome O_j will occur if decision-maker I selects course of action C_i in environment N: the efficiency of C_i for O_j in N.

U_j = the *utility* (relative value) of outcome O_j to decision-maker I in environment N.*

If the courses of action and outcomes are defined so as to be exclusive and exhaustive, then the sum of the probabilities of choice over the set of courses of action is equal to unity.

$$\sum_{i=1}^{m} P_i = 1$$

---

* Obviously, a great deal more needs to be learned about obtaining estimates of these parameters. Discussion of these estimation problems lies outside the scope of this paper, but a good start in this direction, in my opinion, has been made by Churchman.[7]

and the sum of the efficiencies of any course over the set of outcomes is also equal to unity.

$$\sum_{j=1}^{n} E_{ij} = 1$$

Since utility is not measured along an absolute scale we will let a represent the sum of utilities over the set of outcomes:

$$\sum_{j=1}^{n} U_j = a, (a \geqslant o)$$

(In some systems negative values of utility are possible. The minimum and maximum values of the measures given below can easily be adjusted if such is the case.)

Now the decision-maker I can be said to be in a purposeful state (S) if the following conditions hold:

1 There is a pair of possible outcomes (O_1 and O_2) in the environment such that their utilities are not equal ($U_1 \neq U_2$). Hence at least one outcome is preferred to another. Let O_1 represent the preferred outcome. .

2 There are at least two courses of action available in the environment (C_1 and C_2), of which the efficiencies for O_1 are greater than zero and are not equal: $E_{11} > 0$, $E_{21} > 0$, and $E_{11} \neq E_{21}$. That is, the decision-maker has a 'real' choice, one that can make a difference to him.

In ordinary English I can be said to be in a purposeful state if (a) he prefers one possible outcome to another, and (b) he has alternative courses of action which have some, but unequal, probabilities of resulting in the preferred outcome.

The expected utility (EU) of a purposeful state (S) to the decision maker is given by

$$EU(S) = \sum_{i} \sum_{j} P_i E_{ij} U_j.$$

This value can range between a minimum of 0 (where he has no chance of obtaining anything of value to him) and a maximum of a (where he is certain to obtain everything of value to him).

CO-OPERATION AND CONFLICT

Now let us introduce a second decision-maker, I_2, into an environment already occupied by decision-maker I_1.

Let
($S|I_2$) represent a state in which I_2 is part of I_1's environment, and
($S|I'_2$) represent a state in which I_2 is *not* part of I_1's environment

If I_2 is part of I_1's environment, his behaviour may affect the outcome of I_1's behaviour. If I_2's presence in the environment adds to I_1's expected utility, I_2 can be said to *co-operate* with I_1. If I_2's presence decreases I_1's expected utility, I_2 can be said to be in *conflict* with I_1. The *degree* of *co-operation* and *conflict* of I_2 with I_1 can be defined as

$$DC_{21} = EU_1(S|I_2) - EU_1(S|I'_2)$$

If this quantity is positive, I_2 co-operates with I_1; if it is negative, I_2 is in conflict with I_1. Hence, the degree of conflict is the negative of the degree of co-operation. If $DC_{21} = 0$, then I_2 has no effect on I_1 and is not part of I_1's environment in the behavioural, not physical, sense.

The maximum value which the degree of co-operation can take on is $(a - 0) = a$, and the minimum is $(0 - a) = -a$. Negative values, of course, represent conflict.

EXPLOITATION

The degree of co-operation of I_1 with I_2 is given by

$$DC_{12} = EU_2(S|I_1) - EU_2(S|I'_1)$$

DC_{21} and DC_{12} do not have to be equal. Their difference is a measure of *exploitation*. The degree to which I_2 exploits I_1 is given by

$$DE_{21} = DC_{12} - DC_{21}$$

Correspondingly,

$$DE_{12} = DC_{21} - DC_{12} = -DE_{21}$$

Hence, the degree of exploitation is a measure of the asymmetry of co-operation or conflict.

If I_1 and I_2 are co-operating with each other, but unequally, the exploitation can be said to be *benevolent*. This is the type of exploitation that has characterized most enlightened colonization of one country by another and most employer–employee relationships.

If I_1 and I_2 are in conflict with each other, but unequally, the exploitation can be said to be *malevolent*. Most wars and feuds have been examples of such exploitation. If I_1 co-operates with I_2 but I_2 is in conflict with I_1, the exploitation might facetiously be called 'normal' (e.g. the slave–master relationship).

It should be noted that the parties to conflicts or co-operation may not be conscious of, or intend, the effect that they have.

COMPETITION

The term *competition* is frequently used as a synonym of conflict. I shall not so use it here. Rather, I shall adopt the notion that competition is *regulated* conflict, and that the function of the regulation is co-operative. Let me be explicit. Consider a third party, I_3, that may either be distinct from I_1 and I_2, or be the group containing I_1 and I_2. Now suppose I_1 and I_2 have some desired outcomes with respect to which they are in conflict. If this conflict efficiently serves an outcome desired by I_3 and if I_3 at least partially controls I_1's and I_2's choices of action, I_1 and I_2 can be said to be competing relative to I_3. If I_3 is simply the group that is formed by I_1 and I_2 the competition can be said to be *intrinsic*; for example, in a tennis match between friends, where the group objective is recreation. If I_1 and I_2 are not part of I_3 the competition can be said to be *extrinsic*; for example, in a prize-fight before an audience. Competition can, of course, be both intrinsic and extrinsic at the same time, as in a tennis match between friends before an audience.

In the theory of economic competition, it is argued that the more intense the conflict between competing suppliers of desired goods or services, the better the consumers' interests are served.

Hence, competition consists of conflict embedded in co-operation that is regulated so as to assure its efficiency for a 'third' party. It can be characterized by many measures, some of which are the following:

1 $|DC_{12} + DC_{21}|$, the absolute sum that may be called the *intensity* of the conflict.
2 $|DC_{12} - DC_{21}|$, the absolute difference that may be called the *asymmetry* of the conflict.
3 The efficiency of the conflict for the 'third' objective.

At present I see no way of containing all the possible dimensions of competition within one measure. It is not rare, however, to find that a concept is multidimensional.

Modes of affecting conflict

The definitions through which we have just travelled yield some insight into the ways in which a participant or an outsider can intervene in a conflict situation. That is, it yields a classification of the types of thing that can be done to a conflict situation. Such a classification will differ from the very provocative one formulated by Anatol Rapoport.[1,2] Rapoport was concerned with modes of conflict which intensify, stabilize, and decrease conflict. In this context he considers *fights*, *games*, and *debates* which he defined briefly as follows:

'. . . in a fight the urge is to eliminate the opponent; in a game the problem is to outwit the opponent; in the debate, the goal is to convince the opponent (ref. 2, p. 215).'

Rapoport's classification of intentions may be exhaustive, but his classification of means of intervention is not. It was not intended to be, it was intended to illustrate ways of intensifying conflicts (fights), stabilizing them (games), and reducing or eliminating them (debates).

Conflict, as defined here, involves the effect of one decision-maker's behaviour on the outcome of another's. The conflict situation is completely specified by

1 The presence of both parties in an environment, N,
2 The P_i's of I_1 and I_2,

3 The E_{ij}'s of I_1 and I_2, and
4 The U_j's of I_1 and I_2.

Consequently, the things that can be done to change a conflict situation are as follows:

1 *Environmental*

(*a*) Remove one or both parties from the environment. Removal may be either voluntary or forcible, as in a fight. Incapacitation of one of the parties is virtual removal.

(*b*) Change the environment so that the effect of the behaviour of one on the other is removed. This is really a division of the environment. For example, erection of a sound barrier may prevent transmission of noise which is a source of conflict. If both parties want to sit down and only one chair is available, making another similar chair available will remove the conflict.

2 *Behavioural*

Change either the actions selected (the P_i's), the way they are carried out (the E_{ij}'s), or the utilities placed on outcomes (the U_j's).

Manipulation of the last type is normally accomplished by communication: the transmission of messages between the opponents or to them from outsiders. I take such efforts to correspond with what Rapoport has called a *debate*, but I feel this term connotes too restricted a class of communication. Another possible way of affecting behaviour that does not involve communication is considered in Ackoff.[6]

As I indicated earlier, I have used the concept of a purposeful state to define concepts and measures of human communication.[4] In brief, messages which affect the probabilities of choice of an individual (P_i) transmit *information* to him; those which affect the efficiency of his actions (E_{ij}) transmit *instruction*; and those which affect the utility that he places on outcomes (U_j) transmit *motivation*.* The amounts of these which may be transmitted, in my scheme, can be negative. A single message may have any one, two, or all three communicative functions.

Structural conflict within organizations

Now the particular type of conflict which I want to explore with you here is a type of conflict involving objectives, desired outcomes. Parties I_1 and I_2 have objectives O_1 and O_2, respectively, such that, to the extent that one is obtained, the other is not, relative to any of the courses of action which are available to them in the environment. The only way such a conflict can be resolved is by changing the objectives of the parties. But there are many cases in which these objectives are imposed on the decision-makers, and hence are not theirs to

---

* Since means and ends (courses of action and outcomes) are 'relative' concepts, so are these modes of communication.

change. In such cases all the beating of a behavioural scientist's head against the participants cannot hurt the conflict, but it can hurt the scientist's head.

The type of conflict to which I refer is endemic to most organizations. It is a type of conflict which emanates from the structure of the organization itself. Before discussing it in precise terms, consider a few commonplace examples.

A great deal of small group research has been directed towards determining whether co-operative or competitive groups are better in solving problems or completing some other type of task. In a recent review of past work and a presentation of their own, Raven and Euchus [8] came to the conclusion that, in situations in which the group members' actions do not affect each other's performance,* competition is likely to produce better results than co-operation; but if the members' actions are interdependent, co-operation is likely to be more effective. This seems to me to be rather an obvious conclusion that could have been derived directly from knowledge of the structure of the two types of situation.

If group performance is the sum of n individuals' independent performances (i.e. they cannot affect each other's performance), there is no question of co-operation or conflict in what they do because they can do nothing to each other. Their performance, however, may affect the way in which they are rewarded. Little wonder that in such a situation 'The competition (for reward) might add additional interest to what might otherwise be a dull task' and 'motivation would be great in the competitive situation'. [8, p. 308] Recognition of this fact is what lies behind many incentive schemes which are based on competition for prizes.

If, on the other hand, each member's performance depends on what others do, and if they are made to compete for reward they can and do try to gain an advantage by obstructing the others. Only if it is clear that they cannot gain an advantage in the long run do they eventually resort to co-operative behaviour. This is apparent from the results which Anatol Rapoport has obtained in his experiments with the Prisoner's Dilemma (see Chapter 28 in this volume). Contrary to previous research findings – that players tend to select conflict behaviour most frequently – he found, by continuing the plays well beyond the number used in previous experiments, that most players eventually tend towards co-operative behaviour with only occasional defection.

The question as to how to reward interacting members of an organization rests on the question: how should their performance be measured? It is easy to show that the way in which the measures are set up affects not only individual, but also collective, performance. Measures are frequently used which deprive the organization as a whole of effectiveness, even if the members do their best, and which place the members in conflict with each other. In fact, it is very difficult to avoid designing inefficiency and conflict into the structure of most organizations.

Consider the following oversimplified example of a type of situation which

---

* Expected utility of outcome.

is very familiar to those who have worked in and for industrial organizations. The organization involved might be in retailing or merchandising. Its purchasing department buys a particular product at the beginning of each month in quantity q, the value of which it selects. The purchased items are placed in stock until sold. The sales department sets the price at which the item is to be sold. The lower the price, p, is, the more that can be sold on the average. The amount that is sold in any period can only be predicted within a known range. Only items in stock can be sold; back orders are not possible.

Suppose the purchasing department is assigned the objective of minimizing the cost of inventory while at the same time providing sufficient stock to meet their own estimate of demand. The sales department is assigned the objective of maximizing gross profit:

number sold (sale price – cost of purchase)

Now, if the sales department sets a price, p_1, for the next period the purchasing department will make a pessimistic estimate of sales and buy only an amount sufficient to meet this level because, if it overbuys, inventory carrying costs increase and the department suffers. The sales department, of course, wants the purchasing department to use an optimistic forecast of sales because its performance suffers if orders are not filled, but not if anything is left over in inventory. When the purchasing department selects an order quantity, q_1, to meet a pessimistic forecast of sales based on price p_1, the sales department is likely to raise its price to p_2 for which q_1 is an optimistic estimate. If it does so, the purchasing department will revise q_1 to a lower value, q_2, which corresponds to a pessimistic estimate of sales for price p_2; and so on. The limit of this process is reached when the purchasing department buys nothing and, hence, nothing can be sold.

This limit is not reached because both departments want to keep the company in business. What usually happens in practice is that the sales department does not inform the purchasing department what price it is going to set, and the purchasing department does not tell the sales department how many items it is going to buy. Each predicts what the other is going to do. In this way the conflict is 'stabilized'. The two departments convert the situation into a competitive game in which there is no communication between the participants.

No amount of psychologizing or sociologizing on the parties of the conflict can resolve the conflict as long as these measures of performance are operative. Clearly, the measure of performance of the purchasing department ought to take account of lost sales, and the measure of performance of the sales department ought to take account of unsold items. By getting appropriate measures of performance, the company's profit can be maximized and the internal conflict can be resolved.

Now let us see if we can come to grips with the basic nature of such conflict. To begin with, let us consider the simplest type of organization, one involving only two members, I_1 and I_2. The objective of this organization, like that of any other, can be expressed as

$$\max (G - L),$$

where G is a gain (acquisition of desired resources and/or attainment of a desired state), and L is a loss (consumption of desired resources or loss of desired state properties). In this simplest of possible organizations the gain, G, would be a function of one controlled variable, x, and L would be a function of another, y:

$$G = f_1(x)$$
$$L = f_2(y)$$

Therefore,

$$\max (G - L) = \max_{x,y}\left[f_1(x) - f_2(y)\right] = \max f_1(x) - \min f_2(y)$$

The optimal organizational structure follows simply from this last equation. I_1 should be assigned the objective sub-function, $\max f_1(x)$, and I_2 should be assigned the sub-function, $\min f_2(y)$. These two subfunctions are independent, and hence no conflict can arise between I_1 and I_2 because of them.

Most real organizations are more complicated than this one in a variety of ways, but let us consider only one 'dimension of complexity'.

Suppose

$$G = f_1(x, y)$$
$$L = f_2(x, y)$$

Both the gain and the loss functions depend on the same two controlled variables. Hence,

$$\max (G - L) = \max_{x,y}\left[f_1(x, y) - f_2(x, y)\right]$$

Now it is for only very rarely experienced functions f_1 and f_2 that

$$\max_{x,y}\left[f_1(x, y) - f_2(x, y)\right] = \max_x f_1(x, y) - \min_y f_2(x, y).$$

In those cases in which the equation holds, if I_1 is assigned the first function, $\max_x f_1(x, y)$, and I_2 is assigned $\min_y f_2(x, y)$, I_1 and I_2 will be *interdependent* because the performance of each depends on the value that the other selects for the variable which he controls. Optimization can occur only if there is perfect communication between them with respect to these variables.

In general, however,

$$\max_{x,y}\left[f_1(x, y) - f_2(x, y)\right] - \left[\max_x f_1(x, y) - \min_y f_2(x, y)\right] = K > 0$$

Consequently, if the objective sub-functions, $\max_x f_1(x, y)$ and $\min_y f_2(x, y)$, are assigned to I_1 and I_2, at best the organization will fail to meet its objective by amount K, which is a measure of its structural inefficiency.

There are, of course, two other possible sources of organizational inefficiency:

1 I_1 and I_2 may not communicate effectively relative to the variables that they control, x and y.
2 Even where they do, they may not optimize their respective sub-objective functions.

Hence, organizational inefficiency may derive from structure, communications, and decision-making.

The behavioural sciences can contribute significantly to the reduction of inefficiency due to communication, but, at present, they can make little contribution to the reduction of structural and decision-making inefficiency. The converse is true for operational research. Here, then, is an important basis for co-operation between the two disciplines.

Now let us take another step towards organizational realism. In most organizations the organization's overall objective function is seldom explicitly formulated, and, where it is, the formulation is seldom quantitative or operationally useful. Sub-objective functions are *more* frequently (but *not very* frequently) formulated adequately. When these functions are adequately formulated we are likely to find, for example, that if an organization's objective function is

$$\max_{x,y} \left[f_1(x, y) - f_2(x, y) \right]$$

then I_1 and I_2 have been assigned the sub-functions

$$\max_x f_3(x, y)$$

and

$$\min_y f_4(x, y)$$

If

$$\max_{x,y} \left[f_1(x, y) - f_2(x, y) \right] - \left[\max_x f_3(x, y) - \min_y f_4(x,y) \right] = K > 0$$

as is usually the case, it is possible either to change f_3 and f_4 or to develop organizational controls (e.g. the introduction of shadow prices) which will reduce organizational inefficiency, K. But more relevant to this discussion is the fact that once such an explicit formulation has been given to the organization's objective functions and sub-functions, it is possible to determine the extent of structural interdependence of sub-units and whether or not conflict is built into the sub-objective functions which have been assigned to sub-units.

Suppose, for example, I_1 and I_2 have the sub-objective functions:

$$\max_x f_3(x, y)$$

and

$$\max_y f_4(x, y)$$

In practice, an initial value of one of the control variables, say x_1, must be selected. Using this, I_2 finds the value y_1 which minimizes f_4. I_1 can now use y_1 and find the value x_2 which maximizes f_3. I_2 can now modify y_1, and so on. If the successive steps in this process yield values of x and y which improve I_1's and I_2's performance the procedure can be said to *converge*. In such cases it is obviously advantageous for I_1 and I_2 to co-operate. If, however, successive steps in the process of iteration described lead to poorer performance of I_1 and I_2, then it is advantageous for I_1 and I_2 to conflict. Such conflict, as we have already noted, is inherent in the organization's structure; that is, in the sub-objective functions which have been assigned to sub-units. Because this conflict is structural, changes of personnel, their attitudes towards each other, or the communications between them cannot remove the conflict or its source. By use of operational research it is beginning to be possible to identify the nature of such conflict and prescribe for it. Carrying out the prescription may require all the knowledge and skill that the social engineer can muster. Furthermore, an improvement in structure may reduce effectiveness of communications or decision-making with a net loss to the organization. The social scientist should be able to assist the operational researcher in anticipating and preventing such a harmful backlash.

Let me hasten to point out that the capacity of operational research to identify structural conflict and inefficiency is seldom used. In practice, operational research usually serves a sub-unit of the organization, accepts its sub-objective function, and tries to optimize relative to that. That is, it deals with the decision problem, not the structural problem. Sub-optimization (optimizing a sub-function) may actually reduce the efficiency of the organization as a whole. Here is where behavioural scientists can make a major contribution to operational research. They can induce organizational management to have its structure analysed, and they can develop a capacity for diagnosing structural conflict and inefficiency by identifying the behavioural symptoms of such malfunctioning. They may also be able to help persuade operational researchers that more of their effort should be directed towards analysis of organizational structure.

Epilogue

I have discussed the behavioural sciences and operational research as though they were different species of the same genus. This is not true. Operational research is a multidisciplinary activity, not a discipline. In principle, it should involve behavioural science in all its efforts. I have so argued in other places. Unfortunately, the operational researchers have not promoted involvement of behavioural science in their activity largely, I believe, because of the 'language barrier'. But behavioural scientists are becoming more proficient with mathematical language, and this problem may solve itself in time. I wish it would not take so long.

Communication, however, is not the only barrier to involvement of the behavioural sciences in operational research. I have found, when proposing collaboration to behavioural scientists, that they usually respond with, 'Find a problem with a behavioural science component of interest to us, and we'll be glad to collaborate.' This request shows a fundamental misunderstanding of the nature of the 'multidisciplinariness' of operational research. Operational research does not proceed by dividing a problem into disciplinary components and dishing these out to the appropriate disciplines. Rather it seeks to bring as many disciplines as possible to bear on every aspect of every problem. In operational research physicists, mathematicians, engineers, philosophers, and others work on economic, physical, behavioural, and other aspects of organizational problems. The behavioural scientist must be willing to work on every problem and on every aspect of each problem. He must be as willing to bring his knowledge and techniques to bear on what he considers to be a problem outside his domain as he is willing to bring them to behavioural problems. It is not by a division of labour that the behavioural sciences and other disciplines can benefit themselves and each other in operational research, it is by labouring on the undivided. Such collaboration will succeed, however, only if the operational researcher becomes more willing than he is now to face and deal with behavioural variables explicitly.

REFERENCES

1 A. Rapoport (1960)
2 A. Rapoport (1961)
3 R. L. Ackoff (1962b)
4 R. L. Ackoff (1958a)
5 R. L. Ackoff (1962a)

6 R. L. Ackoff (1963b), pp. 99–104
7 C. W. Churchman (1961)
8 B. H. Raven & H. T. Euchus (1963), pp. 307–16

32 · Industrial Conflict
and 'Industrial Democracy'

EINAR THORSRUD and F. E. EMERY

In 1962 the Trade Union Congress and the Confederation of Employers in Norway agreed to finance jointly a research project on industrial democracy. The Institute for Industrial Social Research at the Norwegian Institute of Technology in Trondheim launched the project in co-operation with the Tavistock Institute of Human Relations in London. The theoretical frame of reference was mainly that of socio-technical analysis developed by the Tavistock group (described briefly by Emery and Trist[1]). However, the project must be viewed in a wider perspective. The concept of industrial democracy always had a political undertone. This was also the case in Norway at the beginning of the 1960s, although the concept meant something more than *workers' control and employee representation.* In conjunction with their major role in collective bargaining and maintenance of industrial peace, the main organizations in Norway have had considerable experience with all aspects of joint consultation on the company level – a well-established part of the Scandinavian system of industrial relations. However, the results of works councils, production committees, suggestion systems, etc., were not impressive. Leaders in the trade unions and in industry felt that political stability and steady economic growth could hardly prevail unless the human resources of the country were more fully engaged. *Improved conditions for personal participation might represent a different and perhaps more important basis for democratization of the workplace than the formal systems of representation.* The human resources must, in a country like Norway with limited natural resources, be the major basis for standing up to competition in a new international market situation. Whatever shape this market will take, it will not leave untouched the economic and social structure of a small country.

To most scientists it might sound over-ambitious to accept such a basic political and social challenge as the starting-point for a research project. (To some it might even seem unethical or beyond the scope of social science.)

After initial exploration with leaders on both sides we felt, however, that we were being seriously asked to join in the search for new ways and means to release productive human resources. We felt that whatever the social scientist had to offer it would be seriously considered by those who should properly take social and political responsibility.

A genuinely joint committee was set up by the trade unions and employers, and the programme formulated by the research group was presented to it in the late autumn of 1962. The first part (Phase A) of the research programme would concentrate on a limited aspect of the problem of industrial democracy, namely the *representation of employees on the boards of companies*. Since this aspect was a pressing political matter, we agreed to study it while we made preparations for what the joint committee agreed would be the major research task. In the next phase (Phase B) we would conduct two or three major field experiments to explore the possibilities for improved *conditions for personal participation* in the concrete work situation.

The preliminary report on Phase A was brought to the joint committee for discussion in the late autumn of 1963. In February 1964 the report was published and was the subject of serious discussion among labour and industrial leaders, in all the major newspapers, and on radio and TV. The detailed research programme for Phase B had already been agreed upon by the joint committee, and the financing of a three-year-plan was granted on a tripartite basis between trade unions, employers' organizations, and government. The first field study in Phase B started in February 1964, in a steel plant in Oslo selected for the experiment by the joint committee. The second field study began in a pulp and paper mill in September 1964.

Phase A: Formal mechanisms for conflict resolution

It was accepted by all parties concerned that *the representation of employees on the boards of companies* is only a limited aspect of industrial democracy. This was not the aspect that we were primarily engaged to study. Nor is it an aspect with which social science is as yet particularly well equipped to deal. To place employee representatives directly on the boards of companies is such an apparently simple and seductive solution that we agreed to analyse relevant foreign experience, and to collect the experience accumulated in five significant companies in Norway in which the employees have had representation at board level for a number of years.

We were faced with several difficulties. The concept of industrial democracy is so diffuse that it is difficult to detect just what purposes were intended by having employees represented on the board. This made it difficult to decide what degree of success had been achieved and also to decide what other arrangements might have served the same purposes.

The functions of a board and the role of a board member have not as yet been the subject of much research. This has made it difficult to determine what is involved for the company and the board, as well as for the individual representative, when he takes on the role of board member.

The meaning of industrial democracy in the Norwegian setting was first clarified by analysis of statements made about this matter by leaders in politics, trade unions, and business and by interviews with them. The following themes emerged:

1 It was clearly recognized that industrial democracy must be considered in the context of existing Norwegian industrial conditions, where there is a framework of broad, but tried and secure agreements about labour–management co-operation, arbitration, and conciliation. Not the least of these agreements being that about the important dependent relation of income policies on national productivity.

2 In considering the purposes of industrial democracy there was no apparent willingness to sacrifice what has already been achieved with regard to living conditions or labour relations. At the same time, however, there was a generally shared feeling that steps towards industrial democracy should be taken in order to:

(*a*) Bring Norwegian industrial life into closer accord with the democratic social life that individuals now enjoy;

(*b*) Create the conditions of fuller individual commitment that will lead to increased productivity and efficiency.

There was no indication that people believed that both ends must be served conjointly, although there was some suggestion that it would not be acceptable for one to be achieved at the expense of the other.

3 There was common uncertainty about the organizational forms that would create greater democracy in industry. Different spokesmen refer to the shortcomings of different schemes for formal representation of the employees, and there appears to be a common belief that industrial democracy in Norway must mean something more than just formal democratic arrangements of elections, representation, decisions by committee, etc.

4 From several quarters came the suggestion that this 'something more' pertains to the conditions under which individuals carry out their ordinary day-to-day tasks in the workplace, i.e. something akin to what political scientists identify as the necessary conditions or requirements of democracy.

It seemed to us that the relevant criteria would have to be sought in the social conditions necessary for democracy rather than in some political definition of democracy. General agreement about democracy, and to that extent about industrial democracy, is not limited to agreement about the definition and the correct use of the term. If we limit our relevant public to those who specialize in the study of institutions, then there is very considerable agreement about the social conditions that are in practice necessary for a democratic distribution of social power. Quite briefly, the conditions necessary for effective democracy are broadly agreed to be:*

1 That men are assumed to be equally human. If, on the contrary, some are assumed to be of inferior caste or second-rate members, then, despite any formal arrangements, they will tend to be deprived of effective representation.
2 That all men have a degree of free movement in their daily life such that they may, if they desire, make an autonomous contribution to the life of the community. If, on the contrary, men are extremely hemmed in by the need to earn a living, by censorship, and such like, then no formal arrangements for representation will create an effective democracy.
3 That the leadership is removable by and responsible to the many. If the available leadership is, on the contrary, controlled by some political party or machine or by their loyalties to a narrow social stratum, then the presence of elections, etc., will not ensure effective democracy.

It is easy to see why in recent decades political scientists should have had to spell out the differences between real and apparent democracy and why what we take to be political democracy is treated a little lightly by some students of Classical Greece and some anthropologists. It is also not difficult to see that parallel distinctions need to be borne in mind in considering industrial democracy.

However, the point of particular relevance to our purpose is that general agreement disappears the moment people attempt to make industrial democracy a meaningful concept in a particular social setting. This made it important for us to interview persons who had the experience of functioning as employees' representatives on boards. We expected them to be more specific. When asked to review the results of their representation, they would be forced to specify what objectives had been pursued in their case and how these were modified to meet circumstances.

To limit the danger of over-generalizing from the evidence, three points must be borne in mind with respect to the views expressed by the representatives we have interviewed:

(a) The five companies are, according to Norwegian standards, large manufacturing firms which are all wholly or in part financed by state capital. One might expect the situation here to be more favourable for this experiment than would be the case in private companies in Norway.
(b) The representatives have accepted a personal commitment to their role which might lead to an over-estimation of what they have achieved.
(c) We interviewed some thirty people who had had personal experience on these 'mixed' boards. Twelve out of these had acted as representatives, the others in key roles as chairmen or managing directors.

* This particular formulation is derived from Karl Mannheim.[2]

Apart from simply re-asserting that representation on the boards implemented the employees' right to be heard (i.e. that it was a step to greater democracy), the interviewees pointed to several specific purposes that could be served by representation:

(*a*) It could serve as a control on the way management carried out its personnel functions.
(*b*) It could restrain the board from considering measures that would be very unpopular with the employees.
(*c*) By making available to the board the special experience and contacts of an employee, it could increase the chances that the board's decisions would take into account the interest of their employees. Thus, an employees' representative could help to draw the board's attention to the need for investment in welfare (housing, pensions, etc.)

These are possibilities, and by no means all of the representatives thought they had realized all of them. The critical questions are: how effective are these influences, and how far do they contribute to the intended aims of democratization, compared with alternative means? Several relevant facts emerge from the interviews.

(*a*) There is little evidence of active communication and feedback between the electors and their representative. This in itself renders suspect the effectiveness of the representation, particularly because the representatives are not responsible over a longer period to party or programme.
(*b*) Nine out of the twelve representatives interviewed made some reference to their having to take a board or company view of some matters, particularly production.

These facts were in agreement with information from the other interviews (of chairmen and managing directors) and with the records of board meetings. Together, these points suggest that it may not be easy in practice for representatives to exercise control over the managers in personnel matters, to restrain the board, or to push welfare demands too hard in the face of other company requirements that they may be ill-equipped to judge.

A detailed analysis of experience with these matters in Yugoslavia, Germany, and the United Kingdom confirmed the general picture.[3]

The Norwegian cases bring into sharper focus some of the issues that emerged from the foreign experience. In particular, there is the distinction between, on the one hand, matters that involve negotiation and reconciliation between different but related sources of power (as, for instance, when trade unions exercise their power in negotiations for the interests of employees) and, on the other, matters that seem to involve sharing of power. A necessary condition for the continued sharing of power is that there must be agreement on means and goals that are reconcilable with each other. If in the extreme case the power is used for contradictory and mutually defeating purposes, then the basis for sharing will almost certainly be disrupted. Effective sharing does, of course, require more than the absence of contradictory ends or means; it would seem to require that the various ends and the various means should be mutually supportive. Moreover, if sharing of any source of social power is not to be disruptive of other parts of the society, it must go hand-in-hand with the sharing of responsibility. Examination of the behaviour of employee representatives on Norwegian boards makes it clear that, although they legally share in the power of the board, they find it very difficult to see how to use that power in ways that both accord with usual board purposes and make a direct impact on the working life of their constituents. The power of the board relates to, and is appropriately used for, the economic prosperity of the firm. Most of the known and obvious ways of furthering the employees' interests at board level involve an increase in labour costs, with no assurance of an off-setting economic gain for the company, or they involve interference in managerial execution of board policy which a board will be naturally reluctant to allow. The possibilities for jointly furthering the interests of the employees and the company seem to lie more in the power-field of the manager than at board level. As a consequence, the representatives find themselves in a position where they can do only one of the following:

(a) Work along with the rest of the board, in the hope that increased prosperity for the firm will result in greater job security and increased rewards for the employees. In this way there can be a genuine sharing in the power of the board, but this is at a personal level and does not depend upon their being representatives of the employees. The responsibility that they assume when they act in this way is a responsibility to the board.

(b) On issues that concern employee interests (in line with the preceding alternative) act as members of the board who happen to have some information about the temper of the workers, etc., which might help them to decide on their strategies.

(c) If, however, they decide to stick to their role as employees' representatives they will find themselves negotiating for greater fulfilment of employee interests against the interests represented by the rest of the board. This could not be pushed far without involving, explicitly or implicitly, the power of the employees *vis-à-vis* the company.

Quite apart from any other consideration, the critical consideration for our analysis is that the power involved is independent of and external to the board's power. It arises from the qualities and needs that the workers bring with them on to the job, and, unlike the power of the board, is not intrinsic to the organization of production. Thus, when the employees' representatives adopt the position of bargaining for their electorate, it has very little to do with democratic participation in the powers of the board, but a great deal to do with the trade unions' efforts to secure industrial justice. The representative who so exercises his powers as a board member is at the same time asserting that his primary responsibility, at least on these matters, is to an external group, not to the board.

Over and above these possible lines of action, the representative may take it upon himself to seek redress for injustices that are seen to be done to some individual by the way in which policy has been executed. In this case a representative is not ordinarily seeking to do more than work with the board to prevent misuse of its powers. However, these matters are generally delegated to management and are not the sort of thing that a board feels it can usefully work on. In practice, representatives tend to learn that these matters lie outside their role on the board.

Thus, we are suggesting that, in designing these representatives roles, there has been a failure to distinguish clearly between the industrial power that is exercised by Boards and management, in which employees wish to share, and the power that is exercised by employees (e.g. to withhold labour), which they seek to use more effectively. When employees or their representatives speak about industrial democracy they are usually referring to the sharing of managerial power, but when they come to the practice of industrial democracy they tend to assume that steps to increase the effective application of their independent power (and hence their ability to get what they define as a fair deal) automatically lead to greater sharing of managerial power (and presumably responsibility). In the cases we have examined there is no evidence that this happens.

If this distinction is kept firmly in mind, then it is possible to sum up fairly succinctly the lessons emerging from the above cases and at the same time to avoid some of the prevailing confusion.

(*a*) There seems to be a case for extending the area of negotiations within the firm. Works councils and the like are potentially capable of handling a large number of problems as they arise in their concrete work setting. These problems might otherwise remain unresolved and create bad relations, or they might be translated into some other, even more difficult, problem so that they can be handled by the existing trade union organization.

The general experience is that the problem-solving potential of representational systems can be realized only if matched by an effective management.

In this, as in other matters, the management must recognize that the success of their enterprise depends upon how it works as a socio-technical system not simply as a technical system with replaceable individuals added to fit. In particular, management needs to have a personnel system that keeps them informed of the conditions of their employees and makes it possible for management to exercise some initiative in the matter, and thus demonstrate their sincerity and goodwill. Furthermore, management requires an effective appeals system. Without this the work of the representative (cum negotiating) system will be too easily disturbed and distorted by individual cases.

(b) In so far as industrial democracy means more than extended negotiations and consultations, there is a need for some transfer of real managerial power to the employees. It is difficult indeed to see how this sharing can be started at the top – at board level. If democratic participation is to be a reality, then it seems inevitable that it must be started at a level where a large proportion of employees are *both* able and willing to participate. The problem of creating industrial democracy seems in fact to be inseparable from the problem of 'the split at the bottom of the executive chain' which has plagued all attempts to create effective representational systems.[4] Fortunately, this latter does not seem to be an insoluble problem. Holter's recent survey[5] of the attitudes of Norwegian workers confirms the findings from other comparable democratic societies that the majority of the lower grades of industrial workers feel that they: (a) could cope with more responsibility in their daily work, and (b) want more such responsibility. Industrial experiments in the United States, the United Kingdom, and India (in engineering, coal-mining, and textiles) have shown that democratic sharing of managerial power at this level can be stable and effective because it furthers the ends of both employees and managements.

In these last remarks we would seem to have forgotten the skilled workers and functionnaires. This is only because the evidence suggests that 'the split at the bottom' is a major factor constraining any development of democratic work relations for the other levels. Unless this split is resolved, there is not a great deal that can be done for foremen or skilled workers.

Phase B: a détour round formal resolution

The Phase A research has been reported in full and fed into a setting where there is acrimonious national debate about legal forms of industrial democracy. This debate is conducted by others and for interests that are not identical with ours as researchers. However, this phase of research gave us the chance to build the power network that is essential if the Phase B research is to have a satisfactory outcome. The technical problems of overcoming the split at the bottom do not appear to be insuperable, but our earlier experience [1,6] has shown that demonstrations of how to do this are of no value unless great care and effort have been put in beforehand to create a social mechanism for diffusion. This network must command powerful support from management and unions with a likely, but as yet, indeterminate, input from government. Furthermore, the network must mesh with these interests at each level of their organization. The experiments-cum-demonstrations must themselves be so designed that they can be treated as valid communications by those who have committed themselves to act. The first experiment is well under way in the metal-working sector of Norwegian industry, and the second has started in the pulp and paper sector. It is too early to judge Phase B because the essential criterion of success is whether the diffusion process develops. No amount of expertise in the experiments will avail us if the structure devised by the joint committee of the Trade Union Congress and the Confederation of Employers should fail.

REFERENCES

1 F. E. Emery & E. L. Trist (1960)
2 K. Mannheim (1958), pp. 177–9
3 E. Thorsrud & F. E. Emery (1964)
4 E. Jaques (1951)
5 H. Holter (1965)
6 F. E. Emery, O. A. Oeser & J. Tully (1958)

Q

33 · Activating National Plans

BERTRAM M. GROSS

Introduction

How to get action under national planning?

What are the basic problems in plan execution?

'We've had lots of advice from experts on how to make plans,' Nehru of India is reported to have complained, 'but when shall we hear something on how to implement our plans?'

With the spread of national planning these questions are raised with increasing vigour. Before national planning is seriously undertaken the task of getting action seems relatively simple – particularly to the proponents of planning. Afterwards the national planners themselves find shocking gaps between plans and performance. Their self-confidence is rudely shaken. Their supporters' hopes may be quickly replaced by disillusion with the planners, if not with planning itself.

The problem of implementing plans in any country at any particular period is always a unique problem, one that can be rationally dealt with only by diagnosing the specific obstacles and fashioning an implementation strategy in terms of estimated feasibilities. Furthermore, even the most laudable steps to carry well-designed plans into effect may result in a considerable degree of frustration. Any economy – and particularly the social system in which it is embedded – is only partially controllable. Unforeseeable complications may always produce unpreventable 'shortfalls'.

To analyse the process of plan implementation, we must first introduce the concept of 'activating' as an alternative to the more traditional concept of 'command'. We shall then analyse the obstacles to effective activation, and the processes of building an 'activation base', developing an 'activation mix', coping with conflicts, and developing campaign strategies. This analysis will lead us into many delicate areas usually glossed over by those who approach economic planning in the restricted terms of economic analysis or 'nuts and bolts' administration. It will bring us face to face with such 'unmentionable' realities as conflicts of interest, the distribution of power, and the strategy and tactics of influence.

Activating: the basic concept

Any study of plan implementation, unfortunately, is seriously impeded by certain immaturities in the popular approach to government administration. Many people think of administration as a small 'a' affair involving nothing but staff tools and formal structures, rather than as a large 'A' affair involving the guidance of complex systems in difficult environments. Many too readily accept, and even act in accordance with, over-rigid dichotomies between planning and administration, policy-making and execution, ends and means. They fail to see the intimate and indeed inextricable interrelations among the administrative processes of planning, activating, and evaluating.

Indeed, the traditional language of both public and business administration places an inordinate emphasis upon command (or orders, directions, or instructions) as the way of getting action.* 'After an organization has been formed, it must be made to work,' wrote Fayol, 'and this is the function of command.'[2] 'Directing' was the central element among the seven processes in Gulick's famous POSDCORB.[3] Many more recent analyses of administration, or management, approach the problem of getting actions with the concepts of: (a) command, (b) control (usually conceived of either as command in the first instance or else as subsequent commands to correct action not in accordance with plans), and (c) co-ordination (usually conceived of as commands to keep different actions in conformance with plans). The same spirit is inherent in such terms as 'the chain of command' and the 'span of control'. This tendency to get away from the many difficulties involved in initiating action has often been reinforced by modern theories concerning problem-solving and decision-making. The analysts of decision-making and rationality often prefer to limit themselves to cognitive processes and get away from the nastier problems involved in deciding how to get people to act in accordance with the decisions that are made. The same tendency is promoted by exaggerated ideas of the great power that a prime minister, president, or cabinet minister could exert if he really made the effort, if he really chose to use the directive power allegedly at his fingertips.

In actual practice, however, as every experienced administrator knows, people cannot be moved to action by commands alone. First of all, command is one-directional. One can give orders to a subordinate but not to an associate, superior, or competitor. A government agency may give orders to people who are not in its employ – but usually only in accordance with certain customs, laws, or regulations that subordinate certain people and activities to

---

* The concept of 'activating' has been more formally presented within the framework of general management theory in the author's *The Managing of Organizations*[1] in Ch. 10, 'The Management of Organizations' and Ch. 29, 'Rationality: Administrative Processes'. The following material also draws upon the discussion of conflict resolution in Ch. 11, 'The Conflict–Cooperation Nexus'.

its command. As a form of feasible action, therefore, command tends to be relevant mainly for people in the higher hierarchical positions and, in a general sense, only for the chief of state himself. Reliance on command as a means of getting action, therefore, may readily produce the very inaction that seems to be inherent in overcentralization.

Second, the power of a command rests upon the receivers' assumption that evasion or disobedience will be punished. Few people can draw upon all the punishments needed to back up reliance on command as the sole means of activation. This is particularly true when available punishments may be evaded. Hence the finding of Dahl and Lindblom that 'command is possible only under conditions of social organization that prevent subordinates from fleeing the reach of the superior'.[4]

Third, if command is relied on too much it can readily lose its effectiveness. Punishments may lose their sting. Indeed, they may be converted by the punished into badges of glory.[5] Both commands and punishments may be evaded – sometimes with impunity. When not evaded, the after-effect may be to undermine initiative or even to bring people and organizations to a point where they may lose their ability to act without instructions from others. In the case of some people and organizations, the very whispering hint of command may lead the proud and headstrong to refuse to take action that they might otherwise have wanted to take of their own accord.

In contrast, a full-blooded approach to the implementation of national plans requires attention to *all* the methods whereby the major actors on the national stage take steps to get action. Commands must be included, but must be put into focus by being set alongside other methods of influencing human behaviour. The concept of 'activating' provides an effective instrument for doing this. As shown later, activating may be defined generally as the 'use of influence' and – more specifically – as something done through any combination of various methods of persuading, pressuring (which includes commanding), and promoting self-activation.

Before discussing these methods of activation, however, it is necessary to identify the major obstacles to activating and the process of mobilizing sources of influence by building an 'activation base'.

Analysing obstacles to activation

Like any other problem, the difficulty of implementing a national plan is often responded to in an irrational manner. The existence of an implementation problem may at first be denied. When admitted, it may be handled in terms of an habitual reaction without an effort at diagnosis. The attempted treatment may be irrelevant to the disease, or may even accentuate it. Indeed, irrational responses of this type seem inherent in the growth of national planning. The rationality of technical calculation, so essential to effective national planning, seems to develop more rapidly than the rationality of dealing with institutional deficiencies, human resistance, and defective processes of planning, evaluation, or activation.

A rational analysis of the obstacles to plan implementation will often point to improved ways of activating plans by overcoming resource deficiencies, human resistance, and defects in evaluation and activation themselves. In many instances, however, such analysis will indicate that the plans, as presently constituted, are simply impossible to carry out. This will necessitate an adjustment of time schedules or, indeed, major changes in the substance of the plans and the process of their formulation.

RESOURCE DEFICIENCIES

In a poor country the greatest obstacle to the activation of any plans for making it richer is its poverty itself. This is particularly obvious in any country that lacks such basic natural resources as good soil, water, forests, and minerals. Heroic efforts are needed to overcome these deficiencies, but the poverty created by such deficiencies is itself a major obstacle to such efforts. A vicious circle is thereby created.

In part, these obstacles are technical. They can be overcome by science, technology, and experience. In this respect they are not absolutes. Their difficulty is relative to the current state of knowledge and skill. Indeed, with modern processes and machinery it is technically possible in any country to achieve results – whether in agriculture, mining, construction, manufacture, or transport – that would have been regarded as impossible a few decades ago. In the not-too-distant future it will certainly be feasible to implement plans for the elimination of cancer, the desalination of salt water, and the widespread control of the weather. In the developed nations of the world it is already possible to abolish involuntary poverty.

But there are no purely technical obstacles. Knowledge and skill are human attributes. Agricultural and industrial objectives cannot be achieved in a given country just because the required knowledge and experience exist somewhere in the world. People with these capacities must also exist in – or be brought to – that country. Natural resources are meaningless without human resources. Underdeveloped human resources are the most serious of all resource deficiencies.

Institutional resources – although overlooked in the formal accounts used by economists – are also of critical importance. Natural resources cannot be used effectively by people acting as individuals alone. Significant plans for progress become feasible only when people are brought together into organizations capable of exploiting and extending available knowledge and experience. The absence of adequately staffed and adequately administered organizations is as much an objective difficulty as any deficiencies in soil, minerals, machinery, science, or technology.

The more ambitious the plans, the greater the resource deficiencies seem. To make the desert bloom, to control a mighty river, to build a progressive steel industry, to develop a national transport system, to provide good housing for the majority of the people, to explore the moon – these are the stuff that national plans are made of. While they may be easy to dream about, they can never be accomplished without facing up to one or another form of resource deficiency.

Unfortunately, human and institutional resources are often neglected by so-called 'planning experts'. Plans are often conceived of in scientific and technological terms alone, particularly by scientists, technologists, and lay-men, whose adoration of science and technology blinds them to the social instruments through which science and technology become useful.

RESISTANCE

Still more remote from solution through science and technology alone are the obstacles created by human resistance to the carrying out of plans. In one form or another such resistance is inevitable.

In its mildest form the energy of planners and activators is pitted against the inertia of others. People and organizations are not easily moved. They are weighed down by habit and custom – just as physical objects are weighed down by their mass. As with physical objects, any effort to move them even a little bit is apt to create friction. An effort to move them far or quickly is apt to create active resistance and bring counter-plans into being.

The most active form of resistance is based upon a felt conflict of interests. In the case of cross-sector plans a certain kind of resistance can reasonably be anticipated from the very nature of the plans themselves. Thus:

Plans for the following . . . will probably be opposed by these groups:

Higher taxes	Taxpayers
Wage controls	Wage-earners, particularly their trade union representatives
Price maxima	Sellers
Price minima	Buyers
Higher interest rates	Borrowers
Lower interest rates	Lenders
Nationalization	Private entrepreneurs

The nature and intensity of the opposition will depend, of course, upon the specific circumstances and upon the degree to which the 'injured' interests are organized. Sector and area plans emerge out of competition for scarce resources by organizations in different sectors and areas. While the distribution of these scarce resources among the various sectors and areas provides the wherewithal for satisfying certain interests, it inevitably implies – at least in part – the denial of resources to others. The process of resource allocation has its negative side also – the distribution of dissatisfactions. These inevitably give rise to efforts to change official plans or impede their implementation.

Moreover, plans for technological progress always produce serious conflicts of interest.

'Technological change of any significance whatsoever is a threat, real or imagined, to the power or security of someone. . . . In its more obvious aspects, any technological change which enables the production of similar output with less labor threatens to reduce employment. But even where such an effect can be counterbalanced by expanded production or by transfers to other work, the change itself threatens established positions and expertise. It renders obsolete the accrued capital of knowledge in the hands and minds of those who operated in accordance with previous processes. It may even suggest that the people responsible for the previous processes are inferior individuals, as compared with the wiser souls who promote the new processes. Furthermore, it may turn upside down the whole world of established relationships and lead to a complete re-organization of work groups, tasks, responsibilities and individual status.' [6]

Finally, plans for changes in social structure – whether they are explicit objectives or merely the corollaries of performance objectives – lead the planners into the heart of deep-felt social conflicts. The elimination of caste or class distinctions, the control of monopolies, the regulation of any powerful interests, the reorganization of industry or agriculture, the promotion of new co-operatives, trade unions, or trade associations, the 'levelling down' of privileged groups, the 'levelling up' of the underprivileged – all such objectives pit planners against plan opponents. In such circumstances it is a rare thing if the social conflicts inherent in (or provoked by) certain plans for changes in social structure are not reflected to some degree in conflicts among the central planners themselves.

To analyse the human opposition to national plans, it is essential to identify the interests and groups directly and indirectly involved in these conflicts and estimate the influence, or power, they may exercise under various conditions. Yet a serious obstacle to such analysis is provided by technocratic conceptions of planning as something divorced from anything so sordid as social conflict. 'There has always been a tendency in economics,' as Myrdal has pointed out, 'to gloss over interest conflicts.' [7] As planning advisers, economists usually use dehumanized models abstracted from interest conflicts. Indeed, many planning technicians see national planning as a 'blackboard' problem exercise far removed from the real world of clashing interests and competing influence strategies.

DEFECTS IN PLANNING, EVALUATING, OR ACTIVATING

Another set of obstacles is always provided by the behaviour of those engaged in the very processes of national planning, evaluating, and activating. These are extremely complex processes that have thus far been subjected to little more than superficial study by social scientists. Most practitioners are guided mainly by hunch, intuition, and trial and error. At best, adequate is associated with inadequate planning, good with bad evaluating, and brilliant with wretched activating. It is unlikely that any foreseeable increase in human knowledge and skill will prevent such defects. Although a full survey of major defects of this kind would be beyond the limits of this paper, brief mention may be made of some of those that seem most widespread.

(a) *Overcommitment.* 'Once settled,' Von Moltke told the Kaiser with respect to the Schlieffen plan for Germany's First World War offensive against France, 'it cannot be altered.' [8] Similarly, once an over-ambitious goal had been set for steel output during India's Third Plan period, fear of criticism prevented the planners from reducing the output targets, thereby accentuating the great progress that had, in fact, been made. The other side of the coin is the tendency of planners to accept the credit for overfulfilment when a sudden change in international markets leads to more foreign-trade income than had been hoped for; to revise goals upward in the light of new opportunities would deny them the illusion of false achievement.

Action-oriented planning, in contrast, is a far cry from the rigid idea of a stable, automatic, and highly predictable system. It is, rather, a highly dynamic process leading from one point of disequilibrium to another. The gap between desired and actual performance is usually rather high. Even the best of planners always fail to anticipate certain new situations. The most successful plans always have unanticipated consequences. The most rational methods always create unanticipated conditions. All these factors lead to unanticipated changes in planners, plans, and planning methods.

Above all, in action-oriented planning there is no 'master plan'. The planning documents, important though they are as instruments of communication and as ways of recording sequences that could not otherwise be arranged in an orderly fashion, are rarely up to date. They can never express the major elements of purposefulness. By the time these points are written down and double-checked, they are usually out of date. A written master plan can be up to date only when it represents a planner's vision upon which no action is being taken or an abstract scheme remote from all operational detail. If the master plan is beautifully printed, with elaborate charts, tables, and pictures, one may be sure that it does not represent what is going on or that – as is often the case – nothing is going on.

(b) *Projectismo.* Discussing Mexican culture, Fayerweather defines this as

'constructing plans without much critical analysis and then assuming the plans to be an accomplished fact . . . the individual is caught up in belief and identification with his schemes as a form of reality . . . *Projectismo* is part of reality for many Mexicans. Listening to one of them describing a plan, you realize that, however unlikely or uncertain of success the plan may be, the man is experiencing in its conception the same type of satisfactions which a man of action would realize only as he carried it out. And for him the satisfactions are the greater because a plan which exists only in his mind does not need to suffer the buffeting of conflicts and obstacles.' [9]

Fayerweather explains *projectismo* in Mexico as a compensating element to offset the frustrations of life throughout Mexican history.

Yet it would be an absurd mistake to regard as a purely Mexican phenomenon the propensity to derive satisfaction from goals in a way that diverts attention from goal attainment. This is, rather, a universal tendency. It is a widespread phenomenon in the public life of all industrially underdeveloped countries, where dreams are easy to concoct but the conflicts and obstacles to achievement are tremendous. It is probably just as widespread in the private fantasies of millions of frustrated or neurotic people in the industrially developed countries. In fact, many of the growth-rate projections developed by frustrated technicians and ritualistically publicized by political leaders can best be described as *projectismo*. They often consist of macro-goals for employment or gross national product, without being related to any specific or identifiable means of attainment. They may be abstract projections unrelated to any specific projects. It is also *projectismo* when planners propose major development 'projects' without the engineering specifications needed to make a decision concerning them, let alone to get them under way.

Another form of *projectismo* is based upon utopian commitments to desired situations that are simply impossible to obtain. In this latter case the elaboration of presumed methods of attaining the unattainable may serve to make the plan more plausible, even though not a bit more feasible. Yet the fact that a plan may be utopian need not prevent its reaching the stage of central decision and commitment. National political leaders often make 'pie in the sky' promises as the only way to distract attention from current suffering. While such promises may lead to bitter disillusionment, they may also start the wheels going around on more realistic planning processes.

(c) *Document orientation.* Over-concentration on documents is one of the occupational pathologies of planning technicians. The preparation of major plan documents is the central task of many technicians. This task is particularly important when the planning documents formulate specific purposes and serve as an essential link in the process of communication between leaders throughout a country or even among the people at large. The written word is essential to record the actions that are to be taken and the reasons for them. Without it, there is no possibility of supplementing the defective memory of people and of providing effective communication among them, particularly on details. The written word – particularly if laden with an impressive array of statistics – also has tremendous symbolic value. It may be of great value in mobilizing support.

Yet plan documents by themselves can never express all the elements of human purposefulness. Some of the more important purposes can never be properly or fully expressed in writing. They must be sensed and felt. Moreover, many points that are clearly written are sometimes out of date by the time of printing. Others are out of date just a little later, and the plan documents can never be brought up to date. In planning, as in the drama, 'the play's the thing' and not the script. When the script is taken for the whole show a major gap develops between plan formulation and action under plans. Plan documents may even be used not so much as an instrument of planning but as a preliminary to planning at some later date or as a substitute for planning at present.

(d) *Under- or over-evaluation.* How well (or badly) is the plan progressing? How effective (or ineffective) are the actions of this organization, in that sector, or in that multi-sectoral programme?

To ask these questions and find answers to them is an integral essential to good planning. Administrators may rarely assume such perfection in planning and activating that the satisfactory nature of ensuing action may be taken for granted. To compensate for past errors and adjust to new conditions, control efforts are invariably needed in the form of additional activation, changes in plans, or both. These, in turn, may require certain changes in personnel or organizational structure. By evaluating past and current action, administrators may complete the 'feedback loop' and undertake these control activities.

Sustained evaluation, however, is often neglected. Performance information is often hard to obtain. When obtained, it may prove unreliable. If reliable, it may prove tedious or unpleasant – particularly in comparison with the more heady exercise of concocting new plans. If fully analysed, the evaluation data may stay in the offices of technical personnel and never get to the more responsible planners. A glaring example of what may happen when attention is not given to actual performance is provided by the following story:

'An Egyptian platoon commander who had been in charge of a number of Archers [British tank] was asked why, when abandoning his guns, he had not spiked them. He insisted that he had done so; he really believed it. And when he was taken back to his own guns and shown them intact and in perfect fighting order, he could not understand it. Of course they had been spiked; he had told somebody to do it.'[10]

In national planning, where matters are usually even more complicated than in war, events like this are always happening.

The other side of the coin is that over-emphasis on evaluation may serve to impede the kind of action it is supposed to promote and promote the kind it is presumably designed to control. As pointed out above, many planners and plan theorists have no concept of activation whatsoever. They may thus tend to think in the limited terms of 'planning and evaluation' or 'planning and control'. Accordingly, when it becomes obvious that for the sake of implementation something else is needed to supplement planning processes, they will often move forward vigorously but unwisely into ill-conceived evaluation and control measures. There are, indeed, many cases in developing countries where faulty plan implementation has been made more faulty through the advice of 'foreign experts' who, with little attempt at diagnosis, have prescribed Western control systems as the remedy for defective activation. In some cases the 'foreign experts' may themselves be totally lacking in practical experience in the handling of evaluation and control activities in their own country.

In diagnosing such obstacles to plan implementation, it is important to keep in mind the major difficulties that may be created by evaluation activities and control systems.

The first is the danger that an overdose of evaluation or control may unwittingly serve to undermine plan implementation. Evaluation and control may divert an undue amount of time and energy from concrete implementation steps to the filling out of forms, the conducting of endless studies, and exhausting appearances before evaluation boards or investigating commissions. They may provoke a debilitating sense of resentment and antagonism against the evaluators, undermine the initiative of those evaluated, and even – what is still worse – destroy their sense of responsibility for their own actions. In reporting on the lack of initiative shown by public enterprises in Burma, Walinsky tells how the Government established a high-level, 'hush-hush' 'board of boards' to investigate their operations.[11] In reading his report, one cannot help but wonder if the investigation itself may not have reduced the initiative and self-reliance of the public enterprises under study. In this connexion it should be kept in mind that close supervision and intensive investigation (particularly by legislative committees) have often been favourite devices whereby interests hostile to a government programme may, in the name of helping it, take action to undermine it.

The second is the ever-present possibility that where tight control is exercised with respect to defined criteria the result may be 'action distortion' – that is, compliance at the cost of neglecting other aspects of performance that cannot be so readily measured. Thus, in Soviet planning control figures expressed in terms of quantitative targets for output have often had the effect of promoting the neglect of quality, production costs, or both.[12] This tendency has also been amply documented with respect to control systems in American government and business.[13]

Third, evaluation and control systems have an innate tendency to produce 'data distortion' as well as action distortion. In providing information under control systems or in response to investigations, administrators often select or 'colour' information to enhance their own performance, 'pass the buck' to others, or tell their superiors what they would like to hear.

> 'Events that may be interpreted as failures, if reported at all, are skillfully underrated and sandwiched between successes,' reports Redfield. 'Through experience the subordinate learns how much to report, what interests the

boss the most, how far one can safely go in confession of his own failures and in pointing out the boss's mistakes, and how coworkers at the same level report.'

Even statistical and financial reports, despite their appearance of cold objectivity, may be based upon a certain amount of fabricated or distorted information at the point where the primary data are first recorded. As these data move through the various channels of processing and interpretation, the distortion may grow. 'Distortion is a cumulative process, starting at the bottom and growing as it ascends the hierarchy, because those at the top foster it through a multitude of expressions and actions.' [14]

Finally, the sheer bulk of information collected through evaluation activities may clog the communication channels of the central planning machinery. This has tended to happen in India, where the creation of evaluation boards and committees has become an almost automatic response to problems of fault implementation. The writing of an evaluation report, in addition to becoming a substitute for action, merely adds to the growing number of reports which pile up on the desks of people too busy to read them.

(e) *Administrative myopia.* Planners often get lost in the clouds by losing sight of the organizational basis for both planning and implementation. On the other hand, they often tend to exaggerate the importance of one particular agency (usually their own), thereby losing sight of the major planning roles to be played by many others among the central cluster of national institutions with major roles in national planning. This myopic self-concentration becomes most dangerous when the effort is made to solve problems of co-ordination by doses of major reliance on stronger doses of formal hierarchical authority. On the other hand, preoccupation with building a central planning organization often diverts attention from the need for building many new organizations throughout the society. Many economists still make the mistake of seeing capital investment as a disembodied process, without giving enough attention to the human organizations needed to invest capital and use it productively. Many educational plans have been drawn up with little attention to the required investment in the educational institutions needed to train teachers, to provide education, and to employ highly trained scientific and technical personnel.

Another form of administrative myopia is nourished by over-sharp dichotomies – both personal and temporal – between planning and activating. The personal dichotomy arrays planners and proposers, on one side, and doers and disposers, on the other. The temporal dichotomy regards planning as something that comes first, and implementation (or activation) as something to be thought about afterwards. Such conceptions create or magnify the fact that doers and deciders always have a role in formulating plans. They ignore the fact that the process of formulation has tremendous implications for implementation. They therefore create or magnify obstacles to plan activation.

Finally, administrative myopia takes the form of totally unrealistic conceptions of what is involved in the management of complex organizations and the still more complex interrelations between such organizations. Many planners seem to have a picture in their heads of administration based on the twin glories of central omnipotence and central omniscience. They envisage all-powerful, all-knowing figures seated on a high pinnacle in an hierarchical heaven, with the rules of reason (as they expound them) carried out by lesser folk. If, in their ignorance, politicians, workers, farmers, and bureaucrats do not co-operate, they must be 'educated'. If they will not be educated this goes to show the depths of man's ignorance and the perversity of the world.

In real life the administration of national planning is quite different. Both power and knowledge are dispersed. There is always competition between divergent interests and purposes, and different methods of activation. Above all, there is competition between competing planners. The idea that planning is non-competitive, something entirely different from market competition, is rather remote from the realities of planning – just as the classical economist's picture of free competition is remote from the realities of actual market practices. Naturally, the competition that exists under planning is not free and unbridled. It is, rather, competition which is resolved through various combinations of integration, compromise, domination, deadlock, and avoidance. It is structured by the common interests, institutions, and procedures that bind groups together and by the interlocking roles that define group conflict. In this sense national planning is always some form of 'structured competition'. The administration of national planning always involves the management of conflict.

Mobilizing influence: the 'activation base'

In warfare strategic plans are not limited to military operations that may be conducted against various enemies. They also provide for a build-up of the forces to be used and the maintenance of vital supply lines.

Similarly, plans for implementing national plans are not limited to what the activators do. They also provide for mobilizing the support and acceptance that make it possible for the activators to do anything. More specifically, they involve the development and maintenance of a network of supporting groups and widespread popular acceptance. These two elements together constitute the 'activation base'.* The nature and strength of these elements are largely

---

* The direct observation of influence, or power, is so difficult that one must often appraise it indirectly by studying the activation base. Thus, Simon[15] suggests that 'if we can measure the magnitude of the influence base, we can infer from this the magnitude of

determined not after national plans are decided upon but in the basic processes of formulating national plans and building the national planning system.

THE SUPPORT NETWORK

'If you want to implement national plans, you have to organize specific support for them.' This is one of the working axioms underlying the efforts of those concerned with plan implementation. It applies to all societies – democratic, authoritarian, and totalitarian.

In any society, however, this practical axiom is subject to misinterpretation. Support may be mistakenly thought of in terms of passive supporters alone, of the 'governed' whose consent or acquiescence is somehow or other obtained. The identity of the 'you' that wants implementation or seeks support may be narrowly regarded as limited to a small circle.

A support network, however, may be more realistically thought of as consisting of three concentric circles:

(a) *Key activators.* These are the people and groups constituting the 'you' in the axiom, who take the lead both in building the activation base and in using the influence thus acquired.

(b) *Active allies.* These are the key people and groups with the power to carry out, or obstruct, various area, sector, or cross-sector plans. Their support is vital for various components of a national plan, although they may indeed be passive or antagonistic to other components.

(c) *Passive collaborators.* These are the large numbers of people and groups who 'go along'. Their acquiescence or neutrality is of tremendous importance, in contrast with the situation which might arise if they should become plan opponents.

The building of a support network is necessarily a selective process. In a totalitarian society, where the key activators will try to mobilize the entire society, there will always be certain individuals and groups who will remain outside (or be pushed outside) the network. In a democratic society the sources of organized opposition will usually be much stronger. In both, there are significant limits on which groups can or should be brought within the inner circle of key activators or the second circle of active allies. In all societies the design of a support network takes into account the differential power of people and groups. Special mention must be made of the following:

(a) *National leaders.* The chief-of-state, his personal advisers, and any informal 'kitchen cabinet' are of tremendous importance for the inner circle of key activators. Even apart from anything he does, the support of

---

the influence (e.g. if wealth is the principal influence base in a particular situation – the principal means of exercising influence – then in that situation we may measure influence indirectly by wealth).'

the chief-of-state is essential to give legitimacy to the plan and to the activation efforts of others.

(b) *Financial management agencies.* The various government agencies playing financial management roles are of strategic importance because of their power over budgets and the money supply. Plan implementation is usually endangered if all of these agencies enter the picture only as passive collaborators. On the other hand, the vitality of the plan may be endangered if they all enter the circle of key activators.

(c) *Major national ministries or departments.* These are usually the most important intermediaries in a national planning system. With tremendous amounts of money and people at their disposal, they can determine the success or failure of major plan components.

(d) *Other national organizations.* The most important of these are usually the national organizations representing enterprises in one or more sectors of production and distribution (chambers of commerce, industry groups, farmers' groups, co-operative federations, etc.). Labour organizations may also be of great importance – particularly when they are the only mass organizations concerned with cross-sector problems of employment, income, and living standards.

(e) *Political parties.* Whenever a support network includes strategic people and groups from among the four preceding categories, some degree of party support is assured. More may be needed. Under one-party dominance it is dangerous not to enjoy the support of key leaders in the party organization. Under competitive party conditions multi-party support is desirable. One of the greatest tests of party leadership is its ability to win 'bipartisan' or 'non-partisan' support for major parts of a national plan. In governmental systems in which significant power is exercised by legislatures, legislative party leaders may occupy a crucial role in the support network.

To a certain extent, the design of a support network fits into the hierarchical structure of government and – if there be such – of society as a whole. The support of subordinates – such as ministries and departments – cannot be taken for granted. It must be won and maintained through specific actions taken by their superordinate national leaders.

But major parts of any support network are made up of coalitions, blocs, or alliances that cut across – and often tend to confuse – the major lines of hierarchical relations. Some of these coalitions may be formalized through co-ordinating committees and councils and serviced through joint staffs. Many consist of informal, collaborative relations. In more authoritarian régimes the dominant coalition tends to be a discrete alliance – say, among party activists, key bureaucrats and managers, military leaders, and the secret police. In more democratic régimes the pattern is usually one of overlapping coalitions. In idealized form these two patterns may be illustrated as follows:

Figure 1

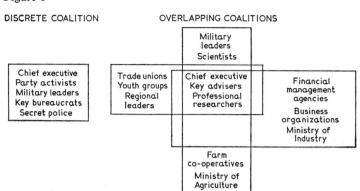

When examined more closely, however, even the discrete coalition may turn out to be composed of a set of smaller, overlapping coalitions. The central core of two or more overlapping coalitions is rarely identical; some advisers and professionals will belong only to one or another. With both types, the coalition structure tends to change with time. In both cases there is a tendency to exclude groups that may threaten the power position of the key activators and a countervailing tendency to co-opt into positions of power those groups whose energy and resourcefulness represent a greater threat if they remain outside. In both, the necessities of the activation base may bring together people and groups that may seem to be, and indeed behave like, strange bed-fellows.

Finally, the organization of a support network cannot always be limited to those groups already in existence. New organizations must often be established – new planning research agencies, new ministries, new public or private enterprises, new forms of agricultural organization, new associations of producers or workers. Organizations must be expanded or replaced. Accordingly, whether or not this is deliberately done on ideological grounds, the very process of building the activation base involves some degree of change – if not reconstruction – in a society's social structure.

UNORGANIZED OPINIONS AND ATTITUDES

Any strong activation base also includes, in addition to a network of supporting groups, a broader and less structured form of support, or acceptance, from large numbers of people in their individual capacity. This is what is often referred to as a 'favourable climate of public opinion'.

'Yet the term "public opinion" is misleading and dangerous if used to refer to some mythical organic entity that comprises the entire society, or to some artificial average that purports to represent all opinions in the society . . . Different opinions are inevitably held by different people. Under most circumstances, except for a few broadly stated issues during a period of national crisis, there will always be less than complete consensus in opinion.

There will usually be at least two different opinions on a single question – and often many more. There may be any one of a varying number of patterns of dispersion among these various opinions. Hence, any meaningful discussion of public opinion must start with a recognition of diversity. It is in this sense that people often talk about the opinions not of the public but of specific "publics".' [16]

The opinions of key elites in strategic positions of power have already been dealt with in the discussion of the support network. We are now left with the opinions and attitudes of unorganized publics. These publics are the various overlapping groups (in the sense of logical categories rather than specific organizations) into which the population may be divided on the basis of age, sex, race, religion, caste, class, kinship, area, sector, occupation, education, wealth, and income.

One reason for the importance of these publics is that their opinions and attitudes have decisive effect on the position of support or opposition taken by specific organizations. Unorganized opinion may always be reflected in the activities of organized groups. It may lead to the organization of new groups or coalitions. It may indeed include the views of the rank-and-file of large organizations and thereby affect the power of the leaders of such organizations to help or impede plan implementation.

Moreover, even in a highly organized society, individuals have important roles. Compliance with laws and regulations, enthusiasm or indifference on the job, voting behaviour in free elections – all these are strongly affected by the attitudes of individuals.

As with the support of organized groups, favourable opinions are usually sought on a selective basis. Although a great charismatic leader may win the support of an overwhelming majority for himself as a person, this support is never automatically transferable to the major components of a national plan. Although most groups may support some aspects of a plan, on other aspects the support of some groups can be won only at the cost of sacrificing support elsewhere. Thus, in a looser and cruder form the strategy of building general support through the favourable opinions of unorganized groups mirrors the coalition strategy of organizing the network of supporting organizations.

Using influence: the 'activation mix'

If command is not the only way to get plans carried out, what else can get things done?

This question may best be answered by regarding command as merely one form of pressure. In addition, an activator may use various forms of persuasion. Also, instead of directly applying persuasion or pressure, an activator may try to get people and groups to activate themselves. The 'activation mix' is the particular combination of these various forms of influence that activators may use in any particular situation. Its composition depends not only on the skill of the activators but also on the activation base, on the resources and energies on which they must rely. In turn, influence must be used to mobilize and maintain sources of influence; the activation base can be built only through the use of an effective activation mix.

PERSUADING

When *A* tries to persuade *B* to do *X* (a course of action) he wants *B* to regard *X* as a way of satisfying or gratifying *B*'s interests (or of avoiding some form of dissatisfaction). If the satisfaction is contingent on something that *A* or someone else may subsequently do (which we may call *Y*), then this is pressure. If it is inherent in the relation between *B* and *X* this is true persuasion.

The following forms of persuasion – informing, expecting, providing an example, proposing, and using propaganda – may be roughly ranked in an ascending order of vigour on the part of *A*. The effectiveness of each depends not only on its combination with other elements in the activation mix but also upon *A*'s and *B*'s perceptions of *B*'s interests.

(a) *Informing.* One of the most effective methods of persuasion is the presentation of data relevant to a desired course of action. Sometimes advisers and others, instead of making specific proposals, will merely present data indicating the desirability of a definite course of action. Often, the process of informing may be quite detailed. In legal briefs, position papers, budget justifications, and plan proposals data are presented to: (*i*) explain the details of a proposed course of action; (*ii*) indicate how and why it will satisfy the interests of the 'activated'; and (*ii*) show how and why alternatives are unfeasible or undesirable. Where no counter-documents are presented, these documents may be extremely persuasive. When many such presentations are made, no point of view will be taken seriously unless backed up by some sort of brief. Even if a brief is too long to be read or too complicated to be understood, its very size and the presumed competence of its compilers may serve to inspire confidence in the proposal.

In a still more pure form the provision of information may be dissociated from any specific proposals. In this sense the annual Economic Reports of the President of the United States, by providing basic information on economic trends and possibilities, undoubtedly have a long-run persuasive effect on the key centres of power in America. Similar forms of persuasion have been adopted in the Netherlands and other countries. The 'indicative planning' of the French, by involving more business leaders in the process of information interpretation, goes still farther. Even in the Soviet Union there is no doubt that the information in basic plan documents *qua information* establishes outer boundaries within which more vigorous forms of activation are used.

(b) *Expecting.* People may also be activated simply by expecting that they will behave in a certain manner. This is particularly effective when the expectation is shared and expressed not only by the activator but also by many others. The tremendous power of mere expectation is illustrated by the extent to which people cling to behaviour patterns expressed in traditions and in informal roles and codes. This power stems from the dissatisfaction created by disapproval and the gratification resulting from approval. It is greatest when the expectation is shared by the 'activated' themselves. It is weakest when there are conflicting expectations and other strong incentives bearing upon them.

Even when unspoken, expectations tend to communicate themselves in mysterious ways. Thus, national planners may promulgate a new programme to reduce tax evasion. But if they themselves expect the programme to fail, their expectations may turn out to be a 'self-confirming prophecy'.

(c) *Providing example.* Another powerful – although often overlooked – form of activation is providing an example to be followed or imitated. An administrator who 'loafs' has a hard time getting others to work hard. The example that he sets may be more influential than anything else he does.

The power of example rests in the satisfactions that people obtain from identifying themselves with a person or group whom they admire or envy. This has often been referred to by political scientists as the 'bandwagon effect', by economists as the 'demonstration effect'. Moreover, providing an example has the additional advantage of communicating far more clearly than may be possible in words the exact nature of the action to be taken.

In national planning the power of example is particularly relevant to such matters as austerity, diligence, and hard work. High government officials who lead a life of conspicuous luxury may thereby undermine plans that call for widespread sacrifices by all the people. Example is also important in improving administrative performance throughout the planning and implementation system. If central planners want more administrators to promote initiative and creativity in the lower ranks of their organizations they, in their own behaviour, set some concrete examples of how this may be done. Conversely, a technical assistance agency which tries to improve public administration in a developing nation may undo all its good work by providing, in its own operations, a conspicuous example of red-taped rigidity or corruption.*

(d) *Proposing.* One of the major functions of advisers is to propose courses of action. This may be done by a direct recommendation or by indirectly discussing alternatives. The incentive lies in the implicit assumption – which may or may not be clearly stated – that acceptance of the advice is in the interests of the advised. Advice is most readily accepted when it shows people how to do what they want to do or to organize their conflicting wants. The process of acceptance is usually quicker if the advised is led to believe that the suggested course of action is really his own idea.

Sometimes, as with command, proposals will be listened to only when

* The author has seen this happen in a number of countries.

coming from someone authorized to offer them. The authoritative nature of a proposal also has a major bearing on the likelihood of its acceptance. When a person is confident that professional advisers are directly concerned with his interests and that there is no conflict among them, the presumption is that the rejection of an authoritative recommendation will lead to some form of dissatisfaction. In these circumstances, which are fulfilled in many practitioner–client relations, an advisory proposal may have tremendous power.

The making of proposals is a vital part of planning and plan implementation. Some proposals are backed up by commands or other forms of pressure; some are backed up by other forms of persuasion; many stand on their own feet. Often, the great merit of a concrete proposal by national planners is that it may inspire others – including key implementers – to come up with counter-proposals that are more easily achievable, if not even inherently more desirable.

(e) *Using propaganda*. In a colloquial sense 'propaganda' is often used to refer to someone else's efforts at persuasion, while one's own are described as informational or educational activities. Even in a more technical sense, the line between using propaganda and informing is hard to draw. Data must always to some extent be structured. They clearly become propaganda only when the facts are strongly 'slanted' or a serious effort is made to appeal to emotions and feelings. Any symbols, slogans, or acts identifying the desired course of action with the interests and aspirations of those who are activated may be used to do this.

Some administrators become effective leaders within their organizations by themselves becoming the personal symbols of their followers' interests. Those who have learned this secret of present-day charisma do not merely persuade people; they convince people by establishing an emotional link with their deeper interests. Similarly, many organizations try to become symbols of interests widely shared by large publics. This is the object of institutional advertising.

It is not always easy to tell whether propaganda is designed more for a broad or a narrow audience. Much public relations and publicity activity ostensibly for external consumption has its greatest utility in keeping the members of an organization persuaded. Election propaganda, it has long been observed, is often listened to mainly by a party's supporters. The public relations activity of the U.S. Forest Service 'is intended to affect the internal forces acting on the Rangers while it strengthens "inside" them, by heightening their identification with the organization, their tendencies toward conforming with agency decisions'.[17] Some planning propaganda probably has its greatest effect upon the self-image and self-confidence of the central planners and their key allies. The most effective propaganda is that which is directly geared to efforts at building the network of organized support and popular acceptance by unorganized publics.

PRESSURE

As already suggested, the difference between persuasion and pressure is that, with the latter, A makes X more desirable (or less undesirable) by promising or threatening Y (subsequent action by the activator in the form of a reward or punishment). The difference between the two forms of Y is not always sharp. The unused stick may be seen as a reward, the withdrawn carrot as a punishment.

The following forms of pressure – bargaining, manipulating, command, and physical force – may be roughly ranked in an ascending order of 'toughness' by an activator. As with the forms of persuasion, the effectiveness of each depends on its position in the total activation mix and upon A's and B's perceptions of B's interests.

The degree of certainty is also important. Severe sanctions (or great rewards) mean little when there is no likelihood of applying (or receiving) them. On the other hand, if the reward–punishment system is automatic and no follow-up is needed, all the activator has to do is demonstrate the inevitable results of a given course of action. Pressure has thus been reduced to persuasion.

(a) *Bargaining*. In bargaining the process of using pressure works in both directions. Both the activators and those activated wield incentives. Each modifies his promises or threats in the light of the actions of the other. Moreover, the desired actions themselves, as well as the rewards and punishments, are also subject to negotiation.

The power of bargaining as a form of activation lies in this flexibility. Both the *quid* and the *quo* may be adapted to the actual needs and strategies of the people and groups involved, as these needs are discovered and modified in the light of shifting relationships. The activators escape many of the resentments and frictions that may easily result from one-way activation. Bargaining on specific points becomes the basis of such co-operative relations as reciprocity, log-rolling, and the exchange of favours. It also enters into the formation of longer-term alliances and coalitions. Bargaining between buyers and sellers constitutes some form of economic market.

Bargaining is an inherent part of the process of making and implementing national plans. Under more dictatorial planning there are fewer bargainers. Under more democratic planning more people and groups are involved in the endless process of negotiation, manoeuvre, and reciprocal adjustment – with much of this taking place in various markets. At times, however, ultra-rational planning technicians may deny any place to bargaining in their own services with respect to plan formulation. By this act of self-denial they may thereby decrease the rationality of the bargaining process itself.

(b) *Manipulating*. In manipulation the activators use pressure to get action without directly stating what they want done. They create situations and influences that impel the activated to move in the desired direction. The successful coquette may use negative signals in order to induce positive action by the ardent male. A central bank may manipulate the money supply and the interest rate in order to obtain – without direct commands – certain desired changes in economic activity or price levels.

'Because command is a more ostensible, direct, person-to-person relationship, perhaps it can offend status, self-respect, and dignity of individuals more than does manipulating of operating penalties,' Dahl and Lindblom observe. 'Manipulation of field seems to be more suitable for creating "permissive situations", i.e. situations in which a particular response is attained although the individual can choose among a variety of rewards and penalties.' [18]

The manipulation of markets has always been a treasured device of money-making by powerful market operators. It is now coming to be regarded as an invaluable device for plan implementation – even when its use may mean the extension of old market situations or the promotion of new ones.*

(c) *Commanding.* A command (order, regulation, instruction, or direction) is a direct presentation of the desired course of action backed up by at least an implied threat of punishment if the action is not taken. Because other forms of activation are so widely used, command is often a residual method, used only when nothing else will do. When used, moreover, it is often closely associated with persuasion and with other forms of pressure.

In some circumstances command is the best method of activation. No other method can be as useful in times of emergency or in any situation when rapid action and co-ordination are needed. Some people will respond only to command. In some programmes nothing else is conceivable. Remove command from a tax plan and it becomes a plan for seeking voluntary contributions.

There are many prerequisites for the effectiveness of commands. As military officers learn in their training schools, a command must clearly specify the action to be taken. It must be feasible; the impossible can be expected of no one. If there is time a command may also be explained and justified; one's action in carrying out a command is not hampered by being persuaded of its desirability. It must come from a legitimate source; an army officer will not usually obey an intelligible, feasible, and well-justified command given him by a newspaper reporter. It must be acceptable. In the language of Barnard and Simon, it must be within the receiver's 'zone of indifference' or 'area of acceptance'. The giver of the command must be prepared to check on the action taken and to take corrective action wherever needed. In national planning, let it be added, these requirements may become extremely onerous –

---

* Market manipulation often involves firm commands (or regulations) at certain points. The manipulation is inherent in their indirect effects.

particularly because of the great complexity often involved in the course of desired action, its explanation and justification, evaluation systems, and the handling of specific sanctions.

Above all, there is a difficult relation between the frequency of commands and their effectiveness. If national planners and activators go too far in issuing vast numbers of regulations and orders, their quantity may quickly outrun the available supply of meaningful rewards and punishments. Resentment and opposition may be promoted. Widespread evasion and deception may result. On the other hand, the art of issuing firm regulations and orders cannot be developed without sustained use. The value of command as a 'last resort' can never be exploited if the 'gun behind the door' is allowed to grow rusty.

(d) *Using physical force.* The use of physical force, or coercion, is one of the oldest means of influencing the actions of others. It is based on two unpleasant but unavoidable facts. The first is that the application of force usually creates intense dissatisfactions which, when felt or feared, may serve as incentive or deterrent. The second is that when applied in certain forms – such as confinement, crippling, murder, or destruction – it may reduce or eliminate the recipient's capacity to act at all.

With the advent of the industrial and administrative revolutions and the accompanying decline in slavery and forced labour, physical force has declined as a conspicuous form of activation. Even the most authoritarian administrators of the modern world no longer dream of relying on the whips of the taskmaster. More effective modes of pressure are always available and are generally used. Even when used as a last resort, physical force is accurately seen as something that, at best, has negative value only, and, at worst, may unleash counter-forces which may damage if not destroy its users.

Although the area in which physical force is used has narrowed considerably, government's traditional monopoly on the legitimate use of organized violence has been maintained. Police forces and courts are indispensable instruments of government – and also of national plan implementation. In fact, together with military forces, they are often essential to provide an environment of law, order, and national security – an environment which, whether in peace, war, or in-between stages, is essential for the implementation of national plans.

PROMOTING SELF-ACTIVATION

One of the unique characteristics of people and human organizations, as distinguished from machines, is that they are more self-activating. Although dependent upon their environment for necessary inputs, they can take steps by themselves to obtain these inputs. They do not have to rely, as do machines, upon messages from makers and operators. Both the individual cells which form the organism and the organism as a whole are independent systems of energy, systems which will recharge themselves and even grow in power until the inevitable day of disintegration. There is thus a realm of self-activation beyond direct persuasion, or pressure, seduction, or coercion.

To penetrate this realm, national planners may use persuasion and pressure to get people and groups to activate themselves by self-administered rewards and punishments.

(a) *Encouraging participation in decision-making.* The most immediate way to promote self-activation is to involve people in the process of themselves determining the desired course of action. To the extent that a decision or plan is regarded as one's own, activation boils down to getting oneself to do what one wants to do. Although this may not be easy, particularly when wants are conflicting and capacities limited, the problem of interpersonal influence is largely by-passed. Also, the problem of accurately communicating the nature of the action to be taken is tremendously eased.

Many studies have demonstrated that in the operation of single, large-scale organizations various forms of broad participation in decision-making and planning have reduced labour turnover, eased adjustment to changes in production methods, raised output, and provided better environment for professional employees.[19,20,21,22] Selznick[23] has demonstrated the value of external participation in building support for a controversial programme. Salter[24] has shown its value in co-ordinating international operations.

The framework for participation in national planning decisions is provided by the social structure itself – particularly by the distribution of power among various groups. The more decentralized the structure, and the larger the role of economic markets, the greater the participation of each part in planning its own affairs. Within such a structure the use of persuasion, bargaining, and manipulation – as distinct from enforced command – may enlarge the possibility of such participation. This may be referred to as 'dispersed responsibility'. In contrast, there is also 'shared responsibility', which usually involves some form of adjustment in the formal or informal structure. Within single organizations, such adjustment may be made by setting up management committees, management teams, or labour–management councils. In government, it may take the form of formal or informal representation of non-government interests within government – both in the official personnel of government and in representative committees of various types.

Two interesting examples of the promotion of large-scale participation in national planning are provided by the short-lived N.R.A. experiment in America during the early New Deal of President Roosevelt and the more recent use of sector and cross-sector commissions in French national planning. Under the N.R.A. each major industry in the United States was asked to organize a 'code authority' which would develop its own code to maintain prices and prevent 'unfair competition'. Within very general policies, each authority – composed almost entirely of private business interests – was left alone. By the time the whole structure was ready to collapse under its own weight, the Supreme Court destroyed its foundations by a decision that it was based upon an unconstitutional devolution of government power to private interests.

In French national planning, in contrast, the sector and cross-sector commissions have been given no formal power whatsoever. Nor are they strictly advisory groups in relation to the Government. Indeed, each group contains a substantial number of government as well as private representatives. Their function, rather, is to work together in formulating joint goals and policies. The national plan is, to an important extent, the product of such joint effort. It is therefore not the *Government's* plan so much as as it is *du plan*. It belongs to all the participants. It is expected, therefore, that those who helped make the plan will do their best to carry it out. In fact, the clearest principle in modern French national planning is the principle of '*the participation in policy-making of those who will have to bear the brunt of the implementation of measures decided upon*'.[25]

The use of such methods to promote self-activation is fraught with technical difficulties. Wide decentralization requires greater central efforts to keep decentralized operations in line with general policy. The more informal representative and consultative relations require large amounts of time and energy and still larger expenditures of patience and skill. The more formal ones seem to require long and frequent meetings, carefully prepared agendas, and strong supporting services. Both involve continuous experimentation.

The greatest difficulty, however, is the danger of either bluff or breakdown. On the one hand, 'participative' techniques are often used to provide ritualistic rather than genuine participation. Planners may merely want to give private groups the 'sense' of participation in order to manipulate them into accepting as their own predetermined decisions and plans. Similarly, many representatives on consultative committees, both intra- and inter-organizational, are mainly interested in the prestige accruing to themselves or their constituents through symbolic rather than actual participation. On the other hand, too much participation may lead to organizational breakdown. As Selznick points out in his TVA study, leadership needs participation in order to get cooperation, but 'if participation is allowed to go too far, the continuity of leadership and policy may be threatened'.[26] This danger is particularly great in the case of participation by external groups eager to penetrate government in order to exploit it for their own narrow purposes. This, in part, is what happened under the N.R.A. This will also happen whenever market mechanisms are relied upon for resource allocation in periods of acute shortages.

The possibility of avoiding these two extremes depends upon the capacities of both the national planners and those whose participation they may want to promote. The planner who favours wide participation must be able to cope with the fact that the plans and actions that emerge can never be precisely known in advance. He must be able to take the risk that the self-activators may decide to go in directions he had not previously contemplated. He must be willing to share power in order to help to build a larger system of power. On the other hand, the other participants must be mature and self-confident enough to escape the tendency to rely too much on central government (as in many developing nations) or to regard central government with ingrained suspicion and distrust (as is also the case in the United States and many developed nations). Above all, there must be enough organizations outside central government to make such participation conceivable. In some countries steps to build such organizations must be taken *pari passu* with efforts to promote their participation in national planning.

(b) *Educating.* Education may promote self-activation by helping people to acquire more knowledge, abilities, and interests. To the extent that this may be done, individuals and organizations will be more capable of rational participation in planning and implementation. They will acquire more confidence in the handling of their own tasks and in co-operating with others on shared tasks.

In a certain sense every national planning effort is a large-scale exercise in nation-wide education. Planning documents and planning discussions raise the level of knowledge about important phenomena. Planning and implementation activities develop new and better abilities. The vision of future goals may awaken new and deeper interests. Moreover, both in the developed and the developing nations, increasing attention is being given under national plans to the expansion of formal education and training at all levels.

Nevertheless, two different approaches – sometimes combined – may be discerned. The first sees education as an instrument of conformity. This is much like the educational efforts in some large-scale organizations that aim to 'control what goes on inside each individual organization member, to get them to do of their own volition what the managers want them to do, and to equip them with the resources of skill and knowledge for these duties'.[27] Here education becomes a combination of general propaganda and indoctrination in the proper response to prescribed incentives. Self-activation is allright, just so long as it takes place within carefully prescribed limits.

The second approach aims at the promotion of greater autonomy. Both individuals and organizations may be encouraged to learn how to deal with new and more challenging situations. They may be helped to broaden their perspectives and seek creative solutions of their own – even if this means challenging approved plans.

The second approach can rarely become significant if the national planners see themselves as the repositories of high wisdom, and education as something needed only by others. One of the most important things that good national planners learn from experience is the shocking extent of their own ignorance. One of the greatest contributions they can make to the nation-wide process of learning through planning is to set a clear example of people who are diligently trying to educate themselves through research, theory, and the fearless examination of their own failures and successes. A dramatic example of such an attitude was provided by Julius Nyerere in a public speech to the effect that 'we all must learn'. 'All Tanganyikans must accept that they knew nothing' and continue their search for knowledge. Many conferences, he held, were needed to show the people, including parliamentary secretaries, that 'they knew nothing'. The newspaper reports indicate that Nyerere drew cheers when he told the gathering 'that he himself was learning to be President. He had been a teacher earlier, and he was now learning his new job'.[28]

Coping with conflicts

National planners and plan activators, it has already been emphasized, are inevitably involved in handling conflicts between people, groups, organizations, and underlying interests. In building the activation base, they prepare for conflict. In using any series of activation mixes, they aim at certain conflict outcomes.* The implementation of national plans, therefore, may also be seen from the viewpoint of the types of outcome that are sought and attained.

1 VICTORY–DEFEAT

Victory by one party to a conflict (or defeat to others) is the neatest of all outcomes. The victor receives a clear-cut gain. The defeated suffers an unambiguous loss.

It is also a highly circumscribed form of outcome. Even in games and debates, where there are agreed-upon rules for keeping the score, a victory in one round may be quickly followed by defeat in the next, and vice versa. In more complex forms of conflict, the possibility of such change is still greater. Clear defeat may be transformed into a psychological victory by propagandistic success in calling it something else – as when President Nasser of Egypt embellished his political victory over the forces that had seized the Suez Canal by convincing Egyptian supporters that it was military superiority which forced the withdrawal of the invaders from the canal region. The very act of surrender, as Coser pointed out, may involve an 'assertion of power'.[29] It may be used to establish conditions for subsequent gains. The anguish of defeat may, in fact, be a contribution to future victories by providing the unseasoned with an invaluable baptism of fire and by teaching lessons that could otherwise never be learned. Above all, victory or defeat on one issue may be inextricably associated with defeat or victory on other issues. In such circumstances, either is merely an aspect of a compromise outcome. Ac-

---

* The term 'conflict resolution' could also be used. Yet 'resolution' (like 'solution' and 'problem-solving') suggests a finality inconsistent with the ongoing process, whereby every desired conflict outcome creates new problems. It also suggests a purely intellectual operation that could be handled with a computer.

cordingly, national planners can rarely afford the luxury of seriously seeking a complete victory in all their battles. To do so would be to risk far too many defeats.

COMPROMISE

A compromise occurs when each party to a conflict wins something and loses something. It may take place with respect to a single issue. Or it may emerge as the aggregate of a set of specific victories and defeats on various issues. It is thus the most widespread outcome of conflict resolution. The shaping of compromise is thus an inherent part of both formulating and carrying out national plans.

The necessity for compromise is something that can never be learned painlessly. It is particularly difficult for those who have discovered the ease with which a purely logical problem can be solved through the processes of deduction but have not learned the difference between such a problem and a genuine social conflict. For these, who may play extremely important roles in national planning, compromise is often seen as an unmitigated evil. If it is to be tolerated the condition is often laid down that at least there shall be no compromise on matters of principle. But principles are usually the first things to be yielded, for the simple reason that they are so rarely a clean-cut expression of fundamental high-priority interests. Because they are sometimes willing to sacrifice principles which are not directly related to basic interests but are rather propaganda devices for the extension of support, the most effective national leaders often appear to be totally unprincipled men. In a world of sharp divisions and dispersed power, they may even have to yield on basic interests. It may be added that since interests and principles are always multiple and diverse, the safeguarding or serving of some invariably requires a yielding or even sacrifice of others.

At the same time, to laud compromise as a value in itself may lead to an eating away of moral values and the growth of a cynical 'anything goes' attitude that may undermine the integrity of national planning. It may also lead to an over-size role for those planners and activators who are skilful in serving as brokers and 'go-betweens'. These are people who usually care more about making a deal or keeping peace for its own sake than about making progress towards achieving substantive goals.

INTEGRATION

As Follett [30] pointed out long ago, integration is a conflict outcome in which the interests of all sides have found a place without any side sacrificing anything. The process of working towards an integration involves getting behind the symbols that may hide the true state of affairs and bringing conflicts out into the open so that the underlying interests can be analysed and re-examined. This is very close to the 'working through' process developed by psychoanalysts. Its application to organizational conflict is well illustrated in the way in which the Tavistock consultants helped to bring about an integration as an outcome to certain managerial conflicts in the Glacier plant.[31] Its application to national planning was envisaged by Mary Follett's discussion of achieving integration through a continuous process of interpenetration and 'reciprocal relating' at many levels.[32] Such a procedure is approximated in many ways by the national planning system in France. Thus, the French plan, to an important extent, represents an integration of major interests in the French society.

Enthusiasm for integration should not lead one to believe that it is possible to resolve all or most conflicts in this manner. Although such an outcome is generally more desirable, and although integration probably plays a much greater role than many cynics would think, there are undoubtedly many occasions when nothing is possible except some sequence or combination of avoidance, deadlock, victory–defeat, or compromise. An integration of any complex conflict, moreover, is a many-sided operation that must usually include within it some elements of mere compromise.

One of the reasons for the difficulty of attaining integration as an outcome of conflict is that it always involves a broadening of the framework. It requires the conflicting parties to become involved in issues beyond the current agenda of attention. It takes into account the many and diverse interests of the combatants, apart from those which are the basis of contention. It is based upon an examination of new and hitherto unexamined courses of action. This requires on the part of at least some of the planners and activators a broad perspective towards life and a varied acquaintance with the total environment. To get beyond the narrow confines of mere compromise, one must be able to analyse the wide range of people's interests and have a sense of what is and is not feasible in a complex environment. These are not common capacities.

DEADLOCK

Deadlock is such a negative state that it may be difficult to regard it as an outcome. As with the stalemate conclusion of a chess game, neither side can win. But unlike chess, the broader game of social conflict can often continue in a state of deadlock for long periods of time.

'The possibility of deadlock – or to use a closely-related term, stasis – is inherent in the democratic process of peaceful group conflict. When few victories are ever complete, when power is widely dispersed among many veto groups, when every solution is a compromise that is objectionable to many, and when every settlement itself creates new problems, you have the makings of a stalemate.' [33]

The negative aspect of deadlock is probably one of the reasons why peace is not always as attractive as the hatred of war might suggest it should be. A 'no win' peace is never as appealing as a victory. It becomes more desirable only when the dangers of defeat make 'no loss' seem more comfortable.

'Peace through stalemate, based on a coincident recognition by each side of the opponent's strength, is at least preferable to peace through common exhaustion.' [34]

However, deadlock may have more positive aspects. It may keep an opponent's energies concentrated upon a certain front, while one tries to advance on other fronts. It may provide a breathing-space, with or without withdrawal, during which one mobilizes forces for renewed efforts or – as with many plans for land reform in developing nations – for substantial modification or even withdrawal of ambitious plans.

AVOIDANCE

Divergence of interest among human beings and groups is so great that it is highly doubtful whether social intercourse would be even tolerable without many forms of avoidance. In fact, withdrawal from conflict seems to be one of man's most natural and traditional ways of coping with conflicting interests. Internal conflicts may be unconsciously repressed. Family conflicts may be avoided by having children sleep in separate rooms, taboos on the discussion of delicate subjects, or – as in some societies – rules against husbands talking with mothers-in-law. Within organizations interpersonal conflicts are avoided by people 'keeping out of each other's hair', by developing codes of non-interference in another's 'territory', by suppressing deeply felt differences of opinion, and by postponing or evading decisions. In conflicts between nations avoidance is achieved through disengagement, a *cordon sanitaire*, isolationism, or the division of disputed territory into spheres of exclusive influence. At the national level avoidance takes the form of regarding certain desirable courses of action as taboo – or at least as not to be incorporated in planning objectives for the present.

If avoidance is carried to an ultimate extreme it may indeed mean the end of conflict – as when a central government avoids dealing with a run-away inflationary crisis. In such circumstances the price of peace may mean the end of both planning and plan implementation. Yet within bounds many issues must always be dodged – at least temporarily. The only alternatives may be defeat, deadlock, or an unsatisfactory compromise.

Developing campaign strategies

For the purposes of analysis it has been necessary in the preceding sections to discuss in an artificially separated manner the interrelated processes of mobilizing sources of influence, using influence, and resolving conflicts. In actual practice these processes are combined in a series of interlocking events that move towards or away from various objectives in national plans. The more effective activators see these events not as single, sporadic acts, but as a series of campaigns. To conduct these campaigns, in the face of obstacles, inertia, and uncertainty, they develop various campaign strategies. In the eyes of a few national leaders these separate strategies may be seen as part of some overall Grand Strategy for the implementation of national planning as a whole. For the major activators, however, the important things are specific campaigns to carry out certain parts of a national plan. Grand Strategy has meaning in the sense of interrelating major campaigns on such matters as agricultural production, industrial expansion, export promotion, price restraint, tax revision, and improved education.

EXPLOITING CRISIS

One of the most delicate aspects of campaign strategy is the use of crisis situations. A period of widespread complacency does not lend itself easily to the accomplishment of great social changes. At the time of sharply perceived crisis, however, many things are feasible that might otherwise be impossible. Leighton explains the difference as follows:

> 'Communities under stress, with their labile and intense emotions and shifting systems of belief, are ripe for change. While this is a situation fraught with danger because of trends which may make the stress become worse before it gets better, there is also an opportunity for administrative action that is not likely to be found in more secure times. Skillful administration may be able to seize the moment not only to guide spontaneous shifts in constructive directions but even to achieve extensive changes that would otherwise be impossible or extremely difficult. . . .
> 'At periods of great emotional stir the individual human being can undergo far-reaching and permanent changes in his personality. It is as if the bony structure of his systems of belief and of his habitual patterns of behavior becomes soft, is pushed into new shapes and hardens there when the period of tension is over.' [35]

The opportunity for initiating extraordinary action is created by this softening. In exploiting this opportunity administrators can, by seizing the initiative, both unify their followers inside and outside the organization and divide and surprise their opponents. As Hirschman has pointed out in his discussion of social reform in Latin America, 'crisis may make it possible to take action against powerful groups which are normally well entrenched and invulnerable, [and] . . . may stimulate action and hence learning on a problem on which insight has been low and which for that very reason has not been tackled as long as it was in a quiescent state'.[36] Above all, in time of crisis, administrators themselves must act. The crisis calls a halt to the many prior acts of postponement and avoidance. In discussing United States participation in international relations, Cleveland points out that 'the President, the Secretaries of State and Defense, the Director of Central Intelligence and several dozen other men do spend a very large part of their time working on the crises of the moment'. He adds that 'it is often at moments of crisis that the most basic long-range decisions about foreign policy are made'.[37] The same observation is relevant to the top officials of government in their handling of domestic plans.

To exploit crisis, national planners are usually continuously alert for sources of stress. To be forewarned is to be forearmed; the penalties are great for not recognizing a crisis until too late. Long-range planning – particularly contingency planning – provides one way of getting prepared to deal with crises. Yet planners often fail to anticipate the profile of the actual crises that emerge. Contingency plans 'must normally deal with many contingencies which do not, as things work out, come to pass'.[38] The utility of the plans, rather, is that their preparation may help to develop a more 'ready' organization or at least a set of organizations better geared to facing uncertainties.

The only sure way to anticipate a crisis is to bring it into being. Thus, 'crisis creation' has become a widespread instrument in the implementation of plans. In a narrow sense the planners create a sense of crisis within the planning system whenever they initiate a difficult and extremely risky operation; the sense of crisis emerges from the fear of failure. In the Soviet Union the system of setting high output norms for sectors and enterprises is an institutionalized method of creating and maintaining a sense of crisis in all major sub-systems of the society. This is what has been referred to by Wiles [39] as 'planner's excess demand' or 'planner's tension'. In a broader sense, a sense of crisis has been maintained throughout the nation by sustained international tensions and by the attitudes towards the external world developed by national leaders. The theory of capitalist encirclement, the drive after the Second World War for the extension of Communism in Eastern Europe and other parts of the world, the ideology of the cold war and, more recently, the theory of competitive coexistence – all these in different ways, have contributed to the sense of crisis. Similarly, in many countries of the industrialized West plan activators have often been obliged to describe their plans as weapons in the cold war or competitive coexistence. In a still broader sense the national leaders in industrially underdeveloped countries have often found no way to combat the apathy and inertia of tradition-ridden masses other than the active awakening of discontent with low living standards. The elites who spread the 'revolution of rising expectations', by stirring up aspirations for the immediately unattainable, deliberately create personal crisis in the lives of those with high aspirations.

TIMING

Time is the medium in which operations are led. 'What time is it?' is the ever-present question in the minds of the plan activators.

A major question is when to start – or expand – a campaign. If one waits until plans are perfected and all the needed support is obtained, valuable time may be lost. The best way to improve a plan may be to test it in action. The

R

best way to get support may be to demonstrate that something is really under way. On the other hand, it is sometimes better to wait until a situation 'boils over' and people are complaining about the lack of leadership. This may provide the most favourable situation for leaders to initiate action.

By bringing together a host of area, sector, and cross-sector plans, national planning may provide a highly rational picture of the most desirable course of development. The picture is still more rational if feasibility takes its place alongside desirability. When this is done it usually becomes evident that it is not feasible to initiate all desirable programmes at the same time. It is even less feasible to time operations in such a way as to have each one support and supplement the others. When opportunities arise to move ahead rapidly in one campaign it is often wise strategy to act – even though this may result in mining more coal than the railroads can move or bringing more students into school than the present teaching staff can handle. To wait until similar opportunities develop on all other fronts may slow up everything and may, indeed, postpone the day when there will be enough freight cars or school teachers. Thus, to a certain extent unbalanced development is made inevitable by what we might call the 'principle of differential feasibility'.* This principle is particularly applicable to planning in industrially underdeveloped countries. Here it is extremely difficult to do anything important – because of the great shortage of appropriate organizations, man-power, physical resources, and the great resistance offered by custom and tradition. Anything important may seem unfeasible, and the choice becomes one between 'differential unfeasibilities'. In such circumstances the higher rationality of plan implementation often suggests the desirability of a vigorous campagin for action at any points of 'least unfeasibility'.

MAINTAINING A POSITIVE STANCE

One of the greatest dangers to the implementation of plans is that a cumulative series of failures or shortfalls will put the planners in a negative and defensive position. This is what seems to have happened in India during the middle period of the Third Plan period (1961–6).

To maintain a positive stance it is important to keep the initiative. In simpler operations this means maintaining a style and a tempo of action that provide continuous results – even if only small ones. It means setting deadlines and dealing directly with problems that might lead to a breakdown. But in the panorama of national planning as a whole there are always breakdowns. If these are allowed to get out of hand the results may be disastrous. One way of keeping them in hand is to conduct enough campaigns at points of 'least unfeasibility', as discussed above. Another is to direct greater public attention to advances and successes rather than allow them to be neglected.

* The case for 'unbalanced development' is presented with considerable illustrative detail in Albert O. Hirschman's *The Strategy of Economic Development* [40] and *Journeys Toward Progress*. [41]

There is a general tendency under national planning for the escalation of public criticism, as the national planners become the conspicuous targets for dissatisfactions which would otherwise be vented in smaller circles. As a counter-measure, national planners must 'pat themselves on the back' by advertising their successes. This is most effective when it is not done by themselves, but when, indeed, the credit is taken by and given to people and groups that play a major role in the activation base. Direct and conspicuous self-congratulation can undermine the support for national planners and their plans.

In situations of conflicting pressures and bitter controversy a major problem is how to respond to criticism and attack. To keep the initiative it is often essential to ignore some attacks, refusing to be put on the defensive. Sometimes the best defence is a counter-attack on another front, the formation of a new alliance, or capitulation on one front in order to advance on another. When a detailed defence is needed it is often more appropriate if it comes not from the national planners themselves but from their active supporters or, indeed, from those who have previously been neutral bystanders.

THE ART OF THE 'IMPROBABLE'

Politics has often been called the 'art of the possible'. This phrase calls attention to the necessity of trimming the sails of desirability to the winds of feasibility. In national planning, where the political arts are required to the highest degree, the phrase is particularly applicable.

Yet in the politics of national planning, as in any other art, there are many degrees of artistry. At one extreme there are the novices, learners, or bumblers. In the middle there are the steady, reliable craftsmen. At the other extreme there are the great artists. One's place on this scale is not determined by occupation or hierarchical rank. We may find novices and bumblers among political leaders as well as among technicians. Although the best opportunities for the exercise of great artistry may arise in or near the offices of chiefs-of-state, some of the greatest artists are often found among the career service bureaucrats and the leaders of intermediate or peripheral organizations.

In this form of art the criterion of greatness is results achieved in the face of serious obstacles, both technical and human. The lesser artists are those who manage to break through the 'feasibility barrier' at various points. The bumblers are those who break their heads on the barrier or else (in a burst of epiphenomenal planning) merely usher in what was already inevitable anyway. The great artists are those who transcend the limits of small feasibilities and achieve results that, in the eyes of careful observers, might have been regarded as highly improbable, if not impossible. By developing flexible campaign strategies for analysing obstacles, building an activation base, using an appropriate activation mix, and resolving human conflicts, they become the masters of the 'art of the improbable'.

REFERENCES

1 B. M. Gross (1964)
2 H. Fayol (1955), p. 97
3 L. Gulick (1937)
4 R. A. Dahl & C. E. Lindblom (1953), p. 103
5 G. M. Sykes (1958)
6 B. M. Gross (1964), Chapter 15
7 G. Myrdal (1954)
8 B. Tuchman (1962), p. 79
9 J. Fayerweather (1959), pp. 77–8
10 R. Henriques (1957), p. 58
11 L. J. Walinsky (1962), pp. 465–74
12 J. S. Berliner (1957)
13 P. Blau (1955)
   E. P. Learned (1951), p. 132
14 C. E. Redfield (1953), pp. 131–2
15 H. A. Simon (1957), p. 69
16 B. M. Gross (1964), Chapter 17
17 H. Kaufman (1960), pp. 196–7
18 R. Dahl & C. E. Lindblom (1953), p. 121
19 T. Burling *et al.* (1956)
20 L. Coch & J. R. P. French, Jr. (1947–8)
21 F. Mann & C. Williams (1960)
22 S. Melman (1958)
23 P. Selznick (1949)
24 Sir A. Salter (1921)
25 J. Hackett & Anne-Marie Hackett (1963), p. 365
26 P. Selznick (1949), p. 261
27 H. Kaufman (1960)
28 *Tanganyika Standard* (1964)
29 L. Coser (1961)
30 M. P. Follett (1940), pp. 30–49
31 E. Jaques (1951)
32 See particularly 'individualism in a planned society', in M. P. Follett (1940), pp. 295–314
33 B. M. Gross (1953), p. 26
34 L. Hart (1954), p. 370
35 A. H. Leighton (1945), pp. 359–60
36 A. O. Hirschman (1963), p. 261
37 H. Cleveland (1962), p. 3
38 H. Cleveland (1962), p. 4
39 P. J. D. Wiles (1962), pp. 259–61
40 A. O. Hirschman (1958)
41 A. O. Hirschman (1963)

34 · Conflict,
a Battle of Strategies

Discussion and Commentary

JULIUS MAREK

Conflict occurs when a state of affairs between at least two parties requires an action to bring together, or to separate, opposing forces. The latter are motivated by needs which are seen as threatened by at least one side. The problems encountered during attempts at resolving conflicts centre upon the kind of action which is appropriate to the problem at hand and relevant to the goals whose satisfaction is the focus of the conflict. This is a question of strategies, and conflict is a battle of strategies.

The six papers on conflict span the full range of human relations, from the interaction of two persons locked in a game that rewards co-operation but exposes it to the temptation of sheer egoism, to the problems of designing national plans in such a way that they become a reality rather than dreams. The conflicting strategies vie for the attention of the decision-maker – how will he choose? This is the question that confronts the science of man.

The total contribution of the papers rests on five propositions which in a sense epitomize the hopes of a scientific inquiry into human affairs:

(i) Man is capable of rational decisions. The deviations from 'objective' rationality have structure and are determinate.
(ii) It is possible to assign values to conflicting issues, so that there is a basis for preference.
(iii) Given *adequate* information, the decision-maker will choose rationally.
(iv) It is possible to structure human organizations in a way that is conducive to the resolution of conflicts.
(v) Design and even acceptance of a solution are not sufficient to implement it. Knowledge of the problem must go hand in hand with the knowledge of *wider* feasibilities which provide an operational context for the problem.

As is to be expected, individual papers concentrate on some propositions more than on others. *Table 1* indicates this distribution of interest, though inevitably the classification is simplified.

The contribution of the papers is directly reflected in, and expressed by, the arguments which they serve. Short summaries of the arguments are therefore given in the hope that they will orient the reader and encourage him to digest the originals. There is yet another reason for their inclusion. As Professor Ackoff observes, many of the behavioural scientists have little mathematical preparation. They are likely to skip those papers which contain

Table 1   *Orientation of the articles*

Author	Propositions (i)	(ii)	(iii)	(iv)	(v)
Rapoport	✓				
Flagle	✓	✓			
Ackoff		✓		✓	✓
Walton				✓	✓
Thorsrud & Emery			✓	✓	✓
Gross					✓

mathematical expositions as being too difficult to handle. This would be a pity, since the weight of their contribution does not lie in the mechanics of mathematical manipulation, but in the argument which dictates the selection and use of the model; in that respect they are particularly instructive for the social scientist.

For the opposite reason the richness of content of the non-mathematical papers may be confusing and discouraging to the operational researchers. Yet it is the substantive content of the problem which must be adequately represented in the mathematical model if it is to be relevant. The paper by Professor Gross may serve as a characteristic example. It brings together a wealth of experience, and it thus offers a substantive basis for a theory. It is already structured, but, most significantly, it points the way to an ordered reduction of the problem and by that to what a model of it ought to be like – one thinks of Ashby's Law of Requisite Variety.[1]

The summaries are arranged according to their level of inclusiveness, starting with face-to-face relations between individuals and ending with those involving complex and extended social structures. It is clear, however, that problems of one level have implications for other levels, some considerations being directly transposable.

Finally, three general issues are raised. The first concerns the conditions of conflict resolution; the second, the function of mathematical models; and the third, co-operation between operational research and social science. These issues are central to the content of this book and the conference from which it derives.

Arguments

Face-to-face relations: papers by Rapoport and Flagle

Rapoport's contribution is twofold. In addition to reporting a piece of empirical research, it is an open exercise in model-building, and the latter, because of its importance, will be discussed separately (pp. 494-6).

Rapoport had pairs of subjects playing seven symmetrical, non-zero-sum games, exemplifying the Prisoner's Dilemma. The subjects were paid off after each play, which consisted of two moves, one for each player. Each player had to choose from two alternatives: either to co-operate with his partner or not. They were isolated and had no means of verbal communication. Consequently, each move was decided on in ignorance of the partner's choice. The only information fed back to the subjects was the outcome of each play, which determined the gain or loss of each participant. If both co-operated they were both rewarded. If they did not co-operate, i.e. they defected on each other, they were both punished by losing small sums of money. If one co-operated and the other defected, then the first was the 'sucker' and lost, while the other was rewarded; since the reward was large, there was a considerable temptation to defect.

The parameters of the game were therefore reward (R), punishment (P), temptation to defect (T), and the 'sucker's' loss (S). The values of these parameters were varied systematically over the seven games, but the basic inequality of the pay-offs such that $T > R > P > S$ was retained throughout, i.e. the gain for one-sided defection was always greater than the reward for mutual co-operation, which in turn was greater than the pay-off (actually a loss) for mutual defection and so on. For example, in Game IV, $T = 2$, $R = 1$, $P = -1$, and $S = -2$. The uncertainty of the situation was likely to raise mixed motives in the participants, and therefore internal conflict.

Rapoport found that the responses of the players tended to polarize, i.e. they 'locked-in' either on co-operation or on defection. Second, the process of play was self-enhancing, i.e. once the co-operation set in, it tended to persist. Intuitively, 'trust breeds trust, distrust breeds distrust'. For the self-enhancing process to set in, a definite threshold point must be reached. If the threshold of trust was exceeded the trust increased, and with it co-operation; otherwise the situation changed to defection. Third, there were typical 'martyr' runs in which one of the players persisted in giving co-operative responses despite repeated defection of his partner. They were usually rather short and tended to end in the martyr's turning to defection rather than converting his partner to co-operation.

Rapoport presents a mathematical model which, with minor discrepancies, accounts for the relative frequency of co-operation observed in the seven games. He stresses that the purpose of a model is heuristic, i.e. it does not have to explain or predict the data, but should lead to the derivation of 'principles' underlying the situation. The instability of the Prisoner's Dilemma situations shown by the existence of the threshold is a principal feature of this kind. Furthermore, the examination of models leads to the identification of variables worthy of attention. In this case the propensities of the players to act in a certain way depending on previous responses of their partners are interesting variables, since they are components of the transition probabilities of a Markov chain. The author presents 'profiles' of different populations of players in terms of these propensities and demonstrates how they increase the power of interpretation and further search.

It is this fruitful flexibility of a model, its tractability rather than its realism, that facilitates the growth of interpretation and a construction of relevant psychological theory.

The interpretation given by Rapoport is in terms of the maximization of rewards by the players. It is possible, however, that their responses had an additional function, namely to communicate with the partner, since all other means of communication were denied to the participants. In order to communicate the players had to sacrifice their reward, hence the long 'martyr' runs. Dr P. G. Herbst, who raised this criticism, felt that both functions of the responses ought to have been considered explicitly.

It is possible that the question would have been covered had direct data been collected on the players' assessment of the situation and on their motivations.

Dr Herbst also suggested that a simple formula of $R + P - T$ accounts for the frequencies of co-operative responses in the seven games rather more closely than the author's model. In addition, the logic of the formula points out the possibilities of extending the range of game conditions. The seven games are such that the sum of reward and punishment is either lower than the value of the temptation to defect or equals that value. At the same time Rapoport's data suggest that the less temptation there is relative to the balance of reward and punishment, the more co-operative responses are obtained. It is likely, therefore, that by intensifying the rewards, the incidence of co-operation would be considerably increased. The formula also leads to an intuitive understanding of the differences in the threshold values.

Flagle's paper is concerned with the problem of whether or not to embark on an expensive medical treatment where the diagnosis is doubtful. If the diagnostic procedures cannot be relied on, the physician is faced with the decision whether: (i) to play safe and to give treatment, even though the patient may not need it, or (ii) not to treat the patient and run the risk of exposing him to the effects of the disease if he is in reality ill.

In the first case, that of unnecessary treatment, the physician risks the cost of the treatment and the involvement of medical resources that may be scarce. In the second case, that of withholding the therapy, the physician risks the life of the patient and his value to his relatives and the community, as well as the possibility of contagion to others and damage to his own reputation or to that of the health service which he represents.

The problem is complicated by differences in responsibilities which the physician may have in a given case. If he is in an individual patient–doctor relationship he is responsible for the well-being of the one patient. If he is an administrator of health services he is responsible for their utilization to a whole community.

Flagle formalizes the problem in terms of a game against states of Nature. Given two states of Nature: 'ill' and 'not ill', an imprecise diagnosis (levels of sensitivity stated), the *a priori* distribution of the disease, and the conditional probability that when the symptoms existed the patient had the disease, it is possible to estimate the utilities or costs in the loss matrix for 'treatment' or 'no treatment' – *Table 2*.

Table 2   *Loss Matrix*

Action	State of Nature Ill	Not ill
Treated	$c = 1$	$c = 1$
Not treated	Q	0

Of the four strategies specified two are particularly relevant:

(i) Follow the action indicated by the diagnosis, i.e. treatment if the diagnosis is positive and no treatment if it is negative. This is a 'faith in diagnosis' strategy. The problem arises when the diagnosis is uncertain, since a deferment of treatment under false negative indication involves the high risk of human life. But by noting what decisions would be made at various probabilities of false negative indications it is possible to specify thresholds of acceptability of a negative diagnosis as a basis for deferment of treatment.

(ii) When diagnosis is uncertain a 'play safe' strategy could be adopted, i.e. the patient is treated no matter what the diagnosis says and no matter what it costs. As a policy of 'minimization of maximum regret' this strategy is likely to be chosen by the parents of an ill child.

The question is whether to treat or not to treat, and Flagle shows that from graphical representation of the loss functions for all strategies under successively diminishing precision of diagnosis it is possible to find the point of indifference between: (*a*) the optimum strategy under certainty, and (*b*) the safe strategy under uncertainty (the parents' strategy). At this threshold both are Bayes strategies minimizing expected loss.

By mathematical analysis it is possible to determine what value of Q will satisfy the condition of indifference between the two strategies. This threshold value (the cost of failure to treat in case of illness) is expressed in terms of the *a priori* probabilities of actual illness* in patients displaying the symptoms, the conditional probabilities of the diagnosis for a given state of Nature, and the cost of hospital treatment.

Since the threshold value of Q is expressible in terms of c, the cost of treatment, either Q or c, could be regarded as the unknown. The formulation is useful in situations where the cost of treatment c, and not the cost of failure to treat Q, is at issue. This is the case, for example, of large public health programmes in which there is competition for restricted resources, and conflicts over choice of strategy arise frequently. The threshold method of utility estimation provides a rational basis for their resolution.

Flagle then exposes his method to a test of a substantive analysis of conflict resolution by Mary Parker Follett and demonstrates its flexibility and rigorous meaningfulness. According to Follett, conflict could be resolved by dominance, compromise, or two types of integration, namely, integration through environmental change and integration through conciliation of conflicting values. For all of these, and especially for the two notions of integration, the idea of a threshold of some probability or of some utility beyond which a new strategy becomes preferable is relevant.

Flagle's closing remark points to the psychological aspect of decision processes. '. . . dealing with utilities . . .' he states, '. . . is a problem of psychometrics rather than statistics . . .' Nowhere is this clearer than in Mary Follett's discussion of conflict resolution through conciliation of opposing values. It is here that the next questions could be posed: What is the reference point of conciliation? This will be considered later on.

Relations in an enterprise: papers by Walton and Ackoff

Walton's is a theoretical paper. He concentrates on three aspects of life within organizations:

(i) Lateral relations, i.e. interactions between sub-units of an organization, such as sales and production departments, whose respective status is not that of authority and subordination;
(ii) Joint decision-making, and
(iii) Conflict versus collaboration.

The author stresses that the general area is neglected despite its manifest importance. Increased specialization within organizations requires co-ordination, which for the most part depends on co-operation between members of the sub-units rather than on explicit rules and procedures. Hence joint decision-making.

Depending on the orientation of the participants, different types of joint decision process evolve. If the situation is seen as requiring an 'open decision process', then the parties will search for 'solutions which . . . involve maximum

---

* I.e. of states of Nature ill/not ill.

gain to both parties considered together' and will freely exchange all relevant information – this is a *problem-solving* type of decision process. Otherwise, the parties settle on *bargaining*, in which their respective gains and losses are considered in isolation and the flow of information between the units is restricted. Problem-solving results in co-operation, bargaining in competition and conflict.

Walton makes the point that the decision processes are rarely observed in pure form, but it is possible to assign them to one or other end of the continuum on the basis of the measures of exchanged information.

The two types of decision process lead to different and appropriate struc-. tures of interaction. Briefly, the co-operative problem-solving process, as compared with bargaining, has an interaction structure characterized by more frequent interactions between the departments and more accurate information,* more people involved in these interactions, less restriction on the types of contact allowed, less coercion and fewer appeals to higher authorities, fewer formal rules for handling mutual problems, and flexible procedures and organization.

Finally, the problem-solving decision process and its open interaction structure engender positive attitudes between the departments, whereas the bargaining process, with its restricted interactions, is accompanied by negative feeelings. The two complexes represent contrasting syndromes of behaviour, the first being 'integrative' and the latter 'distributive'.

The author's dynamic model derives a great deal from the theoretical work of Heider[2] and Newcomb[3] discussed at length in Walton and McKersie's[4] work on attitude change. It makes good sense in terms of the consistency between how one sees a problem, what one does, and how one feels about it, which these students of interpersonal relations postulate. The two syndromes are thus contrasting types of balance that could evolve between organizational units linked by a mutually relevant task. Significantly, Walton places his model within a wider context of demands, opportunities, and limitations (his *Figure 2*, p. 416), which should answer the vexing question of why the participants prefer one orientation to the other. For the view presented here, this is the egg before the chicken, and although it is not discussed, it carries a genuine promise and a reminder that social relations encompassed within a model are open to wider influences.

The purpose of Ackoff's paper is to draw attention to conflicts arising from structural inefficiency and faulty decision-making, rather than from inadequate communications. He also considers co-operation between operational research and behavioural science – discussed here on pp. 496–8.

His approach to co-operation, conflict, and competition is normative.

---

* As stated in the paper, the dependence between the decision processes and the interaction structures appears to rest on a circular argument. Walton, in a personal communication, denies that this is the case.

From a rather familiar basis of decision theory and utility estimation, Ackoff develops a hierarchy of unconventional and stimulating definitions of social phenomena in this area and presents a mathematical model for structural analysis.

The individual in a given environment is faced with a range of courses of action and their effects (outcomes). His choices are based on the utilities of the outcomes, i.e. on their relative values to the decision-maker.

Whether for co-operation or for conflict, the presence of at least one other decision-maker (B) is necessary, so that his behaviour affects the utility of the first individual (A). If the behaviour of B adds to the expected value which an outcome has for A, B is said to co-operate. Should B's behaviour decrease A's expected utility, B is said to be in conflict. The degree of co-operation or of conflict derives, then, from the difference between the presence of the 'other' and his absence. A positive value, that is a gain, reflects the degree of co-operation; a negative value, that is a loss due to the behaviour of the other, reflects the degree of conflict. Conflict is the negative of co-operation.

Ackoff defines thus the values of co-operation, or conflict, for each participant. When the values are not equal a situation of exploitation obtains, and the extent of their difference reflects its degree.

The conventional notion of exploitation applies only when one party gains owing to the behaviour of the second party (co-operation), and the second party loses (conflict); this is the situation of the master–slave relationship. There are two more types of exploitation. When both parties gain, the exploitation is 'benevolent', even though their gains are unequal, as is the case of enlightened colonialism, or of most employer–employee relationships. When both parties lose the exploitation is 'malevolent', as in the case of most wars or feuds.

Ackoff does not accept that competition is equivalent to conflict. Rather, competition is a conflict regulated so as to ensure that a third party gains. A typical example is that of a trading enterprise whose purchasing and sales departments are the principal participants competing with each other. The sectional interests of these departments are in conflict: the buyers want to avoid having to stock unsold items, whereas the salesmen want the buyers to have large enough stocks to cover all orders. Despite the conflict, however, both departments are interested in keeping the enterprise going.

The sectional conflict is imposed on the buyers and salesmen by the structure of the organization, i.e. by the way in which their performance is measured. Criteria of performance that reflect only the sectional interests are more obvious, and therefore more likely to be formulated. Yet from the point of view of the total enterprise, they are sub-optimal and lead to internal conflict.

Since the conflict is structural, it could not be resolved by using psychological and sociological methods of changing the personnel or their attitudes or the communications between them. Only when the total organization's objective functions have been explicitly formulated is it possible to determine the extent of structural interdependence of its sub-units and to assign to them goals which support the objectives of the total organization. This is essentially the work of the operational researchers, who have the necessary tools at their disposal. The behavioural scientists can help by inducing the management to have its structure analysed, by improving the diagnosis of dysfunctional symptoms, and by inducing the operational researchers to pay attention to structural analysis rather than be satisfied with serving sub-units exclusively.

The division of labour between the behavioural scientist and the operational researcher suggested by Professor Ackoff rests on the equation of structural analysis with the evaluation of 'structural performance'. The latter requires mathematical tools, the former does not. Structural analysis has been the concern of behavioural scientists for some time now, and it has included both the clarification and the co-ordination of performance measures (see Trist *et al.*[5, Chapter 13]).

National problems: papers by Thorsrud & Emery, and Gross

Thorsrud and Emery are concerned with the strategy of resolving industrial conflicts. They report on the first phase, Phase A, of an action research project being carried on at a national level and supported by the trade unions, the employers' federation, and the government – the three most directly interested parties, the Holy Trinity, of modern industrial life. The project is carried out in Norway, whose democratic tradition expresses itself in a narrow range of personal incomes, a generally high standard of living, a well-developed network of social services, and a minimum of industrial strife. Furthermore, both the workers' and the employers' representatives agree with the Government on the necessity of maximizing the human resources and are prepared to be actively involved in bringing this about, hence the project on industrial democracy.

The authors examine the meaning of industrial democracy and find its criteria in the conditions necessary for a democratic distribution of social power. These conditions involve agreeing on means and goals which are reconcilable with each other, mutually supporting the means and goals agreed on, and sharing the responsibilities.

The issue concerns the best way of bringing the 'industrial life into closer accord with the democratic social life that individuals now enjoy' and achieving 'fuller individual commitment that will lead to increased productivity and efficiency'. Two ways are considered:

(i) The representation of employees on the boards of companies; and
(ii) The improvement of conditions for personal participation in the work situation.

This paper concentrates on the examination of the first alternative, which attempts to resolve the problem on the level of formal organization. It is, in the authors' words, a 'seductive solution', but analysis of the actual experiences of employee representatives on the boards of some Norwegian companies has shown that such formal representation on the highest executive level of the enterprise does not satisfy the requirements for a productive sharing of power.

The representative is responsible to his electorate, whose power placed him on the board. But by becoming a member of the board and by sharing in its power, he is expected to accept a new set of responsibilities not necessarily congruent with those to which he is primarily committed. On some matters, especially those concerning production, he might have to accept the board's point of view. On others, such as personnel administration, he usually finds that reference may be made more appropriately to the managers than to the board. He may also find that he is ill prepared to contend with the full range of problems on which the board deliberates and in the light of which he has to establish the priorities of his own demands.

Thus, although the representative formally shares the power of the board, it is difficult for him to exercise it in accordance both with the purposes of the board and with the requirements of his electorate. Nor is the Norwegian experience isolated. Similar pictures emerge from the analysis of corresponding approaches in Yugoslavia, Germany, and the United Kingdom. As a way of dealing with the problems of industrial production, formal representation is a misplaced solution.

The authors affirm the need for the sharing of managerial powers by both blue-collar and white-collar employees, but in an area in which they are both willing and able to participate, i.e. at the level of their daily work. On the development of these 'grass roots' of industrial democracy, work is now in progress. This is Phase B of the Norwegian project, which includes, as an integral part, the diffusion of the appropriate organizational measures. For this to take place, a supporting social network is necessary, and its creation was, for the authors, an essential aspect of the initial Phase A.

The main purpose of Professor Gross's paper is to dispel two myths – that knowledge by itself is enough to resolve a problem situation, and that command power is enough to get action. He stresses that, although the design and content of a plan are generally considered to be primary, and separate from the problems of implementation, the two aspects are inevitably connected. The design of the plan must be sensitive to the existing feasibilities, and the latter refer directly to the conditions of plan implementation.

From the analysis of the usual obstacles to efficient planning, Gross proceeds to the notion of a flexible campaign strategy. This involves:

(i) Creating the base for measures of activation, i.e. mobilization of the sources of influence necessary to implement a plan.

(ii) Use of an appropriate composition of these resources – the 'activation mix'.

(iii) Coping with the problems arising out of both mobilization and use of influence.

Implementation of a plan is conceived of as a series of interrelated campaign strategies aimed at carrying out specific parts of the overall plan. These may take place on different levels of social organization, and care must be taken to integrate them so that, for example, a national plan is supported on regional and community levels.

An essential aspect of planning is the exploitation of a crisis. Any significant social change is impossible unless there is a perception of 'acute interest frustration' which softens the positions and attitudes entrenched by tradition and makes the uncertainties of new solutions acceptable. Crisis is thus an important instrument in the implementation of plans, and in fact it is desirable to create it.

Gross's paper is rich in content. It is obviously an initial public statement of a programme of research in this vast field. A major part of his discussion on campaign strategy consists of enumeration of the measures of activation and their uses.

It may well be that an analytic survey of well-documented national plans would lead to a further definition of the connexion between the activation base and activation mix. That is, depending on the objectives and context of the plan, specific sources of influence would have to be mobilized to ensure its feasibility. It is also possible that such different constellations of the sources of influence would require appropriate methods for their activation and that these would vary from one constellation to another. These may create characteristic sets of problems requiring appropriate means of coping with them. What is the content of such coupled systems; how and to what extent do they vary; and what are the parameters of the plan contexts in which they occur? These questions are open to systematic assessment. The sheer scale of such a project presents formidable difficulties, but its contribution to social science would justify the effort.

Similarly, the proposition that crisis is a welcome component of plan implementation calls for further differentiation. Whether a sense of crisis helps all the planners who, for example, depend on international credits is debatable. On the other hand, as Gross points out, the sense of crisis is a well-established instrument in the politics of planning. Again, one may ask: what types of crisis fit given contexts and are there situations in which they should be avoided?

A systematic evaluation of national plans is undoubtedly difficult. But it is inconceivable without a careful substantive preparation such as this paper presents.

Reference level for the resolution of conflict

Most papers in this section imply that the evaluation of issues contained in the domain of conflict must be referred to a higher level of organization than that on which the conflict takes place. A clear expression of this notion is given by Churchman and Emery: [6]

'Societies as admittedly full of conflict as ours could hardly hang together unless there were very pervasive strands of common interest. Our own experience is that community of interest can usually be found at the next higher level of social organization.'

The operational domain of conflict is thus extended, and the measures aimed at its resolution must have a corresponding temporal and hierarchical span. For instance, departmental wage adjustments are invariably embedded in the network of interdepartmental connexions, status positions, and expectations. These in turn are governed by the general wage level within the industry and, farther afield, by national agreements, national wage drift, and national economic policy. Disregard of these wider connexions may initiate disturbances difficult to overcome. They form the context of feasibility.

Use of mathematical models

The use of mathematical models has often been a bone of contention among social scientists. Lack of mathematical preparation prevents a full assessment of the possibilities of existing models. To this is added the fear that their use involves a wholesale reduction of content, and for many behavioural scientists the notion that they faithfully reflect the field of their inquiry is an article of faith.

Yet the appeal of mathematical models is strong. It derives from their orderliness, and from their capacity to relate components to each other, to state the consequences of these relationships, and to take them into account simultaneously. Their power of pushing the logic of underlying assumptions to extremes is a source of fruitful insights and a check on the sanity of the theoretical structure.

The advantages of mathematical formulations are explicitly and elegantly demonstrated in Rapoport's report on the study of co-operation. But his contention that 'we are not seeking a realistic model, only a heuristic one' is likely to reinforce the fears of behavioural scientists, and it bears examination.

The contention is fully developed in his second paper, [7] in which he proposes an approach to general systems theory based on mathematical homology. The use of models may be summarized as follows:

(i) The study of a real-life situation leads to its description by a supposedly adequate model.

(ii) Once the model has been formulated, the researcher concentrates on the properties of the model, i.e. he identifies and examines the characteristics of its structural components.

(iii) The properties of the abstract model then suggest questions about the real-life situation: they suggest new hypotheses and the kind of data necessary to test them. In other words, the abstract properties are translated back into empirical equivalents, and

(iv) The derived hypotheses and their corrections become the components of an empirically relevant theory.

Whereas many a behavioural scientist would be particularly concerned about point (i), i.e. about the extent of the initial correspondence between the model and the real situation, Rapoport stresses points (ii) and (iii). Accordingly, even if an assumption about the empirical situation is unrealistic, and subsequently refuted by the data, it is useful as a starting-point for a theory. The assumption could be modified and its implications examined anew. Meanwhile, the researcher is learning about the principles underlying the real situation. It is in this sense that the heuristic value of the model is more fruitful than its realism.

The stress on one or the other concern should not make much difference, provided the initial model is reasonably adequate. The question of *adequacy*, however, may raise practical difficulties since it is inherently connected with the operations which the model requires. If the model is complex the problem of parameter estimation becomes intractable. An initial reduction of psychological complexities is necessary. To solve the problem, Rapoport suggests constructing 'experiments which are in themselves extremely simple but which at the same time provide opportunities for deriving psychological richness from an intricate analysis of the data'.

Seen from this point of view, the shift in emphasis from point (i) to point (ii) becomes important, since both the richness of the theory and its relevance depend ultimately on the substantive reduction of the problem. Unless there is some basis for a relevant reduction, the emphasis on heuristic derivation rather than on realism of the model may lead to highly developed structures which are at best tangential to the problem at hand. Nor is the empirical validity, as such, a guarantee that all be well in the end. A restricted outlook leads to restricted data, and even sophisticated developments within an originally restricted domain yield an impoverished theory.

For the pure theorist the point is trivial. In time a situation will be found which will fit the model he has developed. The applied social scientist, however, and the operational researcher, usually work under an obligation to their initial brief, and they must have a realistic model.

The question of how to reduce the detailed multiplicity of the empirical field to a tractable representation is difficult to answer. A general notion of homology is most useful. The individual's behaviour is *appropriate* if it takes into account the environmental circumstances. There is thus a correspondence between behaviour and particular physical and social environments, and the individual's perception acts as the mediating bridge.* Since these

---

* For a general discussion of appropriateness and adaptation see Sommerhoff [8, esp. pp. 38-66]. On the correspondence between perception and social context see Marek.[9]

personal interpretations bear on the adequacy of behaviour, research on behaviour must provide opportunities for the assessment of what given situations *mean* to the subjects involved in them.

The argument is directly relevant to the economy of parameter estimation. Since behaviour is relevant to situational requirements, it should reflect the differences in its contents dictated by the levels of organization at which it occurs. And so should the suggested research observations, thereby reducing the labour of computation.

Rapoport's example is quite apposite. Should a stochastic model for a single individual that contains 4 parameters be applied to two interacting individuals, there will be $4^4 = 256$ parameters to estimate – a gigantic and irrelevant exercise. Quite probably, the learning parameters of two interacting individuals are different from those of a single individual since they refer to their *interactions*. The economy of the initial problem-setting is most directly achieved by the selection of relevant behaviour categories. In that case a systematic observation of natural life-situations and their analysis does not present special difficulties.

The difficulty lies in gaining knowledge of the behavioural setting in sufficient detail to allow the researcher to capture the relevancies of the situation. This may be an arduous task, and there are no short cuts, since systematization of ecological categories has not hitherto attracted much attention.* The labour ensures, however, that realism is injected into the process of theory-building right from the beginning. It may also significantly extend the co-operation between the mathematicians and behavioural scientists.

Co-operation between operational research and social sciences

The conditions under which the two professional groups may co-operate fruitfully have been discussed by Ackoff, characteristically, as an integral part of the paper on structural conflict. He has done much to bring the two groups together both in the United States and in Great Britain. The following remarks are my own reflections on the problem.

Let me assume relatively 'clean' groups of the two professions, i.e. consisting of:

(i) Individuals relatively uncontaminated by previous co-operation, and
(ii) Products of the traditional education conceived within the confines of their fields.

The group of operational researchers composed of applied mathematicians, mathematically sophisticated technologists, and others who are actively en-

---

* The theory of behaviour settings of Barker [10] and the classification of organizational environments of Emery [11] are significant contributions to the field. For a discussion of Barker's approach and its extension to technological contexts, see Marek. [12, 13]

gaged in the practice of operational research may be accepted as familiar with mathematics. Anthropologists, sociologists, psychologists, political scientists, and some economists would be classified as social scientists, generally not versed in mathematics. Hybrids between the two strains are ruthlessly excluded.

Let me further endow them with a minimal openness to each other, i.e. with a preparedness to talk to each other professionally about problems which they both agree are of mutual interest.

Finally, let them come together as they did during the Cambridge Conference.

Their reactions to each other after a mutual exposure are characteristically different. The operational researcher thinks of the social scientist's contribution as perhaps rich in content, but vague, lengthy, and logically incomplete: he takes up many threads, but somehow loses them. The social scientist's verdict on the operational researcher is equally definite: crisp and articulate but hasty in reaching for conclusions and essentially poor in contextual reference. (This does not prevent him from admiring the operational research group for what they can do with modest beginnings.)

For all their openness to each other, their reactions carry their own professional mark. It is also clear that they talk past each other and would continue to do so for a long time, even though each group feels that it could enrich the other.

I have no data, but I should think that the bulk of the two professional groups are of this 'clean' type. It may be noted that both groups are multidisciplinary, but only within their own spheres. The traditional demarcation of disciplines is softening up, but, despite extensive overlaps and shifts in boundaries, groups of professionals are likely to retain their own fields of competence. A characteristic slant of this kind ensures in fact a richness of diversity.

Professional differences are therefore likely to persist within the teams. The meaning of 'multidisciplinary' will continue to be, as it is now, a mix. The change will be mainly in the kind of operational involvement across the boundaries.

The capacity to engage in an intelligent dialogue with each other can be accepted as a broad principle of such an involvement. On a minimal level it means a shared knowledge of the input requirements of each field with an ability, of the kind considered by Rapoport, to translate the outputs into empirical categories.

The lack of a working knowledge of the other's language need not prevent a fruitful collaboration, provided there is a sustained effort by each party to translate its own insights into everyday language. In this way varied contributions become mutually accessible and the growth of understanding can be shared. Of the social scientist this demands sympathy for order and a readiness to drive the argument relentlessly to its limits. Of the mathematician and operational researcher it demands sympathy for content. The mood of the times and the pressure of problems work towards the attainment of such co-operation. The conference itself contributed to it in no small measure.

REFERENCES

1 W. R. Ashby (1956)
2 F. Heider (1946)
3 T. M. Newcomb (1953)
4 R. E. Walton & R. B. McKersie (1964)
5 E. L. Trist, G. W. Higgin, H. Murray & A. B. Pollock (1963)
6 C. W. Churchman & F. E. Emery, this volume, Chapter 6, theses 13 and 22

7 A. Rapoport (1964)
8 G. Sommerhof (1950)
9 J. Marek (1963b)
10 R. G. Barker (1960)
11 F. E. Emery (1963)
12 J. Marek (1963a)
13 J. Marek (1966)

Part V
The Systems Concept
as a Common Frame of Reference

SPONSOR: S. LANER

35 · Introduction

S. LANER

Faced with an invitation to write an introductory passage to this group of papers, I find myself in something of a quandary: for it is surely a sponsor's duty and privilege to be neither seen nor heard – and for a number of very good reasons. Why should he be given leave to air his own pet views, protected from the public criticism to which he wilfully exposed his contributors? What title has he to pontificate from the sheltered seclusion of his armchair on what he happens to consider the merits or shortcomings of the papers he solicited? On the other hand, if he cannot decently do either, how many degrees of freedom are there left for him to operate with?

Probably only one: he may just be entitled to indicate what were his expectations in proposing the topic for his session and in persuading his colleagues on the programme committee to include it. Any more degrees of freedom? Possibly he might, with a lot of tact and circumspection, estimate the extent to which the actual proceedings tallied with his anticipations. To do this he should, of course, at least have been there – and I wasn't. Nevertheless, Tom Burns's detailed account of what went on does allow me to avail myself of this second degree of freedom in some measure.

About the selection of the 'Systems' topic there was nothing particularly original. Any scientist or engineer who wants to be considered in vogue must nowadays talk systems (formerly sets of relationships?) and construct models, conceptual or otherwise (formerly theories?). One can understand and even sympathize with the exasperated engineer who, on reading the title and 'blurb' of the Systems session, complained to me that engineers had been dealing in systems long before the scientists had got hold of them and turned them into a science. Then again, is it not symptomatic of the contemporary state of affairs that out of some queer, scientifico-chauvinistic motivations, many a scientist and engineer is fighting a furious rear-guard action to maintain the walls about his particular piece of garden as high and impenetrable as possible, chiefly by assisting in the proliferation of esoteric jargon?

501

Once again I wish to deny any claim to originality. What I have just said has been noted before, and one of the most impressive commentaries on this point was written by Kenneth Boulding in his contribution to the April 1956 issue of *Management Science*.[1] Which lets the cat out of the bag: it was this paper that constituted the inspiration for the Systems session – coupled with my own personal curiosity about the interactions likely to take place when people from a mathematically highly saturated sphere and from one not so saturated are constrained to integrate on a topic they individually claim to be de-segregating. It could have been a fiasco, but it wasn't, if Tom Burns's assessment is right: 'In this last session, the conference discovered its common ground and began, belatedly but profitably, to explore it.' These are sweet words to the ears of a sponsor.

At the same time it is too soon to start cheering the salvation of the Republic of Learning from a total communications breakdown on the slender grounds that at a single session of a small conference those present managed to decode some of their mutual messages. By and large, the signal-to-noise ratio appears to have been distressingly low, even in the Systems session. I wonder if the participants in the discussion, on reading the report of it, will be as struck as I was, especially with the amount of noise generated around Professor Rapoport's paper? Could it be that this paper more than any of the others evoked the strongest defensive reactions: among the mathematically oriented because, deep down, they harbour doubts whether the razor-sharp edge of that same weapon which has helped with one victory after another in the pure and applied physical sciences might not prove too blunt for the social sciences, after all; among the social scientists, on the whole non-mathematically oriented, because they feel self-conscious about their own shortcomings in wielding this same weapon with the requisite skill?

Other features of the discussion, when all is down in black on white, compel attention only slightly less forcibly. The way, for example, in which the sort of game Dan Howland tried to bring within the framework of game theory turns out with every move that carries it closer to real life to have at least as many outcomes as there are players. The way in which Welford's contribution was seen both by its supporters and by its critics exclusively as an exercise in reductionism, and at no point and by nobody, evidently, as an attempt at suggesting that the rules found useful in introducing some order into the data of one scientific discipline might be helpful in doing the same for the data of other, neighbouring disciplines.

However, I now seem to be launched on doing the very things I promised to abstain from and which, moreover – I fear with some justice – may look suspiciously like a *tour de force*, or, in plain English, trying to be too clever by half. So, instead of continuing along this hazardous path, let me turn to the question of whether the Systems session is likely to have effects other than temporary and trivially semantic. Here again I have only Tom Burns's report to go by and – in so far as he has allowed his personal judgement to seep into his summary – he does not appear excessively sanguine. At times, it seems, the 'hard' side displayed symptoms of impatience with the helplessness, even muddle-headedness, of the social scientist, in his attempts to bring social phenomena into the framework of systems theory. In the endeavour to put him to rights, however, most of the 'hard' scientists clearly found themselves enmeshed in the multivariable web in which these phenomena invariably manifest themselves. The question is, have they enmeshed themselves deeply enough to pursue their brief excursions into the social field after the Conference was over?

Regarding the social scientists' contributions to the discussion, some of their remarks at any rate strike one (a social scientist himself, as it happens) as attempts to convince the 'hard' side that the problems in their field are so singularly complex and intractable that the rules found to govern the behaviour of non-social systems can be dismissed *a priori* as inapplicable. At the same time they clearly had some difficulties in coping with some of the notions coming from the other side, and their objections to the legitimacy and serviceability of mathematico-symbolic formulations of social science problems never looked really convincing. The question here is, did the brief encounter heighten their receptiveness or reinforce them in the attitude that there is little to be gained from dialogues with operational research men, engineers, and physical scientists?

It would be foolhardy to venture, or ask for, answers to these questions. They are much more likely to be given, directly or indirectly, when the Systems concept as a common frame of reference comes to be discussed at future operational research/social science conferences.

REFERENCE

1 K. Boulding (1956)

36 · A Regulatory Model
for System Design and Operation

DANIEL HOWLAND

Introduction

As man–machine systems increase in size, cost, and complexity, there is a growing requirement for theory to guide system designers and operators in the selection and management of man and machine system components. Trial-and-error solutions for design and operational problems are excessively costly, both in terms of resources expended and time lost between the establishment and fulfilment of requirements. In order to reduce costs and time-lags, and ensure the development of equipment which meets military criteria of effectiveness, procedures for predicting the operational consequences of man and machine component selection are needed. Systems theory can satisfy this requirement by providing a basis for the integration of men and machines in the operational environment. In order to provide a basis for integration, the theory must describe the complexity of the real world. System models based on such simplifying assumptions as linearity and independence of components may not be sufficiently descriptive to provide a valid basis for prediction. Models must be developed which are 'rich, accurate, precise, and decidable' (Minas [1]).

If we look to operational research as the source of systems theory, we find two major types of model: (a) normative or prescriptive theory based on economic concepts of utility, value, and 'rational' man, and (b) regulatory or descriptive theory with its roots in the behavioural and biological sciences (Dorfman, [2] Shubik, [3]). Flagle [4] has summarized the differences:

'From the beginning there have been two main streams of thought in operations research. The first has been, like the natural sciences, an effort to understand the behavior of systems, to determine the functional relationships between an interesting property of a system and the variables which affect it.

'A second major facet of operations research has been the study of decision processes and values. Here the traditions of the economist are most clearly evident. The Theory of Games and Economic Behavior of Von Neumann and Morgenstern, being a revival and development of utility theory, represent a normative influence in operations research which reflects a motivation to change, improve, or even "optimize" the behavior of a system.'

Although normative models have been helpful in the solution of many types of problem, difficulties have been encountered when attempts were made to use them for decision-making in large systems (Ackoff,[5] Hitch,[6] Ackoff[7]). Nevertheless, most of the methodological interest in operational research has been focused on their development. A growing need for theory to predict the consequences of system design and operational decisions, however, is leading to interest in the development of descriptive models. Clearly, description must precede prescription.

Not only are there two main types of model, but there are also two major methodological procedures for developing them. The first is deductive, the formal procedure of developing a logical structure from axioms, postulates, and theorems. The second is inductive, based on the empirical development of functional relationships between observed and measured variables. Since formal models capable of describing the complexity of man–machine systems do not exist, they must be constructed and validated by a combination of inductive and deductive procedures. As Bronowski[8] has pointed out, this combination provides the foundation of modern science.

The first step in developing a descriptive system model is to identify the real-world problems which must be solved. Starting with a problem, rather than a technique (Maslow[9]), permits the formulation of questions which must be answered to solve the problems. Different concepts of the real world lead to different kinds of question. Since we are interested in the design and operation of systems, we find it convenient to view them as adaptive, goal-seeking organizations made up of man and machine components. These components are linked by information feedback networks, and their performance is regulated and controlled by comparing the difference between actual and desired system performance.

Such systems, or organizations, perform tasks in a wide range of environments. In order to adapt to different environments, they may be required to respond to disturbances which were not foreseen in their design. Such systems must have:

'. . . a certain measure of flexibility and adaptability so that incidental and unexpected mistakes in design will be automatically corrected by the (control) system itself without external human aid. Such a (control) system is thus capable of *learning* how to behave properly and has almost the *homeostatic mechanisms* of living organisms which enable them to survive under varying conditions of environment' (Tsien [10, p. 253]).

The simulation of an air defence centre by Chapman and Kennedy [11] at RAND was a pioneering attempt to come to grips with the adaptive–interaction problem of man–machine systems. They developed task and response models and a descriptive theory of organization. Although their models were not meant to provide design information, they do provide valuable insights into the learning capability of organizations.

The real-world problems

Before discussing problems of developing descriptive system models, the real-world design and operational problems will be discussed, and the information required to solve them will be indicated.

Design may be defined in the traditional engineering sense as the selection of components. The selection of a man or a machine component is one of the most critical system design decisions. The designer must have both man and machine performance data to serve as the basis for such decisions. Since these decisions often require trade-offs among alternatives to a wide variety of criteria, it is essential that system models should explicitly predict the consequences of these trade-offs on overall system performance (Howland [12]).

Operation is the management, or regulation and control, of the components selected by the designer to ensure that system objectives are met. The design–operations interaction is shown in *Figure 1*. As indicated in the figure,

Figure 1   *Interaction between Design and Operation*

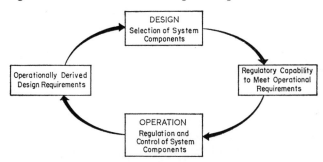

design decisions place constraints on operations. In order to avoid costly and time-consuming refit programmes, design specifications should be based on operational requirements. If other criteria, such as cost, override performance as the basis for design, serious operational problems may be encountered.

In order to provide information for the solution of real-world problems, system models must meet three criteria: (*a*) relevance; (*b*) feasibility; and (*c*) utility.

Relevant theory answers the right questions. It is problem-oriented and serves as a guide for action for the system designer and operator. In order to ensure relevance, the researcher must be intimately familiar with the real world and its problems.

Feasibility implies that the methodological problems encountered in the development of relevant theory can be solved. The general procedure for the development of descriptive models is the traditional hypothetico-deductive method of science (Stevens[13]). In order to utilize these methods, the researcher must have data describing system performance and conceptual schemes for organizing the data. By combining formal and empirical methods of theory construction, we hope to

'. . . arrive at the same conclusions about the real world by two different routes: one is by experiment, and the other – by logical argument' (Coombs, Raiffa, & Thrall[14]).

The most difficult problem raised by the application of the hypothetico-deductive method to systems phenomena is the requirement to deal with the large numbers of variables which must be functionally related. These include not only physical and economic variables but sociological and psychological factors as well. Although science has not traditionally dealt with phenomena as complex as man–machines systems, where complexity is measured in terms of the number of interacting components, procedures for dealing with this problem are of growing concern in a number of disciplines. 'Prominent among the methods for dealing with complexity is cybernetics' (Ashby[15, p.5]).

Our last model criterion, utility, implies that system theory, once developed, can be used by the system designer and operator to answer design questions of component selection and operational questions of regulation and control.

An adaptive model

With these general requirements for theory in mind, a system model is being developed within an homeostatic (Cannon[16]), adaptive (Yovits and Cameron[17]) frame of reference. Viewing systems as adaptive organizations, regulatory action is taken to maintain selected variables within specified limits. Man–machine organizations are thus conceptualized in the same way as the physiologist conceptualizes a living organism. The man and machine components of the organization are analogous to the sensors and effectors of the organism. This view of an organization leads to two related system models: (a) a design model, and (b) an operational model. In the present stage of their development these models are qualitative statements of relationships between variables, not formal functions. Our research objective is to develop the functions suggested.

DESIGN MODEL

The design model takes the following form:

$$P = F(R, \theta)$$

where: P = Set of system performance measures; the set of essential variables which must be maintained within specified limits if system goals are to be achieved.

R = Measures of the performance of system components.

θ = Set of environmental measures which constrain or facilitate component (and consequently overall system) performance.

F = Functional relations between overall system and component performance. Given an environmental and a set of component performance measures, this function allows us to predict consequent system performance.

In this form the model is too complex to be manageable. We, therefore, break it down into a hierarchy of relationships. Adopting a military task-mission scheme, we have:

$$M_i = f(T_1 \ldots T_i \ldots T_n) \tag{1}$$

where M_i = Measure of mission accomplishment.

T_i = One of the tasks which must be performed to accomplish the mission.

f = Functional relationships between task and mission performance.

At the next descending level:

$$T_i = g(y_1 \ldots y_i \ldots y_n; \quad \theta_1 \ldots \theta_i \ldots \theta_t) \tag{2}$$

where T_i = Tasks of equation (1).

y_i = Performance of ith basic system or organizational unit viewed as a black box. In a naval organization this might be an individual ship.

θ_i = External environment; factors influencing performance of basic components.

g = Functional relation between system task and component performance in a given environment.

The performance of the basic system unit must then be broken down into its man and machine components:

$$y_i = h(x_1 \ldots x_i \ldots x_n \ldots; \quad \phi_1 \ldots \phi_i \ldots \phi_t) \tag{3}$$

where y_i = Performance of basic system unit.

x_i = Performance of system man or machine component.

ϕ_i = Internal environment of the unit.

h = Functional relationship between unit and component performance.

Our last relationship is:

$$x_i = k(x_j)$$

indicating component interactions.

Ultimately, then, $M = F(x_1 \ldots x_i \ldots x_n)$, indicating that mission performance depends on the performance of system man and machine components. Given this general formulation of the system model, the research problems are:

(*a*) To partition the system into integrated levels, defining tasks and missions at each level, and identifying the fundamental system unit and components upon which overall system goal achievement ultimately rests.

(*b*) To select the key task of the fundamental unit selected.

(*c*) To select and measure dependent and independent variables which influence performance of the key task.

(*d*) To determine functional relationships between these sets of variables.

(*e*) To validate the functions by testing their predictive capability.

Once the model has been validated by predicting the operational consequences of design decision in different environments, the functions may be used to predict the performance of unbuilt future systems. That is, given the model $P = F(R, \theta)$ and measuring P, R, and θ variables, the functional relationship, F, is determined. Using this F, the performance of future systems can be predicted for various R–θ combinations.

OPERATIONAL MODEL

The operational model extends the design model to the time domain – $P = F(R, \theta, t)$. Given a system in being, design decisions have been made and operational problems remain. The fundamental operational problem is to regulate the performance of system man and machine components $(x_1 \ldots x_n)$ over time so that system performance objectives $(M_1 \ldots M_n)$ are met. In order to do this, a set of system performance variables $(y_1 \ldots y_m)$ must be held within limits prescribed by the controller in the operational environment (θ). The limits are maintained by adjusting, or regulating, the performance of the man and machine resource variables $(x_i\text{'s})$. Instead of predicting expected system performance characteristics on the average, this model describes system performance as components are adjusted in time. In Ashby's terms [18] it describes the behaviour of a system as the trajectory of a time-varying vector.

Ashby's concepts of regulation and control [19] provide the basis for the construction of this model. It is similar to the game-theoretical model in that enemy play and own response are related. It differs from game theory, however, in that cell entries in the table represent the state of the system following play and counter-play, rather than the value, or utility, of the play. That is to say, the table predicts the expected value *outcomes* of tactical decisions, i.e. the adjustment of y's, not the *utility* of the outcomes. Assignment of utility is taken to be a *command decision*, based on factors external to the model. This is the control function, in Ashby's terms. Regulation is the adjustment of system resources $(x\text{'s})$ to maintain the system in the state specified by the controller in the face of external threats or disturbances from the environment. These general relationships are suggested in *Figure 2*.

The first step in the construction of a regulatory model is to identify the performance variables that must be maintained within specified limits if the

Figure 2   *Basic Elements of an Adaptive System*

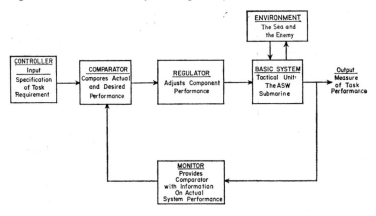

system is to achieve its objective. The regulator's ability to maintain these variables within the limits specified by the controller provides a dynamic measure of system effectiveness.

The submarine weapon-system

Given these related system models, procedures which are being used to develop them in the context of a specified system will be described. Because of its central role as a naval system and its great potential for the development of the resources of the sea, and since it is representative of a wide range of man–machine systems, the submarine was chosen as the basis of our study. Performance data generated during submarine exercises at sea provide the data for model development, and Professor Ashby's cybernetic concepts [15,20] provide logical schemes for organizing the data.

The design–operations cycle may be entered from either the design or the operational frame of reference. We have elected to start with the operational problem in order to select the essential performance variables which must be related in the model.

Our study is concerned with the tactical employment of submarines of known performance capability. We are developing the operational model to predict the consequences of tactical decisions for utilizing system resources, given disturbances from the environment. The model relates disturbances, tactical employment of resources, and the consequent levels of task accomplishment as shown in equation (2) which becomes a time function in the operational model:

$$T_i = q(y_1 \ldots y_i \ldots y_m; \quad \theta_1 \ldots \theta_i \ldots \theta_t; \quad t)$$

S

In the submarine system, $T_1 \ldots T_m$ are the tasks of detecting, classifying, localizing, and destroying a target; $y_1 \ldots y_m$ are the variables describing the tactical performance of the attacking submarine; and $\theta_1 \ldots \theta_i$ represents environment variables, such as the sea and the enemy.

Given that a target has been detected and classified, the variables which must be regulated to ensure effective weapon employment are range and bearing. The killer submarine must hold these variables within limits which depend on weapon capability. Specifically, a closing range and constant bearing rate are required. The ability to maintain range and bearing in the desired relationship depends on the submarine's capability for information acquisition and analysis, its propulsion system, the skill of the crew in manoeuvring it, solving the fire-control problem, and providing instructions for the torpedo; and, finally, the weapon itself. Since the ultimate objective of the ASW submarine system is to place the torpedo within acquisition range of a target, attention is focused on the torpedo. For much of its voyage, it travels in the submarine, and torpedo performance is the same as submarine performance. For the last part of its voyage, however, the torpedo is free-swimming. Given a reliable mechanism, hit probability depends in large part on the instructions to the torpedo prior to launching. These instructions must overcome the effects of disturbances, such as manoeuvres of the target and noise in the sea, which tend to drive the essential attacker variables out of limits. These disturbances may be 'actively hostile as are those coming from the enemy, or merely irregular, as those coming from the weather' (Ashby[21]).

The operational model integrates the interactions between regulator and controller. For example, it describes the commanding-officer/executive-officer relationships in a submarine. The commanding officer makes tactical decisions on the basis of his training and experience, given information on the situation at the moment, and directs the executive officer to manoeuvre the submarine to ensure that his tactical decisions are implemented, i.e. that own ship tactical variables (y's) assume values which will lead to a successful attack.

Since isomorphic models of systems as complex as the attack submarine do not exist, the operators must rely on information feedback for regulation and control. Operational decisions are made, the consequences are noted, and further adjustments are made to reduce the difference between actual and desired performance. Thus, problems of information acquisition, display, interpretation, and analysis loom large. The regulator must detect disturbances originating in the environment and adjust his resource to maintain the system in the state specified by the controller.

In the operation of an adaptive system, hypotheses about the nature of the disturbances are continually being tested. The regulator 'acts as if' he were regulating against disturbances of known characteristics. If regulatory action leads to the predicted system states, the hypothesis is accepted. If it does not, it is rejected, and further regulation is tried. This procedure raises the monitoring problems of the Type I and Type II errors, i.e. responding to signals which did not occur, and not responding to signals which did. Because of the regulator's crucial reliance on *information* presented on abstract displays, the monitor assumes a role of central importance in the regulation of adaptive systems (Howland and Wiener [22]).

The empirical problem

With the development of models to predict future system states as our ultimate research objective, we began our analysis with a description of the performance of target and attacker submarine in the ASW role during submarine exercises. In the conduct of these exercises performance is recorded for both target and attacker submarines on data sheets which resemble Ashby's 'Protocol'.[23] Own ship course, speed, and depth, for example, are recorded as a time sequence. By combining data from target and attacking submarine, it is possible to describe their trajectories as a time-varying vector. According to Ashby,[24] the next step in the analysis is to 'look for regularities, for repetitiveness in the behaviour'. We are plotting relative position and velocity data for submarines and torpedo in order to relate target and attacker behaviour. Using Ashby's [25] concept of the 'ultra-stable' system, we are attempting to develop a set of differential equations from exercise data. These equations, once developed, can then be validated by using them to predict future performance in specific situations.

Summary

The development of research methods for constructing regulatory models of complex systems presents many problems. Among these are the formulation of design and operational questions, the selection and measurement of variables, and the development of functional relationships between them. Our research objective is to develop procedures for combining experimental and formal concepts in models which will provide system designers and operators with information to assist them in their complex decision-making tasks. Methodologically, our problem is one of extending the hypothetico-deductive procedures of experimental science to complex system phenomena. Viewing man–machine systems as adaptive homeostatic organisms, we are applying Ashby's [15,20] cybernetic concepts to the problem of developing system models.

In this frame of reference the regulatory capability of a system depends on the availability of resources which maintain it in states specified by the controller, given disturbances from the environment. Because of the complexity, i.e. number of variables which must be considered, isomorphic models which would permit open-loop system control are not feasible. Closed-loop feedback models make regulation and control possible; cybernetic models are capable of dealing with complexity because they possess this essential feature.

In addition to performance criteria, costs must be considered. It is important, however, that design decisions be made first to operational criteria, and then to cost. As Senator John O. Pastore [26] of Rhode Island remarked:

'Our potential enemies may not use the same cost-effectiveness criteria and thus oppose us with the best weapons their technology can provide. This could create an intolerable peril to the national security.'

Once a system has been designed, and the man and machine components have been selected, operational problems are raised. Since it is necessary continually to adjust component performance so that overall system performance requirements are met, the consequences of component adjustments must be predicted. The kinds of system with which we are principally concerned are those which are designed to hold some set of variables within predetermined limits. The attacking submarine, for example, must establish and maintain its position relative to a target within limits which depend on characteristics of each submarine, the torpedo, and the environment. The operational problem, then, is basically one of establishing and maintaining a set of variables within limits.

The research problem is one of developing the information needed by the designer and operator. It is *not* one of specifying limits. Given limits, specified by responsible commanders, the regulatory problem is one of utilizing system resources to maintain the system's essential variables within limits specified by the controller. A cybernetic formulation of the problem leads to adaptive regulatory system models capable of learning from experience, and dealing with disturbances not anticipated by their designers.

ACKNOWLEDGEMENT

This investigation is supported in part by the Methodology Division, Naval Analysis Group, Office of Naval Research under Contract Nonr 495(28).

REFERENCES

1 J. S. Minas (1956)
2 R. Dorfman (1960)
3 M. Shubik (1963)
4 C. D. Flagle (1963)
5 R. L. Ackoff (1957b)
6 C. J. Hitch (1957)
7 R. L. Ackoff (1958b)
8 J. Bronowski (1951)
9 A. H. Maslow (1954)
10 M. S. Tsien (1954)
11 R. L. Chapman & J. L. Kennedy (1956)
12 D. Howland (1963)
13 S. S. Stevens (1951)
14 C. H. Coombs, H. Raiffa & R. M. Thrall (1954)
15 W. R. Ashby (1957)
16 W. B. Cannon (1932)
17 M. C. Yovits & S. Cameron (1960)
18 W. R. Ashby (1957), Chapter 3
19 W. R. Ashby (1957), Part 3
20 W. R. Ashby (1960)
21 W. R. Ashby (1958)
22 D. Howland & E. L. Wiener (1963)
23 W. R. Ashby (1957), p. 88
24 W. R. Ashby (1957), p. 89
25 W. R. Ashby (1960), p. 98
26 *U.S. News and World Report*

37 · Conceptualization of a System as a Mathematical Model

ANATOL RAPOPORT

Introduction

The notion of system is used in such a wide variety of contexts that it is not easy to extract a meaning common to all of them. One aspect of all the referents, however, is clear, namely that of organization. Organization, in turn, means that the relations of the parts to each other and to the whole can be more or less specified. If this can be done, the organized entity deserves to be called a system.

Living organisms deserve to be called systems, because the structure and the functions of their parts stand in specific relations to each other. If these relations are disturbed, the organism ceases to exist as an organism. Aggregates of organisms, e.g. ant-hills, cities, universities, armies, and the like, are systems to the extent that certain aspects of the behaviour of their members are functionally circumscribed. On the other hand, it is sometimes argued that heaps of sand or milling mobs are not systems, because arbitrarily selected parts of them can be removed without significantly changing the character of what is left. However, the line between a system and a non-system depends to a considerable extent on what aspects of it one has selected for attention. Thus, from a certain point of view a mob may be considered a system, because it sometimes acts like a unit and in predictable fashion. Even a heap of sand can exist only in certain geometrical configurations and not in others, and so has certain (admittedly weak) features of an organized entity.

The system concept is a potentially integrating one, because system properties can often be abstracted from the specific embodiment of a system. Thus, all organisms, viewed as systems, have certain features in common. For example, all individuals of a given species have a distinctly recognizable structure. Moreover, modifications of structure which differentiate organisms from each other are graded, so that meaningful classifications of organisms into species, genera, classes, phyla, etc., is possible. Common to all organisms are certain processes by which their organization is maintained.

515

These features are observed also in systems other than organisms. Engines, like organisms, operate by transforming some forms of energy into others. Like organisms, engines require constant maintenance, i.e. restoration of the ordered arrangement of parts and the co-ordination of their function. Organizations, like organisms, persist in spite of the turn-over of personnel. None of the original members of an organization may remain and yet the organization preserves its identity. In the same way every material particle composing an organism may be replaced many times during its life-time while the organism nevertheless preserves its identity.

The existence of features and aspects common to all organized systems has given rise to a point of view now known as general systems theory. It is a point of view rather than a theory in the scientific sense, because there is little in general systems theory that can be embodied into the sequence of related propositions that one usually conceives a theory to be. More properly, general systems theory is a certain approach to describing and investigating systems, an approach that singles out the system characteristics of objects and phenomena and so classifies objects and phenomena according to the kind of system characteristics they exhibit rather than according to their content, which has been the traditional scheme of organizing knowledge.

It seems useful to distinguish between the systems concept as it pertains to technology and as it pertains to science. Furthermore, there have been at least three different conceptions of general systems theory in science. This paper deals with only one of them. However, in order to place this topic in perspective, we shall briefly mention the other points of view.

The concept of a system in technology differs in one important respect from the corresponding concept in science. The systems dealt with in technology have been deliberately constructed for specific aims. Thus, there is no problem of discovering what are the important components or elements of an artificially constructed system and in what functional relation they stand to each other. The elements have been put there and do not need to be discovered. The problem posed in technology, for which answers are sought in a general theory of systems, is how to put components in relation to each other in order to achieve certain specified aims. In science, on the other hand, the characteristic problem is the inverse of the one just mentioned. Certain entities are obviously systems, for example organisms. Other entities also give definite indications of organized function, for example certain social aggregates, institutions, and the like. Even entities to which material existence cannot be ascribed, in the sense of occupying circumscribed portions of space, strongly suggest systems, for example languages, religions, legal codes, patterns of social arrangement, etc. Here the role of a systems theory is to discover fundamental entities and relations among them in terms of which the structure, the behaviour, and possibly the genesis of the alleged systems become understandable.

There have been three different conceptualizations of a general systems theory as it pertains to scientific investigations as contrasted with the problems of synthesis, with which technology is concerned. The first explicit conceptualization is associated with the writings of Ludwig von Bertalanffy, [1] who emphasized that the open-system-in-steady-state aspect of life could explain phenomena which biologists of the vitalist persuasion tended to ascribe to specific vital forces: for example, 'equifinality', that is, the apparent ability of living systems to attain preset goals regardless of disturbances or obstacles. Bertalanffy's proposal for a general systems theory centres upon investigations of systems with specific boundary conditions, which determine the character of interaction of a system with its environment. The crudest classification of systems into closed and open is the first step in this programme. The study of open physico-chemical systems is closely connected with the thermodynamics of irreversible processes. The latter are important in chemical kinetics. Thus, the most direct application of Bertalanffy's concept of system would seem to be in the study of the general laws of metabolic processes and cycles.

Another conceptualization of a general systems theory was proposed by R. W. Gerard.[2] Gerard views the general investigation of systems as proceeding along two dimensions. One dimension represents hierarchies of levels of organization. Typically the hierarchies are progressively inclusive. Molecules are organized into cells; cells into tissues and organs; organs into individuals. Aggregates of individuals may be viewed either as hierarchies of biological systems – species, genera, classes – or of social systems – small groups, tribes, institutions, societies. These levels form the rows of Gerard's matrix. The columns are three fundamental aspects in terms of which a system can be described, namely its structure ('being'), that is, the relations of its parts to each other at a given moment of time; its behaviour ('acting'), that is, its reactions, usually reversible, to environmental changes; and its history ('becoming'), which may include the development of an embryo, the maturation of an individual, the growth of an institution or a society, or the evolution of a species. (History contains hysteresis effects, hence historical changes are typically irreversible.)

Both approaches clearly aim at an integration of knowledge and research. Bertalanffy points towards an integration of 'mechanistic' and 'organismic' views in biology by suggesting how organismic properties emerge from properties of open systems hitherto not investigated. Gerard's view is primarily a plan for integrating the life sciences by showing how both the biological and the social aspects of living aggregates (whether of cells or individuals) are subsumed under certain general features of living systems.

Mathematical homology

My concern in this paper is with a third approach to general systems theory, that of mathematical homology. The strongest type of mathematical homology is an isomorphism. Two mathematical objects are said to be isomorphic if:

(i) there exists a one-to-one correspondence between the elements of one and those of the other, and

(ii) the relations between the elements are preserved under the same correspondence.

The following example illustrates the principle of isomorphism by exhibiting two mathematical objects isomorphic to each other and a third, apparently similar object, not isomorphic to either of the other two.

As a first object, consider the set of permutations of three elements. Give each permutation a name. Call the original order (123) of the elements the Identity Permutation I. Call the permutation $\begin{pmatrix} 123 \\ 231 \end{pmatrix} A$. Then A^2 is the permutation $\begin{pmatrix} 123 \\ 312 \end{pmatrix}$, since it is obtained from I by applying A twice. To get the remaining three permutations define B as the interchange of 1 and 2. Thus $B = \begin{pmatrix} 123 \\ 213 \end{pmatrix}$. Then $B^2 = I$, $BA^2 = \begin{pmatrix} 123 \\ 132 \end{pmatrix} = AB$, $BA = \begin{pmatrix} 123 \\ 321 \end{pmatrix} = A^2B$. The six distinct elements of this mathematical system (technically called a non-abelian group) are, therefore, I, A, A^2, B, AB, and A^2B. There are no others, since $BA = A^2B$, $A^3 = I$, etc.

Consider now a tray in the shape of an equilateral triangle, with a coin placed in one of its corners. Let A be the act of turning the coin over and B the act of rotating the tray clockwise through 120°. It is easily verified that the two operations are commutative; that is, the result of any two operations is the same in whatever order the operations are performed. Moreover, A^3, being a rotation through 360°, is equivalent to (I), the rotation through 0°, and so is B^2, the act of turning the coin over twice. Therefore there are six distinct operations, namely, I, A, A^2, B, AB, and A^2B. This 'system' is not isomorphic to the group of permutations on three objects, because here $BA = AB$, whereas in the group of permutations $BA = A^2B$.

Now consider a triangle with a circle in one corner. Let A, as before, be a clockwise rotation of 120° around an axis perpendicular to the plane of the triangle and B a rotation of 180° around an axis through the vertex. Now it is easily verified that $AB \neq BA$, indeed $AB = BA^2$. This 'system' also consists of six operations, and it is isomorphic to the system of permutations of three objects.

From the point of view of mathematical homology, then, the three mathematical objects just described represent just two non-equivalent ones. Moreover, any system whatsoever which can be described by one or the other of these mathematical models belongs to the one class or to the other. All systems within such a class are mathematically equivalent.

A well-known example of two physical systems represented by isomorphic mathematical models is that of a harmonic mechanical oscillator and an electrical circuit with an inductance, a resistance, and a capacitance. The equation of motion of the former is given by the second-order differential equation

$$m\ddot{x} + r\dot{x} + kx = F(t) \tag{1}$$

where m is the mass of the oscillating point-mass, r the coefficient of resistance of the medium, k the elasticity modulus, i.e. the constant of proportionality between displacement x and the restoring force, and $F(t)$ is the externally applied force, which may be a function of time.

The analogous equation of the electrical system is

$$L\ddot{x} + R\dot{x} + Cx = E(t) \tag{2}$$

where L is the inductance of the circuit, R the ohmic resistance, and C the capacitance, and $E(t)$ the externally impressed electromotive force. Here x stands for electric charge. The two equations, (1) and (2), are isomorphic. The solutions of one correspond exactly to those of the other. From the point of view of mathematical homology, the two physical systems are not distinguishable from each other in spite of their widely different physical contents. Furthermore, the mathematical isomorphism suggests analogies between physical quantities which may not have occurred spontaneously, for example an analogy between electrical inductance and mass, a rather far-fetched idea, but one which appears understandable upon reflection, once we realize that, in a way, mass is responsible for inertial resistance and so is electrical inductance: when an electromotive force is suddenly applied, the response of the system is not instantaneous. Inductance plays the part of inertia.

The main function served by mathematical homology is that it makes analogies rigorous. Analogies are the very essence of creative thought. Ordinarily, however, there is danger in analogical thinking, since it is easy to fall prey to delusions instigated by superficial resemblances. The method of mathematical homology guards against the delusions of superficial analogical thinking.

As we have said, from the point of view of mathematical homology two systems are considered equivalent if they can be represented by two homologous mathematical models, as in the case of the mechanical and electrical harmonic oscillators. Further, a system is *defined* in terms of the mathematical model which describes it. A definition of system which is both rigorous and general flows from this identification.

Mathematically speaking, a system is defined not in terms of its content (as it would be from the point of view of hierarchy of organization) but in terms of its abstract structure. Every system is an aggregate of elements (or components) and relations. The totality of elements and relations constitutes the structure of the system. If the structure is assumed to be constant in time the theory of the system is a static one. If the structure changes in time, and if the laws of change can be specified, the theory of the system is a dynamic one.

If a system can exist in any of a given set of configurations these configurations are called the *states* of the system. A complete dynamic theory of a system must specify how, given the state of a system at a given moment or throughout a given period, the sequence of future states can be predicted, or a history of past states post-dicted. If the sets of possible states of two systems are in one-to-one correspondence, and if their dynamic theories are mathematically isomorphic, the two systems are isomorphic. From the point of view of general systems theory the two systems are identical.

The classification of systems now flows naturally from the classification of mathematical models in terms of which they are described. The task of systems theory now becomes the investigation of the properties of the mathematical models, considered as mathematical objects in their own right without any concern for the possible referents of these models.

Naturally, the models are not invented arbitrarily. Usually some real-life situation instigates the study of a model supposedly adequate to describe it. Once the model has been formulated, however, the investigation concentrates on the properties of the abstract mathematical object. It is from this investigation that hypotheses (not conclusions!) are derived, from which a theory of the situation originally envisaged is constructed.

It sometimes turns out that the model fits some other situations better than the one for which it was formulated. If so, then the systems theorist is led to wherever the model leads him. In short, he is as frequently in the market for situations to fit the model he has investigated as on a quest for models to fit a given situation.

Example: population and conflict dynamics

Let us examine some general classes of mathematical models frequently used in a great variety of situations. In classical mathematical physics the dominant model is a system of second-order ordinary or partial differential equations. These systems describe the motions of particles in classical force fields (gravitational or electro-magnetic). From this point of view the solar system is a system, because it can be described by a system of differential equations. The state of such a system at any moment of time is given by the configuration of positions and velocities of its elements (the planets). The fact that from any given state a sequence of future states can be predicted with great accuracy furnishes convincing proof that the underlying system theory is valid. Moreover, any system of this type yields to a theory of the same type.

Another class of systems is describable by systems of ordinary linear differential equations of the first order. As an example, consider the following such system:

$$dx/dt = ax + ky + g$$
$$dy/dt = mx + by + h$$

where a, b, g, h, k, and m are constants. All such systems can be regarded as belonging to the same class regardless of the signs of the constants. A finer analysis differentiates the systems according to the signs of the constants. For simplicity, let us disregard the signs of g and h and consider only two cases, namely (i) where a and b are positive while k and m are negative, and (ii) where a and b are negative while k and m are positive. Before we look for situations which such systems may describe, let us examine the mathematical properties of these two kinds of systems.

(i) If a and b are positive, while k and m are negative, it can be easily shown that the system is unstable. For consider the two lines in the phase space (x, y) along which dx/dt and dy/dt vanish respectively. Replacing k and m by their absolute values, we write

$$ax - ky + g = 0 \qquad (5)$$
$$-mx + by + h = 0 \qquad (6)$$

If the lines intersect, both derivatives vanish at the intersection. Therefore, if there is an equilibrium it must be at the intersection. Suppose, however, x increases by the smallest amount above this equilibrium value. This immediately makes dx/dt positive and dy/dt negative, which facilitates a further increase in x and a further decrease in y. The system continues to move in the direction of increasing x and decreasing y indefinitely. Just the opposite if y increases from its equilibrium value or if x decreases from the equilibrium value. 'Coexistence' of x and y is impossible in such a system.

(ii) If a and b are negative, while k and m are positive, then the system may be stable or it may be unstable. The former is the case if $ab > km$; the latter if $ab < km$.

Such systems were considered by Lewis F. Richardson [3] as models of arms races between two rival blocs, in which the armament level of one stimulates the other to increase its rate of armament (as represented by the mutual stimulation coefficients k and m), but where the rate of growth of armament expenditures of each bloc is inhibited by its own burden of armaments (the coefficients of self-inhibition a and b). Depending on the relative magnitudes of these parameters, stabilization of the arms race is or is not possible. If it is impossible there are still two possibilities, either a runaway arms race or total disarmament, depending on initial conditions.

If the second sort of system is stable it can be interpreted in a biological setting as a symbiotic relation between two species. Let x and y be the respective populations, and let g and h be zero or negative. Then in the absence of one population the other will die out. For if, say, $y = 0$, the rate of change of x is always negative (if $a < 0$), and similarly for y if $x = 0$. Only when both populations are present can an equilibrium be maintained, provided $ab > km$.

There is, however, another model which is more realistic biologically and leads to the same result. Let the net rate of natural increase of each species be positive, but let there be a 'crowdedness' term, which detracts from the birth rate or adds to the death rate. These 'crowdedness' terms will depend on the frequencies of contacts between the members of the same species and the members of the different species, hence on the products of the population densities. We write accordingly,

$$dx/dt = ax - kx^2 - gxy \qquad (7)$$
$$dy/dt = by - my^2 - hxy \qquad (8)$$

An investigation of the dynamics of this system leads to the conclusion that the species can coexist in equilibrium provided $km > gh$ but not otherwise.[4]

From these examples we see how theoretical concepts can emerge from the interpretations of the model rather than being the starting-points in the construction of the model. This need not be the case, of course. One might well start with hypothesis that 'crowdedness' may have something to do with the existence or non-existence of equilibria in species competition and on the basis of this conjecture construct a mathematical model in order to verify the conjecture by deducing the consequences of the model. But one might also have started with investigating the properties of a pair of logistic-type equations like (7) and (8), and, noting the dependence of stability on the parameters, seek the proper interpretations of the parameters.

This whole approach, it must be stressed, is typical of the scientific aspects of systems theory rather than of its technological aspects. When a hardware system is being designed or has been built we know what the parameters stand for. The only problem is to pick the right values of the parameters in order to give some desired features of performance. Typically, the electrical engineer wants to know how to connect his elements and what magnitudes of impedance or electromotive force to put into his system. There is no problem of interpretation here. The natural scientist, on the contrary, trying to understand a system given by nature or, as sometimes happens, inventing a conceptual system which, he believes, will fit some portion of the world, has a serious problem of interpretation. The way he interprets the parameters will determine the direction of his theory.

I should like to illustrate this principle by two examples from my own work. The first example is meant to illustrate the shift of interest which frequently results as one pursues the implications of a mathematical model quite aside from the original context to which the model was meant to apply. The second example is meant to illustrate the emergence of a theory or, at least, of a sequence of hypotheses from the interpretations given to the parameters of the model.

Mathematical theory of nets

About fifteen years ago I became interested in mathematical models of neural nets. A detailed empirical investigation of a real neural net with a view to constructing a mathematical model of its structure, let alone of its dynamics, was out of the question. The complexity of these objects defies any kind of description that yields to mathematical treatment. Therefore, those of us who were interested in this subject were driven willy-nilly (mostly willy, for we were theoreticians, not experimenters), to the study of artificial mathematical objects, which we called 'neural nets', trying to remember that this label was no more than a nickname.

We postulated laws of propagation of impulses determined by distributions of thresholds, inhibitory and excitatory connexions, and so on. We hoped to deduce some sort of general principles of propagation based on the postulated model. A number of formal papers were the result, which bore no necessary connexion to real neural nets or to any events going on within them for want of data relevant to our mathematical models.

After two or three years of this work I heard of some experiments on the West Coast designed to study the spread of information through a population. Specifically, items of information were given to schoolchildren and contests were arranged to see who could pass on and receive most information of these items. The experiments were so designed that information could be recovered concerning the path of an item of information (which was on cards) through the population. This permitted the construction of a model of information spread through 'removes'; i.e. one could tell how many new receivers of information were contacted on each remove from some original source.[5]

If one supposed (on the basis of a null hypothesis) that the contacts were made at random, the equation governing the numbers or fractions of the population newly contacted on each remove could be written down, namely,

$$p(t + 1) = [1 - x(t)][1 - e^{-ap(t)}] \qquad (9)$$

where $p(t)$ is the fraction of the population contacted on the tth remove, $x(t) = \sum_{j=0}^{t} p(j)$, and a is the average number of individuals ever contacted per individual.

This was the same equation as was used in the theory of propagation of impulses through a neural net, assuming (probably quite unrealistically) totally random connexions. But whereas in the context of neural excitation there was no opportunity of comparing the results predicted by the equation with observed results, there was such an opportunity in the context of information spreading among a population of schoolchildren. This comparison we undertook. We proceeded in the following way. Solving equation (9) for a, we obtain

$$a = \alpha(t) = \frac{1}{p(t)} \log_e \frac{1 - x(t)}{1 - x(t + 1)} \qquad (10)$$

where we have equated a to $\alpha(t)$ to indicate that formally it is a function of t, as shown by the right-hand side of (10). But, of course, if (10) holds, then $\alpha(t) = a$, a constant. Therefore whether $\alpha(t)$ is indeed independent of t

becomes a test of the model embodied in (9), i.e. whether the communication net is indeed random.

As one could have expected, the communication net along which the children passed the information was not random. Plotting $\alpha(t)$ against t revealed at first a precipitous drop from $\alpha(0) = 7\cdot2$ to $\alpha(1) = 1\cdot3$, and thereafter a steady rise of $\alpha(t)$ with t. The reason for the drop was immediately apparent. It was traced to the 'inbred' character of the net, i.e. to the fact that the friends of one's friends are also likely to be one's own friends. The magnitude of the drop was accordingly interpreted as the measure of this 'inbreeding'. The subsequent steady rise in $\alpha(t)$ was more difficult to explain. We conjectured that this was the effect of increasingly more randomized contacts as the immediate 'acquaintance neighbourhoods' of the carriers of information no longer yielded fresh contacts. Clearly this effect, if indeed it was such, stemmed from the way information was being disseminated in the net, not from the structure of the net itself. Therefore, we conjectured, if we studied the communication net itself, applying similar methods, the rise of $\alpha(t)$ following the initial drop ought not to be observed.

The problem lay dormant until it was revived some three or four years ago. This time we concentrated on the study of net structures without anything going on in the nets. This simplified immensely the problem of gathering the data, since this part of the task became independent of special experimental arrangements. One obtains a net in any situation whatsoever provided one has identified a population of elements (or 'nodes') and a binary relation which may or may not exist between members of an ordered pair of such elements. The following are obvious examples of nets:

1 A sociogram. Here the elements are a population of individuals. The relation in any ordered pair (A, B) may be 'A chooses B as his best friend' or 'A talks to B' or 'A dominates B' or whatever.

2 A communication net. Here the elements are stations and the relation is 'messages may pass from A to B'.

3 A neural net. The elements may be neurons; the relation may be 'neuron A sends a functional connexion to neuron B'.

4 A system of trade between firms or nations.

Etc.

The principle of mathematical homology obviously applies to these systems. Isomorphism of two nets is defined in the usual way. Also homologies weaker than isomorphisms can be defined, and this brings out a natural method of classifying nets according to the degree of mathematical homology between them rather than by the specific content.

Nets can be classified, for example, by the logical nature of the relation that defines them. In some cases the relation is clearly symmetrical, as in 'A is connected to B by a telephone wire'. (If A is connected to B, so is B to A.) Some relations are clearly asymmetrical as 'A is B's superior in a chain of command' (if so, then B is not A's superior). Some relations may be neither symmetrical nor asymmetrical, as 'A calls B his best friend'. Nets can also be classified by the extent to which the nodes are connected with each other. A completely connected linear graph is a net in which the relation in question exists between every pair of nodes. A connected graph is one in which paths exist from any node to any other node via the links established by the relation, etc.

As an example of an investigation in which the general aspects of the mathematical model are at the centre of attention, I shall mention some studies on word association nets that we have recently been conducting. A net of this sort is constructed by each subject. A subject is given a list of words and asked to find for each word a certain number of its closest connotative associates chosen from the same list. The result is a net. Such nets are quite easy to obtain by the hundreds, and they can be studied entirely at leisure. The large numbers at hand enable us to study the statistical properties of such nets – a great advantage, because a detailed description of a large net is so complex that hardly any general consequences can be drawn from it. One can, however, single out a few statistical properties to construct a 'profile' of a net from the few parameters defining these properties. Once this is done, one could ask 'content' questions, such as how the general properties of the word association nets constructed by one class of subjects (differentiated, say, by age, sex, culture, diagnostic procedures) differ from those of another class. One can ask what are the similarities and what the differences between a word association net and a network of international trade or between a sociogram and a neural net. These questions may seem pointless if one views them as comparisons of contents, since the contents are so far apart as to preclude meaningful comparison. But the questions are not pointless if viewed as comparisons of structural characteristics. In terms of such a comparison one might discover that a certain bias (departure from randomness) plays in a word association net a role quite homologous to that of a certain bias in a net of international trade. Such a comparison might not have occurred in terms of content, but seems naturally to occur in the context of mathematical homology, and may lead to an important insight.

Such discoveries had been made before. The example of a mathematical homology between electrical inductance and inertial mass has already been mentioned. Another example of recent discovery is the mathematical homology between entropy and negative information. Still another is the parameter characterizing the rank-size distribution of words, which in Mandelbrot's mathematical model of this distribution plays a part mathematically homologous to temperature as derived in statistical mechanics. This makes it possible to speak of the 'temperature' of a verbal output. This metaphor, on the face of it absurd, has no relation to the emotional qualities of the output but has a rich meaning in the context of mathematical homology between information theory and thermodynamics.

Dynamics of non-zero-sum games

As a final example, I will mention another line of investigation where the systems approach proved valuable as a generator of theoretical ideas. For a number of years some of us have been conducting experiments on a class of two-person non-zero-sum games, known as Prisoner's Dilemma.[6] The pay-off matrix of this game is shown in the following matrix:

	C_2	D_2
C_1	R, R	S, T
D_1	T, S	P, P

Prisoner's Dilemma is defined by the inequality $T > R > P > S$. The dilemma arises from the circumstance that although strategy D dominates strategy C for both players, the choice pair $D_1 D_2$ is worse for both than $C_1 C_2$. This conflict between individual and collective interest has naturally intrigued psychologists, and a considerable amount of experimental work has been done with games of this sort. We have performed experiments in which pairs of players play Prisoner's Dilemma type games some hundreds of times in succession. The players cannot communicate with each other, but the result of each play of the game is made known to them.

Certain questions naturally arise concerning a situation of this kind. A psychologist interested in personality may ask what sort of people predominantly play C rather than D, and vice versa. A social psychologist or a group dynamicist may be interested to know how the interpersonal relations between the two players will affect their way of playing. To the strategist, on the other hand, the game presents no interest, since calculation of consequences of choices (which makes games of strategy interesting to the strategist) plays no part in this game. Indeed, game theory has little to say about a game of this sort. Each player has only two choices, and each of these has only two outcomes. Since the outcomes of one choice are better than those of the other, regardless of how the other player chooses, the game-theoretical 'solution' of this game (with communication between the players disallowed) is obvious: D is the rational choice. The fact that D leads to a loss for both players makes the dilemma, but it cannot be resolved within the framework of strategic analysis. The choice of C can be rationalized only by invoking notions like mutual trust and trustworthiness, which have no place in the vocabulary of game theory. It is this dependence of choices upon quasi-ethical considerations that makes the game psychologically interesting.

The systems approach to this problem eschews the raising of either psychological or of strategic questions. It concentrates instead on the examination of a system, that is, of a mathematical model which might be expected to represent the process of repeated plays of a Prisoner's Dilemma game.

As has been said, a dynamic theory of a system is based on a set of assumptions concerning the laws which stipulate how the system passes or is likely to pass from state to state. It is natural to assume that the corresponding model of Prisoner's Dilemma is a system that can be in any of four states, each corresponding to a pair of strategy choices, namely, C_1C_2, C_1D_2, D_1C_2, and D_1D_2. Next, it is natural to assume that the passage from state to state is governed by stochastic rather than deterministic laws, since clearly no one can predict with certainty how a given player will choose on a given play.

One of the simplest stochastic processes is a Markov chain, which specifies a constant transition probability for every one of the 16 possible transitions. Let the matrix of transition probabilities be (α_{ij}) $(i, j = 1, \ldots 4)$, where we have assigned subscripts 1, 2, 3, and 4 respectively to the four states mentioned above. Then, if the initial frequency distribution of the four states and also the sixteen transition probabilities α_{ij} are known, the frequency distribution of the four states can be deduced as a specified function of time. In principle, then, we have a mathematical model of the process which can be tested against the data. However, in order to test the model, the above-mentioned distribution and the transition probabilities must be estimated. Any such estimates will be based on certain assumptions, that is, on a preconceived theory of the process. Of course, such a preconceived theory underlies every theoretical development. The characteristic virtue of mathematical models is that their construction forces the theoretician to state the preconceived theory rigorously and explicitly. Usually these *a priori* assumptions will have to be modified in the light of the discrepancies between the model and the data or in the light of the interpretation of the parameters. It is these continual modifications which provide the 'theoretical leverage' of the mathematical method.

To continue with our example, let us see what role the transition probabilities α_{ij} can play in our theory. Take some α_{ij}, say α_{24}. It represents a transition of our system from state 2 to state 4, i.e. from state C_1D_2 to state D_1D_2. This transition indicates that player 1, having co-operated and having been 'betrayed' (since player 2 did not co-operate on that play of the game) switched from C to D on the succeeding play; while player 2, having defected successfully (because player 1 co-operated), continued to defect on the next play. The transition probability α_{24} multiplied by the probability of state C_1D_2 represents the probability that this event occurred.

As we have seen, the event is a composite one, involving acts of both players. Moreover, in the absence of communication the acts of the players *on a particular play* (as distinct from the overall patterns of their plays) may be assumed to be statistically independent; and so our transition probability α_{24}, as every other α_{ij}, is a product of two probabilities, each being a conditional probability of co-operating or non-co-operating on the part of a player, *given that the system is in one of the four states*. These conditional probabilities are the following:

x: the probability of co-operating following rewarded co-operation.
y: the probability of co-operating following betrayed co-operation.
z: the probability of co-operating following successful defection.
w: the probability of co-operating following unsuccessful defection.

These probabilities are psychologically interpretable. Therefore any *a priori* assumptions about them constitute elements of a psychological theory. For example, we might assume that every individual in the experimental population is characterized by the same value of *x*, *y*, *z*, and *w*, which are, moreover, independent of time (i.e. of what happens in the course of the experiment). This is, of course, an extremely strong assumption and, as it turns out, an unrealistic one, refuted by the data. However, it serves as a starting-point of a theory. For the assumption can be modified in any of several directions. We can assume, for example, that the system can be in more than four states. This can be done by introducing a 'memory' of what has happened previously. In particular, some of the states may be so-called 'absorbing states' which, once entered, persist thereafter. Such an assumption is suggested by the characteristic divergence of the observed realizations of the process towards the extremes: most pairs of players 'lock in' either on the CC state or on the DD state. On the other hand, this effect can be deduced also from other assumptions, such as that the conditional probabilities *x*, *y*, *z*, and *w* are themselves modified in the course of the experiment. This links the Markov process model to a stochastic learning model in which the parameters of interest are no longer the conditional co-operative propensities *x*, *y*, *z*, and *w* (which are no longer constant, and hence do not characterize the players), but the learning parameters, which determine the operators, which transform the successive conditional co-operative propensities, which determine the time course of the frequency distributions of the four basic states of the system.

Finally, we may assume that the parameters themselves, although constant for a given individual, are characterized by a frequency distribution in the population. These parameters might be taken to be the unconditional co-operative propensity C, or the conditional propensities, *x*, *y*, *z*, and *w*, or the still 'deeper' learning parameters.

One would think that the last-mentioned type of assumption, namely that the parameters are distributed in the population, is an eminently reasonable one and should be made from the start. However, the method of mathematical models is guided not so much by the realism of the assumptions as by the tractability of the model. For example, the model which postulates a stochastic learning process superimposed upon a Markov chain involving the conditional propensities *x*, *y*, *z*, and *w* contains in its most general form 256 parameters. Such a model would provide no real understanding of what goes on, even if the 256 parameters could be accurately estimated. The idea is not so much to account for the details of the data as to provide an overall view of what determines its most important features, for example, to what extent the observed process *seems* to be determined by the interactions between the paired players and what remains to be accounted for by individual differences between them. If it turns out that even if the players are assumed to be all identical a great deal can be accounted for, we can concentrate on the important features of the interaction process; if not, we can concentrate on the important personal determinants of the process. In this way the method of the mathematical model *suggests* psychological hypotheses on the basis of its own structure and at the same time suggests what must be observed to test the hypotheses, whereas the connexion between what should be observed and what can be conjectured on the basis of the observations might not occur to the unaided imagination.

In summary, the mathematical homology approach to a general systems theory possesses its own characteristic theoretical richness in its essential feature, namely, the initial indifference towards the content of phenomena with a view to investigating their logical (mathematical) structure. The content theory emerges from what is learned about the structure. The unifying potential of the method resides in the opportunity of tying together phenomena of widely different contents if they have mathematically homologous structures.

REFERENCES

1 L. von Bertalanffy (1956)
2 R. W. Gerard (1958)
3 L. F. Richardson (1939)

4 G. F. Gause (1934)
5 A. Rapoport (1956)
6 A. Rapoport (1964b)

38 · Individual Capacity and Social Demands

A New Look at Social Psychology

A. T. WELFORD

Introduction

Attempts to consider social phenomena in psychological terms go back at least as far as the pioneers of scientific psychology in the latter half of the nineteenth century. The development of social psychology as we know it today can, however, be said to begin with the publication of William McDougall's famous book *Introduction to Social Psychology* in 1908. This was essentially an outline of certain principles of individual behaviour likely to be of significance in social settings and an attempt to show how these could account for a number of social and anthropological observations.

In the twenties and thirties of the present century a new approach appeared which examined the effects upon individuals of influences in their social environment. This approach was greatly facilitated by the development at that time of methods of scaling and assessing attitudes and of public-opinion polling, but there were also some notable studies in which measurements were made of social influences on individual perception under experimental conditions. There has continued to be a stream of researches in which social variables have been manipulated and their effects on individual attitude or behaviour assessed.

A true social psychology dealing with the behaviour of groups as such has come to the fore since the Second World War in the study of small groups performing tasks under laboratory or quasi-laboratory conditions. The basic technique is to record the 'interactions' between different members of the group and to note how these interactions change under different conditions. Some of these studies are little more than descriptive, but others have attempted to relate the behaviour of the groups to theoretical frameworks, notably that of 'utility theory' or 'decision theory'.

Although it is unfair to criticize pioneering attempts of this kind, they seem to display serious difficulties of technique. Plotting interactions between members of a group tends to generate an enormous mass of data and, if this

531

is not to prove indigestible, studies must begin with leading ideas and theories to be examined. Commonly, authors seem to have used a single leading idea, such as that the group will in some way try to maximize 'pay-off' and minimize 'cost'. Following this idea, they have set up a substantial set of hypotheses to be tested against the observed data. The shortcoming of this method is that confirmation or denial of the single leading idea is almost inevitably unclear, and the rigidly defined hypotheses act as a strait-jacket to the treatment of the data, diverting the experimenter's attention from many intuitive leads. To put it another way, at the present stage of investigation, when relatively little is known, studies of group behaviour are not wholly satisfactory when made with a single leading idea from which a substantial set of hypotheses have been derived. Rather they should start from a range of leading ideas in terms of which the data can be examined, not so much to provide proofs or disproofs of detailed hypotheses, as to stimulate intuitive thought and generate ideas for future studies in which more precise questions can be answered.

The purpose of this paper is to consider one such set of leading ideas, wide enough in range to be able to cover some of the complexity with which any adequate theoretical treatment in social psychology must eventually deal. They arise from the fact that there are obvious similarities of relationship between one man confronting another and a man confronting a machine. Both can be treated in terms of a 'systems' approach. Research on skill and human capacity generally has provided a considerable wealth of knowledge about the factors that determine the performance of a man–machine system, and these suggest a powerful method of conceptualizing certain social relationships and of analysing them in terms of individual human capacities operating in a definable dynamic system.

Man and machine

Much of the recent advance in laboratory studies of human performance has been due to the application of 'information theory'. The subject, taking action in response to signals, is found to be able to transmit information from 'display' to 'control' at a maximum rate: if the demands of the task exceed this rate he will make errors. The rates differ for different types of task, but show enough predictability to be useful as measures of many types of performance in terms of the degree of *choice* required between alternatives or potential alternatives. More recently, quantitative treatments have also been successfully made of laboratory *discrimination* tasks by using somewhat more detailed 'decision-theory' models than those commonly used in social psychology.

Recent researches have also emphasized a number of other factors which seem to be crucial in determining the level of performance in a wide variety of tasks. Among these special mention may be made of the short-term retention of data, the recognition of sequences in events and the building of routines, the servo-characteristics of the human operator when feedback information is available about the results of his performance, and the effects of loading, not only in the sense of physical effort producing muscular fatigue but more especially of over- or under-loading as regards mental work.

In these terms let us look at some of the main types of demand made upon the operator of a process plant and, by way of example, compare these with the demands made by one man learning from another to use a hand-tool: for simplicity we shall think of the trainee as analogous to the operator and the instructor to the plant, although the comparison could equally validly be made with the roles reversed. Let us also, as a further example, consider the questions that each of these demands suggests for a study of management communications in industry.

(a) *Information transmission and translation*

A process plant will provide a flow of information from instruments such as meters and gauges which the operator has to perceive and use to guide the controlling actions he takes. The translation of such information into action is a mental operation, often of considerable complexity. It takes an appreciable time, which increases with the range of possible different control actions that may be required, and is affected by the precision with which the instruments have to be read and the straightforwardness or otherwise of the relationships between the indications on the instruments and the corresponding control actions.

Similarly, in the training situation the instructor will provide a flow of information to the trainee, describing the use of the tool in words and demonstrating it by actions. The trainee will have to translate these words and his sight of the instructor's actions into a co-ordinated control of his own actions. Demonstration, being more directly related to the actions required, is likely to be more quickly and readily understood than verbal statements. The time required by the trainee to comprehend what he has to do will also depend on the type of tool, rising as the actions required become more varied or complex. It will further depend on the skill shown by the instructor in describing the operation accurately and sufficiently without introducing confusing side-issues or changes in terminology – in information-theory terms the time required will be increased if the instructor fails to convey the necessary information free of 'noise'.

Turning to the analysis of communications in industry, the organization charts plotting the course of communications, whether intended or actual, which are commonly drawn up provide only the barest beginning of the data necessary for a meaningful analysis. A much fuller and more satisfactory treatment would be available if questions could be answered such as: What decisions does each person in the chain of organization have to make? What is their range and what are the relative probabilities of different decisions within the range? From how many sources do the data come on which these decisions are based, and with what relative frequencies from the various possible sources? In what form do the data arrive, and how directly are data related to the actions taken: for example, are indications for action immediately clear, or is it necessary to make elaborate assessments or inferences before action can be decided?

(b) *Short-term retention*

It may be necessary for the operator of a plant not only to react to the indications present at any one instant but also to relate these to previous data, as, for example, when observing trends developing over a period of time. If so, he will have, unless instruments are provided which make a record or he makes one himself, to carry data from one point of time to another in some form of short-term memory.

In the training situation some hand-tool operations involve a fairly elaborate series of actions, all of which will have to be described or demonstrated. The trainee may thus find learning more difficult if he is expected to master the whole operation at once than if he can learn each part separately before combining them together. There seems to be, on the way to permanent registration of data in long-term memory, a stage of short-term, temporary registration in which the amount that can be held at any one moment is relatively small. An attempt to learn a complex operation as a whole right from the start may overload this short-term memory, so that, by the time the instructor has dealt with the last items of the operation, earlier items will have been forgotten.

Short-term retention is of obvious importance in communications within industry, giving rise to questions whether all the data required for a decision are present together at the time it has to be made, or whether relevant items have to be carried in some sort of 'running memory' from one point of time to another. Also it needs to be asked whether a decision, once taken, can be put into effect at once, or whether the man responsible has to remember to initiate action at a point of time in the future.

(c) *Sequences and routines*

In the course of experience the operator of a plant may come to recognize that certain sequences of events recur, so that when the first appears he can confidently predict that the others will follow and can initiate a routine series of controlling actions. When this happens, his load of decision-making will be reduced, since he no longer needs to deal with each event and action separately, but can treat the sequences as single wholes. The task will become in an important sense easier because it can be handled on a broader scale.

During training the communication between instructor and trainee is likely to change in two ways: first, as the trainee masters the use of various tools, the instructor's treatment can shift from detailed methods to the broader aspects of using tools in different types of job. Second, the trainee will come to recognize subtleties in the way the instructor frames his material, so that a great deal comes to be conveyed by implication instead of by overt statement. The first of these changes is clearly akin to the building-up of larger units of performance by the process operator. The analogy in the case of the second change is not so obvious, but nevertheless valid: the trainee comes to recognize the unspoken assumptions and implications of what the instructor says, i.e. to recognize the larger units of the instructor's thinking from which his specific statements have come.

On the management side, we may ask whether long-term experience enables the making of some decisions to be reduced to a routine so that the man responsible is free to give his attention to broader aspects of his work, or whether he has to deal with every incident in detail, using only the most general principles derived from past experience to guide him.

(d) *Feedback*

Variation in the readings of the instruments in a process plant will signal not only changes occurring spontaneously within the plant but also the effects of the operator's actions. There is thus a feedback loop which enables the operator to make his control adjustments accurately. Laboratory studies have shown that, if the feedback is to be maximally effective, it must occur quickly and give precise quantitative information about discrepancies between actions required and those taken. Feedback, as well as providing a corrective, seems to have an incentive effect: when it is absent or unclear the operator may become careless or may cease to be sufficiently 'vigilant', failing to notice signals for action when they occur.

There is an obvious analogy between the feedback of man–machine systems and the correction of the trainee's performance and answering of his questions by the instructor. Such exchanges are virtually essential if accuracy is to be attained quickly, and without them the trainee is likely to lose interest, because it will seem to make no difference how much or how little he exerts himself. As in the man–machine system, the feedback must, if it is to be maximally effective, occur quickly and be as precise as possible. Detailed information about the nature and extent of errors and measures necessary to correct them, if given as soon as they are made, promotes much more rapid learning than an overall comment, mark, or grade given after a whole training session.

The corresponding questions about industrial communications are concerned with what kind of feedback or knowledge of the results of his decisions a manager obtains. How clear and detailed is this knowledge? How far can he differentiate the results of his actions from those of actions by others? How long does he have to wait for feedback to arrive? Does he receive several feedbacks at different times? If so, do the indications of those which come quickly differ from those which are slower – for example, does action have to be taken which is immediately unpopular in order to bring long-term benefits?

(e) *Over- and under-loading*

The mental 'work-load' imposed by different plants, and under different conditions varies widely. If it is too great, actions will be hasty and ill-considered and, over a period of operation, performance may deteriorate owing to fatigue. If the load is too light, performance may again be poor and accompanied by feelings of boredom. The most boring conditions seem to occur when information arrives at a rate too slow to occupy the operator's whole attention, but spaced out in time in such a way that he cannot attend to anything else during idle periods. Between these fatiguing and boring conditions is an optimum rate of demand which permits the operator to fill his time while working at a comfortable speed.

Correspondingly, the instructor will be less than maximally effective if he teaches either too fast or too slowly. If he tries to cover too much ground the trainee will not have time to comprehend the information provided, and may become confused by his efforts to keep up. If the trainer goes too slowly, especially if he is wordy and repetitious, the trainee will become bored, since much of what is said will require him to pay attention, but will not convey any new data. It would be fair to define a bore in the present terminology as one who engages attention without conveying information.

Turning once again to management communications, we may ask what are the frequency and timing of requirements for decision? Even if the average frequency is within the capacity of the person concerned, are there occasional periods of over-loading; if so, how great is the over-load and how long does it last? Are there periods of under-load; if so, is the person concerned able to switch his attention to other activity?

It should be emphasized that just as we have dealt with a single operator of a process plant and a single trainee receiving instruction, so our questions regarding communications need to be asked of each individual in the chain. Not only do individuals differ, so that, for example, what may constitute an over-load for one will not do so for another, but also the whole essence of the approach is to look in detail at the various links in the chain and consider how failure of one will affect the performance of others. The important difference between this approach and some others commonly used is that it is not concerned solely or mainly with the *overall performance* of the system in terms of efficiency or reliability or capacity. Rather, it examines the detailed way in which the system functions and the *process* whereby the overall performance is attained. In this respect it presents a joint challenge to psychology and operational research: it is for the psychologist to point to leading individual characteristics and for the operational research worker to consider the stochastic processes of their interaction.

Further applications of this approach

The rest of this paper will outline some attempts to illustrate the possibilities of this approach in two further social problems well recognized in industry and in three of the traditional areas of social psychology. In none is it claimed to reach any radically new conclusions, but the treatment does take sides in some existing controversies, try to place various operative factors in perspective, and suggest lines for future research.

LEADERSHIP AND SIZE OF GROUP

Suggestions of how limitations of individual capacity for processing information would affect the optimum size of group and organization of leadership have already been outlined elsewhere.[1] A working group will generate for a leader an amount of information which depends upon the nature of the job being done, the conditions under which it is done, and the personal characteristics of individual members. Information from these sources will summate, and the size of group that one person can lead will depend on the total amount of information generated for him by all of them. This implies that if members of the group are all doing the same routine job under stable conditions and are of even temperament, one leader can deal satisfactorily with a large number. If, however, the work is not of a routine nature so that it requires constant detailed attention, or if various members are doing different jobs, or if working conditions are unpredictable or there are unstable personalities among the team, the maximum size of group that one man can lead effectively will be reduced.

Consideration of the capacities of both leader and group members together suggests possible reasons for relationships which have been claimed to exist between morale and size of working group. It has been urged that a small group is more 'democratic', while a large group tends to generate an 'authoritarian' leadership which is less acceptable. Evidence on which type of organization leads to better results and greater job-satisfaction is, however, conflicting. A possible reconciliation is provided by the results likely to follow if a group generates more information than a single leader can deal with. In the terms we have been using, a 'democratic' system means that there is a possibility of effective feedback from group members to leader, whereas an 'authoritarian' system means that members of the group are unable to influence the leader's decisions. One of the common reactions to over-load in laboratory tasks is that the subject sheds part of the load by ignoring some of the signals he should observe and omitting some of the actions he should take. Usually these are the less frequent ones, so that the subject concentrates on the main features of his task and ignores side-issues. In this way he often manages to put up a reasonable, although not, of course, wholly adequate performance. One way in which an over-loaded leader could readily 'shed

load' would be to rely on routines established in his group to keep it functioning while ignoring feedback from members. This would in effect mean that
leadership would become 'authoritarian'. It would doubtless have little
adverse effect for a time, so at first it would seem to be working well, but an
important means of recognizing needs for modification or change would
have been lost, so the group's performance would tend to become progressively
less effective.

On the other hand, the alternative procedures available when a group
becomes too large for one person to lead are not without difficulties of their
own. There seem to be two main possibilities:

(a) Members of the group can be required to refer particular problems to one
of a range of specialists added to the group as deputy leaders. The disadvantage of this system is that individual members may have to make
difficult decisions about which specialist to go to, and may find themselves making a tedious round from one specialist to another until the right
one to deal with their particular problem is found. They may well feel
that a reasonably benevolent authoritarianism is preferable.

(b) Alternatively, the group can be split into smaller sub-groups, each with a
leader who can call on specialists and is responsible in turn to a leader
higher in a hierarchy. In this way the members are still able to refer all their
problems to one person, and although the difficulty of getting the right
specialist service may merely be transferred to him, the morale and
effectiveness of the group as a whole is likely to be higher than if such
decisions have to be made by individual members. The superiority of
the second system is likely to increase with the frequency of problems
requiring decisions for individual members. Thus, with a routine operation under stable conditions, there may be little to choose between the
effectiveness of the two methods of organization, but if technical and
management functions are highly complex the second could be expected
to yield better results.

INCENTIVES AND STABILITY

Feedback would appear to be important in other facets of industrial organization than those already discussed, in particular in various problems of
motivation.

Willingness to undertake a course of action may be thought of as depending
upon some balance or ratio between the worth of what is likely to be achieved
and the cost in effort, unpleasantness, etc., of achieving it. Achievement must
obviously be perceived for this balance to be recognized, and this in turn
depends upon the feedback of adequate information about the effects of
actions that have been taken. As we have already noted, laboratory studies
have shown that such feedback must give accurate quantitative indications

and occur quickly if it is to be maximally effective. If these principles can be transferred to the field of industrial work, three points follow:

(*a*) The effectiveness of *incentive schemes* is likely to depend very largely upon the directness and immediacy with which bonus payments, etc., are related to extra effort. Any delay, even to the end of the week, is likely to reduce the subjective value of any benefits the scheme confers. This point has been urged for some time now, but is seldom if ever realized in practical schemes. There are, of course, difficulties in making bonus payments available quickly, and this gives some support to views that incentive-payment schemes are seldom worth the trouble of installing and maintaining.

(*b*) Elliott Jaques [2] makes the interesting suggestion that the *responsibility* required in a job can be measured in terms of the length of time that elapses between action being taken by the operator and checked by a supervisor. In the present terms 'responsibility', or this facet of it, is conceived as being a function of the extent to which feedback is delayed, and thus of the time for which the operator has to perform 'open-loop'. Common observation suggests that individuals vary in their ability to do this and that it is one of the ingredients of the personal quality of 'reliability' or 'integrity' – a 'reliable' man is one whose performance will not suffer in quality or vigilance if he is allowed to work with little or no supervision.

(*c*) An ability to perform well without knowledge of the results of actions implies that the subject has built up *internal standards* against which he can match his performance. Although as regards feedback from the job as a whole he is working 'open-loop', he does in fact almost inevitably obtain some feedback from his own performance: his internal standards, formed during the course of experience, enable him to infer the results of his actions to some extent from this restricted feedback. However, such internal standards will be reliable only if the relationship between action and result remains stable. Under unstable conditions, performance will show insufficient flexibility unless feedback over the whole job is available.

All these points apply essentially to individual performance, or to groups where conditions are similar for all the individual members. They will also apply in a more truly group sense where an organized team is engaged on co-ordinated work. It is commonly recognized that such groups need clear guidance about the overall aims of their job. It would seem that they also need clear feedback at each stage of their work indicating how far these aims are being attained. If a group is to work as a team with the actions of members fully co-ordinated there will have to be an elaborate mixture of feedback covering the job as a whole and each individual member's contribution. Plotting the many feedback lines within such a team, and relating them to efficiency and morale, would be a rewarding research exercise.

BEHAVIOUR OF CROWDS

One of the traditionally difficult problems of social psychology is to account for the uniformity of the behaviour of crowds. Accounts in terms such as 'social facilitation' are not truly explanatory, since they are essentially *ad hoc*, and thus little more than descriptive. The present terms, however, provide the attractive and simple hypothesis that, when the members of a crowd are all acting alike, the sight and sound of others provides each individual with a kind of augmented feedback of his own behaviour. This would be especially so if the crowd were, say, shouting slogans in unison. It has its analogue on a smaller scale in the feeling of 'unusual power' reported by crews of rowing eights when their boats are 'going well': when all are pulling precisely together each man gets the feeling that the whole result is due to his own effort. The seeming ratio of effect to effort is thus greatly enhanced, and it is reasonable to suppose that the satisfaction gained from the activity is correspondingly increased.

How far other aspects of crowd behaviour could be accounted for in the same terms is not at present clear, but seems to be worth serious study. For example, how far is the effect of size of crowd to be explained in terms of signal-to-noise ratio, in the sense that, as the crowd becomes larger, augmented feedback increases in strength, and individual differences of behaviour tending to blur the unison are smoothed out?

RACE RELATIONS

The terms we have been using are clearly insufficient to deal fully with the vexed problem of race relations, yet the general line of approach seems able to deal with some aspects of them.

There can be little doubt that economic fears of cheap labour by those with a lower standard of living often play a part in creating tension between races, and that in countries with, or contemplating, universal suffrage there may be fears of a political takeover by a section of the population which has a high birth rate. The latter fear would not, however, exist unless there was some other reason for disapproving of those concerned. This may, perhaps, arise in part from deep-seated, irrational antipathies akin to the almost universal dislike of loud, high-pitched noises. These seem unlikely, however, to be a major factor, since race antipathies are commonly less evident among young children – the antipathies concerned depend upon a developed experience.

This suggests that a more likely source of friction lies in differences between races in habits and methods of everyday living. When two races are living in close proximity any differences in behaviour between the two will increase the variety of data with which any one person will have to deal. In other words, the information load of everyday living will rise. With it will rise the likelihood of error or misunderstanding in dealing with the opposite race, and these may in turn spark off fear and hatred. The problem will be particularly acute if there are conflicts of meaning; if, for instance, a style of dress implies one set of personal characteristics among one race and another among the other, or if the same action may be interpreted differently by different races so that courses of action have to be chosen more carefully than would otherwise be necessary.

If this view is correct, two implications follow that do, in fact, seem to hold broadly true:

(*a*) Friction will arise most where substantial numbers of two races are settled in close proximity so that they are having to take account of one another at all times. Rare, isolated members of another race met only for limited periods are likely to excite curiosity and interest rather than hatred.

(*b*) Attempts to reduce the extra informational load by partial segregation are likely to be unsuccessful: they will cut the races off from the possibility of gaining a thorough understanding of each other, so that the uncertainty inherent in such contacts as remain will be increased. The easiest relationships seem likely to exist when the members of the two races understand each other's reactions thoroughly.

It would probably be wrong to conclude that, if economic and political fears could be allayed, sympathetic understanding could entirely eliminate antipathies between races. Any differences of reaction or behaviour between the sections of a multi-racial society mean a higher informational load than in a uni-racial society living under comparable conditions. Whether present racial differences of reaction and behaviour would disappear after a generation or so of thorough integration short of intermarriage it is hazardous to predict: it depends on the extent to which racial behaviour tendencies stem from differences of environment or experience, as opposed to inherent factors of mental and physical constitution.

SOCIAL NORMS AND CUSTOMS

We are on much surer ground with a systems approach to social norms and customs. These can be thought of as pre-formed decisions or routines regulating action in particular sets of circumstances. The learning of such norms and customs is an important process in the structuring of individual perception and behaviour. It is reasonable to suppose that they represent the codifying of insights and techniques for dealing with the environment which survive because of their value, if viewed in a broad enough perspective, for the individuals and groups concerned. Modifications take place in the course of time, presumably as a response to changing circumstances or fresh insights into methods of dealing with the problems of living. There is, however, usually a substantial time-lag before adjustments become effective, so that there is clearly the possibility of oscillation, with swings of over-adjustment and readjustment taking place over a period of years.

We have already noted that the building-up of routines in individuals as the result of experience makes for greater efficiency in stable conditions but greater rigidity in the face of change. The gradual accumulation of norms and customs in a society seems likely to have similar effects, making a mature society more stable, since fewer decisions of policy are open to question, but less capable of absorbing new ideas quickly than societies in which rules of conduct are less developed and entrenched.

Concluding note

A well-known sociologist once remarked in conversation, 'I have no use for psychologists: they always want precision.' It would be idle to suggest that the type of approach that has been outlined in this paper is capable of being applied to social situations with the same accuracy as has been possible in its use with systems consisting of man and machine. It seems fair to claim, however, that it paves the way for a more precise and quantitative treatment of many social processes in the future when methods of measuring decision processes are more advanced than they are at present.

The systems approach is in no sense a 'grand theory' of social behaviour, nor is it a foolproof, 'cook-book' method of obtaining significant data about social processes. What it does do is provide a closer link than has hitherto been possible between, on the one hand, certain facets of individual capacity and function and, on the other, social behaviour. In this way it bridges the gulf between those who regard social groups as nothing more than an agglomeration of individuals and those who seek to establish natural laws of social interaction which are entirely different from those which govern individual behaviour.

REFERENCES

1 A. T. Welford (1962)   2 E. Jaques (1956)

39 · Discussion and Commentary

TOM BURNS

Implicit in the title of this section was a manifesto. Both Rapoport and Welford tried in their very different papers to write it out in full. Howland's paper took the manifesto as read and agreed, and staked out a claim for the definition of a class of models which he called descriptive, and which others chose to regard as cybernetic. In the event, the manifesto was left unwritten; neither papers nor discussion resolved any of the controversies or solved any of the problems that made themselves evident. What it did was to demonstrate the effectiveness of the systems concept as an organizing theme.

General systems theory emerged afresh as a language in which people from a wide range of disciplines could not only cast their own ideas and comprehend those of others but also extend analytical competence within their own fields with ideas and instruments devised for very different purposes. But the utility of systems theory, or rather of systems theorizing, as a medium of communication and even of concept formation, has been clear for many years. What was, and is, still not clear is whether its usefulness resides in its providing a fashionable currency for interdisciplinary discussion, and useful mostly because fashionable, or whether it fills the role of what Kuhn[1] calls a 'paradigm' in science.

As language, systems theorizing provides a kind of scientific ideology and an up-to-date universe of discourse in which new ideas, new formulations, and new syntheses can be promulgated and understood. Sociologically, one could say that, in this role, systems concepts perform something of the function of a cultural enclave for an in-group of theoretical pacemakers, cutting down the rate of critical exchange with established ideas which might have proved destructive, and promoting a close intellectually symbiotic relationship to counteract the estrangements which increasing specialization brings.

As paradigm, systems theory would have to stand as a fundamental scientific achievement, 'which includes both theory and some exemplary applications to results of experiments and observation . . . and is an accepted

T 543

achievement in the sense that it is received by a group whose members no longer try to rival it or to create alternates for it'. Kuhn's paradigmatic virtues, that is, lie not in their theoretical consistency or novelty, or in the dramatic significance of discoveries, or in their wide acceptance, but in a special combination of all three.

The serviceability of the systems concepts at the first level, that of language, is amply demonstrated by the contrast this last section afforded with the first general section (Part II), in which the absence of this common language was matched by the apparent absence of common interests, and in which the general mood swung between polite disbelief and truculent challenge. In this section the conference discovered its common ground and began, belatedly but profitably, to explore it.

The issue of whether or not systems theory attains the status of paradigm had to be left unresolved, largely because of the variety of positions taken up at the outset by the authors of the three papers.

Both Ackoff (introducing Rapoport's paper) and Howland distinguished 'normative' (Howland) or 'technological' (Rapoport–Ackoff) models from those ('descriptive' or 'scientific' respectively) which are devised in an effort to represent and explain the behaviour of aggregates of natural objects, events, acts, and so forth in terms of the functional interaction between them and perhaps between them and other objects, events, acts, etc. Howland, having made this distinction, then went on to put his own 'adaptive model' in the second category – an odd decision which may have been defensible but went unchallenged and tended therefore to sow some confusion. Rapoport's paper, for its part, went on to establish a third category, described, like his previous two, as 'an approach to general systems theory' and contrasted with the 'technological' and 'natural science' approaches. This third approach turned out to be a statement of the heuristic rewards of establishing mathematical models which: (a) could reveal isomorphic patterns in real life, and (b) were susceptible to homological transformation, thereby achieving important second-order generalizations and reducing the pattern variations one had to deal with.

Welford's presentation, in rather stark contrast, amounted to a plea for a thoroughgoing reductionism along familiar lines. Sociology and social psychology had typically to do with collectivities and with the multivariant relationships and processes which occur in social systems. Such studies typically generated very large quantities of data. In looking for ways in which to reduce the complexities of such data, it seemed to him logical and proper to look for guidance in the models developed in connexion with individual psychology, and, beyond that, to neurophysiology. There was, he thought, a fruitful correspondence to be found between the model developed in the study of the acquisition of individual skills and the adaptive processes which groups and organizations went through when confronted with new tasks or new situations.

Marquis and others argued that there were a number of well-articulated concepts, such as role, status, expectation, convention, which were necessary elements in the consideration of interpersonal relationships which were simply not reducible to the analytical units appropriate to individual psychology or physiology. Later discussion did nothing to resolve this antithesis, although it was presented by Welford and his critics in two or three fresh guises.

Discussion concerning the applicability of systems theory both to operational problems and to the social sciences was necessarily interwoven with, and generated by, debate over the particulars of the introductory papers – especially Rapoport's and Howland's. I have suggested that the main upshot of the papers and discussions was the consensus which made itself felt in the use of systems concepts as common ground; and that the discussion itself showed that the value of systems theorizing lies in its currency as a language rather than in the limited homologies which may be struck from time to time between solutions to different kinds of empirical problem. But I must emphasize that this is my own interpretation of what was said. The debate was concerned with the limitations of the operational model formulated by Howland, and with two questions raised about Rapoport's paper: were not the virtues he claimed for his special class of system models simply those of mathematics; and were not the particular homologies he discussed of very limited value because they applied only to those special sections of real-life situations in which evolutionary, developmental, or dynamic change could be disregarded.

One of the main themes of the discussion was set by Emery. He began by referring to the papers contributed to the *Fifth General Systems Year Book* (1960)[2] by Lektorsky and Sadovsky, by Kel'zon, and by Kremyanskiy. All three papers argued in different ways that there was a fundamental distinction between the structural characteristics, and the mathematical formulations appropriate to them, of processes which were essentially time-independent and of those which were time-dependent. Rapoport's paper was devoted to time-independent models. In systems in which sequential process was determined by evolutionary development rather than by a logic internal to the system it was impossible to start, as Rapoport implicitly claimed, with an initial indifference to the content of phenomena. It was, of course, true that one had to become indifferent to phenomenal content at some stage, but not at the beginning when these phenomena were time-dependent. In this latter case, he suggested, one had to follow the path proposed by Somerhoff, who had built developmental considerations into his model from the outset. It was perfectly true that in social science, no less than in technology and in the natural sciences, one could often isolate from the general problem area a section, a part-problem, susceptible to solution by Rapoport-type models. This was the kind of procedure involved in component analysis. The diffusion process instanced by Rapoport was an excellent example of this.

Beer, ignoring the categorical differences between the models principally discussed by Howland, on the one hand, and Rapoport, on the other, launched into a criticism which he claimed linked both. Rapoport's promotion of mathematical isomorphism was not, he suggested, either novel or appropriate. Operational research models had to deal with the complexity of real life and had therefore to involve 'many-to-one reduction', whereas isomorphism connoted 'one-to-one correspondence'. The correct prescription for any operational research model must allow for reduction along homomorphic lines – i.e. for reducing information content through step-by-step transformations while preserving inter-element structure; the adequacy of the eventual model would be determined by the adequacy of the transformations. Turning to Howland's paper, he saw the cybernetic procedure described in it as based on an acceptance of the necessity of a one-to-one identity mapping, a reporting of all information. But whereas the two black boxes of Howland's model did make structural provision for this isomorphic relationship, the necessity of providing for requisite variety in these two matching components of the system made the demand for redundant channel capacity ('required by Shannon's 10th theorem') impossible to meet whenever the system was confronted with the variance for which Howland's submarines presumably had to be prepared. Thus, the attempt to build a system on servo-mechanical lines to measure and control (through the regulator's decisions) task performance in highly complex situations was bound, he thought, to fail; requiring, as it did, the inclusion of elements capable of sensing, communicating, and correlating a range of information of unknown dimensions, the system would go into uncontrollable oscillation.

Ackoff responded very briskly to Beer's criticism of Rapoport by suggesting that he, Beer, had not read the paper. Rapoport, he said, was not concerned with operational research models, and had gone to some trouble to make this clear. What he had been discussing was models of natural scientific systems. Second, he thought Beer had confused methodology and personality. A great deal of what was put forward as scientific method was in fact a projection of our own personality preferences or styles. This meant that there was bound to be a great diversity of approach, and personally he welcomed this. It was nonsense to claim for any approach, let alone model, that it was the only valid procedure; this held true even when it could be demonstrated that such an approach was productive. Third, he thought that Beer's remarks were shot through with naïve assumptions about the existence of an objective, immutable reality lying 'out there' to be used independently of our perception of it. Reality for us was a product of the perceptual model which we brought to it. The 'complex reality' mentioned by Beer was as much a model as was a set of mathematical symbols in the form of equations. All that could be argued was the replacement of one model by another, not the representation of reality in some ontologically prior sense.

The conference fortunately declined to enter into the epistemological debate thus offered it. Later discussion of Rapoport's paper was initiated by Easterfield, who welcomed Ackoff's appeal for tolerance of diversity but went on to suggest that what was required was not so much tolerance as a higher level of sophistication. The sophistication required was of the sort demanded by the acceptance of the Athanasian creed, of a principle of unity in diversity, and of diversity in unity. During the conference, and especially in this section, he had thought that, under the same heading, models were being propounded and discussed that had in fact three different kinds of property. The first type of model was one that contained a minimum of information consistent with its capacity to predict. Second, there was a class of models aimed at the widest possible scan or comprehensiveness, instanced in Howland's paper; the apparently relevant endeavour was to ensure the inclusion of all information that could conceivably be relevant. In this case one had to balance the assurance that comprehensiveness gave against the possibility that the model might be quite unmanipulable and of no predictive use. The third property, which had been mentioned only marginally, was that the model might frequently suggest hypotheses and concepts that would not otherwise have been suggested. The outstanding instance of this known to him (Easterfield) was Lewin's use of topology. Although, in his view, Lewin's understanding of topology was quite primitive, it had nevertheless been of exceptional value in generating a number of extremely valuable insights.

Stansfield and Howard resumed the criticism of Rapoport's contribution on the ground that what he had claimed and exemplified in his paper as the virtues of a third general systems approach were in fact no more than the properties generally attributed to mathematical formulations. The scientist's problem, said Stansfield, was to describe what he observed in nature, and the relationships between the phenomena, in terms that were as precise as possible while remaining understandable to others. A great deal of information in any situation had to be condensed through the use of symbols. The symbols used were words, as used in definitions, and mathematical symbols. He did not see that Rapoport's paper, at least in its earlier part, said anything more than that the most precise and economical way of describing nature was in terms of mathematical relations. If this was so it was something which was assumed at the outset of any scientific career; he personally had done this during his first year at his university, but had had to spend his next five years contending with the difficulties of definition. One began by thinking one knew what an atom was, and then spent several years in discovering how much experience and consensus had built up over several generations in such a way that other people knew what one was talking about, a way, moreover, that would take several volumes to spell out at length. The difficulty in social science was that this common experience and consensus did not exist. He himself was uneasy about the devotion of so much attention to the development of a mathematics for the social sciences, in the absence of a common understanding of what the mathematics could possibly stand for.

Howard asked why Rapoport had advanced his very interesting paper as an account of a third general systems approach, when what he had been illustrating was how pure mathematics was applicable to a variety of natural phenomena.

The point of Rapoport's paper, Ackoff suggested, was not so much to construct the model that would arrive at an interpretation of the Prisoner's Dilemma problem, but to find structural similarities between this situation and others, the hope being that when he saw other situations with the same structure, which were perhaps better understood, they would give him insight into the content of the experimental situation. He was, in short, looking for a principle by which argument by analogy could be made more rigorous. But was this, Howard asked, any more than what happened when the same mathematical procedures were used by econometricians and by engineers (in dealing with problems of heat transfer) and so on? If enlightenment did arise from the exploration of what was common to the structure of both these kinds of phenomenon it arose because of one's activities as a pure mathematician.

Gayer reinforced the doubt raised by Stansfield by pointing to the history of the natural sciences. It was true that mathematics served as the common language of the natural sciences, but progress in any individual science had been dependent on theoretical formulations related to the specific content of those sciences. Mathematics could hardly have served as the language of chemistry without the prior existence of such terms as element, atom, molecule, valency, atomic weight. These were verbal terms with a firm and virtually universal definition without which one would not know what the mathematics was about.

Scheff added a material point to the debate. Rapoport had noted, he said, that his exponential equation did not fit the actual diffusion of messages in human groups. When James Coleman had replicated this experiment he had introduced a simple representation of social stratification and had obtained a very good fit. This, he thought, emphasized the importance of a kind of dialectical movement between mathematical treatment and content in the development of social science models.

Ackoff suggested, finally, that Rapoport was concerned with treatment of natural phenomena at a level in which mathematics, so to speak, lay in the middle. On the one hand, he was concerned with experimental situations and, at the other end of his range, with the consideration of international problems on the widest possible scale. For Rapoport, the homologies and rigorous analogies of a kind that only mathematics could provide were essential.

The concluding point of Beer's opening criticisms repeated an observation he had made immediately following Howland's presentation of his paper. Howland had then replied that the system was in fact inclined to go into oscillation; all he felt they could do was to provide 'feed-forward' in the hope that the oscillations could be damped. (It was this response, repeated later, which prompts the doubt about the correctness of locating his 'adaptive model' in the descriptive rather than the normative (or, to use Rapoport's equivalent and rather more revealing term, 'technological') class; from his account and the critical discussion of his model, Howland seemed to have committed himself to the extrapolation of Ashby's concepts to the design of a super, or collective, brain.) Nevertheless, Howland contended that it was still feasible for the system to operate within the limits of control; improvements in sensing equipment might reduce noise and raise the information content of the data considerably 'if it were possible to see through the ocean in more effective fashion than one can, much of the confusion would be reduced'. Moreover, he said, it was beginning to look as though the number of variables actually involved was smaller than was first thought. When the adaptive model was applied – as it had been – to the organization of surgical operations the number of variables was much more prescribed and the system operated well within limits.

It was also apparent, from later contributions, that the model presented in the latter part of the paper was predictive rather than adaptive (and, consequently, 'technological' rather than 'normative') if the 'controller's' actions were regarded as outside the system, as Howland's remarks suggested. Was the actual operational objective, one speaker asked, 'to get the system running stably or even to get the system running'? Was it not rather to 'provide information to the controller on what he can expect to happen if he does something'?

Emery criticized the effectiveness of the model on other grounds as empirically inefficient and technically, or theoretically, inadequate. He saw the 'real-life situation' assumed for Howland's model as oversimplified in that as soon as an enemy was sighted, information must be – or should be assumed to be – imparted to the enemy; thereafter, one was dealing with at least two coupled systems. Developing this same point later, he instanced the success obtained by a minority of submarine commanders who acted on this assumption, as against the majority who operated as if the total amount of information obtainable through sensory equipment both about the outside environment and about events and action inside the organization of the submarine were all relevant (i.e. they operated on the same set of assumptions as Howland's system). To assume that enemy vessels and their escorts operated according to an organized body of procedural rules, and by means of a system of data-collection and information-processing similar to their own, enabled a submarine commander to emit information which would affect the decisions and course of action of enemy vessels in predictable ways, and thus increase the chances of destroying them. Baiting traps, that is to say, was a way of reducing the variance which a hunter was trained and organized to handle, or, in other words, of reducing the information which the feedback loop had to bother about. But the act of baiting a trap depended on assuming that the quarry was operating within a means–end system of his own and that one was involved in a plurality of interacting systems.

There were two corollaries to this thesis. First, Emery suggested, it was possible that individuals and groups reduced the amount of information and the variables they needed to treat as relevant by *presuming* a conflict situation. It enabled one to posit system characteristics in the social environment and, at the same time, to simplify the system within which one operated. The information received could be collapsed or filtered drastically, and reduced to easily manageable categories. This might, he thought, account for the distance between the theoretical treatment of duopolistic competition and empirical reality which presented many alternatives to a straight fight; in terms of individual psychology, too, the dichotomous, or, at times, oscillating relationships of love and hate might be seen as simply a means of reducing the amount of information relevant to social behaviour which, for some people all the time, and for everybody some of the time, was over-large.

This interesting inversion of Osgood's semantic–differential thesis had repercussions. A little earlier in his argument, Emery referred to Sommerhof's formulation for 'directive correlation' as a logical statement of his point. Strategic control was facilitated by the postulation of disturbance (sc. information) being itself the product of (interpreted as) organized behaviour in a coupled system; disturbance (Ashby's term) being replaced by Sommerhof's coenetic variable. Beer asked whether the coenetic variable – i.e. the organization strategically assumed to exist for the supply of information from the environment – was not, in this sense, the rules governing the practice of war. Emery suggested that the biggest advantage which one side could gain at the outset of a contest was to obtain possession of the other side's operating doctrine, and the curriculum of the training school for their commanders. This, Beer went on to suggest, was the system concept applicable to the conflict of police and criminals. The determination of the coenetic variable would enable one to reduce the variety of information; the side which could formulate the coenetic variable (i.e. the principles of organization within which opponents would operate in dealing with them) would be able to regulate its own action successfully – i.e. escape with the loot or capture the criminals. Emery agreed. The problem presented by bank-robberies could only, in principle, be solved by gaining information about the operating doctrine of the criminal group – by trying to infer their strategy and mode of operation. The course of action suggested was to change the routines and procedures of banks not with the immediate hope of capturing criminals but in such a way as to induce them to follow a certain predictable strategy; thus, they ought to be allowed initial successes the better to ensure subsequent capture. This was, McDonald said, a reasonable description of the model they were trying to fit to the police–criminal situation. Nevertheless, they were operating in an extremely dense situation. It was perfectly clear, for example, that a strategy devised to trap bank-robbers by manipulating variables in this way might itself result in more considerable reverses in other terms or in other sectors; how did one marry partial solutions so as to produce improvement as a whole? and how did one use this concept when the coenetic variable itself seemed to be hopelessly complex?

It was suggested that there was a connexion between this discussion and the difference between theoretical and practical solutions. Engineers often had to be satisfied with partial or sub-optimal solutions when full or optimal solutions were theoretically feasible; there was also the familiar experience of step-by-step progress in practical design towards the ideal solution which might have been postulated at the outset. These might be seen as cases in which strategic constraints had to be placed on information content so as to promote control. The move into models which included human behaviour components might oblige even greater simplification, and thus an acceptance of 'satisficing' as a theoretically justifiable goal. The relationship between 'theory' and 'practice' was a valuable object of study in itself.

Verbal gestures of incomprehension by Ackoff and Beer notwithstanding, the discussion then moved into a further development of the theme broached by Emery. If, one speaker suggested, both sides in a conflict operated according to systems which included an inferred, controlled, or even vaguely imputed operating system to the other side, was not conflict an admittedly very special case of co-operation? While the particular formulation was hardly acceptable, it was nevertheless argued that both sides could read the behaviour of the other side only because of the existence of some consensus about means and ends.

For a brief period, the discussion drew in all three papers. Stringer suggested that Welford had seemed to point to a distinction between a 'structural approach' and a pluralistic 'population approach', one characteristic of psychology and the other of sociology. Sociology and psychology were both considering a set of items (viz. persons) with attributes, some of which were related; so there was a set of relationships over a set of items. In the 'real world', then, relationships were not binary 'yes–no' relationships, as in logic, but were blurred and mixed, or partial. So in practice, social scientists made a drastic reduction in the range of actual situations by considering, for the most part, two extreme types of case; the fully connected set of relationships, in which case one could devise notions of system and structure, and, at the other extreme, the fully unconnected set, from which one derived statements about population of a statistical, including stochastic, nature. Each gave an admittedly partial picture of the situation as a whole; but, interestingly, the systems approach lent itself to a static analysis, whereas treatment of the items as a population led, through stochastics, to a rendering of dynamic aspects. It was not a question of one approach being right and the other wrong, but of each being complementary to the other. And since a great deal of attention had been paid in recent years to the development of structural models, was it not time to redress the balance and exploit the possibilities of the statistical approach? Welford said that he had argued not merely for the application of static models, such as that derived from a learning situation, to the analysis of organizational behaviour and collectivities, but the development of models that would be applicable to the evolution of situations over time; he cited as an example the development of interracial hostility from the point of initial contacts. In the social sciences one was confronted with situations in which a class of individuals were behaving in identical or similar ways for reasons which had nothing to do with their interrelationship or common membership of a collectivity, and with situations which moved from that class to one in which activity was related entirely to their membership of a closely integrated group. One had to develop models that would comprehend this range of complication and of relative structural coherence. For this to be done, it was essential *not* to try to build models specific to these several situations, but to refer content to formulations and models that were devised from content outside the social investigations with which one was actually concerned; this content, he urged, was to be found in the study of individual human performance and, ultimately, in the study of physiology.

Again, it was argued from the floor, this reductionist thesis ignored what Durkheim had called social facts: phenomena which were analytically independent of individuals. The example of submarine warfare again offered an instance. Durkheim's theory had accounted for the existence of social conventions, regulations, and norms by suggesting that in situations in which two people were operating in the same social field, action by one would become recognized by the other, and so matched, supplemented, or countered. The next logical stage was the *emergence of knowledge of intent by the other*; the next, of realization that this knowledge was mutual, and so on. What would develop was an infinite regression of mirrored awareness of intent and purpose – 'I know that you know that I know . . . etc., etc.' But this regression did not happen, and so destroy the possibility of action in a psychological impasse. Instead, this awareness became, as it were, imputed to the social system. In place of the impossible over-load of information-reading, analysis, and decision-making in single one-to-one relationships, there were conventions which people saw themselves and others as 'obeying'. It was in this sense that submarine warfare could be envisaged as taking place within a set of conventions. Conventions were simply not reducible to psychological elements. R. D. Laing had suggested that there were three discernible stages of mutual knowledge of intention: agreement on a rule; understanding that the rule was mutually accepted; and realization that mutual acceptance was based on a similar understanding. But the variety of possible states was very considerable, even at the elementary stages of mutual comprehension. The familiar process of institutionalization was a way out of the analytical paradox as it was out of the psychological impasse. Schelling, Laing said, had made essentially the same point in his discussion of the decision not to bomb the Yalu River bridges. The UN command had decided that they would not; the Chinese knew that they wouldn't; and the UN forces knew that they knew, and so on; in other words, the understanding had in a sense passed out of individual appreciation and lay in the collectivity comprising the combatant forces and interested governments. This was inherent in the social system, and not understandable at the level of physiology or even of psychology.

Another speaker suggested that the combat situation threw light on the whole debate over model-building. The development of strategies, counter-strategies, and counter-counter-strategies, etc., was an evolutionary, developmental, or dialectical process by which each side in turn was able to include a wider span of considerations (i.e. systematization of more and more of the notionally infinite totality of variance) in devising the operational system in which its strategy was articulated. After all, so long as conflict was waged according to a model simple and stable enough to be mutually understood and applied by both combatants, what obtained was a simple game structure with a predictable outcome; in conflict properly so called, each side endeavoured to build a model more 'complete' than the other side's, taking more account of 'reality', and thus continually reintroducing conflict into a situation which would otherwise have predictable outcomes. This, said Ackoff, was exactly the point of Rapoport's last book, in which he discussed possible solutions to this same process of conflict by model escalation; a solution which involved a qualitative change in the conceptualization of the problem. There were, Ackoff remarked, other possible solutions, most of them derived from social science, which represent what might be termed meta-conflict strategies.

REFERENCES

1 T. S. Kuhn (1962)

2 L. von Bertalanffy & A. Rapoport (1960)

Part VI
Models, Decisions, and Operational Research

SPONSOR: P. A. LONGTON

Present tools for describing an organizational structure – plan of research – overall results – individual and unit results – discussion and conclusions

40 · Introduction and Commentary

P. A. LONGTON

Introduction

The aim of this preface to the six papers that follow is to relate them to one another and to the field of operational research as a whole. This it proposes to do through suggesting a broad classification of the set of problems which fall under the rubric of operational research and by then relating the papers to this schema. In this way it is hoped that the preface may be of some interest in its own right. The penalty to be paid for this two-pronged and ambitious effort is that neither are any six papers selected on other criteria likely to provide a good basis for any general scheme of classification nor does a general framework necessarily provide the best setting for any six specific papers. In the event, however, the match between the general scheme of classification and the particular set of papers is surprisingly close.

It is perhaps an excellent thing that operational research as an activity remains difficult to demarcate completely from other related fields. It may then adopt a protean form and adapt to the changing circumstances in which it finds itself. It can, for example, take in successively key problems as they emerge from its changing environment and as the distinctive competences change of that particular body of individuals who label themselves operational research workers. Its effectiveness and viability are in this way enhanced.

At any particular stage of its evolution, however, it may be defined in terms of the connected set of problems with which, by common consent, it concerns itself, and in terms of its 'traditional' approach to these problems as typified in certain 'classic' studies which act as paradigms for its disciples.

Alternatively and more generally, however, it may be described in terms of certain key features that characterize it. Features which by themselves do not suffice to distinguish operational research from other disciplines, although as a unique combination they may do so. They serve as constant landmarks in an otherwise shifting landscape.

Models of and models for decisions

Two such features are the notions of 'model-building' and 'decision-making', to which a third, 'optimization', should perhaps be added to indicate its practical orientation. Almost invariably any description of operational research includes the building of models directed to the making of decisions. Furthermore, as well as being characteristic attributes, these two notions of 'model' and 'decision' can be employed to bring order to much of the work done in this field and in particular the papers in this section. To do this a distinction must first be drawn between models of decisions and models for decisions.

In the first case, models are built of the decision-making process itself so that, through a better understanding of the mechanism and the factors involved, improvements may be made in the machinery and process of making decisions.

In the second case, the model does not represent the decision process itself but the situation in the external world with regard to which a decision must be made. By manipulation of the model, the consequences of alternative decisions may be evaluated and the optimal selected.

The first may be said to look inwards, whereas the second looks outwards.

Of the six papers the first two, by Professor Menges and Dr Farquharson, fall into the category of 'models of decisions' and the four others into the category of 'models for decisions'.

Models of decisions

It is perhaps unfortunate that the process of choosing between alternative courses of action should have the label of decision-making so firmly attached to it in the field of operational research.

It seems premature to label it in this fashion, since it prejudges the question of whether the process of choice performed by a manager is more akin to that of deciding or of learning. Both are processes of choice, but, in a frivolous vein, they can be distinguished in that the first is studied by economists while the second is studied by psychologists. In their extreme variants of the closed decision model of the classical economist and the classical stimulus-response learning model of the psychologists they are two distinct phenomena. In a decision a rational choice of the optimal course of action is made instantaneously from the complete set of alternatives *a priori* with perfect information; while learning is a gradual process of modifying behaviour *a posteriori* with experience.

More recently, however, attention has shifted from the closed decision model to the open decision model incorporating both searching for a satisfactory rather than an optimal solution and the feedback of attainment discrepancy, thus converting the instantaneous into a gradual process. In learning theory the S–R theories have been challenged by the S–S theories where learning is visualized as the accumulation of expectancies and the development of a mental map of the problem situation. The two lines of thought possibly meet in the principle of situational logic, which proposes that the individual acts logically according to the situation as he perceives it, where this perception flows from some acquired cognitive framework. Choice, therefore, may be rational choice or may be conditioned response, but is probably best represented by a more complex model involving aspects of both deciding and learning. A general term such as discretion would therefore be more appropriate to refer to this topic of research.

As an example of research in this field the type of model discussed by Professor Menges falls under the heading of closed decision-making in the individual.

MODELS OF DECISIONS: COLLECTIVE

Discretion, however, often involves a group of individuals rather than a single individual. 'Group decision-making' becomes pervasive in modern society as the complexity of the situation outstrips the capacity of the single human brain. Such discretionary behaviour as purchasing and voting may be individual, but most of the decisions taken within organizations, for example, are the result of group activity in management committees, design teams, boards of directors, planning groups, and so on.

As important as, if not more important than, the consideration of individual decision-making is therefore that of making 'decisions' in groups. This involves the study of the processes and factors concerned in obtaining a consensus of agreement within a group with regard to a course of action to be pursued by that group. In the case of a management group, for example, the problem is that of obtaining most quickly and economically a consensus of agreement on the 'optimal' (or a feasible) programme given the differing backgrounds, specialities, and professions of the members of the team.

Studies of this kind must be rooted in empirical investigation, such as action research, into how such groups do in fact proceed, in order to isolate the particular and specific problems that arise, to determine the relative importance of the various factors that may be involved and thus abstract the set of operative variables, and lastly, since operational research is an applied study, to facilitate implementation of the conclusions. Nevertheless, logical and mathematical models have an important part to play in providing a logical framework for organizing the empirical findings, in demonstrating the effect of given conditions, and in suggesting hypotheses for subsequent validation. Science proceeds most effectively through the interplay of rational framework and empirical facts.

Dr Farquharson illustrates in his paper what can be done in demonstrating the consequences to certain procedures for a committee.

Models for decisions

However, it is probable that the majority of the models so far developed within the field of operational research represent models for decisions. The aim of these models has been to facilitate making some specific decision such as 'How much stock should we hold?' or 'How many cranes should we install?' These are not models of the decision-making process itself but rather models of the outside world with respect to which a decision must be made.

MODELS FOR DECISIONS: POPULATION

These models of the world for decision-making fall into two secondary categories depending on whether they are population- or system-oriented.

Population-oriented models are based on the assumption that the world may be considered as a collective population of individual items. Any pattern of behaviour abstracted from observations is therefore a cumulative picture of the behaviour of the items. The unit of analysis, however, is fundamentally the elementary item, and the techniques associated with this approach are normally statistical or stochastic.

Population-oriented models are typically exemplified in mathematical models of market behaviour, as for example the class of these models based on Markov processes. Here it is first assumed that the purchasing behaviour of the individual consumer may be adequately described in terms of a Markov process. It is further assumed that the behaviour of the market as a whole represents the cumulative sum of the behaviour patterns of the individual consumers and may correspondingly be described in terms of an aggregate Markov process. Although these are fairly drastic simplifications of the real situation, nevertheless a balance has always to be struck between validity and tractability, and in this case the rather idealized model furnishes some interesting and useful conclusions about the dynamics of consumer markets.

MODELS FOR DECISIONS: SYSTEM

System-oriented models, on the other hand, are based on the assumption that the world or object of study must be considered as a single whole of the form of a unitary system of multiple interrelated components, and that it cannot be validly treated as a collection of disparate items. Any pattern of behaviour abstracted is that of the system as a unit and not the simple sum of the behaviour patterns of its elements. The unit of analysis from this viewpoint can only be, therefore, the molar system, and the importance of the individual items lies only in the part they play in the system as a whole. Furthermore, in 'higher' or 'true' systems it is possible to distinguish a relatively stable configuration of relationships between the components of the system, which forms its structure. Each component may then be said to occupy a certain station in the structure and to play a certain role in the processes of the system. Moreover, it may be appropriate to relate each component to the system in terms of function or of its contribution to the fitness of the system as a whole. In this way is obtained the familiar structure-function framework for the analysis of systems.

The fundamental definition of a system as a complex of interrelated components parallels the specification of a graph in terms of a set of points together with some function which relates one point to another in ordered pairs. Graph theory, in its many variants and derived forms, provides, therefore, an especially appropriate battery of techniques for developing and manipulating system models. By means of it the essential features of a system can be represented precisely and concisely in graphical form, the concepts and terms of systems theory can be subjected to rational analysis and exact specification, comparison and generalization can be facilitated, and, lastly, the conclusion following from given premises can be logically derived.

As with all models, however, the relevance of the system graph to the real world depends on the appropriateness of the key variables and their relations that have been incorporated as premises into the model. The model will give out no more than has been put into it, and its quality depends on the proverbial 5 per cent inspiration and 95 per cent perspiration.

The use of graph theory in studying systems is illustrated in mathematical models for structural role theory. For example, three types of element may be defined:

(i) 'Task', meaning simply something that has to be done;
(ii) 'Person', indicating someone who has no characteristics and no relationships to other persons other than those of his office;
(iii) 'Position', defined as a location on an organization chart.

Graph theory may then be employed to describe how sets of these elements may be logically interrelated and what invariant structural properties such relationships possess.

MODELS FOR DECISIONS: PROBABILISTIC SYSTEMS

In fact, neither the population- nor the system-orientation gives a complete picture of the world, although each has its usefulness in representing particular facets of it. The operational research worker uses a population or a system 'filter' depending on the particular problem confronting him. The methodological situation would seem parallel to that in physics prior to the emergence of the quantum theory and the notion of wave packets, when certain phenomena were best explained in terms of the corpuscular theory of light, while others were more appropriately explained by a wave theory. Presumably the unifying notion for operational research lies in that of the probabilistic system, in the sense of a system specified in statistical terms.

In this case a system might be defined as a set of items that are interrelated in some given context to a significantly greater degree than they are related to other items outside that context. Such a system is based on a statistically defined structuring of a population. It follows, incidentally, that a boundary may then be hypothesized separating the system from its environment and dividing the domain as a whole into these two sectors.

The paper by R. N. Howard entitled 'Classifying a population into homogeneous groups' shows, among its other applications, how the structure of such a 'system' might be abstracted from the underlying 'population'.

MODELS FOR DECISIONS: SYSTEM AS A BLACK BOX

The notion of the system embedded in and interacting with its environment is a common framework for all branches of science. The simplest and most direct approach to the study of this situation is to concentrate on the responses of the system to the stimuli of different states of its environment – i.e. the outputs it produces in response to different inputs. A model is then constructed that behaves in a similar fashion. Here, the intervening variables between stimulus and response or between input and output are neglected, the system being treated as a black box whose internal workings are unknown, perhaps even irrelevant.

When, for example, a system such as a firm, a hospital, or an airport is considered as a unit, and a model is constructed of its output with respect to different inputs, without investigation of the internal mechanism determining the output to each specific input, then the system is being treated as a black box. The investigation is taking the system as a constant quantity or as a pre-set machine transforming some given input into some other output.

Dr Steinberg is essentially concerned in his paper with determining the basic relation between hospital size and the cost of medical care, and in so far as he concentrates on this relation he is treating the hospital as a black box. He then, however, starts to take it to bits when he breaks down the cost of care per patient into its various components, and this process is taken further by Professor Revans in the next paper.

MODELS FOR DECISIONS: SYSTEM AS A COMPLEX

Sometimes it is required to change the response that a system makes to different situations, that is to change the system 'transfer function'. It is then necessary to study the system itself or, in other words, to get inside the box and analyse the complex of intervening variables between stimulus and response, or input and output. Only when the system mechanism within, which produces the particular response to the given situation, is understood will it be possible to modify that mechanism to produce a 'better' response to the situation. The term 'better' here is, of course, with reference to some criterion or set of criteria for effectiveness or efficiency. With regard to hospitals it might be cost or it might be some other measure of performance, such as mean length of patient-stay; with regard to firms it might be cost per unit output; and with regard to airports punctuality of flight departure.

It is exactly this process of getting inside and unravelling the complex of intervening variables that Professor Revans illustrates so admirably in his contribution.

MODELS FOR DECISIONS: SYSTEM AS A STRUCTURE

Implicit in Professor Revans's paper is the notion that the hospital as a system has a certain structure. The references to superiors and subordinates implies ranking, and those to communication imply relationships. The system, with its complex of persons, roles, and relations, might be represented in graphical form with points representing roles and/or persons and with lines joining them representing their relationships. A complete and realistic graph would undoubtedly contain a myriad of lines and present a blurred and confusing picture. Certain arcs of the network, however, would be denser than others and some more significant than others. A certain relatively stable and significant pattern of relationships might therefore be abstracted from the full network, and this would form the structure of the system.

This notion of structure is itself an idealized model of one aspect of the real system which can be mapped on to any real situation in all its complexity, first, as an aid to interpretation and understanding and, second, as an initial step to improvement. In practice, however, it is not an easy concept to handle.

Professor Weinshall in his paper discusses some of the problems involved in constructing this structural model of an organizational system.

Conclusions

In the introduction to this preface it was suggested that any scientific activity could best be defined in terms of the connected set of problems with which it concerns itself and of the particular approach to these problems it 'traditionally' employs. It might be added that the type of solution resulting from this particular approach also tends to be characteristic.

Following from this, an attempt has been made to scan the field of operational research and to draw up a broad classification of its contents in terms of models of and for decisions, population- and system-oriented models, and systems as black boxes, complexes, and structures. The resulting array of problems closely resembles that of the applied social sciences. The distinguishing feature between operational research and the applied social sciences lies, therefore, rather in the approach or methodology and in the consequent type of model than in the subject matter of study.

Operational research from this viewpoint, then, represents a new approach to old problems complementary to the 'traditional' methods and frameworks of the social sciences themselves. The emergence of new theoretical constructs and conceptual frameworks throughout the history of science has often been associated with the members of one discipline crossing interdisciplinary boundaries to bring their methods to bear on some other discipline. That is what this preface and these papers are really all about.

BIBLIOGRAPHY

1 S. Beer (1959a)
2 S. Beer (1959b)
3 F. M. Bass, et al. (1961)
4 E. R. Hilgard (1956)

5 M. G. Kendall (1958)
6 T. S. Kuhn (1962)
7 O. A. Oeser & F. Harary (1964)
8 R. D. Luce & H. Raiffa (1958)

41 · The Suitability of the General Decision Model for Operational Applications in the Social Sciences

GÜNTER MENGES

Introduction

NORMATIVE, CONTEMPLATIVE–EXPLICATORY, AND OPERATIONAL SCIENCE

Scientific investigation of the subject-matter of the social sciences, viz. the behaviour of man in society, follows, as is well known, three different lines:

(a) *Normative:* according to Husserl,[1] it is the essence of normative science '. . . that it establishes general propositions in which certain attributes are stated in relation to a standard basic measure – e.g. an idea or a supreme goal – attributes the possession of which warrants that they are suited to the measure . . .'* In a wider sense, however, every science may be regarded as normative, provided that the 'standard basic measure' in the sense of Husserl is logic itself. In the social sciences the concept 'normative' is usually interpreted in a different and narrower manner, namely as an ethical 'standard basic measure'.

(b) *Contemplative–explicatory:* the non-normative and non-operational domain of the social sciences ranges from pure contemplation, i.e. mere viewing and description of (social) phenomena, to the orderly explanation of social reality, its causal interpretation ('explained' means shown to be the effect of a cause). In the past this domain was always the dominating one.

(c) *Operational:* the operational variant of the social sciences (though as old as the social sciences themselves) has become increasingly important in the past two or three decades. The characteristic of the operational variant, as it presents itself today and as it is about to dominate the social sciences, is the

---

* Since I may not have done too well in the attempt to translate Husserl's virtually untranslatable German into English, I quote the original passage as well: '. . . dass sie allgemeine Sätze begründet, in welchen mit Beziehung auf ein normierendes Grundmass – z.B. eine Idee oder einen obersten Zweck – bestimmte Merkmale angegeben werden, deren Besitz die Angemessenheit an das Mass verbürgt . . .'

substitution of the formerly central concepts of 'action' or 'behaviour' by the new central concept of 'decision'. The well-defined 'object' is being replaced by the operation and the algorithm, conceived to be of almost general validity (whereas explanation is concerned only with the case in hand).

'OPERARI SEQUITUR ESSE' (ET DESTINATUM)

I believe that the trend of the social sciences towards the operational variant does not render the other two types superfluous. It may be argued, however, that the operational form is nothing but the synthesis of the other two forms, i.e. normative science (as thesis) and contemplative–explicatory science (as antithesis) may come to be united in operational science (the synthesis), without being destroyed thereby as distinct and separate forms. This is supported by experience: master and control presuppose targets as well as knowledge of the causal structure of the relevant factors of the problem in hand. Whatever the particular problem under consideration, only the answers to the normative question – 'What should be?' – and to the contemplative–explicatory question about the *phenomena* and their *conditions* – 'What is, and why is it?' – permit the final answer to the operational question about the decision to be taken – 'How are we to operate?'

THE GENERAL DECISION MODEL

The decision-maker is at the centre of the modern decision–theoretical model, an idealized figure like the homo oeconomicus or the homo rationalis, taken to be equipped with unlimited logical faculties and with unlimited computational capacity. Thinking does not make him feel displeased.

A certain number of actions or ways of conduct are at his disposal:

$$A_1, A_2, \ldots, A_i, \ldots, A_m$$

(For the sake of simplicity we assume that the number of possibilities is finite.)

He is confronted with a certain number of states of Nature (which we also for simplicity's sake assume to be finite):

$$R_1, R_2, \ldots, R_j, \ldots R_n$$

If the decision-maker knows which R is the true one, then he has a decision problem under certainty.

If he does *not* know which R is the true one, then he faces a decision under uncertainty, a decision involving as a rule a conflict.

The uncertainty can appear in three different forms:

First: Nature is his opponent and wants to do him maximum harm;
Second: Nature does not behave like a rational opponent but is *unmeasurable*;
Third: Nature does not behave like a rational opponent but is *measurable*.

Several possible states of Nature can appear, we do not know which is the true one, *but* we do know a probability distribution *F* over the states of Nature, e.g.

$$F: P_1, P_2, \ldots P_j, \ldots P_n$$
$$R_1, R_2, \ldots R_j, \ldots R_n$$

In this important case we like to say that the decision-maker makes his decision under risk.

The states of Nature *per se* do not interest the decision-maker, they only concern him as transition stages in the determination of the consequences of the decision, the outcomes, to be denoted by E_{ij}. An outcome E_{ij} unambiguously corresponds to each possible combination of an action A_i and a state of nature R_j. The E_{ij} can be defined as ordinal or cardinal utility indices or as losses or profits evaluated in terms of money or other cardinal values. For the sake of simplicity, the E_{ij} will be regarded below as losses in terms of money.

In order that the decision-maker can make his choice between competing A_i's, it is necessary that there shall be a preference ordering among all the E_{ij}'s, at least the E_{ij} must obey a weak ordering, i.e. first, the decision-maker must be able to say which of any two outcomes he would prefer or that he is indifferent towards both of them, and, second, the decision-maker, if he does not prefer an outcome to a second outcome and does not prefer this second outcome to a third outcome, will not prefer the first outcome to the third outcome.

The decision-maker is now confronted with a set $\mathfrak{E}$ of outcomes which is at least weakly ordered; on the product of the set $\mathfrak{A}$ of actions and the set $\mathfrak{R}$ of states of nature, there is defined an outcome function E which maps this product into $\mathfrak{E}$:

$$E: \mathfrak{A} \times \mathfrak{R} \to \mathfrak{E}$$

Finally, the decision criterion *C* is a rule which, on the basis of the mapping *E*, selects one $A^\star$ out of the set $\mathfrak{A}$ of actions. This is the solution of the decision problem: $A^\star \in \mathfrak{A}$.

Applications of the general decision model

NORMATIVE APPLICATIONS

As can be seen, the general decision model allows for a normative interpretation, provided we focus our attention on the decision criterion *C*. The 'standard basic measure' in Husserl's sense could well be an ethical postulate (e.g. Select $A^\star \in \mathfrak{A}$ in such a manner that the outcome is just. However, what is just?). In many modern normative applications of the general decision model *rationality* is the 'standard basic measure'. The definition of rationality will necessarily differ according to whether it is formulated with respect to a decision problem under certainty or uncertainty about the states of Nature. In the first case, simple maximization or minimization of the outcome function *E* would seem to supply a straightforward definition. In the second case, the definition of rationality is more difficult. If uncertainty is measurable rationality can be effected by the application of the Bernoullian utility concept, unless the dominance principle (or even simple rules of ordering) can be taken to represent rationality. In the other two uncertainty cases, the definition of rationality is particularly difficult. Lately, it has become customary to consider the minimax criterion of J. Von Neumann and O. Morgenstern as an expression of rational behaviour both when Nature is looked at as a hostile opponent and when Nature is neutral but nevertheless unmeasurable. (See ref. 2 for a detailed discussion.)

CONTEMPLATIVE–EXPLICATORY APPLICATIONS

No doubt the general decision model has a very large number of potential applications when used as an explanatory device, both in the social sciences and in the natural sciences.[3]

It may even assist contemplation, for instance in psychological questions of the type: Do people decide rationally?

The possibilities of explicatory applications may be classified according to the manner in which uncertainty manifests itself; no normative implications are involved in this context. In the past, explicatory theory has dealt little with the various forms of uncertainty but rather with the two sets $\mathfrak{A}$ and $\mathfrak{R}$ as well as the outcome function E.

The most important among modern explicatory applications of the general decision model is game theory. Unlike classical marginal analysis, game theory drops the basic assumption that the conditions considered important in the case in hand can be controlled. The resulting consequences are well known.*

Since it would be outside the scope of this paper to investigate these consequences in full detail, suffice it to mention that game theory (as such) is nothing (and cannot be anything else) but a theory to *explain* economic reality; it is – directly – no operational technique. While it is true that (contrary to other explicatory applications of the general decision model) the criterion C is of central interest for game theory, this is only so for C as a hypothesis of behaviour or as a mathematical algorithm of solution, 'eidetically not interpretable'.[4]

OPERATIONAL APPLICATIONS

It has been shown that the general decision model has both normative as well as contemplative–explicatory uses. In what follows we shall deal exclusively with its operational application.

---

* 'In game theory the assumption characteristic of marginal analysis, i.e. the complete controllability of all factors is discarded. In this way the "mechanical" determination of "action" is abolished, and the new object, the *decision problem* preceding the "action", results. Thus, the essentially economic event is no longer seen to be the action as the moving force of economic variables but the *decision* as the *moving force* of *action*.' [4]

That the general decision model is suitable for normative applications in the social sciences is self-evident; its suitability for explicatory applications in the social sciences was convincingly demonstrated by Oskar Morgenstern.[5]

But what about the suitability of the general decision model for *operational applications* in the social sciences?

Some minor obstacles to application (and/or reductions)

TWO CASES: A PRIORI *versus* A POSTERIORI KNOWLEDGE OF THE PROBABILITY DISTRIBUTION

Nobody, I think, has seriously argued that there exist specific social science decisions under certainty. Of course, decision problems under certainty relevant for the social sciences may be conceived, for instance technological or psychological or biological ones, and decision procedures under certainty, such as linear programming, provide satisfactory solutions for these problems. But as soon as human behaviour comes into play as a specific component, predictability, and hence certainty, comes to an end. Thus, I feel justified in excluding the certainty case from the following considerations. Since decisions under complete uncertainty, on the other hand, cannot but be called irrational,[2] whether they follow the minimax criterion or not, we should be content to distinguish two cases:

(*a*) The decision-maker has *a priori* information about the probability distribution over the states of Nature.

(*b*) The decision-maker has no such *a priori* information, but he can acquire *a posteriori* knowledge from other sources. (If you do not share the opinion that the subject-matter warrants this restriction, please accept it as a reduction of the problem under discussion.)

TRANSFORMATIONS AND MODIFICATIONS

If the states of Nature are characterized by a statistically measurable variable X, then (*a posteriori*) information will be supplied by observing a sample

$$\mathfrak{x} = (x^{(1)}, x^{(2)}, \ldots x^{(s)}),$$

where the x's denote realizations of the random variable X.

The decision-maker is thus given the opportunity to approach his initial situation of total uncertainty to the case of partial uncertainty as he reduces the uncertainty by means of a sample $\mathfrak{x}$.

Accordingly, a rule enters in place of action A_i, a rule telling us which action A_i is selected by the sample $\mathfrak{x}$. This rule is the strategy or (in a narrower sense) the decision function d. For simplicity's sake we consider only so-called pure strategies, i.e. the choice of an action depends only on the sample drawn and not also on any kind of random mechanism that is extrinsic to the sample.

Whether information is supplied by means of samples or not, a further modification is worthy of regard: if X is a random variable which character-izes the states of Nature and has the possible values

$$x_1, x_2, \ldots, x_k$$

then its possible states are described by probability distributions

$$\mu_1, \mu_2, \ldots, \mu_g$$

These probability distributions now characterize the states of Nature directly.

Just as the states of Nature are replaced by their possible probability distributions, the outcomes are replaced by their expectations. If we define the outcomes as losses, then the mathematical expectation of the outcome is the risk r that arises if strategy d_Q is selected and μ_j is the true state of Nature:

$$r(\mu_j, d_Q) = \sum_{x} \mathfrak{L}(\mu_j, d_Q(x)) f(x \mid \mu_j)$$

where f is the probability for the sample x, if μ_j is the true state and $\mathfrak{L}(\mu_j, d_Q(x))$ is the risk that arises if the action is chosen according to $d_Q(x)$ and μ_j is the true state of Nature.*

Finally, if we place the possible probability distributions opposite the pos-sible strategies and if we ascribe the risk r to every possible combination of strategy and probability distribution, then we get the following *statistical decision matrix*:

$$
\begin{array}{c|c}
 & \mu_1 \ldots \mu_j \ldots \mu_g \\
\hline
d_1 & \\
\cdot & \\
\cdot & \\
\cdot & \\
d_Q & \text{—}r(\mu_j, d_Q)\text{—} = \{r(\mu_j, d_Q)\} \\
\cdot & \\
\cdot & \\
\cdot & \\
d_r &
\end{array}
$$

The decision criterion is applied to this matrix.

MATHEMATICAL REQUIREMENTS

The mathematical assumptions required for the existence of the solution of a decision problem imply but minor restrictions. In all practical applications of decision theory the sets of states and actions ($\mathfrak{R}$ and $\mathfrak{A}$) can be assumed to be finite. Likewise, the outcome functions (E) can be taken to be bounded

---

* If mixed strategies are admitted, then

$$r(\mu_j, d_Q) = \sum_{x} \sum_{i=1}^{m} p(A_i, d_Q \mid x) \mathfrak{L}(\mu_j, A_i) f(x \mid \mu_j)$$

where $p(A_i, d_Q \mid x)$ is the probability that the application of strategy d_Q, given the sample x, leads to the action A_i.

functions. In no case will this imply an important loss. At any rate, the assumptions mentioned guarantee a mathematical solution of the problem in hand. (See ref. 6 for the exact assumptions.)

PRE-DECISIONS

The general decision model possesses a high degree of idealization, even when it is exactly specified and when it has been modified in order to make it more adequate in relation to reality.

Given a number of models ready for operational application and given a certain empirical decision situation in the social sciences, the problem arises of fitting the specified model as closely as possible to the empirical situation, i.e. of selecting a model from the set of all models that corresponds as exactly as possible to the situation in hand. Let this adaptation be called *accommodation*. Accommodation requires a certain number of decisions, which I call *pre-decisions*, about which model is to be selected from the set of all models under consideration. These pre-decisions follow more or less objective criteria and are made in such a way that the model selected maps the decision complex presented for solution in an optimal fashion (optimal with respect to the solution of the decision problem).

The pre-decisions are mainly concerned with the set of actions, the set of states, the set of distributions over the set of states, the procurement of information (if any) and the set of information, the set of decision functions and the selection of the decision criterion considered adequate. I shall call these pieces the *constituents of a decision* problem. Given these constituents, the model is 'constituted', i.e. exactly specified. Once the model is 'constituted', all that is necessary in order to arrive at the final decision sought for is the application of the corresponding mathematical calculus.

Although this accommodation problem is familiar to all operational applications of the general decision model, it is not saying too much that its solution is particularly urgent and particularly difficult in social science applications. This is so because of the characteristics of the social sciences and, above all, because of the general interdependence of social phenomena.

I cannot discuss these points in full detail; I shall, however, outline a few of the important questions and try to answer them as far as possible.

(*a*) Is it possible and how is it possible to enumerate all actions and states of Nature *essential* (which are essential?) to the decision problem? In the field of social science this possibility is obviously conditional on a rather precise knowledge of the social environmental factors (the social milieu or the 'social peristases' [7]) of the specific decision problem, as well as of the way in which they interact, and also on the knowledge of the true aims of the decision-maker as well as of the initial position of the decision situation before the calculus is applied. As a rule, the decision-maker is unable to pay attention to other than (taken in pairs) disjointed actions and states, and furthermore, he will have to introduce *a priori* restrictions with respect to technical, financial, and social possibilities.

(b) Is the existence and measurability of a preference ordering among the outcomes guaranteed? Evidently the decision-maker must have an unlimited sensitivity for utility differences, because otherwise the indifference would no longer possess the required property of transitivity and hence would empirically lead *ad absurdum*.

(c) If information procurement is under consideration, should a sample be drawn or not? Which variable(s) should be measured? Should a sequential procedure be employed? Etc.*

(d) Which decision criterion should be applied? Frequently, this pre-decision will be the most difficult of all. (I have discussed this problem on several occasions.[2,10,11])

The main obstacle to application: 'The basic agnosticism'

FURTHER NOTATIONS

The difficulties listed so far are, it seems to me, relatively harmless and in principle superable – in contrast to the specifically statistical problems to which we now turn.

Let us return once more to the decision matrix $\{r(\mu_j, d_Q)\}$ and add some more notations and transformations. The characteristic element of the decision matrix is $r(\mu_j, d_Q)$. It denotes the risk, i.e. the expected loss which is suffered if the decision-maker selects strategy d_Q and if μ_j is the true state of Nature. $\mu_1, \mu_2, \ldots, \mu_g$ on their part are probability distributions of the state variable X. In general, this stochastic state variable X will have at its disposal not only a finite number of values $x_1, \ldots, x_k$ but also an arbitrary space of events Z. Over the space Ω of states of Nature probability distributions λ can be defined which fill a space $\bar{\Omega}$.

If we denote the sample by $\mathfrak{x}$, then $d(\mathfrak{x})$ is an action, namely the one prescribed by the strategy d provided the sample $\mathfrak{x}$ is observed. Then the risk function r, in the general case, is to be defined as

$$r(\mu, d) = \int_{\mathfrak{X}} \mathfrak{L}(\mu, d(\mathfrak{x})) \, d\tilde{\mu}$$

where $\tilde{\mu}$ is the probability distribution induced by μ in the sampling space $\mathfrak{X}$.

If a distribution $\tilde{\lambda}$ is given uniquely from the space $\bar{\Omega}$ of probability measures over Ω, then the risk with respect to $\tilde{\lambda}$ is given by

$$r^\star(\tilde{\lambda}, d) = \int_{\Omega} r(\mu, d), \, d\tilde{\lambda}$$

and the decision problem can be solved by Bayes's theorem. The solution is the choice of that strategy for which the risk – with respect to $\tilde{\lambda}$ – is a minimum.

* Some answers are given in refs. 8 and 9.

THE *a priori* APPROACH

But how do we determine $\bar{\lambda}$? This question is old and has a long tradition. In the analogous terminology of the Continental school of mathematical statistics, let $\bar{\lambda}$ be called the distribution law over the states of Nature. How, then, does one get to know this distribution law? One possibility, which was taken into consideration by Bayes and before him by Bernoulli, is *a priori*: you know in advance, prior to observation, that $\bar{\lambda}$ is a specific distribution, for example, a binomial distribution with a known Bernoulli parameter or a normal distribution with a known mean and variance. Such *a priori* knowledge will be rare even in physics and other disciplines adjacent to physics in degree of exactitude. In any case, wherever such *a priori* knowledge exists it will be used, Bayes's solution will be arrived at, and the decision problem will have been solved in a brilliant way. In the social sciences, however, such *a priori* knowledge is non-existent. As a rule, the *a priori* way is not open.

THE *a posteriori* APPROACH

If one does not possess *a priori* knowledge, one will take refuge in procuring relevant information, thus taking the *a posteriori* way. Experiments are carried out, and even if these experiments do not permit one to draw unique inferences about the distribution law, one will nevertheless gain knowledge about the class of probability measures, for which, given certain circumstances, Bayes's solution can be computed, too. Wherever reliable *a priori* knowledge is not available but where exacting experiments can be made, the *a posteriori* way will be tried.

There are, however, numerous situations in the social sciences where the *a priori* approach as well as the *a posteriori* approach are blocked. These situations occur where experiments cannot be made or where the conditions under which the experiments are made cannot be controlled.

It was this unfavourable situation, characteristic for the social sciences, which Tschuprow [12] had in mind when he coined the phrase 'basic agnosticism': *ignoramus, ignorabimus*. The natural sciences, on the other hand, seem to be in a better position. Then and now they may have *a priori* knowledge about the distribution law; if not, they will be able to procure reliable *a posteriori* knowledge by using experimental observations. With respect to this basic difficulty, the suitability of the general decision model for operational applications in the natural sciences must be rated high.

SUBJECTIVE PROBABILITIES

The operational application of the general decision model in the social sciences would seem to require different solutions.

Some modern decision theorists will not be willing to accept the epistemological pessimism expressed above. They substitute lacking *a priori* knowledge by subjective or personal probabilities. 'Subjective probability refers to the opinion of a person as reflected by his real or potential behaviour,' [13] Savage writes.

Some arguments of the probability subjectivists are worth considering. You can compute subjective probabilities as well as objective ones. There is a certain rational logic in subjective probability reasoning: if the decision-maker evaluates the probabilities for the occurrence of the various states of Nature wrongly, then this is his own fault and he will have to take the consequences. Therefore he will try hard to produce as 'true' an impression of the probabilities as possible. Even if he does not succeed, he can still act subjectively, rationally, and without contradicting himself.

Nevertheless, I should like to question the argument that subjective probabilities are scientifically applicable. I believe it can be shown that the subjective–psychological root of the probability concept is pre-scientific and precarious, since probabilities cannot be possible *Erlebnisinhalte*. There exists no scientifically demonstrable relation between the assertion: I feel or think or believe that an occurrence has a certain probability, and the actual probability for this occurrence.

NORMATIVE JUDGEMENT INSTEAD OF KNOWLEDGE?

If one rejects the solution of the probability subjectivists as a fallacy, then one again faces the dilemma which we have called 'basic agnosticism', following Tschuprow.

But perhaps our *a priori* knowledge is not as insufficient as to prevent us from defining a more or less narrow class $\bar{\Omega}$ of probability measures which contains the true distribution law as an element. Or we can, using the *a posteriori* knowledge given by the sample, define a class of probability measures which is still narrow enough to have a demonstrable reference to Nature – though not narrow enough to make Bayes's solution possible. Perhaps you are inclined to follow Wald and a number of modern decision theorists and to abandon the latter condition, i.e. perhaps you find it reasonable to solve a decision problem even if $\bar{\Omega}$ forms the class of all possible distribution functions.

In either case the problem arises to select *one* probability distribution from the set of those that are admitted and to go ahead with Bayes's solution. Wald has solved this third problem by means of the criterion of minimaximal risk. For each strategy, that distribution is to be chosen which is the most *unfavourable* in regard to the risk to be expected. Then, according to the minimax rule, we are to decide for *that* strategy which, considering its most *unfavourable* distribution, turns out to be the best.

In this way the problem of the 'basic agnosticism' leads to the question of rationality: is the minimax criterion an expression of rational behaviour? If this question is answered in the affirmative, then (by means of a normative judgement) the operational applicability of the decision model is saved for the case, characteristic for the social sciences, that exact knowledge of the distribution law over the states of Nature is impossible. In doing so we commit a logical flaw: in place of knowledge required for the operational application a normative judgement is used. Instead of the question 'What is, and why is it?' the question 'What should be?', which was not asked, is answered.

A further difficulty: instability

PROCESS INTERVAL AND STABILITY INTERVAL

A final difficulty must be discussed: the stability of the decision situation. We could neglect this question, if the sequence 'formulation of the decision problem – pre-decisions – procurement of information – computation of the optimal strategy – concrete action – coinciding of the action with a state of Nature – appearance of the outcome' took place with such speed that no change would occur within the decision situation during the process. This is precisely what theory assumes. Actually this assumption is questionable.

In social reality the sequence will take a certain amount of time, say, a time-interval of length G. If the decision situation is stable in the interval of length T, and if the process interval G is included by the stability interval T, then the empirical situation is obviously equivalent to the situation theory assumes.

As the process interval becomes longer and/or the stability interval becomes shorter, the empirical situation departs from the assumption of the model. We shall not inquire further into the length of the process interval; as a rule it is determined by technological factors, among others by the computing time necessary to arrive at a solution of the decision problem. The stability interval, on the other hand, implies a number of specific problems. Since I have dealt with these problems in a contribution to the *Festschrift* for Hans Kellerer,[14] I shall limit my discussion here to a brief sketch of what is treated more extensively there.

LIMITATIONS TO THE STABILITY INTERVAL

Among the factors limiting the stability interval are:

1 Changes of the decision-maker's targets as far as these changes are reflected in the set of admissible actions A_i, or
2 Changes of the set of states of Nature that are considered essential, or
3 Changes in the evaluation of the outcomes E_{ij}. This limitation is likely to occur even when we are dealing with consequences of decisions which can be measured cardinally and which can be expressed in terms of money units, if the prices of the goods that make up the consequences change irregularly in time. Changes of an ordinal preference field over the set E of outcomes can occur easily, if the decision-maker is not completely certain and consistent in evaluating the possible outcomes. Such stability in his evaluations will probably be the harder for him, the smaller are the utility differences between the various outcomes. In particular, the empirical

U

transitivity of indifference relations will hardly be preserved for a longer period of time.

The stability interval is furthermore limited

4 By changes of the standard of behaviour as it is reflected in the choice of a certain decision criterion, for example, on account of structural changes in society, changes of market conditions, price changes, political changes, or

5 By changes either of the *a priori* distribution or of the class $\bar{\Omega}$ of probability distributions established *a priori* or *a posteriori*.

The corresponding five stability conditions are also an obstacle to application, in the natural sciences as well as in the social sciences, but particularly in the latter, where the free will of human individuals rather than natural determinism is dominant.

Conclusions

IMMEDIATE CONCLUSIONS

The general decision model

Meets the requirements of explicatory applications in the social sciences well (as has been shown by O. Morgenstern),

Meets the requirements of operational applications in the natural sciences well (as is intuitively plausible);

on the other hand, it

Meets the requirements for operational applications in the social sciences poorly.

This is the conclusion to be drawn since it has been shown:

(*a*) That the accommodation between the empirical decision situation and the decision model specified can reach a low degree only; this is mainly because of the following difficulties –

(*a*1) Complete enumeration of all 'essential' actions,

(*a*2) Complete enumeration of the 'essential' states of nature,

(*a*3) Existence and measurability of a preference ordering among the outcomes;

(*b*) That certain knowledge of the distribution law over the states of Nature is practically never achieved –

(*b*1) Neither objectively *a priori*,

(*b*2) Nor *a posteriori* (since the social scientist's data are passive),

(*b*3) At most subjectively *a priori* (if one is willing to leave firm ground and to tread the treacherous sands of probability subjectivism),

(*b*4) Or by Wald's trick of substituting a normative judgement for missing *a priori* knowledge;

(*c*) That in social science applications the stability interval is, as a rule, likely to be considerably shorter than the process interval, chiefly because –

(*c*1) The decision-maker's targets may change,

(*c*2) The space of states may change,

(*c*3) The preference field over the outcomes may change (very quickly, for example on account of price variations),

(*c*4) The decision-maker's standard of behaviour may change (e.g. because of structural changes in society),

(*c*5) And in particular because the class $\bar{\Omega}$ of probability distributions may be highly unstable.

The chief reasons for this negative result would seem to lie in the following simple properties (corresponding to the foregoing list):

(*a*) Social phenomena are interdependent.

(*b*) The possibilities for controlled experiments in the field of the social sciences are rather limited.

(*c*) Social phenomena are not (or at least only to a minor degree) determined by natural law.

FINAL CONSIDERATIONS

I should like to emphasize that I do not consider the high level of mathematical sophistication of decision theory responsible for the negative result we have encountered. Mathematics is a tool of science which is ontologically totally neutral. Of course, it may well be the case that the mathematical apparatus which modern decision theory uses is not the one best suited to the purpose. It may be that 'decision mathematics' appropriate to the social sciences have not yet been developed.

The negative outcome we have arrived at will not surprise the perceptive social scientist who knows the ends and means of his science. We shall have to go a long way before social processes can be mastered and controlled, before a satisfactory answer to the question 'How are we to operate?' can be found.

REFERENCES

1 E. Husserl (1928), p. 26
2 G. Menges (1963c)
3 G. Menges (1958)
4 H. Ache (1962), pp. 82–3
5 O. Morgenstern (1963), pp. 111–28
6 A. Wald (1950)
7 G. Menges (1959), p. 74

8 G. Menges & M. Behara (1963b)
9 G. Menges & M. Behara (1962)
10 G. Menges & M. Behara (1963a)
11 G. Menges (1963b), pp. 585–94
12 A. Tschuprow (1924)
13 L. J. Savage *et al.* (1962), p. 11
14 G. Menges (1963a), pp. 84–94

42 · The Application of Game Theory to Committee Procedure

ROBIN FARQUHARSON

Let us consider a committee charged with the welfare of a club. It has been proposed that a clubhouse be built, and there is a further proposal that it be equipped with a bar. Opinion is divided on both proposals. Altogether there are three possible decisions which may emerge:

A. No clubhouse;
B. A clubhouse without a bar;
C. A clubhouse with a bar.

We shall suppose that the committee is composed of three members (or three blocs), each having one of these three outcomes as first preference. No outcome, therefore, is the choice of an absolute majority. Each member has a definite preference between the two outcomes that are not his first choice.

The first procedure is that described by Sir Reginald Palgrave [1] as 'the popular mode of procedure on amendments'. It will be referred to as the *Amendment Procedure*.

Under this procedure, a motion would be moved: 'That a clubhouse be built.' To this motion, an amendment is moved: 'That the words "equipped with a bar" be added to the motion.'

The voting proceeds as follows. The amendment is put to the vote first. If it is passed, the substantive motion 'That a clubhouse be built, equipped with a bar' is put for acceptance or rejection. But if the amendment is defeated, the original motion 'That a clubhouse be built' is put to the vote without change.

The second procedure is also frequently used. It consists in a first vote on the main issue (the motion, or the 'question of principle'); only if this is passed is a vote taken on the minor issue (the amendment, or the details). Let us call this the *Successive Procedure*.

Under the Successive Procedure, then, the committee would vote first on the proposal 'That a clubhouse be built'. If this motion were rejected there would be no further vote. But if it were passed there would be put the further motion 'That the clubhouse be equipped with a bar'.

The main difference between the two is that in the Amendment Procedure the question of a bar is voted on before the main question, but in the Successive Procedure it is left until afterwards. The two questions are necessarily linked, since there is no possibility of a bar without a clubhouse.

It has been assumed that there are three members, each with a definite scale of preferences: and that there is no outcome which has an absolute majority of choices. Under these conditions there are only eight distinct ways in which the preference-scales of the members can be distributed. If one member most strongly desires A, then his second preference may be for B, or for C; the scales compatible with the assumptions are thus the eight which may be made up by drawing one each from the pairs

$$\{ABC, ACB\}; \{BAC, BCA\}; \{CAB, CBA\}$$

Let us suppose, first of all, that every member of the committee votes 'sincerely'. That is to say, he votes strictly in accordance with his preferences. If he prefers the amendment to the motion, he votes accordingly. If his first choice is a clubhouse without a bar, then under the Successive Procedure he votes for the clubhouse, but against the bar. He makes no use of 'voting strategy'.

With such sincere voting, the decision of the committee is determined uniquely by the preference-scales of the members and by the procedure which they use. There are eight possible combinations of preference-scales; in four of these eight the decision reached under the Amendment Procedure will be different from that reached under the Successive Procedure.

In other words, if each preference-scale is equally likely, then there is an even chance that the decision which the committee reaches will be decisively affected by its choice of procedure.

Consider one of these cases. The member's preferences can be summarized as ABC, BAC, CAB. More picturesquely, they may be called:

The Miser (ABC). He is opposed to spending money on any part of the project; his first choice is no clubhouse at all, his second choice a clubhouse without a bar.

The Prohibitionist (BAC). He is strongly in favour of a temperance clubhouse; but if a bar were installed he would resign from the club.

The Alcoholic (CAB). He is interested only in the bar; and feels that a clubhouse without one would be worse than none at all.

Examine what happens if this committee votes sincerely. Under the Amendment Procedure the Prohibitionist moves 'That a clubhouse be built'. The Alcoholic moves an amendment to add the words 'equipped with a bar'.

On the first vote the amendment is at issue. The Miser is necessarily against it, and so is the Prohibitionist. Only the Alcoholic supports it, and it is defeated by two votes to one.

The motion is then put unamended, in its original form 'That a clubhouse be built'. The Prohibitionist is for it, but both the Miser and the Alcoholic are against it. It is defeated by two votes to one, and no clubhouse is built.

Compare the effect of the Successive Procedure. The Prohibitionist moves his motion as before – the Alcoholic's proposal, however, is not accepted as an amendment; he is told that it may not be put until the main question, that of a clubhouse, has been decided.

The first vote, therefore, is taken on the building of a clubhouse, without considering the question of a bar. The Prohibitionist is for it – it is his motion. The Alcoholic is necessarily for it, since otherwise his own proposal falls away. Only the Miser is against it. So it is passed by two votes to one.

The Alcoholic's addendum is now put 'That the clubhouse be equipped with a bar'. He is for it; but both the Miser and the Prohibitionist oppose him. So the voting results in a barless clubhouse being built.

It is evident, in these circumstances, that the fate of the Prohibitionist's motion has depended entirely on the choice of procedure. And there are three other possible combinations of preference-scales (making four out of the eight) for which the same would be true.

All this depends on the assumption of sincere voting. If the Alcoholic had known that his addendum would be defeated he would have been able to obtain at least his second preference by voting against the Prohibitionist's motion in the first instance. Then he would not have seen his own vote help to pass a motion which resulted in a temperance clubhouse, the very last thing he wanted.

Such behaviour can be called 'strategic voting', as distinct from 'sincere voting'. The extent to which strategic voting can be advantageous varies, similarly, according to the procedure. In this case recourse to strategic voting by the Alcoholic gives him a better result, provided the other two vote sincerely.

This is not true, however, for the Amendment Procedure in the same circumstances. Sincere voting gives each of the three voters as good a result as he could have obtained by strategem.

The Miser, in fact, gets his first preference, so he could have no motive to act differently. By changing his vote the Alcoholic could have changed the result to 'clubhouse without bar', but he would not wish to. Likewise, the only effect which the Prohibitionist could have produced by a change in his vote (e.g. to supporting the amendment and then the motion) would have been to secure the triumph of the Alcoholic's cause.

In such a case – where voting takes a course such that each voter can say, 'Even if I had known exactly what the others planned to do, I would not have voted differently' – we can say that there exists a 'stable situation', or an individual equilibrium. (Such an equilibrium has exactly the character of an 'equilibrium point' in the theory of Games of Strategy.[2,3])

It is always possible to say, for a given procedure and set of preferences of the voters, whether or not sincere voting constitutes an individual equilibrium. Here it does so under the Amendment Procedure. But under the Successive Procedure it does not, since the Alcoholic can say, 'If I had known the bar would be defeated, I would have voted against the whole thing in the beginning.'

To say that a situation is such an equilibrium, however, is only to say that no voter could have improved his position by voting differently *on the assumption that the others' votes did not change*. If the others' votes were not 'held constant', then a departure from sincere voting by one, for whatever reason, might make a similar departure advantageous for another. And, in general, a voter does not know with any certainty what the other voters' preferences are; so that he may be unable to determine whether or not an equilibrium in fact exists.

It is more to the point to ask: under a given procedure, is it *ever* advantageous for a certain voter to depart from sincere voting? Consider the situation of each of the voters. Not knowing what the others may do, can one decide definitely what course of action is best?

The Miser can do so under the Successive Procedure. No clubhouse (A) is his first choice, and voting accordingly can never be disadvantageous; since even if he is outvoted, he has not prejudiced his chance of at least defeating the bar proposal on the second vote. Sincere voting is his best course of action in all eventualities.

But under the Amendment Procedure his choice is much more difficult. For there exist some possible circumstances in which sincere voting, and sincere voting only, gives the best result; but there exist others in which it is definitely inadvisable.

Suppose that, instead of the Alcoholic, the third member of the committee had been an ordinary clubman. Though strongly in favour of a bar, such a man would not be so dedicated a drinker as to disdain a clubhouse without one. 'No clubhouse' would come last on his scale, with a barless clubhouse second – his scale would be *CBA*.

In these circumstances the Miser would be ill advised to vote sincerely under the Amendment Procedure. If he did so, and opposed the amendment to add 'equipped with a bar' to the motion, then the amendment would be defeated. On the second vote the original motion 'That a clubhouse be built' would be carried by the support of the Prohibitionist and the Clubman, and a clubhouse would have to be paid for. Whereas if he had insincerely supported the amendment the words 'equipped with a bar' would indeed have been added to the motion on the first vote, but on the second vote would have ensured that the Prohibitionist's support would be withdrawn, so that the substantive motion would have been rejected altogether (by a majority composed of the Prohibitionist and the Miser). Thus, for the Miser, voting for his *bête noire* would, paradoxically, ensure his first preference, no clubhouse.

Yet such tactics, effective in this instance, are clearly unsafe. They might easily have resulted, with a different distribution of preferences, not in no clubhouse, his first preference, but rather in a clubhouse with bar – and in circumstances where sincere voting would have given him at least his second preference, a clubhouse without a bar.

To vote effectively, in fact, the Miser must know how the other members of the committee intend to vote. We may therefore say that the Amendment Procedure is not 'straightforward' for him. It is straightforward both for the Prohibitionist and for the Alcoholic (though it would not be so for the Clubman).

The Successive Procedure, however, is not straightforward either for the Prohibitionist or for the Alcoholic; each of them has two plausible courses of action open to him and, whichever he chooses, he may later regret it.

In general, no procedure can be constructed which will be straightforward for all scales of preference. But in cases where the scales obey certain conditions of compatibility [4] an appropriate procedure can easily be determined. We can show that this is possible here – a procedure exists which gives each member of the committee a course of action which can be called 'best' without qualification.

Let the committee proceed as follows: a motion is moved

'That a clubhouse be built, equipped with a bar.'

If it is passed, the decision is final, and no further vote is taken. If it is defeated, the committee proceeds to accept or reject the motion

'That a clubhouse be built without a bar.'

Under this procedure, sincere voting by the Miser, the Prohibitionist, and the Alcoholic will lead to the defeat of both motions. If the Alcoholic were replaced by the Clubman the first motion would be defeated and the second passed, so that a barless clubhouse would be built.

But in both cases, and indeed with any committee of three selected from these four, it would be true that *no member of the group has any incentive to depart from sincere voting*, whether or not he knows the preferences of the others, and whether or not they vote sincerely.

The 'model' of a committee which has been presented here is a very much simplified one. No mention has been made of the strategic difference between secret ballot and open voting; [5] of the effects of more complex preferences; [6] or of the possibility of coalitions between voters. [7,8] Each of these aspects permits of rigorous treatment; and I have found it possible, by applying known general results in the Theory of Games, [3,9] to reach conclusions about them which could not easily have been attained directly.

Yet the results, when they are reached, are not necessarily esoteric. Indeed, it appears always to be possible to give them a clear intuitive interpretation, and to explain the concepts which they employ in terms not unduly remote from the ordinary language of politics.

ACKNOWLEDGEMENT

This paper is based on work done at Nuffield College, Oxford, between 1953 and 1955, under the supervision of Mr Norman Chester and Professor D. G. Champernowne. I am also grateful to Professor R. B. Braithwaite and Dr Martin Shubik for their interest.

REFERENCES

1 Sir R. Palgrave (1877)
2 J. Von Neuman & O. Morgenstern (1944)
3 J. Nash (1950)
4 D. Black (1958)
5 R. Farquharson (1956a)
6 R. Farquharson (1956b)
7 R. Farquharson (1955)
8 M. Dummett & R. Farquharson (1961)
9 H. Kuhn (1953)

43 · Classifying a Population into Homogeneous Groups

R. N. HOWARD

Description of the problem

The problem is that of partitioning the elements of a multivariate population into homogeneous sets. A simple example of the problem is: we have a population of people and, knowing their incomes, we want to say of each person whether he is 'rich' or 'poor' relative to the others. What is the best dividing line? The example differs in complexity from the general problem in two ways. We must classify with respect to many variables, not just one (income). And we must form many sets, not just two ('rich' and 'poor').

The example of the general problem which brought me to work on it is the following. The Centre for Urban Studies is subjecting the 1961 Census tabulations for Greater London to a statistical analysis. Figures are available – that is, the values of about forty socio-economic variables are available – for each of about 5,000 small districts in London. In order to present, in an assimilable form, the information these figures contain about the socio-economic structure of London, it is intended to draw a map in which each small district is coloured. A single colour distinguishes a set of districts which are as much as possible like each other and unlike the rest. A key to the colours gives, for each colour, the mean value of every variable for districts of that colour. Such a map and key would be useful to a hypothetical firm with the following problem. The firm employs salesmen all over London. Salesmen of different abilities, equipped differently, and employing different techniques, are the most effective in areas of different character. So a number of different courses of instruction for salesmen are run. What should be the aims of the courses, matching the characters of the areas in which their graduates will work? And where on the map of London should they work? The socio-economic structure of London is most effectively revealed for this firm by our map with colours and a key. Indeed, the firm's two questions are answered respectively by the key and the map. But the classification of the districts of London into homogeneous (that is, like-coloured) groups is useful for more than just drawing maps. The sociologist may find that the objectively determined groups bear a natural interpretation – such as that this is the group of council housing estates, that the group of slums. The applied statistician may be able to use the classification as a general-purpose stratification from which to draw simultaneously samples of a whole range of variables.

A first heuristic approach to the problem might be to think geometrically. Visualize the districts as 5,000 points in forty-dimensional space – the space whose co-ordinate axes are the forty variables. Intuitively, the problem is then to group together districts near to each other in space.

Nomenclature

The word 'classification' in ordinary language may mean assigning an individual to one of a set of predetermined groups or determining groups into which a set of individuals are divided. Discriminatory analysis is concerned with classification in the first sense, and is sometimes called 'classification' in consequence. However, as 'discriminatory (or discriminant) analysis' is the more usual name, I use 'classification' in the second sense. Thus, classification is basic to language, thought, and most human activity. For example, the use of any word presupposes a classification of objects into those which the word means and those it does not. It is not surprising that the problem of classification arises in many different forms which require different mathematical models. I consider only one model here. (I do not, for instance, propose a model for solving the problem of classifying topological spaces.) To distinguish this model one might call it that of 'classification by least squares'. Otherwise, as the references show, the subject has been called 'cluster analysis', 'grouping', and 'optimum stratification'. But most authors refer to it as 'classification' as well.

Statement of the problem

Make the assumption (which I consider discarding later) that we want our classification to reflect the variation of each variable equally and independently, even though this depends on the units in which it is measured, and even though the variables may be correlated. Then the variation of the whole system may be taken to be the sum of the variations of all the variables, since we neglect covariation and are equally interested in a unit of variation, no matter what its source. Now we have, if $P = \{A\}$ is a partition of the population into sets $\{A\}$, the set A having a mean $\bar{a}$ and the population X having mean $\bar{x}$,

$$\sum_{x \varepsilon X} (x - \bar{x})^2 = \sum_{A \varepsilon P} \sum_{a \varepsilon A} (a - \bar{a})^2 + \sum_{A \varepsilon P} n_A (a - \bar{x})^2 \tag{1}$$

where n_A is the number of elements in the set A and the other numbers – $x, \bar{x}, a$, and $\bar{a}$ – are all vectors. They represent points in k-dimensional space, where k is the number of variables. (I have used the notation $(x - y)^2$ for the scalar product of the vector $(x - y)$ with itself, instead of the more usual $(x - y)^T(x - y)$, to save space.) The single term on the left is the sum of the variations (squared deviations from means) of all variables. It is what we have called the total variation of the system, and the two terms on the right show it split up, in the usual way of the analysis of variance, into variation within the sets (groups of the classification) and variation between them. The first term, then, is the variation we lose if for the vector of values associated with each element (district) we substitute the vector associated with the mean of its group, and the second term is the variation we retain. It seems reasonable therefore, if we are given a number p of groups in the classification, to find a p-partition P which will minimize the first and maximize the second. The whole approach is based on the analysis of variance.[1]

Existing theory of least-squares classification

What do we already know about this problem? Rao,[2] reporting his earlier work, describes a rough, intuitive way of classifying a multivariate population using Mahalanobis' D^2 (a measure of distance between multivariate populations or, as here, sub-populations). This measure assumes identical dispersion matrices for the sub-populations. If we make this assumption, and further assume that the dispersion matrix of the sub-populations is the same as that of the whole population, and that all correlations are zero, we merely have to standardize the variables in order to make our approach equivalent to maximizing D^2 between all the groups in a partition. Actually, we do not have to assume zero correlations to make this possible, since we can always begin by transforming to uncorrelated variables.

Dalenius,[3] followed by Dalenius and Hodges,[4,5] considers the problem of optimal stratification in the univariate case. This problem arises as follows. If a sample of fixed size is to be used to estimate the characteristics of a population a more precise estimate is obtained if first the population is partitioned into strata which are homogeneous with respect to the variable which is sampled, then samples are taken separately from each stratum, and finally the samples are combined. The samples may be taken from the strata in various ways, each of which has its merits. If a method known as proportionate sampling is used the optimal stratification, in the sense that it will minimize the standard error of an estimate of the population mean obtained from a sample of fixed size, is such that the within-strata variation (the same as we are minimizing, except that it is considered for only one variable) is a minimum. Only one variable is considered. Yet it is clear that, if the sampler attaches a cost to a unit of standard error in each variable he intends to sample and scales the variables accordingly, he may consider our problem as a formulation of the multivariate stratification problem. However, for a continuous distribution of a single variable, Dalenius obtains the result that a necessary condition for a point dividing two adjacent strata to be optimally placed is that it should be half-way between their means. Meanwhile, in the course of proving something slightly different, W. Fisher [6] proves the corresponding condition for the discrete case – though still considering only one variable. It is

$$\frac{n_A}{n_A - 1}(a - \bar{a})^2 \leqslant \frac{n_B}{n_B + 1}(a - \bar{b})^2 \tag{2}$$

where a is an arbitrary member of an arbitrary set A with mean $\bar{a}$, and $\bar{b}$ is the mean of an arbitrary other set B. It follows that any element is nearer to the mean of its own set than to the mean of any other set, and of course Dalenius' condition follows on letting n_A and n_B tend to infinity. But this actually goes farther than Dalenius' proof. It proves, what Dalenius assumes, that the convex hulls of the sets of points do not intersect (convex hulls, when there is only one variable, being simply lines which pass through all the members of a set and are drawn along the axis of the one variable).

Ward [7] considers classifying elements so as to minimize any objective function whatever to the extent that it is possible by starting with them all in separate groups, and at each stage when there are p groups, examining all $p(p - 1)/2$ ways of uniting two of them to obtain $p - 1$ groups. Cavalli-Sforza and Edwards [8] discuss minimizing our objective function by starting with all the elements in one group and, at each stage when there are p groups, examining all the ways of splitting one of them into two so as to obtain $p - 1$ groups. Thus, if there are n elements their first stage requires $2^{n-1} - 1$ comparisons, as compared with Ward's $n(n - 1)/2$. Furthermore, either method seems as likely or unlikely to reach the optimum, so Ward's is preferred. However, they have an interesting discussion of the objective function. But neither method is intended to solve our problem exactly. Both seek an hierarchical classification – that is, one in which the groups of the p-classification are never split up between groups in going to a classification into less than p groups. They thus focus attention on the whole hierarchy of classifications, for $p = 1, \ldots n$, whereas I consider optimizing for each p separately. An optimal hierarchy is not defined by them except implicitly, as the hierarchy obtained by their algorithms.

The necessary condition: properties of an optimal classification

A necessary condition for a least-squares classification turns out (as in the Appendix) to be (2) when a, $\bar{a}$, and b are interpreted as vectors. In fact, the proof goes through exactly as it does when they are interpreted as single values, all the operations involved being valid also in matrix algebra. We can now relate classification to certain other branches of multivariate analysis, considered as non-probabilistic techniques.

A principal component analysis [9] seeks first that variable, a weighted sum of the original variables, the variation along which is the greatest proportion of the sum of the variations of the original variables – that is, the greatest proportion of the left-hand side of (1). We seek a grouping of the elements into sets such that the variation between the grouped elements is the greatest proportion of – the same thing. This is shown in *Figure 1* for a bivariate population. The first component is the line through the origin. The points representing the means of sets are shown by crosses. Principal component analysis seeks to retain the maximum variation along the line. We seek to retain the maximum variation between the points.

Figure 1

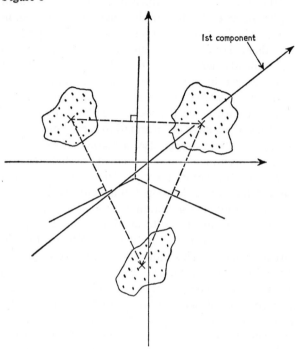

There is a duality here between points and lines. Consider now the question of scaling. Neither the classifications nor the components that are extracted will be the same if the relative scales of the axes are altered, since both depend on measuring squared distances in space. It is customary to standardize (measure the variables in units of their standard deviations). This is not usually justifiable, certainly not if the argument is that to use other scales would be arbitrary. It means that equal weight is given to each variable – a quite arbitrary decision – not that the weights given are somehow left to determine themselves. The difficulty arises when the variables are not comparable. That is, measurements of different variables upon a single element are not comparable, though different measurements of a single variable are comparable. Now suppose that measurements of the same variable upon different elements are not comparable, though the measurements taken of different variables upon a single element are. For instance, we might be measuring length and breadth in inches and be interested in shape, not size. Then again we have duality between lines (variables) and points (elements); for now the same problem of scaling arises, except that now we must choose a scale for each element. And, again, both the principal components and the least-squares classification will depend upon the choice of scales.

Now consider the question of the independence of the information we seek to retain. Classification and component analysis retain the greatest possible proportion of the information contained in each variable, summed over all variables, despite the fact that the variables may be correlated, in which case the classification will be more in terms of some independent sources of variation than others. To take an extreme case, suppose two of the variables are functionally linearly dependent. From the outset, by including both in the set of variables, we have included redundant information. Those two variables constitute one source of information, not two. Yet that one source of information will have twice the weight in the ensuing classification or component analysis of a source of information represented by only one variable. To take now the dual extreme case, suppose that by mistake two sets of measurements have been taken on one element, so that, regarding each element as a source of information, there is again duplication. A single source of information will have twice the weight of a source represented by only one element. And, even without taking extreme cases, we can tell by their distances in space how near two elements are to inhabiting the same point, just as we can tell by their correlation how near two variables are to being collinear, before we start the analysis. This difficulty, if it is felt as such, can be overcome, once the initial scales of the axes have been chosen. The difficulty for classification can be overcome by doing a principal component analysis and standardizing in component space before starting classification, though judgement must be used as to how many components to retain. The difficulty for principal component analysis can be overcome by doing a classification and reducing the elements of a group to one element at the mean of the group – instead of allowing them all to coexist at the mean of the group – before doing the component analysis, though again judgement must be used as to how many groups to form.

Consider the relation of classification to discriminatory analysis.[9] Given two populations, discriminatory analysis seeks for a variable, a weighted sum of the original variables, such that measurements along it tell us to which population an element should be assigned with least probability of misclassification. In our case there is no possibility of misclassification, since we determine the membership of the groups, but we should be interested in a linear function of the variables such that all elements with less than a certain value of the function are in one group, and all those with a greater value are in the other. Indeed, it is intuitively a desirable property of a classification that no two sets in it should overlap in the sense that their convex hulls intersect. But if this property is realized any two sets must be separated by a hyperplane, and such a linear function as we describe will be given by any line passing at right angles through that hyperplane. In view of this, it is pleasing that condition (2) implies the existence of a hyperplane, bisecting at right angles the line between the means of any two sets, which separates all the members of one set from the members of the other. This, too, is illustrated in *Figure 1*. The vector ($\bar{a} - \bar{b}$), which compares the means of two sets, is thus the non-probabilistic discriminant between them, so that it is a characteristic of a least-squares classification that comparing the means of the sets found is a uniquely valid thing to do. The hypothetical firm discussed in connexion with classifying the districts of London can rely on its key as well as on its map.

The necessary condition:

$$\frac{n_A}{n_A - n_u}(\bar{u} - \bar{a})^2 \leqslant \frac{n_B}{n_B + n_u}(\bar{u} - \bar{b})^2 \qquad (3)$$

where U is an arbitrary sub-set with mean $\bar{u}$ of an arbitrary set A (with mean $\bar{a}$) and $\bar{b}$ is the mean of an arbitrary other set B – is proved in the Appendix. It is more general than (2), yielding (2) as a special case. It implies that any sub-set of a set must have a mean nearer to the mean of that set than to the mean of any other set. Thus, if the elements of a population to be classified are actually means of smaller sub-populations they need only be weighted according to the numbers in them for the least-squares classification obtained from them to be optimal for the elements of the sub-populations, subject to the constraint that the sub-populations cannot be split up.

The computer programme

Consider a classification, not necessarily optimal. If an element a is taken out of the set A the right-hand side of (2) gives the decrease in within variation of the set A. If it is put into another set B the left-hand side gives the increase in within variation of B. Thus, given a p-classification, np comparisons will

Figure 2

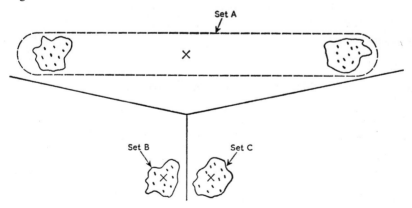

Set A

×

Set B   Set C

tell us whether and by how much it can be improved by a single transfer. Along these lines, one can improve the classification until (2) – and hence (3) – is satisfied. But the condition is not sufficient. One would like to avoid situations such as that illustrated in *Figure 2*, where the sets whose means are shown by crosses satisfy the necessary condition, yet obviously do not constitute an optimal 3-classification. One would like to start from a good place. Ward's [7] algorithm does not lead to a combinatorial number of comparisons – indeed, it is much quicker than the one I describe. I am currently writing a programme which starts with n groups, and when there are p groups applies Ward's step of examining all $p(p-1)/2$ possibilities of uniting two of them, unites the best two into one group, and then improves the resulting $(p-1)$-classification until (2) is satisfied. As compared with Ward's algorithm, I test the truth of the assumption – which is reasonable in, for example, taxonomy [10] – that the data are naturally classifiable hierarchically. (Thus I might test the theory of evolution.) Since, for the purpose of classifying the districts of London, we would like the data to speak for themselves about the number of groups in the classification (within a certain range), the programme prints out classifications for a whole range of values of p, the range being set by the user. Thorndike [11] discusses this question.

Results and conclusions

The main result is the necessary condition (2) for a least-squares classification, with its corollary that the vector which compares the means of two groups in the classification also discriminates (non-probabilistically) between them. It is based on a definition of a least-squares classification as that which minimizes the sum of within-group variations, summed over all variables. I conclude from a comparison of least-squares classification with component analysis that it is about as justifiable, and has corresponding limitations. Whether it is practicable or not must await practical experience, but it seems likely. It can in any case be used to improve proposed classifications until the desirable properties accompanying (2) are realized.

Appendix

Theorem

If $P = \{A\}$ is a partition of a set of vectors such that

$$\sum_{A \epsilon P} \sum_{a \epsilon A} (a - \bar{a})^2$$

where $\bar{a}$ is the mean of A – is a minimum, then if A, B are distinct elements of P and S is a proper subset of A,

$$\frac{n_A}{n_A - n_S} (\bar{a} - \bar{s})^2 \leqslant \frac{n_B}{n_B + n_S} (\bar{b} - \bar{s})^2 \qquad \ldots (1)$$

where n_X is always the number in the set X, and $\bar{s}$, $\bar{b}$ are the means of S and B.

Proof

Write D_Y^X for the sum of all squared distances between an element of X and an element of Y, that is

$$D_Y^X = \sum_{x \in X} \sum_{y \in Y} (x - y)^2 \qquad \ldots (2)$$

so that $D_X^X/2n_X$ is the within variation of the set X.

Consider transferring S from A to B. The decrease in within variation of A is

$$\frac{1}{2}\left\{ \frac{D_A^A}{n_A} - \frac{D_{A-S}^{A-S}}{n_A - n_S} \right\} = \frac{1}{2}\left\{ \frac{(n_A - n_S) D_A^A - n_A D_{A-S}^{A-S}}{n_A (n_A - n_S)} \right\}$$

which we call $-\triangle_A$.

Now $D_{A-S}^{A-S} = D_A^A - 2D_A^S + D_S^S$ because of (2). Hence

$$-\triangle_A = \frac{1}{2}\left\{ \frac{2n_A D_A^S - n_S D_A^A - n_A D_S^S}{n_A (n_A - n_S)} \right\}$$

$$= \frac{1}{n_A - n_S}\left\{ D_A^S - n_S \frac{D_A^A}{2n_A} - n_S \frac{D_S^S}{2n_S} \right\}$$

$$= \frac{1}{n_A - n_S}\left\{ \sum_s \sum [(s - a)^2 - (a - \bar{a})^2] - n_A \frac{D_S^S}{2n_S} + (n_A - n_S) \frac{D_S^S}{2n_S} \right\}$$

$$= \frac{1}{n_A - n_S}\left\{ \sum_s n_A (s - \bar{a})^2 - n_A \sum_s (s - \bar{s})^2 \right\} + \sum_s (s - \bar{s})^2$$

$$= \frac{n_A n_S}{n_A - n_S} (\bar{s} - \bar{a})^2 + \sum_s (s - \bar{s})^2 \qquad \ldots (3)$$

Similarly, the increase $\triangle_B$ in the within variation of B is

$$\triangle_B = \frac{n_B n_S}{n_B - n_S} (\bar{s} - \bar{b})^2 + \sum_s (s - \bar{s})^2 \qquad \ldots (4)$$

and $\triangle_A + \triangle_B$, which must be positive if the partition is optimal, is found to be the difference between the right and left hand sides of (1). *Q.E.D.*

As a corollary, we have, if we consider transferring a single element a of A to B, the necessary condition

$$\frac{n_A}{n_A - 1} (a - \bar{a})^2 \leqslant \frac{n_B}{n_B + 1} (a - \bar{b})^2 \qquad \ldots (5)$$

and we also have, on examining (3) and (4), that the two sides of (5) are $-\triangle_A$ and $\triangle_B$ in this case.

The proof goes through for non-discrete distributions if integrals are substituted for the numbers in sets and for summations over the elements of sets.

REFERENCES

1 R. A. Fisher (1954)
2 C. R. Rao (1952)
3 T. Dalenius (1957)
4 T. Dalenius & J. L. Hodges, Jr. (1957)
5 T. Dalenius & J. L. Hodges, Jr. (1959)
6 W. Fisher (1958)
7 J. H. Ward, Jr. (1963)
8 A. W. F. Edwards & L. L. Cavalli-Sforza (1963)
9 M. G. Kendall (1957)
10 R. R. Sokal & P. H. A. Sneath (1963)
11 R. L. Thorndike (1953)

44 · *Factors in Determining Hospital Size*

N. STEINBERG

Introduction

Within the framework of the policy for the modernization and adaptation of French hospital facilities, considerable investment funds have been allocated for the building of treatment units. The extent of the need and the large amount of funds to be deployed over fifteen years is the basis of a vast research programme undertaken by the Ministry of Public Health on the various problems arising from the work of the hospitals. In particular, the means of recommending the optimal size of a hospital is at the moment the subject of studies in depth.

It is proposed in this article to summarize the basic directions of research undertaken in France on this subject.

Study of existing concepts

In France, just as much as elsewhere, the prevalent view with regard to the size of a typical hospital favours medium-sized units of 600–800 beds. The arguments in favour of this size range will be accompanied later by a detailed critique of various supporting evidence.

CRITERIA FOR HOSPITAL SIZE

The following three criteria are often quoted:

Economic criterion

The cost of treatment is higher in large organizations than in medium-sized organizations, assuming that the latter afford equal security for the patients.

Psychological criterion

The large monolithic hospital gives an impersonal feeling to the patients; vast edifices containing 1,500–2,000 beds are beyond the scale of normal human experience, affecting both patients' morale and the working atmosphere for staff.

Administrative criterion

The large hospital is difficult to organize. Control is difficult to establish, and arising out of this is a wastage of resources, which also explains the observed rise in cost of care.

Support for the medium-sized hospital has many consequences; indeed, if a detailed study corroborates current opinion as outlined above, one may expect a dispersal of French hospital resources in the future. To a certain extent, such a prospect rebuts the common-sense view that links economy with management on a large scale, and is a reaction against the policy of large centres which was the dominant feature before the war. Moreover, this reorientation would constitute a brake on the development of group medicine, which has tended to become an essential feature in the profession.

ANALYSIS OF THE CASE

In the controversy around the optimal size of a hospital, this study will be primarily concerned with clarifying the economic aspects. Parallel studies could later be undertaken on the soundness of the psychological and administrative propositions.

(a) Economic criterion

The economic criterion is basically concerned with rise in cost of treatment. In fact, it is a question of verifying the rise in expenditure by scrupulous analysis of running costs, and demonstrating the process of economic degeneration in the functioning of a hospital as its size increases.

(b) Psychological criterion

Investigation of the 'psychological environment' arising from a large unit size gives rise to the following questions:

To what extent is the feeling of 'impersonality' which has been noted actually due to the scale of the hospital? Or does it arise only out of the way it is run?

What, for example, would be the 'psychological environment' felt by the patient in an establishment of 2,000 beds, divided into five or six treatment units of 350–400 beds, each comprising three- or four-storey buildings at the outside, and spread over a site of the order of 15 hectares (37 acres)?

The results of psychological studies on these lines would give an answer to these questions.

(c) Administrative criterion

The same sort of objection could be raised on the administrative level. Actually, if the management structure is based on the principle of responsibility by the hospital unit, and consequently devolves on the management committee of the hospital, would not the large hospital cease to appear an intractable hydra?

The acuteness of the management problems of large hospital groups arises first and foremost from the lack of adaptation in the present managerial environment. This dates back in history to an era of charity hospitals and workhouses, and is contrary to present needs arising from progress achieved in medical techniques and utilization of health services. It is obvious that the style of management differs radically in organizations according to whether they are small, medium, or large.

(d) *Plan of research*

Arising from the foregoing survey, a research programme has been drawn up, which basically proposes to investigate:

the mechanisms of the cost structure in hospitals;
the management structure of large-scale organizations.

In this outline the main object is to examine the initial results of the costing studies, and the consequences that arise therefrom with regard to hospital facilities.

Cost analysis of hospital care

STRUCTURE OF COST OF CARE

The only evidence with regard to the effect of hospital size on cost of care that was available at the time this study was undertaken is to be found in the report of the Public Accounts Department. Statistics of cost per day by category of establishment, grouped according to number of beds, brought to light an increase in average cost per day (in hospitals in this category) according to number of beds, in all branches of medicine.

Studies were directed towards research into factors that might account for this rise in costs. Parallel to this attempt at interpretation, investigations of a more general nature were undertaken into the mechanism of hospital cost structures.

These studies have made it possible to define a significant unit of measurement of hospital activity (viz. average cost of care per patient) and to highlight the structure of this cost. It is appropriate here to recall that the validity of the results set out in this article is linked to the particular character of the hospitals used as a sample, which consist of thirty-six establishments (of all categories). Research is now envisaged to verify these conclusions over a larger sample of 130 hospitals.

(a) *Components in costs of care per patient*

One can consider, broadly speaking, that the cost of care per patient is broken down into cost of the stay and hospital staffing, on the one hand,

and administrative and medical expenses, on the other (such as use of radio-graphy, laboratory tests, blood plasma, and pharmaceutical products). Statistical analysis made of the different components of cost gives an interest-ing set of results:

average cost of stay and staffing (nursing and auxiliary staff) per patient are related to average length of stay of patients in that branch (medical, surgical, maternity);

administrative and medical costs do not depend on length of stay, and represent therefore an average cost per patient;

hospital staff and medical expenses depend on the average technical level of the department (general or specialized medicine).

(b) *Independence of cost of care and hospital size*

Analysis of costs against different parameters of activity show their markedly linear and proportional form.

From this it follows that the average cost of care per patient does not depend on the volume of activity nor on the bed-size of the hospital.

This conclusion applies only to measures of cost; it is possible that a fall in quality of work is related to the growth of hospital size. In the absence of a worthwhile investigation into the measured performance of various hospitals it is not possible to reach any conclusions on the present state of affairs.

This independence of cost and scale, which is evident at this stage of statistical observation, counters arguments in favour of a positive relation-ship. Actually, the rise in price per day arises from a double coincidence: first, large-scale establishments generally provide specialized and costly services, and, second, their situation in large provincial centres gives rise *ipso facto* to higher prices for consumable goods.

Consideration of the present data shows that the unit cost of care is un-related to the size of hospitals, and thus leads one to ignore the economic factor as a criterion for determining hospital size.

An explanation of the linear character of costs probably lies in the self-same principle of organizing hospital medicine in independent services; the linearity thus reflects to some measure the piecemeal structure of the different branches of treatment.

This structure likewise partly explains the linear nature of the function of the administrative expenses, since a hospital is only a collection and not a juxtaposition of treatment departments.

Another explanation of the proportional nature of administrative costs is probably concerned with a certain type of lower-level administration in the hospitals.

RELATIONSHIPS BETWEEN COST OF CARE AND COST OF ILLNESS

The direct application of these results in appraising hospital managements, or in the drawing-up of budgets for national health, raises a few more problems that originate basically in the present lack of relationship between cost of care and cost of illness, or between cost of care and length of survival period of patients (mainly the elderly).

In this study the cost of hospital care has been studied very closely. Nevertheless, the calculations apply to only one part of the total attributes directed towards cure. An unknown factor still exists at present in post-hospital facilities.

For this reason the explanation of deviations between average cost of hospital care and cost in an individual hospital raises extremely delicate problems of interpretation, for information is lacking on comparable states of health of patients discharged from different hospitals. For example, the length of stay of patients undergoing operations for similar complaints differs widely from one hospital to another, from which it might be deduced that the state of health of patients on discharge also differs widely. This disparity produces a statistical bias in any inter-hospital comparisons, which can be removed only if the problem of hospital treatment is treated on a far more general level.

Since cost of hospital care is only one factor in the cost of illness, it follows that two hospitals may have very different figures for length of stay and cost of care, without it being possible to deduce from the existing state of affairs any conclusions as to the cost of illness. The latter should be investigated as a whole, to include hospital care and all post-hospital facilities in relation to the illness in question.

From the point of view of present collective financing of the health sector in different forms, the basic factor undoubtedly is *cost of illness*. The problem of planning hospital facilities is integral, in this context, with that of health when the global nature of health facilities is considered.

Some conclusions

OPTIMUM HOSPITAL CAPACITY

Running costs do not provide a criterion for hospital size. As far as the cost of building goes, even if it is possible that the cost per bed to the contractor must decrease slightly with the number of beds, it is not clear that the price per unit follows the same curve. Finally, if one takes into account the time or speed of building, we notice that this speed decreases with the importance of the programme. Hence, one can propose a working hypothesis: that as a first approximation economic factors making up running costs and building costs do not permit the *a priori* determination of an optimal size for hospitals.

However, it would appear that the problem of an optimum lies on a level of planning regional facilities which, according to circumstances, would include establishments of varying dimensions. It is a question of 'optimizing' a network of hospitals and not one hospital alone.

Moreover, this planning would encompass the whole set-up of Public Health, with a view to attaining at the lowest cost the desired quality of health facilities. In particular, it is appropriate to provide for wider definition of hospital treatment to include some help for the aged, and general convalescence outside hospitals, etc.

The structure of the network will thus depend on the health organization, on the location of population, physical and economic geography, traffic layout, building land available, etc.

HOSPITAL SIZE AND ARCHITECTURAL CHOICE

If local and regional conditions within the framework of a regional plan lead to the building of an institution of more than 1,500 beds, for example, within a fixed perimeter, the realization of this group of buildings raises the problem of an architectural choice. It is desirable not to equate large capacity with a monolithic style. Actually from the management and human angle, the concept of an architectural unit of medium size, 400–500 beds, called a management unit, presents a compelling argument.

The notion of the management unit arises from research into the working of hospitals, and naturally supposes the existence of a corresponding architectural organization; the structure of the building often dictates the administrative structure. The essential thing is not to confuse large size with any given architectural principle (such as the vast block), but on the contrary, to review the problem in each case, taking into account all the factors and all the data.

STRUCTURE OF THE HOSPITAL GROUP AND POLICY FOR FACILITIES

The structure of regional facilities would seem to be fairly closely linked with the policy of setting up specialist services on a regional health level. One can situate the specialist service on the region in its main hospital (present 'hierarchical' policy); one can equally well scatter these units throughout the hospitals of the region. In the first case it results generally in the creation of enormous establishments (more than 2,000 beds); in the second case the result is medium-sized establishments.

Nevertheless, it should be remembered that applying the former policy by no means implies, as is emphasized above, the automatic creation of single-unit skyscrapers; on the contrary, this problem should be seen in totality, and solved as an equipment problem.

Finally, it is possible to set up highly specialized institutes which are lavishly equipped. This strategy of 'grafting' on to a hospital could equally well lead to the creation of medium-sized hospitals.

The problem discussed here of choosing a doctrine for facilities is closely linked to the nature and importance of the working communications from one branch to another, and to the prospects of significant changes, taking into account the very rapid advances in medical and hospital techniques.

45 · Hospital Attitudes and Communications

R. W. REVANS

The ranking of hospital characteristics

Consider *Table 1*

Table 1   *Rank Orders of Fifteen Acute General Hospitals*

Hospital	Rank order of five parameters				
	P	*K*	*Q*	*M*	*S*
A	1	5	2	1	1
B	2	1	9	2	3
C	7	6	1	5	6
D	4	3	12	8	2
E	3	2	6	6	14
F	6	4	7	7	7
G	8	12	3	4	9
H	5	10	5	14	13
I	14	11	10	3	10
J	13	15	4	12	4
K	11	9	13	9	8
L	9	13	8	11	11
M	12	7	15	13	5
N	15	8	11	10	12
O	10	14	14	15	15

P = Sisters' opinions of senior staff
K = Sisters' attitudes towards student nurses
Q = Stability of qualified nursing staff on wards
M = Mean length of patient stay, general medical
S = Mean length of patient stay, general surgical
Coefficient of concordance,
W = 0·51; significant at 0·1 per cent

THE MEAN LENGTH OF PATIENT STAY

Table 1 ranks fifteen acute general hospitals by five observables. The meaning of two of these, M and S, are already well understood; they are the rank

601

Table 2   Rank Orders of Average Length of Patient Stay for Twelve Large General Hospitals

Hospital	i	ii	iii	iv	v	vi	vii	viii	ix	x	xi	xii	xiii	xiv	xv	xvi	xvii
a	1	1	2	3	1	2	1	5	1	2	4	1	3½	1	2	3	10
b	4	2¼	1	2	2	10	3	1	4	5	5	2	5	7	1	5	1
c	5	8	3	10	3	8	2	2	8	4	3	3	11	9	8	2	7½
d	3	2¼	5¼	8	10	3	6	10	10	6	2	7	2	10	5	11	2
e	7	6	8¼	1	5	5	10	6	2	9	6	12	9	3	6	8	6
f	8	7	4	12	11	6	5	9	11	1	1	4	8	8	3	1	12
g	2	5	5¼	7	4	9	9	7	5	7	8	10	12	4	9½	9	3½
h	6	4	7	5	6	4	12	11	7	10	11	5	10	2	7	6	5
i	10	10	8½	4	9	7	8	4	3	8	9	8	3½	6	11	4	7½
j	9	12	10	6	7	11	4	3	9	12	7	11	1	5	4	7	3½
k	11	9	11¼	11	12	1	7	12	12	3	12	6	6	11	12	12	11
l	12	11	11½	9	8	12	11	8	6	11	10	9	7	12	9½	10	9

Identification of symbols used for each of seventeen diagnostic classes

i   Allergic, endocrine, metabolic, and nutritional diseases
ii Diseases of central nervous system
iii Diseases of arteries and veins, and other diseases of circulatory system
iv Pneumonia
v   Other diseases of respiratory system
vi Diseases of stomach and duodenum
vii Appendicitis
viii Hernia of abdominal cavity

ix   Other diseases of digestive system
x   Diseases of urinary system
xi   Diseases of bones and organs of movement
xii Diseases of skin
xiii Benign neoplasms
xiv Diseases of heart
xv   Malignant neoplasms
xvi Diseases of genital organs; male
xvii Diseases of genital organs; female

The coefficient of concordance of the entries in this table is 0·32 and is very highly significant.

orders of the rapidity with which general medical and general surgical cases are discharged. It is necessary to ensure that as far as possible like is being compared with like. The hospital with the shortest average length of patient stay is ranked first; and the hospital with the longest average length of patient stay fifteenth. These general averages vary from 9 days to 16. In *Tables 2* and *3* two other examples are given to suggest that, although the figures of *Table 1* are drawn from those two wide ranges of diagnostic classes known as general medical and general surgical cases, there is also, within any given general hospital, a significant tendency for all specific diagnostic classes to remain a length of time determined by that particular hospital. There is a significant concordance between the mean lengths of patient stay of all diagnostic classes in the same hospital. Hospitals where appendicectomies or hernia repairs are discharged sooner than average tend also to discharge their cardiacs and diabetics sooner than average, and vice versa. This fuller result is not, of course, suggested in *Table 1*, although there is some positive correlation between M and S as there shown.*

Table 3   *Rank Orders of Patient Stay for Five Common Diagnoses at Five Hospitals*

Hospital	*i*	*ii*	*iii*	*iv*	*v*
I	1	1	2	1	1
II	2	2	3	3	2
III	3	3	1	2	3
IV	5	4	4	5	4
V	4	5	5	4	5

Identification of symbols used for each of five diagnostic classes

i appendicectomy	*iv* cholecystectomy
ii hernia repair	*v* respiratory complaints
iii partial gastrectomy	

The coefficient of concordance of the entries in this table is 0·85 and is very highly significant.

> *N.B.* In this table, rank order is ascending. Hospitals that keep their patients longest rank 5, those which discharge them most rapidly rank 1.

THE STABILITY OF HOSPITAL STAFFS

The variate Q of *Table 1* is the rank order of ability of the hospital staff to retain its qualified ward staff, namely, its sisters and staff nurses. [This ability

---

* It may be suggested that these differences can be explained by the differing demands for hospital beds in different areas. No such effect has been found; indeed, some hospitals with very long waiting lists (above 1,000 surgical patients) may have exceptionally long mean periods of patient stay. This appears to be a simple consequence of a queueing situation with a low service rate.

is expressed by the ratio of the average number of ward sisters and staff nurses (calculated monthly over two whole years) actually on the payroll of the hospital to the average number allowed by the hospital establishment over the same period.] A hospital that is continually short of qualified staff should not only deplore the emaciated service that it must offer to its patients but should also ask itself why the vacancies arise. The results of *Table 1* might have been expressed in other indices of staff stability, such as the mean length of service of individuals in particular grades; it has, however, proved extremely laborious to collect accurate information of individual periods of service in this way. Nevertheless, in the group of hospitals for which *Table 3* is drawn the records of several thousand employees were individually investigated, and it was shown that the hospital with a high wastage rate of one class of nursing staff also tended to have a high wastage rate of other classes. The results of this study are set out in *Table 4*; it can be readily appreciated that, on one hand, Cols. *Q*, *M*, and *S* of *Table 1* and, on the other, *Tables 3* and *4*, taken together, are saying the same thing.* In preparing *Table 1* it was not possible to repeat this detailed analysis, and the index *Q* shown in *Table 1* was accepted as a simpler measure.

Table 4   *Rank Orders of Mean Length of Stay of Different Hospital Staff for the Five Hospitals of Table 3*

Hospital	i	ii	iii	iv	v	vi
I	1	2	2	1	$1\frac{1}{2}$	1
II	4	1	1	2	$4\frac{1}{2}$	2
III	2	3	3	4	$1\frac{1}{2}$	3
IV	5	5	4	5	3	4
V	3	4	5	3	$4\frac{1}{2}$	5

Identification of symbols used for each of six classes of hospital staff.

i Matrons and deputy matrons   *iv* Assistant nurses
ii Sisters   *v* Domestics
iii Staff nurses   *vi* Student nurses

The coefficient of concordance of the entries in this table is 0·59 and is significant at about 0·1 per cent.

N.B. In this table, rank order is descending. Hospitals ranking 1 keep their staff longest, those ranking 5 lose them soonest.

---

* The five hospitals of *Tables 3* and *4* were all in the homogeneous culture of industrial Lancashire; the fifteen hospitals of *Table 1* were drawn from the whole of the industrial North and Midlands. It is to be expected that the residual variances of the data of *Table 1* would be relatively greater than those of *Tables 3* and *4* together.

THE MEASUREMENT OF SUPERVISORY ATTITUDES

The indices P and K are more complex than Q, M, and S; there may be some who even doubt their validity. P is, however, a rough-and-ready estimate of the extent to which the ward sisters in these fifteen hospitals have confidence in their seniors and in the hospital organization; it has been determined through a system of standardized, confidential, and non-collusive interviews. K, which has been determined in the same interview, is an estimate of the extent to which the sisters see it as their responsibility to help in the integration of student nurses placed in their charge. Since this is a paper on the sociology of hospitals, it is necessary to explain how P and K have been measured, and hence what, it is believed, they signify.

The relations between ward sisters and their superiors

The ward sister is a person of great importance, since it is her business to see that the senior organization of the hospital supplies her ward with what the patients need for their recovery; it is also her business, therefore, to report to the senior organization the needs of the patients *as she perceives them*. The most casual observation of the ward sister's difficulties shows that she is continually thrust into situations of tension for three principal reasons. First, she works under a system of authority which, even when understandable, she may find irksome and frustrating; second, she works in a culture of intensive specialization, in which at times any member of another service, medical, paramedical, or lay, may, in an access of insecurity or status awareness, become unco-operative or even hostile; third, she is enveloped by emergency and change, both of which demand that authority and functional specialism shall engage to the fullest extent in effective two-way communication with those who rely upon their help. Since her means of contact are frequently obstructed, there are days on which the life of the ward sister is one crisis succeeded by another. Consider, for example, the sister who has been nettled by the off-hand rejection of a comment which she has made to a doctor about the condition of a patient; the doctor, himself puzzled by the case, may have made it clear to the sister that he regards her opinion as of no importance or even, indeed, as a confusing interruption of his own thoughts. A minute later the sister may relieve her feelings with a comment about that doctor or, indeed, about all the doctors in that particular hospital. She is effectively saying, 'The medical staff here tend to treat suggestions from the nurses with less consideration than they deserve.'

In the same way a sister may have reason to feel that she is not getting from the matron the support that her problems deserve. A ward sister, in a moment of tension, may pass some such remark as this: 'The matron and her administrative staff are no longer as closely in touch with ward problems as they should be.' Sometimes the sisters are aware of the positive part they play in helping to improve the hospital organization; they may make observations such as: 'The sisters in this hospital are confident that any solutions to their problems reached at their formal meetings will always be put into effect.' If this is not so they may briefly remark, 'Formal meetings of sisters with the senior staff at this hospital seem little more than somebody laying down the law.' At other times the situations of tension in which the sister finds herself are more directly connected with the physical organization of the hospital; a conflict has arisen with the diet kitchen, the dispensary, or the X-ray department, and the sister feels she is getting less co-operation than she should reasonably expect. She may then observe, 'Ancillary departments such as the pharmacy, kitchen, or maintenance seem [to the sister] to be organized for their own benefit rather than for that of the wards.' We have collected many such comments upon important matters of hospital organization and culture that seem clearly and vigorously to express the perceptions of the sisters who pass them. Several sets of such remarks have been assembled, and sisters in about forty different hospitals have been invited to say to what extent they themselves agree or disagree with these comments. Consider, for example, the item, 'The medical staff here tend to treat suggestions from the nurses with less consideration than they deserve.' Sisters are invited to suggest, in conditions of complete confidence and anonymity, and also in which it is impossible for any one sister to know the responses of any other, to what extent they agree or disagree with this remark. A five-point scale of response is permitted, namely, strongly agree, agree, uncertain (or don't know), disagree, and strongly disagree. If twenty sisters in a particular hospital strongly agreed with this remark, whereas only five disagreed with it, and in some other hospital only five agreed and twenty strongly disagreed, one would be able to conclude that there were significant differences between the opinions held of the medical staff by the sisters in the two different hospitals. The variate P now under discussion measures the extent to which the sisters feel themselves in easy and fruitful contact with their superiors.[1]

The variate P turns out to be normally distributed. It is also possible to show, by analysing the variance of P, that there are highly significant differences in the average values of P between hospitals; averages taken over all the sisters in different hospitals differ from each other to a much greater extent than do the estimates of P made by individual sisters within particular hospitals. Although the response of any particular sister to any particular statement must be subjective, there is so great a unanimity between the independent responses of all the sisters in the same hospital to the same set of statements that we are obliged to recognize an objective hospital effect. We can therefore assert with confidence not only that the concept P is meaningful but also that we can form a numerical estimate of it for any given hospital.

The relations between ward sisters and their subordinates
Consider such statements as these:

> 'Sisters can devote time to instructing the student nurse only at the expense of what may be more important demands.'

'Even during their preliminary training, student nurses are given glamour-
ized ideas of their future work.'

'The sister who wishes to get on in her profession must seek frequent
changes of hospital.'

'Student nurses should be taught not to speak to the doctor unless spoken
to first.'

'Even in a ward with two or more consultants, the sister should always
deal with them herself.'

These statements, made by ward sisters, throw light upon the attitudes they
hold towards the training of student nurses and their integration into their
ward teams. An analysis of the daily activity of large numbers of sisters
reveals that few of them give more than 1 per cent of their time to their
first-year student nurses. It is not surprising, perhaps, to discover that one of
the major fears of the student nurse is that she will be expected to perform
for a patient some service in which she has not been adequately instructed.
Ward activity studies also show that some sisters spend as much as 50 per
cent of their time on clerical and related duties; nor would it be unfair to
add that some sisters appear to justify their withdrawal from the stresses of
the ward by engaging in elaborate clerical exercises. Other sisters, whether
deliberately or not, diminish the learning opportunities of the student nurses
by forbidding them to ask questions of the doctors; others insist upon themselves transacting all ward affairs directly with the doctors, and hence upon
giving no supervisory responsibility to their juniors. Finally, in some hospitals sisters are a highly transient class and student nurses are perfectly well
aware that they have no deep attachment to the hospital nor to the training
that should be given upon its wards.

This batch of statements may therefore be scored to give some indication
of the extent to which the ward sisters are concerned about their student
nurses, who provide the bulk of the bed-side care; it may be scored, as was
the batch of statements indicative of P, to form another variate, here called
K. This variate is also normally distributed, and an analysis of its variance
shows that there are highly significant differences between hospitals. As with
P, therefore, we are entitled to calculate the mean value for K for each
hospital, and hence to arrange our sample of fifteen in rank order. The
conclusions of a professional sociologist (herself not much older than the
majority of the student nurses among whom she worked) enable us to observe
K through the eyes of the girls themselves:

'There was little evidence of the existence of bad personal relations,
except in individual isolated cases, between the new student nurses and the
other members of the nursing staff. What did emerge from the various
comments made by the student nurses was that they felt there was a
general lack of meaningful relations with other people in the hospital.
Many complained of the break-up of the preliminary school set, saying

X

that it was impossible to meet the other student nurses that they knew. Some felt that the ward sisters did not spend sufficient time instructing them in the wards. They mentioned that the ward sister did not always welcome them to the ward, did not always say "Good morning" and was not always particularly approachable. They did not always know who to go to if they were in difficulties or wanted information.' [2]

Another constraint, called H, upon the student is the commitment of the nursing staff to the observance of hierarchical precedence; unfavourable measures of H suggest hospitals with extensive rules intended to discipline the student nurses. Attitude surveys show not only that the girls often regard such rules and the manner of their enforcement with amused contempt but also that they conspire together in order to break them.

THE CONCORDANCE OF HOSPITAL CHARACTERISTICS

We may now return to *Table 1*. The coefficient of concordance is 0·51. This means that hospitals that rank high in any one of the five variates (P, K, Q, M, S) rank high in the other four; or that hospitals with a low rank in any of these variates have a low rank in the four others. The most casual examination of the table shows, of course, that there are some hospitals that rank high in one variate and low in one or more of the others. One must expect some departures from any general law in real-life situations, even although there is a significant association between high ranking in one variate and high ranking in others. In spite of its obvious exceptions, therefore, we must accept *Table 1* as evidence that the hospital perceived by the sisters, and so by others, to possess a good communication system has not only a stable professional staff but also enables its patients to recover more rapidly. This is perhaps not a surprising conclusion, since the main task of a hospital is to communicate to its patients that optimum succession of biological and mental stimuli that is the sinew of patient recovery. If this communication system becomes opaque, disjointed, uncertain, overloaded, attenuated, or simply ramshackle it must necessarily delay or distort whatever it is that makes for such stimuli; the metabolism of the hospital system slows down, there is an eruption of administrative chilblains, and the recovery of the patient becomes retarded. In simple English, if a message about a special diet is held up because the ward sister is on bad terms with the dietician the patient on the special diet is bound to suffer; if the junior nurse who observes what she believes to be an important change in the patient's condition is forbidden by hospital tradition to report this to the doctor unless he specifically asks her about it she is not only not helping that patient but is also probably accumulating a frustration which will itself contribute at some later date to a decision not to continue with her training. For those whose interest in the clinical affairs of the ward demands more than the arid statistical arguments of this essay, there is abundant evidence in the recent books by Elizabeth Barnes [3] and by Anne McGhee. [4]

Inter-group communication

THE SENIOR STAFF AND THE ATMOSPHERE OF THE WARD

We might argue here that P and K are like two meteorological indices, measuring those qualities of the atmosphere of the ward which, according to Anne McGhee, are so much determined by the attitudes of the sisters. What is important to the administrator is that, as *Table 1* suggests, this ward atmosphere seems to be determined not only by the sister herself but also by that sister's relationships to the senior staff of the hospital; in determining these relationships the hospital itself makes a contribution no less important than that of the individual sister. That this is so is shown not only by the significant concordance of *Table* 1 but also by the significant results found in the analysis of the variance of P, within and between the hospitals.

PROFESSIONAL GROUPS AND COMMUNICATION PROBLEMS

Elizabeth Barnes reaches similar conclusions. Her final paragraphs are on the importance of communications within the hospital and, in particular, on the importance of improving communications between the various professional groups of which the hospital is composed.

STATUS GROUPS AND COMMUNICATION PROBLEMS

Professional expertise is not the only major cause of division within the hospital community. Whatever the need for supervisory effectiveness to be based upon overt authority, the integration of the nursing staff into a cohesive corps is often bedevilled by considerations of rank and status. Consider the responses to this statement, also made by a ward sister: 'The tradition that nursing staff of similar status should keep together at meal-times is essential to the efficiency of the hospital.' About one-half only of several hundred sisters interviewed disagree with this statement; 39 per cent agree with it, and 11 per cent are not sure how to interpret it. There are many other remarks that enable an estimate to be made of the extent (measured by a variate H) to which any hospital is committed to such hierarchical beliefs, and statistical treatment of the results shows some hospitals to be significantly more committed than others. One finds that in hierarchically inclined hospitals the student nurses tend to place great stress upon the importance of their own 'set' or that group of them who enter the hospital training school together at any given time. As any one set (to the extent that it survives) moves upward through the hospital, steadily gaining in seniority, so it may become the shield and refuge of its members; in moments of difficulty each will seek consolation from the others, and the student nurse who finds she needs help, advice, or instruction will often seek it at the next coffee-break from a fellow set-member on another ward rather than on the instant from her own sister or immediate senior. In a few hospitals one finds emphasis in still other directions upon the horizontal (namely, within given status classes) rather than upon the vertical (namely, within given wards or service departments); not only do all, say, second-year student nurses of the April set tend to form a front against all other sets, but resident staff may have little in common with the non-resident, and the full-timers may see themselves positively threatened by the part-timers. The problem for the hospital administration (using that expression in its widest sense) is again one of communication. What, one may ask, is it that endows the organism in the first place with its tendency to hierarchical division? Or, indeed, is the whole idea that it is *possible* to form a team on the ward a misconception that can serve only to distract attention from more fruitful subjects of contemplation?

THE DOWNWARD TRANSMISSION OF ATTITUDES TO THE WARDS

It is easy to show that the perception that the sister has of those in authority above her, whether one of co-operation or of hostility, is substantially transmitted to those in turn responsible to her. The correlation between the P and K scores of several hundred individual sisters is of the order of $+0.55$; the correlation between the hospital averages of P and K for nineteen hospitals in a particular sample was $+0.72$. Both of these results are highly significant. But correlation coefficients alone, although interesting, do not identify causes. It is, however, reasonable to suggest that the attitudes of the senior staff towards the sisters, namely, the attitudes that in turn determine P, are of first importance. The doctor who is not concerned to use the sister's opinion of the patient is not likely to stimulate that sister in teaching her student nurses the value of observation; the sister who has learned to regard her formal meetings with the matron as a frustrating waste of time is unlikely to encourage frank discussion among her own ward staff with a view to contributing fruitful ideas of benefit to the hospital as a whole; the ward sister who is at loggerheads with the specialist departments of the hospital (who may also be at loggerheads among themselves) is unlikely to teach her student nurses much that is useful about the contributions that these specialist departments have to offer the patients. It is more economical to conclude, as Occam's Razor would have us do, that the community of ward sisters who feel themselves unable to help their student nurses is getting little support from those above, rather than that a whole hospital full of unco-operative individual sisters has come together at random. This is not to say that the particular handful of senior staff are, as persons, outstandingly thoughtless, negligent, or insensitive. The fact, however, remains that the key relationship in the social structure of the hospital is that between the ward sisters, with the patients on their hands, and the whole array of central services, from the doctors, the matron, and the secretary to the physiotherapists, the engineer, and the barber. And if, as may apparently so readily happen, this relationship in particular deteriorates, the hospital will have a high rate of staff turnover and a slow rate of patient recovery.

Hospital models and communication needs

The results presented in *Table 1* and briefly discussed in the following paragraphs have been obtained from research into a miscellany of hospital problems; some of these have touched on highly practical issues, such as the location of hospital stores or the improvement of hospital transport systems; other inquiries on the sickness rates of the student nurses and, in particular, the significant changes in these rates as the same individual girls move from one hospital to another in the course of their training; still other inquiries on the success or failure of hospital cadet schemes, the efficacy of hospital costing schemes, and the structure of hospital committee systems. It would be convenient if, as a result of this miscellaneous programme, we could begin to develop what the operational research worker describes as a 'model' of the hospital as an organism. In practice, this organism is so complicated as to defy, with our present limited knowledge of systems analysis and symbolic notation, any simple representation. Of this, however, we can be quite sure: a hospital treats a patient at five distinct stages: (*a*) an admission stage, which must embrace preliminary correspondence with the general practitioner, with another hospital or some other antecedent source, and with the patient's relatives; (*b*) a diagnostic stage, during which the complaint from which the patient is suffering is either discovered or confirmed, and some decision made as to the treatment the patient shall receive; (*c*) a treatment stage, which may consist in a single and decisive act, like a surgical operation, or some slower cycle of therapy during which the patient is likely to remain in the same ward; (*d*) a control stage, during which the progress of the patient after treatment is observed, so that it may be determined whether the operation or the therapy is doing what, at the diagnostic stage, it was expected to do; (*e*) a discharge stage, during which the patient is being prepared to leave the hospital in a condition, it is to be hoped, more satisfactory than that in which he was admitted. Such a model is capable of considerable elaboration, and it is possible to locate in it the roles and interactions of the main physical services of the hospital, such as the pathological laboratory and the medical records section. In trying to build such models one becomes impressed with the importance of rapid communications between one department and another, and, at the patient level, between persons on the same ward. Exercises of this type, therefore, make all the more impressive some of the results stated by Elizabeth Barnes. She describes how the majority of the members enlisting in the seminars set up in the participating general hospitals to discuss their psycho-sociological problems were able to perceive for the first time the importance of communication between different groups. One striking finding of the studies described in her work was that most professional hospital staffs had previously been completely unaware of the necessity for improving methods of communication between themselves.

The development of social sensitivity

As in the interesting essays in self-analysis reported by Elizabeth Barnes, we found that the medical staffs were in general indifferent to the attempts being made to discover how to improve hospital communications.

Little is known about the possibility of making members of institutions or of professional communities more critically aware of the impact that they make upon each other. Some interesting experiments have been reported from the University of California in Los Angeles by Tannenbaum, Wechsler, and Massarik; [5] to some extent the work of Johnson Abercrombie, aimed at sharpening self-perception, belongs to the same field of exploration. The researches of Rensis Likert at the University of Michigan on managerial and supervisory authority support the main ideas of this present essay. [6] The seminars reported by Elizabeth Barnes, although in a detailed sense unplanned, are among the most promising excursions beyond the sombre horizons of our administrative ignorance. The work of D. H. Clark of Fulbourn Hospital, Cambridgeshire, on administrative therapy, is also full of relevant suggestion. [7] Joan Woodward, as in so many other directions, also has something of interest to say upon the social forces at work to help or hinder the quest for enlightenment. [8] The Engineering Experiment Station of the Ohio State University is at present engaged upon a comprehensive and highly original study of social stratification on the hospital ward and its relation to clinical performance; the care with which its experiments are designed offers lessons to all students of institutions as social organisms. [9] The work of Gillian MacGuire on the possible influence that certain hospitals have upon the progress and difficulties of their student nurses is also original and important.

Attitude surveys and hospital problems

From Manchester we have made an attempt to examine, among others, the two hospitals at the bottom of *Table 1* and *Tables 3* and *4*; representative attitude surveys have been conducted, with members of the university meeting in free interviews a total of over 600 persons. These voluntary and confidential interviews, each of which lasted between ten minutes and three-quarters of an hour, were patterned on a stratified sample of all staff at the hospitals. The interviewers merely explained to those who appeared that they were generally interested in the way each particular hospital functioned; they did not solicit opinions upon any particular aspects of hospital life. The programmes of interviewing were spread over about two months in each hospital, and from time to time brief reports were made back to the staff of the main findings and of any actions which the management committees were able to take upon them. It was, however, perfectly clear, after the results of the many hundreds of interviews had been classified, that each hospital had deep and organic problems on which little effective progress was to be expected from mere administrative decisions alone.

One result is of interest, because it tests the reliability of the attitude survey as a research instrument. Three hospitals with markedly different problems were chosen for survey: the first, A, has recently had to close wards because it cannot get nurses to remain in its service, the second, B, was in much the same condition three years ago, but then achieved a change of matron, who worked steadily to improve relations with her nurses; the third, C, is an old building too small for the load it is carrying, but has no serious staff problems. The points raised by the staff at the interviews could be broadly classified under two headings: primarily to do with interpersonal relations (training, promotion, communications, discipline, recruitment, social and recreational functions) and those to do with working conditions (hours, pay, food, living quarters, transport, buildings, uniform, supplies, equipment, procedures). *Table 5* shows the responses from the staff interviewed, drawn at the three hospitals from all ranks, consultants to cleaners; not all comments are critical. But even when favourable comment is offset against the unfavourable, *Table 5* still shows that hospital A has an abnormally high comment rate about interpersonal relationships and hospital C an abnormally low one; at hospital B, where great efforts had recently been made to improve these relationships, the comment rate was about the average of A and C. On physical conditions, on the other hand, hospital C had a high comment rate and hospital B a low one; the rate at hospital A was about the average of B and C. Numerically, these results are highly significant, and the content of the comments is hence of interest to those who are trying to understand the problems of these particular hospitals.

Table 5 *Numbers of Staff Interviewed and Numbers of Comments Passed upon Interpersonal Relationships and upon Working Conditions, for Three Comparable General Hospitals*

		Number of comments	
Hospital	*No. of Staff interviewed*	*Interpersonal relations*	*Working conditions*
A	188	856	461
B	129	478	234
C	120	346	440

Participation as a learning process

A number of problems deeply seated in the hospital organisms have been identified from the attitude surveys, and means must be contrived whereby all who are affected by them must devote time to their analysis and solution. Typical problems uncovered are these: the arrangements for moving patients between the wards and the operating theatres; the preparation of the off-duty rota; the demands of the clerical work created, whether usefully or not, by ward routines and practices. Each of these problems affects many people at different levels within the hospital, from the consultants to the porters. One or two such problems should be carefully studied by an operational research group that includes not only a sociologist but also an administrator and that, as is suggested below, can draw upon the support and advice of the medical and nursing professions; this group should then attempt to initiate a course on administrative therapy by placing its findings for interpretation, analysis, and action in front of a committee representing all the interested factions or professional groups within the hospital; administrative therapy can be a true learning process, in which those who participate get valuable information about their own behaviour.* It should be the first concern of the leader of the operational research group to ensure that all members of the representative committee perceive what the structures of the problems are; if necessary, he should ensure that each of them can clearly state the objections or difficulties of any other faction hostile either to the changes which his own faction would advocate or to the position his own faction is striving to defend. The leader of the operational research group would need to have learned so much about the problems of the hospital as to be able to suggest what the effect would be of taking any action advocated by any particular faction, or of failing to take such action should other factions disagree with it. The operational research group might need to meet the interprofessional or interfaction committee as many as twenty times; the group leader should be free to tell the committee members if, and why, in his view, they are making no useful progress, or even if they are expressing *ex parte* views that can only bring damage to the hospital as a whole. It therefore follows that the leader of the group must not be a paid member of the staff of that particular hospital. Experiments of this type are in progress, but they have already struck one major difficulty. This does not lie within what might be called the operational research exercise itself; it lies in the lack of contact between the management committee and its own hospital problems. While the writer, who has had many years of experience in local government, believes that the judgement of the good amateur or lay committee is, in the final analysis, always sounder than that of the professional experts, he is very conscious of the difficulties of making lay committees face up to the profes-

---

* The study and construction of learning mechanisms shows that inputs about outputs (or knowledge of one's results) form a cardinal link in the learning process. There must also be some desire or perceived utility in the person wishing to learn; it is possible to build into a learning mechanism certain 'penalties' that the mechanism 'learns' to avoid. The 'penalty-avoidance' circuit of the human being may also need rearrangement at an intellectual level; he must perceive that certain types of behaviour (e.g. disparaging a clinical suggestion from a sister as an encroachment upon his professional authority) are contrary to his wider interests as well as to those of the patient and the hospital. Unless he does so he will have no desire to learn, that is, no motivation to change his present behaviour.

sional conflicts within their own authority. No doubt conferences and other educational activities such as are promoted by the Association of Hospital Management Committees all have their place, but something radical also seems to be called for.*

THE PARTICIPATION OF THE PROFESSIONS

Communication systems cannot be improved by the disinterested ministrations of mere experts; these systems begin and end with the attitudes that a few important members of the staff have towards their work and towards each other. One can renovate a hospital lighting system by employing competent electricians to overhaul it; one can deal with confusion in the hospital accountancy system by installing a reliable computer. But whether or not one can in fact do much to improve the communication system of a hospital is a debatable question. Deeply seated human attitudes are involved; the success of any learning process, by the participation of the senior staff of the hospital in the solution of hospital problems, depends, to a large extent, upon those who are called upon to catalyse this participation. It may be that there are some in the hospital service ready to turn to outsiders for help in their present difficulties, but the writer sees little evidence that, when it comes to the point of changing traditional attitudes or established practices, the service as a whole, will listen to those who are, after all, not professionally qualified. It is of no use for the outsider to deplore this fact; the professional palisades justifiably thrown up by the doctor and the nurse in defence against the charlatan and the imposter are not readily lowered to admit the sociologist, the operational research worker, or even the non-medical statistician. There is, of course, every reason why both doctors and nurses should themselves make excellent research workers in this field, since the concept of an organic system is a biological one, although, in the sense now being used, at a level of complexity and abstraction higher than that derived, say, from dissecting a dogfish. The practical difficulty to be overcome is to enable the hospital service to call upon operational research groups in whom the medical and nursing professions would have confidence. Such groups must be drawn partly from institutions, such as universities, interested in social research, partly from within these professions themselves, since the essential problem of communication, involving perception, social awareness, professional status, functional specialism, and so forth, lie behind the palisades themselves. The lay outsider can suggest method, design, and experiment; he can collect

* The relations between the senior professional staff of the hospital and its management committee appointed by the Regional Board deserve closer study than they so far seem to have received. What is needed is not some legalistic appraisal of the terms of reference of Boards, Hospital Management Committees, Hospital Committees, and their retinues of sub-committees, but an analysis of the real distribution of power and responsibility among them and their principal officers. In particular, a good deal of thought could well be given to the powers and duties of matrons, especially in relation to nursing sub-committees, hospital secretaries, and other senior members of the nursing administration.

evidence, carry out complex statistical analysis, point out the significance of results and so forth. To convince the medical or nursing staff he must work closely with professionally qualified colleagues drawn from the ranks of doctors and nurses themselves.

LESSONS FROM THE EMERGENCE AND DEVELOPMENT OF WORK STUDY

Over the past decade the hospital service has become increasingly interested in work study. A large number of hospitals have had both nurses and junior administrators trained in its techniques. What seems to be needed now is that a number of young doctors, future hospital secretaries, and nurses of the rank of deputy matron should be trained in methods of social investigation and, indeed, of operational research. This would demand that they should participate in existing research projects in the social sciences; it would be helpful if some of these projects were in fields remote from hospitals. There are a dozen or more centres of social research in Britain to which, in the first instance, these potential hospital analysts could be attached. The training which they (and others to follow them) would receive should be looked upon as a normal part of their present professional education and would not be intended to deflect them into a wholly new career; they would merely supply the hospital service with a nucleus of senior staff capable of participating, from time to time, in projects of operational research and social analysis. After having received formal training in analytical methods and having gained research experience from two years or so of organized fieldwork, they would return to their particular professions. Apart from the benefit to their own substantive employment that they would gain from such training, the hospital service would have, within its own ranks, a corps of qualified advisers who could be seconded to help with the identification, analysis, and treatment of the social problems of particular hospitals anywhere in the country. For our experience is beginning to show that a true perception of the communication problems of a particular hospital will rarely be gained by persons, whether professional or lay, emotionally or economically involved in the affairs of that same hospital. Nor is it likely that the professional staff, between whom communication is poor or has broken down, will ever accept any diagnosis of their troubles from the lay outsider. What is needed is that some outside commission, containing members of the medical and nursing professions, should be invited to help the socially sick hospital to perceive, to understand, and to treat its own troubles.

Other practical considerations

The hospital service is now endowed with a number of centres of education and research, such as those established by the King Edward's Hospital Fund and the Nursing Studies Unit at the University of Edinburgh. The Nuffield Provincial Hospitals Trust, although it does not support any institutions like these, has given very powerful backing to a wide range of research into hospital problems, including the work of the present writer. There are also many professional associations, like that of the hospital matrons, as well as the Royal College of Nursing, which are interested in questions of hospital morale and efficiency. All of these in their own way can advance the study of hospital communications. What, to the writer, seems most necessary is the development of the concept of self-awareness or social sensitivity. When a profession has been taught for generations that it must not become emotionally involved in those with whom it deals it is perhaps natural that its members should be slow to perceive the effects that they have upon those subordinate to them, or even, indeed, upon their colleagues.

The university medical school must contrive not only to fortify the medical student against the terrifying responsibility that he will be called upon to carry; it must make him aware that he is but one member, even if the most important one, of a hospital team that is dependent upon him, not only for its clinical success but also for its self-respect. The education of senior administrative nursing staff must also bring out more clearly the imperative need for the matron and the sister to adopt a more supportive and a less directive role than at present. A significant volume of young talent is leaving the nursing profession on account of the unrealistic and insensitive attitudes of those in command of it. If, since these are educational responsibilities, the following questions are put by those in charge of education, 'What does this mean in practice? What are we to teach?', let them be referred to some of the researches mentioned in this essay. Let them, for example, ask themselves why it is that over half the ward sisters in a representative sample of British hospitals believe that their matrons are no longer in touch with ward problems; or why over three-quarters of them believe that their doctors should be more co-operative in choosing times for their ward visits. We do not know the answers to these questions. All we can conclude is that the recovery of the patients and the morale of the staff are tied up with them.

REFERENCES

1 R. W. Revans (1961)
2 G. M. MacGuire (1961) p. 83
3 E. Barnes (1961)
4 A. McGhee (1961)
5 R. Tannenbaum, I. R. Wechsler & F. Massarik (1961)
6 R. Likert (1961)
7 D. H. Clark (1964)
8 J. Woodward (1959)
9 D. Howland *et al.* (1960)

46 · The Communicogram

A Method for Describing the Pattern, Frequency, and Accuracy of Organization and Communication

THEODORE D. WEINSHALL

Present tools for describing an organizational structure

Two of the most important problems confronting leaders of organizations are how to describe the structure of their organization to themselves and others and how to decide when, where, and how to introduce changes in their organizational structures.

The most prevalent method of describing organizational structures is the Organization Chart, which represents the formal relationships in the organization as perceived by persons at the top of the hierarchy pyramid of the Organization Chart. It is a mixture of what they believe to be the formal relationships and of what, in their opinion, such relationships should preferably be. Other types of chart present the relationships as perceived by all members of the organization entered in the chart. After each member has indicated how he himself perceives his own formal or informal relationship the overall structure is then drafted. One such chart confined to formal relationships might be referred to as a Formalogram.* Another better-known chart relates to informal relationships. It is known to social scientists as the Sociogram and might also be called Informalogram.†

Various representations of organizational structures can be compared to establish, for example, differences between the formal and informal structures. A graphic method of comparing a Sociogram and an Organization Chart has been developed by Stogdill and Shartle.[1]

---

* Mutually Perceived Formal Relationship Chart, describing the vertical formal relationships (matching the responses to questions like 'to whom do you report' and 'who are the people who report to you') and the horizontal formal relationships ('who else reports to the same person as you report to').

† An Informalogram is the network of mutually perceived informal relationships. Each such mutually perceived informal relationship is defined as the relationship existing between two persons who reciprocate in mentioning each other when responding to the request to 'list the people with whom you generally work most closely, regardless of their position in the organization' (each mutually perceived informal relationship appears on the Informalogram as a solid line between two persons).

The basic difference between the Organization Chart, on the one hand, and the Formalogram and the Informalogram, on the other, lies in the depth of insight they allow into the organizational structure. The Organization Chart is a sort of map, an aerial photograph if you wish, in which all linkages between the individuals listed are complete and no disagreements or omissions occur. In the Formalogram and Informalogram, which consists of the relationships as viewed by the participants, disagreements or omissions between people as to their roles relative to each other always appear; they thus tend to pinpoint people who are 'strongly situated' in the organizational structure, on the one hand, and people who are organizationally 'deviant' or 'isolated', on the other.

Nevertheless, the Formalogram and the Informalogram both have shortcomings, especially inasmuch as they are normally incapable of dealing with communication dynamics in the time dimension.

Thus, in view of the 'single-shot' character of the charts, a person who was missing from work for several days is likely to be overlooked by his colleagues when describing their organizational relationships. It is the events immediately preceding the moment when the respondent is reporting his relationships that would most probably affect his choice of persons and his perception of their organizational positions most. Again, an unpleasant or, alternatively, a very pleasing, recent interaction with somebody would impress the memory in such a way that the particular person in question would undoubtedly be organizationally perceived, while others might be omitted.

Furthermore, the fact that two persons mutually perceive each other as formal or informal colleagues does not really mean that all goes well between them in the organizational sense. The relationship might exist in their minds, but the communications or perhaps even the rapport between them are far from conducive to the maintenance of a healthy organizational climate.

By comparison with the first, this last shortcoming is by far the more important. My first organizational encounter with this type of breakdown in communications was at a lecture describing a study carried out among the top managements of several of the largest department-store organizations in Europe.* The lecturer said that he had interviewed the presidents of these organizations immediately after they had had meetings with their subordinates, who might be general managers of department stores or of factories belonging to the organization; he was interested in finding out how the two participants at such meetings perceived their interaction. He discovered that the character of the interaction was often perceived by each of the two altogether differently. For example, the president might relate that he had given his subordinate information to help him make his own decision, whereas the subordinate, the general manager, would say he was told by the president what to do and felt that he had been given an instruction.

* The lecture was given in Israel by Professor Sune Carlson of Sweden about the time his book on the subject [2] appeared in Stockholm.

Similar observations were reported by Roethlisberger and Rogers,[3] who stated that, unless the meaning and character of a communication is perceived identically by those participating in the interaction, a break occurs in the communications network. Their suggested remedy for such breaks was to have the recipient repeat the statement of the communicating party until the latter was satisfied that it was identical not only in content but also in spirit.

This was the background of the conceptual scheme for the present study. The scheme views the communications network as including not only the total spoken contacts (or interactions) between members of the organization but also the degree of agreement regarding the communication. In order that the organization shall continue to exist and survive, it is not enough that a proportion of these interactions should be mutually perceived by the participants as having occurred; it is equally essential that those transmitting the communication should agree, in a proportion of instances, as to its character and spirit.

To overcome some of the shortcomings mentioned above, attempts were made to incorporate a number of interactions and mutual perceptions in the description of the organization's communication patterns. It was hoped that this would provide a better indication of breaks and informal bridges in communication, leadership qualities existing and required in key communication positions, and various other aspects of the organization. The conceptual tool used will be referred to as the Communications Chart or Communicogram.

Plan of research

AIMS OF THE STUDY

The study was carried out as a part of my research on 'Changes in the Management Structure in a Growing Enterprise'* in the Devon Corporation, a company producing raw materials, semi-processed materials, and finished products. In 1959, the relevant year, the organization comprised about 3,000 employees in three different factories in New England, U.S.A., in vertically integrated form.

The management group at Devon included about 150 professional and supervisory personnel.

The development of the communications study evolved from a previous study of the relationships and attitudes among the whole management group in this company.[4]

In undertaking this study I hoped to be able to answer, or partly answer, the following questions:

1 Do the people really work closely with those they mentioned in their questionnaires, in answer to the question: 'With whom do you generally work most closely, regardless of their position in the organization?'

* Later reported as a doctoral thesis under a different title.[4]

2 What type of interaction do they perceive in their communications?

3 Are the interactions initiated by themselves or by the other party?

4 Do they perceive themselves as 'active' or 'inactive' in the interactions?

5 How many interactions are perceived by both participating parties ('mutual choice'); how many are perceived only by one party?

6 Of the interactions perceived by both parties, in how many cases is there mutual agreement as to the 'type of interaction'?

7 What is the relative use of the telephone in the perceived interactions?

8 Does the relative use of the phone vary much for one person in communicating with different individuals (i.e. is it used to shield the user from individuals whom he would not like to meet face to face)?

9 Do misunderstandings as to the 'type of interaction' occur more frequently in conferences or in conversations over the phone?

And, finally, the main question:

10 What are the informal organization and communication patterns that emerge from these perceptions of the daily management interactions?

METHOD

The information collected consisted of written reports supplied daily by members of management and data on interactions, activities, and attitudes gathered through interviews, observations, and questionnaires.

The daily written reports on perceived interactions were asked for two reasons, one practical and the other theoretical:

(i) In order to observe the simultaneous interactions of a group of executives, sitting in separate rooms and interacting orally by meeting each other or over the telephone, the study would have required a number of observers equal to that of the executives under observation.

(ii) The findings of an outside observer as to the 'content' of the interaction (type of interaction) are irrelevant to the process of communication which takes place in an organization. Let us imagine two participants, A and B, in an interaction: A, the superior, says he gave B information, while B, the subordinate, states that A gave him an instruction. The outside observer, without referring to the participants, might feel either way or might think that A gave B advice; whatever the observer feels or thinks has no bearing, in my opinion, on what is happening in the interaction, and it is therefore unsound to rely solely on such observations when studying the communications process and the informal organizational structure.

Fifty persons were chosen from among the management of the Devon Corporation for participation in the study, mostly higher-echelon managers (with annual salaries of $10,000 and upwards) interconnected in their daily work.

Each person was given a 'Daily Management Interactions' form which he was asked to fill in at least twice daily over a period of two weeks. The forms were collected daily from the participants. The form included information pertaining to every interaction the respondent could recall. Each interaction was to be recorded as 'Telephone' or 'Face to Face' (conference), and the respondent was asked to supply details about:

The corresponding party, i.e. the names of those with whom he interacted

The initiator of the interaction

Topic. A brief description of the subject-matter of the interaction (e.g. production, research, accounting, etc.); if several topics were discussed during the same interaction, the dominating topic (according to the respondent).

Type of interaction. Was the communication regarded as a decision, instruction, information, advice, or any other type of interaction?

Role player. Who played the major role in the interaction, i.e. who gave the instruction, information, advice, etc.

Time of interaction. The interactions were recorded within limits of full hours, so that the reported details could be checked against one another.

Every entry of a respondent (i.e. each interaction he reported) was classified according to time of occurrence (date and hour), number of respondent, number of initiator, character of interaction, and number of role-player. The data were then fed into processing equipment, where each entry of one respondent was checked against all those of the other respondents. This was done in two stages:

Consensus as to the existence of the interaction. Did the corresponding party (the other participant or participants in the interaction) acknowledge the occurrence of the interaction?

Consensus as to the character of the communication. In those cases in which the participants both reported the occurrence of an interaction, it was further checked whether they agreed on the spirit in which the communication was intended to pass, i.e. did they record the same 'type of interaction'?

Overall results

DESCRIPTION OF INTERACTIONS

Thirty-four of the 50 selected participants reported their daily interactions during the two weeks chosen for the experiment. *Chart A* is an Informalogram* of the 50 persons chosen for the study and the 34 who co-operated in the

---

* This Informalogram was derived separately earlier, when the data for the study on the relationships and attitudes of the whole management group (about 150) had been analysed.[4]

research (marked by numbers in the Informalogram).* *Table 1* shows that 5,135 interactions were reported, of which only one-third (1,708) were interactions with others of the group of 34.

Table 1 *Perceived Interactions by Thirty-four Group Members* (over two weeks, i.e. ten working days)

	Total	Daily average per person	Within group		Outside group	
			Interactions	% of total	Interactions	% of total
Telephone	1,514	4·5	380	22	1,134	33
Conference	3,621	10·5	1328	78	2,293	67
Total	5,135	15	1708	100	3,427	100

CHART A

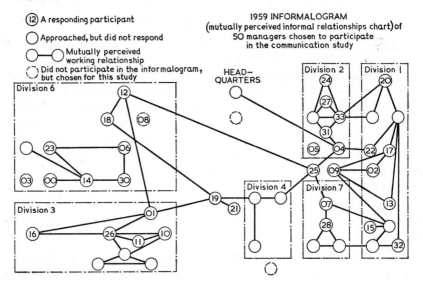

The telephone was evidently perceived as having been used only in 30 per cent of the total interactions (1,514 times out of 5,135).

It is natural that the proportion of perceived conference versus telephone interactions was higher within the group (78 per cent) than when the perceived interactions concerned out-of-group communications (67 per cent) because members of the organization would prefer the phone as physical distances between them increased.

It should be emphasized that we are dealing with perceived interactions. The findings of this experiment strongly indicate that the actual numbers of

* Note that those who declined to report were mostly linked to each other in small groups (Division 4 and the lower groups in Divisions 3, 7, and 1).

interactions, both total and daily average per person, were much higher. The balance of the interactions, those not perceived by either party, were 'forgotten'. The fact that 15–17 interactions per day were perceived on the average in the group of 34 does not mean, however, that these communications 'went through' in every one of the perceived interactions.

CONSENSUS AS TO THE EXISTENCE OF THE INTERACTION

When the perceived interactions were checked against each other for the consensus as to their occurrence it turned out that only in 25 per cent of the cases were the perceptions of one party reciprocated (see *Table 2*):

Table 2 *Mutually Perceived Interactions Among Group Members*

	Total perceived interactions in group	Mutually perceived	
		Interactions	% out of total
Telephone	380	80	21
Conference	1328	356	27
Total	1708	436	25

Seventy-five per cent of the reported interactions thus registered in the mind of one party only, and therefore could be regarded as 'lost' from the communications point of view.* We can assume that the actual proportion of such 'lost' interactions was much larger. The reason is that undoubtedly a not negligible number of interactions remained unperceived by either party involved. This means that probably more than three-quarters of the interactions in this group were 'wasted', not being recalled several hours later, a surprising result. *Table 2* shows that the conference did better than the telephone in impressing the participants in interactions of their existence.† This might be attributed to the visual contact at the conference; a person might be expected to retain better the occurrence of a conference with a person he saw than a telephone conversation where the visual impression was missing.

CONSENSUS AS TO THE CHARACTER OF THE COMMUNICATION

The fact that the participating parties in an interaction agree as to its existence does not necessarily mean that the communication 'went through'. *Table 3* shows that only in less than one-half of all mutually perceived interactions did

---

* A certain proportion of the perceived interactions were unreciprocated because of errors in registration of the time of occurrence. Even so, a somewhat smaller percentage (below 75 per cent) would be amazingly high.

† It should be pointed out that this difference was found to be non-significant and therefore the ensuing speculation is quite tentative.

the 'recipient' of the communication understand the spirit in which it was meant to be delivered by the 'transmitter' of the communication:

Table 3 *Consensus as to what took place in the Interactions (Consensus as to Type)*

		Consensus as to type of interaction	
	Total mutually perceived interactions	Number of interactions	% out of total
Telephone 80		48	60
Conference 356		158	44
Total 436		206	47

The communication did not 'pass' ('go through') in the spirit it was intended to in 53 per cent of the recorded mutually perceived interactions.

Unlike the consensus as to the existence of the interaction, where the conference did better than the telephone, the consensus as to the type of interaction shows that the telephone did better than the conference.* Thus, if the phone conversation is recalled it is recalled more accurately. A possible explanation why this is so refers to the relative brevity of telephone conversations (the expectation being that telephone conversations are usually shorter than face-to-face meetings and cover fewer subjects). Perhaps there is a stronger tendency, in face-to-face meetings, to go from one subject to another, even when the original reason for the meeting was a specific topic. When the meeting terminates every participant might take away a different impression of what seemed to him to be the core of the meeting. These dynamics are worthy of more detailed study.

Table 4 *Proportion of Communications 'Gone Through' out of Total Interactions Perceived within Group (Summary)*

			Consensus as to type of interaction	
	Reported interactions within group	Mutually perceived interactions	Number of interactions	% out of reported interactions
Telephone 380		80	48	13
Conference 1328		356	158	12
Total 1708		436	206	12

Table 4 shows that only in 206 (12 per cent) out of the 1,708 perceived interactions in the group was there agreement as to their occurrence as well as

* The differences in this case was found to be significant (between 0·02 and 0·01 levels).

to their character. The telephone did almost as poorly as the conference (13 per cent vs. 12 per cent).

Individual and unit results

We now take a closer look at one division of the Devon Corporation, namely the Research and Development Division.

In this division the entire management group was requested to participate, while in other divisions only selected individuals were chosen for the experiment. The reason for choosing the research and development as an example for studying the communications pattern of a complete management group, was that research and development managers were expected to have a comparatively higher number of perceived interactions with individuals outside their own division; this assumption, incidentally, was found to be wrong in our case. The response from the Research and Development Division was higher than from any other participating divisional group – nine out of ten managers participated actively in the experiment.

ANALYSIS OF THE INDIVIDUAL RESULTS AND COMPARISON WITH INFORMALOGRAM

Table 5 presents the individual and unit results concerning the first aspect of communication only; namely, the Consensus as to the Occurrence of Interactions. It is necessary, for the purpose of comparison between individuals and between units, to calculate their mutually perceived interactions per day.* An analysis of *Table 5* enables us to reach several conclusions with regard to the persons involved.

Group Orientation. Is the individual 'inwardly' or 'outwardly' oriented? Example: Person 00 is the most 'outwardly oriented' one in this unit (60 per cent 'out of group' interactions), while person 18 is the most 'inwardly oriented' in this unit (94 per cent 'in group' interactions).

Main Role Players. Is the individual an 'informal leader' of his group or does he serve as a 'communications transmitter' (with outer units)? Example: Person 12 is perceived to be the chief role player in interactions out of the group (1·0 interactions per day), and thus seems to be the chief 'communications transmitter' of the group (and this happens to be the formal leader of the group); persons 00 and 06 are additional 'communications transmitters' (0·6 daily out-of-group interactions each). Person 18, on the other hand, is perceived to be the chief role player in interactions within the group (3·0 interactions per day), and thus seems to be the chief 'informal leader'; person 06 seems to be another 'informal leader' (2·7 daily in group interactions). Persons 03 and 30 have been almost ignored in the perceptions of their formal peers and superiors.

* The number of Mutually Present Days varies from one pair of individuals to another.

Table 5 Devon Corporation – Research and Development Division
Comparison of Structural Characteristics (Mutually perceived interactions and relationships) between Communicogram and Informalogram

Person's No.	Formal org. level*	No. of days†	Communicogram — Mutually Perceived Interactions — Total: Telephone	Conference	T + C	Per day	Out of group: Total	Per day	In group: Total	Per day	Informalogram — Informal‡ Relationships: Out of group	In group	Comparison (of role players) — Out of group: Com.	Inf.	In group: Com.	Inf.
1 00	6	8	3	5	8	1·0	5	0·6	3	0·4	0	1	⊤			
%			38	62	100	100	60		40							
2 03	6	2	0	0	0	0	0	0	0	0	0	0				
%			0	0	0	0	0		0							
3 06	5	10	3	30	33	3·3	6	0·6	27	2·7	0	2	⊤⊤		⊤	⊤⊤
%			9	91	100	100	18		82							
4 08	4	8	0	12	12	1·5	3	0·4	9	1·1	§	§				
%			0	100	100	100	27		73							
5 12	3	9	4	21	25	2·8	9	1·0	16	1·8	2	1	=	=	⊤	=
%			16	84	100	100	36		64							
6 14	6	10	1	9	10	1·0	2	0·2	8	0·8	0	4				
%			10	90	100	100	20		80							
7 18	4	5	2	14	16	3·2	1	0·2	15	3·0	1	1		⊤⊤	=	=
%			12	88	100	100	6		94							
8 23	5	10	4	14	18	1·8	3	0·3	15	1·5	0	2			⊤⊤	⊤
%			22	78	100	100	17		83							
9 30	6	11	1	5	6	0·5	1	0·1	5	0·4	0	2			⊤	⊤⊤
%			17	83	100	100	20		80							
Total		73	18	110	128	1·75	30	0·4	98	1·35	3	13				
%			14	86	100	100	23		77							

* According to company's Organization Chart: Level 3 = Divisional Head (usually a Vice President); Level 4 = Departmental Head, etc. † Participating in study. ‡ Mutually Perceived Informal Relationships. § Did not participate in Informal Relationships study. ‖ Chief role player. ⊤ Other role players.

Communications Means. By which means does the individual prefer to inter-act – the telephone or the conference? Example: for all individuals, the conference is the preferable mutually perceived communications tool. Never-theless, there are differences in the relative use of the telephone. Person 08 is not perceived as using the telephone at all, while persons 00 and 23 are perceived as using it comparatively more than others (38 per cent and 22 per cent respectively).

A comparison between the Communicogram and Informalogram in *Table 5* brings to light several differences as to roles played by members of the group:

Communications Transmitters. The chief role player in out-of-group contacts is Person 12, the formal leader of the group both on the Communicogram (1·0 mutually perceived interactions per day) and on the Informalogram (two mutually perceived relationships). As to other main role players in out-of-group contacts, there seems to be disagreement between the two charts. While the Informalogram, based on a 'single-shot' perception, points out Person 18 (one mutually perceived relationship) – the Communicogram tells us that his mutually perceived out-of-group interactions were comparatively few (0·2 per day); on the other hand, Persons 00 and 06 were perceived as much more active in out-of-group interactions (0·6 per day each).

Informal Leaders. The emerging informal leader on the Informalogram, Per-son 14 (four mutually perceived relationships), does not appear as such on the Communicogram (only 0·8 mutually perceived interactions within the group). On the other hand, Persons 14 and 06 appear to be the informal leaders on the Communicogram (3·0 and 2·7 mutually perceived in-group interactions respectively).

COMPARISON OF COMMUNICOGRAM WITH ORGANIZATION CHART

All these aspects of the Communicogram could be presented in graphical form. *Chart B* enables us to compare the volume of interactions that was perceived to exist among members of the research and development manage-ment group with the formal (required) relationships between them, according to the company's Organization Chart.*

Table 6 presents the data on the Communications Chart (*Chart B*) and enables us to find out to what extent the perceived existing interactions con-form with the requirements laid down by the company's Organization Chart. The circled numbers of interactions are between a person and those with whom he is required to maintain formal relationships according to the Organization Chart (with his superior, with subordinates, and with peers).

It is evident from the data in *Table 6* that for some members of the group

---

* The mutually perceived interactions on the chart are the totals over the period of the experiment. In future, when such studies would cover longer periods of time, such a Com-municogram should preferably portray the 'interactions per day' between the participants.

CHART B

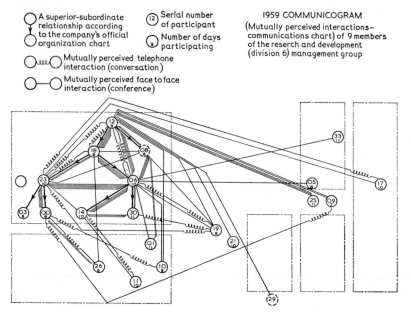

Table 6   *Devon Corporation, Research and Development Division, Mutually Perceived Interactions in Conformity or Non-conformity with Organization Chart*

	Mutually Perceived Interactions* between members of the group ('in-group' only)									required in group	total in group	% with those required out of total
Person Number	12	O8	18	23	O6	O3	OO	14	30			
12		③	⑥	1	6	-	-	-		9	16	56
O8	③		1	1	4	-	-	-		4	9	44
18	⑥	⑴		③	⑤	-	-	-		15	15	100
23	1	1	3		⑥	⊖	③	1		12	15	80
O6	6	4	⑤	6		-	-	④	②	17	27	63
O3	-	-	-	-	-		⊖	-		O	O	-
OO	-	-	-	③	-	⊖		-		③	3	100
14	-	-	-	1	④	-	-		③	7	8	87
30	-	-	-	-	②	-	-	3		5	5	100

* Circled interactions are between members of the group among whom formal relationships are required according to the Organization Chart.

the mutually perceived interactions are confined to the requirements of the Organization Chart, while only about half of their perceived existing interactions with others are as required by the Organization Chart. It is interesting to note that, generally speaking, the higher the management echelon, the more the informal activity (over and above the requirements). This, incidentally, corresponds to similar findings arrived at with different tools in the same organization.*

Discussion and conclusions

A period of two weeks might be too short for establishing statistically valid daily averages of the 'existing' interactions and the communications that 'went through' from one person to another. Nevertheless, the results of this study suggest that the description of the organization by means of a Communicogram seems to be more meaningful, and closer to real events, than that provided by the more traditional Organization Chart, Formalogram, and Informalogram. This is primarily so because the relationships between members of the organization in these latter charts preclude any differentiation as to either quality or quantity of the relationships between various members of the organization. Even in Organization Charts where a solid line is supposed to denote a 'line relationship' and a dotted line a 'staff relationship', all solid lines are identical and therefore do not indicate what the relationship involves – how many interactions, what type of communication, etc.

The Communicogram, on the other hand, enables us to describe the quantities of the relationships and could point out the quality of the relationship (by indicating the types of interactions 'gone through', i.e. the amount and types of communication with regard to which there exist a consensus between the participants). Thus, *Chart B*, which describes only the consensus as to the occurrence of interactions, could have been broadened to include the description of the consensus as to the type of interaction.

The principal findings of this research were that in the organization in question only 25 per cent of the perceived interactions among the participating management group were mutually acknowledged; that is to say, 75 per cent of the perceived interactions did not register in the minds of the other party. From among the mutually perceived interactions, less than 50 per cent of the communications 'went through', i.e. there was a consensus as to the type of interaction. In all, only 12 per cent of the perceived interactions 'went through'. Nobody can establish whether this is 'bad' or 'good' until similar research has been carried out elsewhere.†

Even at this stage, the present communications study enables us to evaluate

* The table on p. 91 of 'Effects of Management Changes on Organisation Relationship and Attitudes' [4] shows that the higher the management level, the more Mutually Perceived Informal Relationships per person.

† The only comparable study was brought to my attention by Professor Robert Dubin. [5] This study was carried out several years earlier by Tom Burns. [6] Interestingly enough, both Burns's and the present projects were related to Carlson's work. [2]

The common denominator of the two projects is their being based on self-recording by the participants, one of the major differences being that in Burns's study all interactions were recorded. For this reason it is impossible to compare the Consensus as to the Occurrence of the Interactions. The Consensus as to the Type of Interaction (Burns refers to it as Exchange of Information) achieved in Burns's case was 60 per cent as against 47 per cent in this study.

the possible uses of the Communicogram as a tool for top management when considering changes for improving the organization. Its potentialities lie in:

Its ability to contrast one organizational unit (e.g. a division) with another. This might give management an insight into why one division is more efficient and effective than the other.

Its ability to contrast top-management requirements (as expressed in an Organization Chart) with the communications pattern as perceived by the people of the organization. This might lead either to modifications in the Organization Chart, that is to say in the working procedures of management, or, if top management is convinced that the Organization Chart in its present form is vital for the organization, to changes in the organization.

Its ability to establish the position of every individual (as compared with others) in terms of his being perceived as a channel not only of interactions but also of certain types of interaction. This again might lead to changes with regard to an individual who, for example, might be a 'good information-transmitter', a 'poor decision-maker', and a 'reasonably good adviser'.

Its ability to highlight 'weak communication links'. A certain position in the management structure might be a 'barrier' to, instead of a 'gateway' of communications, for two main reasons. An individual in this position may act as a 'block in communications', and he should then either be helped in his communications or moved to another position where his communications characteristics are more suitable.

On the other hand, the communications characteristics of a given individual may be suitable, but he may be overwhelmed by the volume of communications; in this case, the position should be reinforced with additional personnel.

All these potentials of the Communicogram could be realized only in conjunction with other tools of management. Such tools include Financial Statements, Budgeting, Cost-Accounting, Marketing and Production Reports, etc., as well as a first-hand knowledge of the people with whom the Communicogram deals. In the absence of collateral information it could be extremely dangerous to act upon the conclusions of a Communicogram alone.

Once changes have been introduced in an organization, an additional communications study would provide an opportunity for determining their effects.

ACKNOWLEDGEMENTS

I gratefully acknowledge the free computer time allotted to me by the MIT Computation Center, the programming by the staff of the Littauer Statistical Laboratory, Harvard University, the encouragement of Professors G. Lombard of Harvard University and W. F. Whyte of Cornell University, and the patience of Professors

J. D. Glover of Harvard University and E. A. Fleishman, Director of the American Institute of Research, Mr B. A. Friedrich of Nahariya, Israel, Mr E. Goldberg, of the Technion, Haifa, Israel – who read the manuscript and offered their helpful comments.

REFERENCES

1 R. M. Stogdill & C. L. Shartle (1955)
2 S. Carlson (1951)
3 F. Roethlisberger & C. R. Rogers (1952) pp. 46–52
4 T. Weinshall (1960)
5 R. Dubin (1958)
6 T. Burns (1954)

Part VII
Conclusion

47 · Closing Remarks

G. KREWERAS

Among the reasons which make it difficult to conclude, there is the fact that the authors of papers and participants in discussions have often placed themselves at the highest level of synthesis; so that my own remarks must find a way to avoid a tedious repetition of already expressed ideas or a subjectivity which would deprive them of any right to stand at this final place. It is to be feared that my remarks cannot meet these requirements; in fact, I am sure that they will offend both criteria.

It seems to me that the organizers deserve especial thanks for having systematically brought together operational researchers and social scientists without trying to force each single participant into one of these two sub-sets. Several times in discussions participants tried to determine the numerical balance, and each time I felt that many people were reluctant to profess a definite place on this or that side of the vertical line:

Social	Operational
Sciences	Research

Even for those who feel that they are unmistakably on one side, no serious reasons for lack of understanding seem to arise with those on the other side. Perhaps this can be accounted for by the individual decisions to attend this conference, which of course have kept away all those who were not struck by or interested in the possible relationship and the need for co-operation between these types of activity.

My starting assertion will be that, if there is anywhere a gap that creates genuine difficulties, it is not so much directed along the vertical line above as along the horizontal line:

Social	Operational
Sciences	Research

This implies that operational researchers and social scientists have probably encountered it more or less consciously within their disciplines, and

perhaps hoped that such a river could be more easily crossed in the neighbouring village than in their own.

It looks as if such a hope were fundamentally utopian and as if the crossing
of the river were at any rate a risky enterprise. On one side there is reality –
operational or social reality – on the other side there is theory, science,
research; the difficulties of bridging the gap are of a common, essentially
philosophical, kind and are linked with the world-old question of the connexions between thought and action.

Have the modern developments of operational research and of the scientific
approach to social problems improved our position with respect to this
quandary? I am not at all sure. Remarkable efforts have been devoted in
recent writings and even in this conference to giving a sound basis to the
concept of a 'normative science' or to the occurrence of the verb 'ought' in
the conclusions of scientific research. May I say that these efforts have not
convinced me so far; rather, I wonder whether, instead of clearing up the
misunderstandings, they have not worsened and deepened them sometimes.

One should never overlook the golden rule, so often referred to, which
reminds us of the pitfalls of language. The more basic or common a word is,
the more carefully its meaning should be agreed upon; and in case the
agreement proves hard to reach, the word itself should be avoided as far as
possible. By virtue of this rule, let me stick to the standard usage which
reserves the word science for non-normative activities of mind.

The scientist's task consists primarily, if not exclusively, in building up
models. This holds as well for the adept of the 'well-established sciences' as
for the operational researcher or the social scientist. Of course, different sorts
of scientist are interested in different 'sections' of the real world. The conventional scientist (physicist, chemist, biologist) studies sections of reality
which are not at all irrelevant to human behaviour and decision, but which
happen to condition such a variety of actions and purposes that the concept
of value seems to be absent from them: everybody knows how well the same
nuclear physics can serve quite opposite political goals.

As for operational research and the social sciences, they cut up reality in
another way: man is always explicitly present, at least as a decision-maker,
often as a subordinate or as an opponent, and often in groups, i.e. in a social
context. Since man is present as a whole, his scales of values or preferences
are present with him, whether they are conscious or not. The latter can, of
course, not be passed over in silence, unless there is an unquestionable
unanimity about them; which means practically never.

In so far as it has sometimes been believed that the main role of operational
research, as an embryo of a 'normative science', was precisely to construct
and/or justify values, the needs of the social sciences have perhaps been
responsible for such a belief: any social scientist has experienced – and
several of them have testified here – how tricky it is to define social values and

to fit them into consistent models. For anyone faced with such difficulties, it may be tempting, of course, to expect from operational research more than it can give.

As things stand, one might wonder whether operational research is feasible at all. At the same time one might wonder whether the social sciences should not limit themselves to describing without any judgement or reference to values, and abide with the old-fashioned reproach of being more concerned with what happens in some Polynesian islands than in the industrial suburbs of London or Paris.

To both questions, this conference seems to contribute with the following reply: values, provided it is not believed that they can be built up from nothing or from 'objective facts', may be – and let me add 'should be' – incorporated in models. If one wished to emphasize a difference between operational research and the social sciences one could say that the latter consider human commitments to specific values as facts which deserve to be described in their static or dynamic characteristics according to appropriate models, whereas the former is primarily concerned with the models which involve a logical connexion between the (true or assumed) adhesion to certain values and the 'preferability' of certain courses of action.

At least the typical operational researcher is familiar with the paradox of the two watches. It is rather easy to induce an unwary person to agree with the statement that the better of two watches is the one that indicates the right time more often. Once the agreement is reached, it is a matter of elementary logic to ascertain that a watch which loses a minute a day gives the right time about once in two years (once in 720 days), whereas a watch that has stopped working gives it twice a day. But this paradox is relevant for the social scientist as well, for it shows how carefully values should be dealt with and how many ambiguities may occur, even though there is no obvious conflict. It would be too easy to say that the victim of such a joke 'should not' have agreed with the premise. Of course this would be true in the case of a watch, because it does perhaps not need too much intelligence to notice that it is not only the frequency of exact time indications that matters but also the magnitude and progressiveness of deviations, the possibility of regulating, and so on. But clearly enough this leads to a more refined analysis, i.e. a better model of what is demanded from a watch; and such an analysis may need much more sophistication if a social institution and no longer a watch is concerned.

The main question to be answered is 'what is a good model?' Undoubtedly, a satisfactory model must be a rational one, i.e. must satisfy internal conditions of logical consistency. But this is not enough; we require the model to fit reality. This is the central difficulty, and I have not the slightest hope that we can solve it; it is as though the tailor were on this side of the river and had to make clothes for customers on the other side.

Some of you might hope that we can achieve what seems to have been

Y

achieved by the sciences of inert matter; has not the transition from Newtonian to relativistic mechanics simply added corrective terms to the initial model, and proceeded by minor alterations as a tailor does in the last fittings?

Although I am a layman in physics, I suspect that even in that case things are not so simple. I am willing to admit, for instance, that for the form of the Earth a sphere is a better model than an indefinite plane, and an ellipsoid a better model than a sphere. But let us assume, for a moment, that the Earth is 'really' an ellipsoid with known dimensions, and that we try to represent it approximately by a sphere: on what basis shall we choose the radius of the latter? The problem arises because of the eccentricity of the ellipsoid, and we should make our final choice either arbitrarily or with reference to an initially unformulated question (to trace a map of Europe, for instance).

Just as doubtful, it seems, is the situation in the sciences of man and society. Whether a model is right or wrong, true or false, is largely a matter of agreement; as long as two persons or more agree upon a model, they may draw interesting and useful conclusions from its development, but they should always – for both philosophical and practical reasons – remain prepared to take quite new elements into account, including the eventuality of being induced to adopt a completely new model. Nothing precludes either of them, even when displaying such a basic scepticism, from remaining true to some higher form of ethics; it is one of the glories of science to authorize a dialogue between supporters of different ethical families. But there are obvious limits in this direction: however refined game theory and conflict theory have become in their modern forms, a theory of ideological war, for instance, will remain out of sight unless the relevant ideologies can be thought of as 'particular cases' of some 'common ideology'; which is not unlikely to imply a contradiction.

Let me summarize my apparently pessimistic position in a style borrowed from our technical jargon: the set of models which are conceivable for a given reality is not necessarily a totally ordered set.

Let me also state, as a conclusion, that this pessimism does not interfere at all with our common feeling of considerable interest in joint meetings like this one. As for myself, I must confess that I had never seen so many prominent scientists devote several days to questions so closely related to the key problems of modern society; I do hope that it is not the last time. Even if this conference had only given to operational researchers an opportunity to go beyond a sometimes too strictly technological horizon, and to social scientists an extensive look at the more decisional implications of their discipline, its organizers would have deserved the gratitude of the participants and their enthusiastic support for further similar initiatives.

Combined Bibliography

ACHE, H. 1962. *Wesen und Voraussetzungen einer operativen Ökonomik* (The nature and prerequisites of operative economics). Dissertation, Faculty of Economics and Social Sciences, Free University of Berlin.

ACKOFF, R. L. 1960. Unsuccessful case studies and why. *Opns. Res.* 8, 259–63.

1957a. *Design of social research.* Chicago: University of Chicago Press.

1957b. Operations research and national planning. *Opns. Res.* 5, 457–68.

1958a. Towards a behavioral theory of communication. *Man. Sci.* 4, 218–34.

1958b. On Hitch's dissent on operations research and national planning. *Opns. Res.* 6, 121–3.

1962a. A definitional note on cooperation, conflict, and competition. *Saertryk Erhvervsøkonomisk Tiddsskrift* 4, 312–15.

1962b. *Scientific method: optimizing applied research decisions.* New York: Wiley.

1963a. Towards quantitative evaluation of urban services. In H. G. Schaller (Ed.), *Public expenditure decisions in the urban community.* q.v.

1963b. Definition and measurement of cooperation, conflict, exploitation, and competition. *U.S. Army Research Symposium, March, 1963.* Durham, North Carolina, pp. 99–104.

ACKOFF, R. L. & RIVETT, B. H. P. 1963. *A manager's guide to operations research.* New York: Wiley.

ALMOND, G. A. & COLEMAN, J. S. (Eds.) 1960. *The politics of the developing areas.* Princeton, N.J.: Princeton University Press.

ALTMAN, I. & MCGINNIES, E. 1960. Interpersonal perception and communication in discussion groups of varied attitudinal composition. *J. abnorm. soc. Psychol.* 60, 390–5.

ARGYRIS, C. 1957. *Personality and organization.* New York: Harper.

1960. *Organization development – An inquiry into the Esso approach.* New Haven, Conn.: Yale University.

1962. *Interpersonal competence and organizational effectiveness.* Homewood, Ill.: Dorsey Press; London: Tavistock Publications.

1964a. *Integrating the individual and the organization.* New York: Wiley.

1964b. T-Groups for organizational effectiveness. *Harv. bus. Rev.* 42, 60–74.

ARROW, K. J. 1951. *Social choice and individual values.* New York: Wiley.

1964. Control in large organizations. *Man. Sci.* 10 (3), 397–408.

ARROW, K. J., HARRIS, T. & MARSCHAK, J. 1951. Optimum inventory policy. *Econometrica* 19, 250–72.

ASHBY, W. R. 1956. *An introduction to cybernetics.* London: Chapman and Hall.

1957. *An introduction to cybernetics.* New York: Wiley.

1958. Requisite variety and its implications for the control of complex systems. *Cybernetica* **1**, 83–99.

1960. *Design for a brain* (2nd Edn.) London: Chapman & Hall; New York: Wiley.

BARITZ, L. 1960. *Servants of power*. Middletown, Conn.: Wesleyan Univ. Press.

BARKER, R. G. 1960. Ecology and motivation. *Nebraska symposium on motivation*. Nebraska: Univ. of Nebraska Press.

BARNARD, C. I. 1938. *The functions of the executive*. Cambridge, Mass.: Harvard Univ. Press.

BARNES, E. 1961. *People in hospital*. London: Macmillan.

BARNETT, H. G. 1956. *Anthropology in administration*. Evanston, Ill.: Row, Peterson.

BASS, F. M., et al. (Eds.) 1961. *Mathematical models and methods in marketing*. Homewood, Ill.: Irwin.

BAUMGARDT, D. 1952. *Bentham and the ethics of to-day*. Princeton, N.J.: Princeton Univ. Press.

BAVELAS, A. & STRAUSS, G. 1961. Group dynamics and intergroup relations. In W. G. Bennis, K. D. Benne & R. Chin (Eds.) 1961. *The planning of change*. New York: Holt, Rinehart & Winston.

BECKHARD, R. 1965. An organization improvement program in a decentralized organized organization. In D. Zand & P. Buchanan (Eds.), *Organization development: Theory and Practice*. q.v.

BEER, S. 1959a. What has cybernetics to do with operational research? *Operat. Res. Quart.* **10**, 1–21.

1959b. *Cybernetics and management*. London: English Universities Press.

BEESLEY, M. E., BLACKBURN, A. J. & FOSTER, C. D. 1963. Urban transport models and motorway investment. *Economica* **30**, 243–61.

BEESLEY, M. E. & FOSTER, C. D. 1965. The Victoria Line: Social benefits and finances. *J. Roy. statist. Soc.* A, **128**, 67–88.

BENDIX, R. & WEBER, M. 1960. *An intellectual portrait*. New York: Doubleday.

BENNE, K. D. & SWANSON, G. (Eds.) 1950. *J. soc. Issues* **6**, Values and social science.

BENNIS, W. G. 1962. Towards a 'truly' scientific management: The concept of organizational health. *Industr. manag. Rev.*, M.I.T., Fall.

1963. A new role for the behavioral sciences: Effecting organizational change. *Admin. Sci. Quart.* **8**, 125–65.

1966. *Changing organizations*. New York: McGraw-Hill.

BENNIS, W. G., BENNE, K. D. & CHIN. R. 1961. *The planning of change*. New York: Holt, Rinehart & Winston.

BERELSON, B. 1952. *Content analysis in communication research*. Glencoe, Ill.: Free Press.

BERELSON, B. & STEINER, G. A. 1964. *Human behavior*. New York: Harcourt Brace.

BERLINER, J. S. 1957. *Factory and manager in the U.S.S.R.* Cambridge, Mass.: Harvard Univ. Press.

BERNARD, J. 1950. Where is the modern sociology of conflict? *Amer. J. Sociol.* **56**, 11–16.

BION, W. R. 1961. *Experiences in groups, and other papers*. London: Tavistock Publications; New York: Basic Books.

BLACK, D. 1958. *A theory of committees and elections*. Cambridge: Cambridge Univ. Press.

BLAKE, R. R. 1953. The interaction-feeling hypothesis applied to psychotherapy groups. *Sociometry* **16**, 253–65.

BLAKE, R. R. & MOUTON, J. S. 1962a. Comprehension of points of communality in competing solutions. *Sociometry* **25**, 56–63.

1962b. *The induction of change in industrial organizations.* Austin, Texas: Scientific Methods, Inc.

1964. *The managerial grid.* Houston, Texas: Gulf Publishing.

1965. A 9, 9 approach to organization development. In D. Zand & P. Buchanan (Eds.), *Organization development: Theory and practice.* q.v.

BLAKE, R. R., MOUTON, J. S., BARNES, L. B. & GREINER, L. E. 1964. A managerial grid approach to organization development: The theory and some research findings. *Harv. bus. Rev.* **42.**

BLAKE, R. R., SHEPARD, H. A. & MOUTON, J. S. 1964. *Intergroup conflict.* Foundation for Research on Human Behavior, Ann Arbor.

BLAU, P. M. 1955. *The dynamics of bureaucracy.* Chicago: Univ. of Chicago Press.

BLAU, P. M. & SCOTT, W. R. 1962. *Formal organizations.* San Francisco: Chandler Publishing Co.

BLUMBERG, M. S. 1957. Evaluating health screening procedures. *Opns. Res.* **5**, 351–60.

BOSKOFF, A. 1964. Functional analysis as a source of a theoretical repertory and research tasks in the study of social change. In G. K. Zollschan & W. Hirsch (Eds.), *Explorations in social change.* Boston: Houghton Mifflin.

BOULDING, K. 1956. General systems theory – the skeleton of science. *Man. Sci.* **2**, 197–208.

BOVEY, R. L. 1964. *The sensitivity of optimal strategies in finite statistical decision problems to variations in parameters.* Doctoral dissertation, Johns Hopkins University.

BRADFORD, L. P., GIBB, J. R. & BENNE, K. D. 1964. *T-Group theory and laboratory method.* New York: Wiley.

BRAITHWAITE, R. B. 1955. *Theory of games as a tool for the moral philosopher.* Cambridge: Cambridge Univ. Press.

BRAYBROOKE, D. & LINDBLOM, C. D. 1962. *Strategy of decision.* Glencoe: Free Press.

BRAYFIELD, A. H. & CROCKETT, W. H. 1955. Employee attitudes and employee performance. *Psychol. Bull.* **52**, 396–424.

BRITISH RAILWAYS BOARD 1963. *Reshaping of British Railways.* London: H.M.S.O.

BRONOWSKI, J. 1951. *The common sense of science.* London: Heinemann.

BROSS, I. D. 1953. *Design for decisions.* New York: Macmillan.

1964. Is it really wrong? *Amer. Statistician.* **18**, 21–2.

BUCHANAN, J. M. & STUBBLEBINE, W. C. 1962. Externality. *Economica* **29**, 371–84.

BUCHANAN, J. M. & TULLOCK, G. 1962. *Calculus of consent.* Ann Arbor, Mich.: Michigan Univ. Press.

BURLING, T. *et al.* 1956. *The give and take in hospitals.* New York: Putnam.

BURNS, T. 1954. The directions of activity and communication in a departmental executive group: A quantitative study in a British engineering factory with a self recording technique. *Hum. Relat.* **7**, 73–9.

1958. *Management in the electronics industry.* Social Science Research Centre, Edinburgh.

1961. Micropolitics. *Admin. Sci. Quart.* **6**, 257–81.

1962a. Des fins et des moyens dans l'entreprise. *Sociol. Travail* **3**, 209–29.

1962b. The sociology of industry. In Welford, Argyle, Glass & Morris (Eds.), *Society*. London: Routledge & Kegan Paul.

BURNS, T. & STALKER, G. M. 1961. *The management of innovation*. London: Tavistock Publications.

BUSH, R. R. & MOSTELLER, F. 1955. *Stochastic models for learning*. New York: Wiley.

CAMPBELL, D. T. 1963. Social attitudes and other acquired behavioral dispositions. In S. Koch (Ed.), *Psychology: A study of a science*. Vol. 6. *Investigations of man as Socius: Their place in psychology and the social sciences*. New York: McGraw-Hill.

CANNON, W. B. 1932. *The wisdom of the body*. New York: Norton.

CARLSON, S. 1951. *Executive behavior: A study of the work load and working methods of managing directors*. Stockholm: Strömbergs.

CAUDILL, W. 1958. *The psychiatric hospital as a small society*. Cambridge, Mass.: Harvard Univ. Press.

CERVIN, V. 1955. Experimental investigation of behavior in social situations: Individual behavior effects of change in group attitude from opposition to co-operation. *Canad. J. Psychol.* **9**, 155–60.

CHAMBERS, D. & CHARNES, A. 1961. Inter-temporal analysis and optimization of bank portfolios. *Man. Sci.* **7** (4), 393–410.

CHAPMAN, R. L. & KENNEDY, J. L. 1956. The background and implications of the systems research laboratory studies. In G. Fitch & F. Cameron (Eds.), *Air Force human engineering, personnel, and training research*. Washington: National Academy of Sciences, National Research Council.

CHAPPLE, E. D. & SAYLES, L. R. 1961. *The measurement of management*. New York: Macmillan.

CHARNES, A. & COOPER, W. W. 1962. *Deterministic equivalents for optimizing and satisficing under chance constraints*. Northwestern Univ. Technological Institute and Carnegie Institute of Technology, July.

CHARNES, A., COOPER, W. W. & IJIRI, Y. 1963. Breakeven budgeting and programming to goals. *J. Accounting Res.* **1**, 16–43.

CHARNES, A., COOPER, W. W. & MILLER, M. H. 1959. Application of linear programming to financial budgeting and the costing of funds. *J. Business* **32**, 20–46.

CHARNES, A. & STEDRY, A. C. 1964a. Investigations in the theory of multiple budgeted goals. In C. P. Bonini, R. K. Jaedicke & H. M. Wagner (Eds.), *Management controls: New directions in basic research*. New York: McGraw-Hill.

1964b. Exploratory models in the theory of budgetary control. In W. W. Cooper, H. J. Leavitt & M. W. Shelly (Eds.), *New perspectives in organization research*. New York: Wiley.

CHEIN, I., COOK, S. W. & HARDING, J. 1948. The field of action research. *Amer. Psychol.* **3**, 43–50.

CHERNOFF, H. & MOSES, L. 1959. *Elementary decision theory*. New York: Wiley.

Chicago Area transportation study. Final report. 1959–62. (Vol. 1, 1959; Vol. 2, 1960; Vol. 3, 1962.)

CHIN, R. 1961. The utility of system models and developmental models for practitioners. In Bennis, Benne & Chin (1961), pp. 201–4. q.v.

1963. *Models and ideas about changing*. Presented at the Symposium on Acceptance of New Ideas, Univ. of Nebraska, November.

CHIPMAN, J. S. 1960. The foundations of utility. *Econometrica* 193–224.

CHURCHILL, N. C. 1962. *Behavioral effects of an audit: An experimental study*. Ph.D. dissertation, Univ. of Michigan School of Business Administration. (Revised in *Behavioral aspects of audits* (in press). Reading, Mass.: Addison Wesley.)

CHURCHILL, N. C. & COOPER, W. W. 1964. Effects of auditing records: Individual task accomplishment and organization objectives. In W. W. Cooper, H. J. Leavitt & M. W. Shelly II (Eds.), *New perspectives in organization research*. New York: Wiley.

CHURCHILL, N. C., COOPER, W. W. & SAINSBURY, T. 1964. Laboratory and field studies of the behavioral effects of audits. In C. P. Bonini, R. K. Jaedicke & H. M. Wagner (Eds.), *Management controls: New directions in basic research*. pp. 253–67. New York: McGraw-Hill.

CHURCHMAN, C. W. 1961. *Prediction and optimal decision*. Englewood Cliffs, N.J.: Prentice-Hall.

CHURCHMAN, C. W. & ACKOFF, R. L. 1950. *Methods of enquiry*. St. Louis: Educational Publications.

CHURCHMAN, C. W. & RATOOSH, P. (Eds.) 1959. *Measurement definitions and theories*. New York: Wiley.

1960. *Innovation in group behavior*. Institute of Industrial Relations, Univ. of California, Berkeley.

CLARK, D. H. 1964. *Administrative therapy*. London: Tavistock Publications; Philadelphia: Lippincott.

CLARKSON, G. P. E. 1962. *Portfolio selection: A simulation of trust investment*. Englewood Cliffs, N.J.: Prentice-Hall.

CLAWSON, M. 1959. *Methods of measuring the demand for and value of outdoor recreation*. Reprint No. 10, Washington D.C.: Resources for the Future.

CLEVELAND, H. 1962. Crisis diplomacy. *Foreign Affairs*, August.

COCH, L. & FRENCH, J. R. P., Jr. 1947–8. Overcoming resistance to change. *Hum. Relat.* **1**, 512–32.

COHEN, B. P. 1963. *Conflict and conformity: a probability model and its application*. Cambridge, Mass.: M.I.T. Press.

COLM, G. 1956. Comments on Samuelson's theory of finance. *Rev. Econ. Statist.* **38**, 408–12.

COOMBS, C. H., RAIFFA, H. & THRALL, R. M. 1954. Some views on mathematical models and measurement theory. In R. M. Thrall, C. H. Coombs & R. L. Davis (Eds.), *Decision processes*. New York: Wiley.

COOPER, W. W. 1961. Some implications of the newer analytic approach to management. *Calif. man. Rev.* **4**, 51–64.

COSER, L. 1956. *The functions of social conflict*. Glencoe: Free Press.

1961. The termination of conflict. *J. Conflict Resol.* **5**, 36.

CROSSMAN, R. H. S. 1964. Scientists in Whitehall. *Encounter*, **23**, 3–10.

CYERT, R. M., DILL, W. R. & MARCH, J. G. 1958. The role of expectations in business decision making. *Admin. Sci. Quart.* **3** (3).

CYERT, R. M. & MARCH, J. G. 1963. *Behavioral theory of the firm*. Englewood Cliffs, N.J.: Prentice-Hall.

DAHL, R. A. 1956. *A preface to democratic theory*. Chicago: Univ. of Chicago Press.

DAHL, R. & LINDBLOM, C. E. 1953. *Politics, economics and welfare*. New York: Harper.

DAHRENDORF, R. 1961. Towards a theory of social conflict. In Bennis, Benne & Chin (1961), pp. 445–51. q.v.

DALENIUS, T. 1957. *Sampling in Sweden: Contributions to the methods and theories of sample survey practice.* Stockholm: Almquist & Wicksell.

DALENIUS, T. & HODGES, J. L., Jr. 1957. The choice of stratification points. *Skand. Aktuar.* **3–4**, 198–203.

1959. Minimum variance stratification. *J. Amer. statist. Ass.* **54** (285), 88–101.

DALTON, M. 1959. *Men who manage.* New York: Wiley.

DYDTZIG, G. B. 1959. General convex objective forms. In Arrow, Karlin & Suppes (Eds.), *Mathematical methods in the social sciences.* Stanford, Calif.: Stanford University Press. 1963. *Linear programming and extensions.* Princeton, N.J.: Princeton University Press.

DANTZIG, G. B. & WOLFE, P. 1960. Decomposition principle for linear programs. *Opns. Res.* **8**, 101–11.

1961. The decomposition algorithm for linear programmes. *Econometrica* **29**, 767–78.

DAVID, G. 1965. The Weldon Study: An organization change program based upon change in management philosophy. In D. Zand & P. Buchanan (Eds.), *Organization development: Theory and practice.* q.v.

DAVIS, O. & WHINSTON, A. 1962. Externalities, welfare, and the theory of games. *J. polit. Econ.* June.

DEBREU, G. 1959. *Theory of value.* New York: Wiley.

DEUTSCH, M. 1949. An experimental study of the effects of cooperation and competition upon group processes. *Hum. Relat.* **2**, 199–231.

1960. The effect of motivational orientation upon trust and suspicion. *Hum. Relat.* **13**, 123–39.

DORFMAN, R. 1960. Operations research. *Amer. econ. Rev.* **50**, 575–623.

DOWNS, A. 1957. *Economic theory of democracy.* London: Harper.

DUBIN, R. 1958. *The world of work.* Englewood Cliffs, N.J.: Prentice-Hall.

DUMMETT, M. & FARQUHARSON, R. 1961. On stability in voting. *Econometrica* **29**, 33–43.

ECKSTEIN, O. 1958. Water resource development. In *The economics of project evaluation.* Cambridge, Mass.: Harvard Univ. Press.

1961. Benefit-cost analysis and regional development. In *Regional economic planning: Techniques of analysis.* Paris: European Productivity Agency of O.E.E.C.

EDWARDS, A. W. F. & CAVALLI-SFORZA, L. L. 1963. A method for cluster analysis. *Fifth Int. Biometric Conf. Cambridge.*

EMERY, F. E. 1963. *Second progress report on conceptualization.* London: Tavistock Institute of Human Relations. Document No. T.125.

EMERY, F. E., OESER, O. A. & TULLY, J. 1958. *Information, decision and action.* Melbourne: Univ. of Melbourne Press.

EMERY, F. E. & TRIST, E. L. 1960. Sociotechnical systems. In C. W. Churchman *et al.* (Eds.), *Management sciences, models and techniques.* London: Pergamon Press. 1963. *The causal texture of organizational environments.* (Mimeo). London: Tavistock Institute. (Reprinted in *Hum. Relat.* **18**, 21–32, 1965.)

EMMETT, D. 1966. *Rules, roles, and relations.* London: Macmillan.

ENTHOVEN, A. C. 1963. Systems analysis and decision making. *Military Rev.* **43**, 7–18.

ETZIONI, A. 1961. *A comparative analysis of complex organizations.* New York: Free Press.

EVAN, W. 1962. Due process of law in military and industrial organizations. *Admin. Sci. Quart.* 187–207.

EXLINE, R. V. 1957. Group climate as a factor in the relevance and accuracy of social perception. *J. abnorm. soc. Psychol.* **55**, 382–8.

FARQUHARSON, R. 1955. Théorie des jeux – sur une généralisation de la notion d'equilibrium. *Comptes rendus* **240**, 46–8.

1956a. Strategic information in games and in voting. In C. Cherry (Ed.) *Information theory.* London: Butterworth.

1956b. Straightforwardness in voting procedures. *Oxford Economic Papers,* February.

FARRAR, D. 1962. *The investment decision under uncertainty.* Englewood Cliffs, N.J.: Prentice-Hall.

FAYERWEATHER, J. 1959. *The executive overseas.* Syracuse, N.Y.: Syracuse Univ. Press.

FAYOL, H. 1955. *General and industrial management* (Trans. Storrs). London: Pitman.

FELDSTEIN, M. S. 1964. Net social benefit calculations and the public investment decision. *Oxford Econ. Papers* **16**, No. 1.

FISHER, F. M. 1956. Income distribution, value judgements and welfare. *Quart. J. Econ.* **70**, 380–424.

FISHER, R. A. 1954. *Statistical methods for research workers.* Edinburgh: Oliver & Boyd.

FISHER, W. 1958. On grouping for maximum homogeneity. *J. Amer. statist. Ass.* **53** (284), 789–98.

FLAGLE, C. D. 1963. Operational research in the health services. *Ann. N.Y. Acad. Sci.* **107**, 748–59.

FLAGLE, C. D. & LECHAT, M. F. 1963. Statistical decision theory and the selection of diagnostic and therapeutic strategies in public health. *Proc. Third Int. Conf. Opns. Res., Oslo.* Paris: Dunod.

FLEISHMAN, E. A. 1953. Leadership climate, human relations, training and supervisory behavior. *Personnel Psychol.,* 205–22.

FOLLETT, M. P. 1940. In H. Metcalf and L. Urwick (Eds.), *Dynamic administration. The collected papers of Mary Parker Follett.* New York: Harper.

FOSTER, C. D. 1963. *The transport problem.* London: Blackie.

FOSTER, C. D. & BEESLEY, M. E. 1963. Estimating the social benefit of constructing an underground railway in London. *J. Roy. statist. Soc.* A, **126**, 46–78.

FOSTER, G. M. 1962. *Traditional cultures and the impact of technological change.* New York: Harper and Row.

FOUNDATION FOR RESEARCH ON HUMAN BEHAVIOUR. 1960. *An action research program for organization development.* Ann Arbor, Mich.

FREEMAN, H. E. 1963. The strategy of social policy research. *Soc. Welfare Forum.*

FRENCH, J. R. P., Jr. 1941. The disruption and cohesion of groups. *J. abnorm. soc. Psychol.* **36**, 361–77.

FRENCH, J. R. P., Jr., KAY, E. & MEYER, H. H. 1962. *A study of the effects of threat and participation in the performance appraisal situation.* General Electric Co., New York.

FRENCH, J. R. P. & RAVEN, B. 1959. The bases of social power. In D. Cartwright (Ed.), *Studies in social power.* Ann Arbor, Mich.: R.C.G.D., Univ. of Michigan.

FRIEDMAN, J. 1963. *Issues in planning theory.* (Mimeo). Cambridge, Mass.: M.I.T. Press.

GAUSE, G. F. 1934. *The struggle for existence.* Baltimore, Md.: Williams & Wilkins.

GEISLER, M. A. 1958. *The simulation of a large-scale military activity.* RAND Corp., P-1555.

—— 1960. *The use of simulation in the design of an operational control system.* RAND Corp., P-1986.

GEISLER, M. A. & STEGER, W. A. 1962. *Determining preferred management techniques in new systems through game-simulation.* RAND Corp., RM-3066.

GERARD, R. W. 1958. Concepts and principles of biology: Initial working paper. *Behav. Sci.* **3**, 95–102.

GIBB, C. A. 1951. The effects of group size and of threat reduction upon creativity in a problem-solving situation. *Amer. Psychol.* **6**, 324.

GIBB, C. A. & GORMAN, A. 1954. Effects of induced polarization in small groups upon accuracy of perception. *Amer. Psychol.* **9**, 376–7.

GIBB, J. R. & LIPPITT, R. (Eds.) 1959a. *J. soc. Issues* **15.** (2); Consulting with groups and organizations.

—— 1959b. Helping a group with planned change. *J. soc. Issues* **15**, 13–19.

GLOCK, C. *et al.* 1960. *Case studies in bringing behavioral science into use.* Inst. Commun. Res., Stanford, California.

GOFFMAN, E. 1961. *Asylums: Essays on social situations of mental patients and other inmates.* Garden City, N.Y.: Anchor Books.

GOODENOUGH, W. H. 1963. *Cooperation in change.* New York: Russell Sage Foundation.

GORDON, M. J. 1963. *The use of administered price systems to control large organizations.* (Mimeo), January.

GOTTHEIL, E. 1955. Changes in social perceptions contingent upon competing or cooperating. *Sociometry* **18**, 132–7.

GOULDNER, A. W. 1955. *Patterns of industrial bureaucracy.* Glencoe, Ill.: Free Press; London: Routledge & Kegan Paul.

—— 1959. Organizational analysis. In R. K. Merton, L. Broom & L. S. Cottrell, Jr. (Eds.), *Sociology today: Problems and prospects.* New York: Basic Books.

—— 1961a. Engineering and clinical approaches to consulting. In Bennis, Benne & Chin (1961), q.v.

—— 1961b. Theoretical requirements of the applied social sciences. In Bennis, Benne, & Chin (1961) q.v.

GRAAFF, J. de V. 1957. *Theoretical welfare economics.* Cambridge: Cambridge University Press.

GROSS, B. M. 1953. *The legislative struggle.* New York: McGraw-Hill.

—— 1964. *The management of organizations.* New York: Free Press.

GROSSACK, M. M. 1954. Some effects of cooperation and competition upon small group behavior. *J. abnorm. soc. Psychol.* **49**, 341–8.

GULICK, L. (Ed.) 1937. Note on the theory of organization. In L. Gulick & L. U. Urwick (Eds.), *Papers on the science of administration.* New York: Institute of Public Administration, p. 13.

HABERSTROH, C. J. 1961. Administration of safety in the steel industry. *Man. Sci.* **7**, 436–44.

HACKETT, J. & HACKETT, ANNE-MARIE. 1963. *Economic planning in France,* Cambridge, Mass.: Harvard Univ. Press.

HAGEN, E. E. 1962. *On the theory of social change.* Homewood, Ill.: Dorsey Press; London: Tavistock Publications.

HAIRE, M. 1962. *Why have the social sciences contributed so little to industrial relations?* (Mimeo). University of California.

HARE, A. P. 1962. *Handbook of small group research.* Glencoe: Free Press.

HARRISON, R. 1962. In C. Argyris, *Interpersonal competence and organizational effectiveness.* Homewood, Ill.: Dorsey Press; London: Tavistock Publications.

HART, L. 1954. *Strategy.* New York: Frederick A. Praeger.

HARVEY, O. J. 1956. An experimental investigation of negative and positive relations between small groups through judgement indices. *Sociometry* **19**, 201–9.

HAYTHORN, W. W. 1959a. *The use of simulation in logistics policy search.* RAND Corp., P-1791.

HAYTHORN, W. W. 1959b. *The use of simulation in estimating intrasquadron logistics: A description of LP-II, Phase 1.1.* RAND Corp., P-1656.

HEIDER, F. 1946. Attitudes and cognitive organisation. *J. Psychol.* **21**, 107–12.

HENRIQUES, R. 1957. *A hundred hours to Suez.* New York: Viking.

HERTZBERG, F., MAUSNER, B. & SNYDERMAN, B. 1959. *Motivation of work.* New York: Wiley.

HILGARD, E. R. 1956. *Theories of learning.* New York: Appleton-Century-Crofts.

HILSMAN, R. 1956. *Strategic intelligence and national decisions.* New York: Free Press.

HIRSHLEIFER, J., DE HAVEN, J. C. & MILLIMAN, J. W. 1960. *Water supply economics, technology and policy.* Chicago: Univ. of Chicago Press.

HIRSCHMAN, A. O. 1958. *The strategy of economic development.* New Haven, Conn.: Yale Univ. Press.

1963. *Journeys toward progress.* New York: Twentieth Century Fund.

HITCH, C. J. 1957. Operations research and national planning — a dissent. *Opns. Res.* **5**, 718–23.

HITCH, C. J. & MCKEAN, R. N. 1960. *The economics of defence in the nuclear age.* London: Oxford Univ. Press.

HOBBS, N. 1962. Sources of gain in psychotherapy. *Amer. Psychol.* **17**, 741–7.

HOLT, C. C., MODIGLIANI, F., MUTH, J. F. & SIMON, H. A. 1960. *Planning production, inventory, and work force.* Englewood Cliffs, N.J.: Prentice-Hall.

HOLT, H. 1964. The psychoanalytic psychiatrist as a management consultant. In G. Fisk (Ed.), *The frontiers of management psychology.* New York: Harper & Row.

HOLTER, H. 1965. Attitudes towards employee participation in company decision-making processes: A study of supervisory employees in some Norwegian firms. *Hum. Relat.* **18**, 297–322.

HOMANS, G. C. 1950. *The human group.* New York: Harcourt, Brace & World.

HOWLAND, D. 1963. The trade-off problem in weapon system design. *Military Rev.* **43**, 72–8.

HOWLAND, D. & WIENER, E. L. 1963. The system monitor. In D. N. Buckner & J. J. McGrath (Eds.), *Vigilance: A symposium.* New York: McGraw-Hill.

HOWLAND, D. et al. 1960. *The development of a methodology for the evaluation of patient care.* Engineering Experiment Station, Ohio State University.

HUME, D. 1957. *An enquiry concerning the principles of morals.* (Edited by C. W. Hendel.) New York: Liberal Arts Press, pp. 24–5 (1st Edn. 1751).

HUSSERL, E. 1928. *Logische Untersuchungen. Erster Band: Prolegomena zur reinen Logik.* (4th edn.) Halle a.d. Saale.

HUTCHINSON, T. W. 1964. *Positive economics and policy objectives.* London: Allen & Unwin.

IJIRI, Y. 1963. *Goal oriented models for accounting and control.* Pittsburg: Carnegie Institute of Technology, May.

JANIS, I. L. & KATZ, D. 1959. The reduction of intergroup hostility: Research problems and hypotheses. *J. Conflict Resol.* **3**, 86.

JAQUES, E. 1951. *The changing culture of a factory.* London: Tavistock Publications.
1956. *Measurement of responsibility.* London: Tavistock Publications.
1961. Social therapy: Technocracy or collaboration? In Bennis, Benne & Chin. (1961), pp. 162–8. q.v.

JASINSKI, S. J. 1959. Adapting organization to new technology. *Harvard bus. Rev.* **37**, 79–86.

JENKS, R. S. 1965. The business-within-a-business. In D. Zand & P. Buchanan (Eds.), *Organization development: Theory and practice.* q.v.

JENSEN, A. & THYGESEN, I. 1963. An O.R. case study in road-investment: A sequential procedure. *Proc. NATO Conf. on O.R. in Economics* May.

JOHNSON, E. A. 1954. 'Introduction' to J. F. McCloskey & F. N. Trefethen, *Operations Research for Management.* Baltimore: Johns Hopkins Press.

JUNGK, R. 1958. *Brighter than a thousand suns.* New York: Grove.

KAPLAN, A. 1964. *The conduct of inquiry.* San Francisco: Chandler.

KAUFMAN, H. 1960. *The forest ranger.* Baltimore: Johns Hopkins Press.

KELMAN, H. C. 1958. Compliance, identification and internalization: Three processes of attitude change. *J. Conflict Resol.* **2**, 51–60.
1962. Changing attitudes through international activities. *J. soc. Issues* **18**, 68–87.

KENDALL, M. G. 1957. *A course in multivariate analysis.* London: Charles Griffin.
1958. The teaching of operational research. *Operat. Res. Quart.* **9**, 265–78.

KIMBALL, S. T. & PEARSALL, M. 1954. *The Tallageda story.*: Univ. of Alabama Press.

KLEIN, L. 1964. *Multiproducts Limited.* London: H.M.S.O.

KLINEBERG, O. 1964. *The human dimension in international relations.* New York: Holt, Rinehart & Winston.

KOOPMAN, B. O. 1957. The theory of search. III. The optimum distribution of searching effort. *Opns. Res.* **5**, 613–26.

KOOPMANS, T. C. 1951. Analysis of production as an efficient combination of activities. In T. C. Koopmans (Ed.), *Activity analysis of production and allocation.* New York: Wiley.

KRUTILLA, J. V. 1961. Welfare aspects of benefit–cost analysis. *J. polit. Econ.* **69** (3), 226–35.

KRUTILLA, J. V. & ECKSTEIN, O. 1958. *Multiple purpose river development.* Baltimore: Johns Hopkins Univ. Press.

KUHN, H. 1953. Extensive games and the problem of information. In Kuhn & Tucker, *Contributions to the theory of games II.* Princeton, N.J.: Princeton Univ. Press.

KUHN, T. 1962. *Public enterprise economics and transport problems.* Berkeley, Calif.: Univ. of California Press.

KUHN, T. S. 1962. *The structure of scientific revolutions.* Chicago: Univ. of Chicago Press.

KURLANDER, A. B., HILL, E. H. & ENTERLINE, P. E. 1955. An evaluation of some commonly used screening tests for heart disease and hypertension. *J. chronic Dis.* **2**, 427–39.

KURLANDER, A. B., ISKRANT, A. P. & KENT, M. E. 1954. Screening tests for diabetes – A study of specificity and sensitivity. *Diabetes* **3**, 213–19.

LANDSBERGER, H. A. 1961. The horizontal dimension in a bureaucracy. *Admin. Sci. Quart.* **6**, 298–332.

LAWRENCE, P. 1958. *The changing of organizational behavior patterns.* Cambridge, Mass.: Harvard Univ. Press.

LAZARSFELD, P. F. & SPIVACK, S. S. 1961. *Observations on organized social research in the United States: A report to the International Social Science Council.* (Mimeo.) New York.

LEARNED, E. P. 1951. *Executive action.* Boston: Graduate School of Business Administration, Harvard University.

LEAVITT, H. J. 1964. Unhuman organizations. In H. J. Leavitt & L. Pondry (Eds.), *Readings in managerial psychology.* Chicago: Univ. of Chicago Press.

LEAVITT, H. J. & WHISLER, R. L. 1958. Management in the 1980's. *Harv. bus. Rev.* **36**, 41–8.

LEEDS, R. & SMITH, T. (Eds.) 1963. *Using social science knowledge in business and industry.* Homewood, Ill.: Irwin.

LEIGHTON, A. H. 1945. *The governing of men.* Princeton, N.J.: Princeton Univ. Press.

LESOURNE, J. 1964. *Le calcul économique.* Paris: Dunod.

LEVINSON, H. *et al.* 1962. *Men, management and mental health.* Cambridge, Mass.: Harvard Univ. Press.

LEVY, B. I. 1954. Some effects of periodic discussions upon the social characteristics of non-laboratory groups. *Amer. Psychol.* **9**, 569.

LICHFIELD, N. (undated). Planning and the land market. In *Contemporary problems of land ownership.* Dept. of Land Economy, Univ. of Cambridge.

— 1956. *Economics of planned development.* London: Estates Gazette, Part IV.

— 1959. Value for money in town planning. *Estates Gaz.* **173**, 245.

— 1960. Cost–benefit analysis in city planning. *J. Amer. Inst. Planners* **26**, 273.

— 1962. *Cost–benefit analysis in urban redevelopment.* Research Report 20, Real Estate Research Program, Institute of Business and Economic Research, Univ. of California, Berkeley.

— 1964. Cost–benefit analysis in plan evaluation. *Town Planning Rev.* **35**, July.

LIKERT, R. 1961. *New patterns in management.* New York: McGraw-Hill.

LIKERT, R. & HAYES, S. P. Jr. (Eds.) 1957. *Some applications of behavioral research.* Paris: UNESCO.

LIPPITT, R., WATSON, J. & WESTLEY, B. 1958. *The dynamics of planned change.* New York: Harcourt Brace.

LIPSET, S. M. 1959. *Political man.* London: Heinemann Mercury Books.

LITTLE, I. M. D. 1950. *Critique of welfare economics.* London: Oxford Univ. Press.

LOOMIS, J. L. 1959. Communication, the development of trust and cooperative behavior. *Hum. Relat.* **12**, 305–15.

LOWE, V. 1962. *Understanding Whitehead.* Baltimore: The Johns Hopkins Press.

LUCE, R. D. & RAIFFA, H. 1958. *Games and decisions.* New York: Wiley.

MAASS, A., HUFSCHMIDT, M. M., DORFMAN, R., THOMAS, H. A., MARGLIN, S. A. & FAIR, G. M. 1962. *Design of water resources systems.* New York: Macmillan.

MCCLELLAND, D. C. 1961. *The achieving society.* Princeton, N.J.: Van Nostrand.

MCGHEE, A. 1961. *The patients' attitude to nursing care.* London: E. W. Livingstone.

MCGREGOR, D. 1960. *The human side of enterprise.* New York: McGraw-Hill.

MACGUIRE, G. M. 1961. *From student to nurse: The induction period.* Oxford Area Nurse Training Committee, Oxford Regional Hospital Board.

MCKEAN, R. N. 1958. *Efficiency in government through systems analysis.* New York: Wiley.

1963. Cost benefit analysis and defence expenditure. In A. T. Peacock & D. J. Robertson (Eds.), *Public expenditure: Appraisal and control.* Edinburgh: Oliver & Boyd.

MANN, F. 1957. *Studying and creating change: A means to understanding social organization.* Industrial Relations Research Association, Publication No. 17.

MANN, F. & BAUMGARTEL, H. 1964. *The survey feedback experiment: An evaluation of a program for the utilization of survey findings.* Foundation for Research on Human Behavior, Ann Arbor.

MANN, F. & LIKERT, R. 1952. The need for research on the communication of research results. *Hum. Organiz.* **11**, 15–19.

MANN, F. C. & NEFF, F. W. 1961. *Managing major change in organizations.* Foundation for Research on Human Behavior, Ann Arbor.

MANN, F. & WILLIAMS, C. 1960. Observations on the dynamics of change to electronic data-processing equipment. *Admin. Sci. Quart.* **5**, 217–56.

MANNHEIM, K. 1958. *Essays on the sociology of culture.* London: Routledge & Kegan Paul.

MARCH, J. G. 1955. An introduction to the theory and measurement of influence. *Amer. polit. Sci. Rev.* **49**, 431–51.

MARCH, J. G. & SIMON, H. A. 1958. *Organizations.* New York: Wiley.

MARCH, J. G., SIMON, H. A. & GUETZKOW, H. 1958. *Organization.* New York: Wiley.

MAREK, J. 1963a. Social and psychological responses to changing environmental demands. Unpublished Ph.D. Thesis, London School of Economics and Political Science.

1963b. Information, perception and social context. I. *Hum. Relat.* **16**, 209–31.

1966. Technological development, organization, and interpersonal relations. *Acta Sociol.* **10**, 1–34.

MARGLIN, S. A. 1963a. *Approaches to dynamic investment planning.* Amsterdam: North Holland Pub. Co.

1963b. The opportunity costs of public investment. *Quart. J. Econ.* 77, 274–89.

MARGOLIS, J. 1955. Comment on the pure theory of expenditures. *Rev. Econ. Statist.* 37.

1957. Secondary benefits, external economics and the justification of public investment. *Rev. Econ. Statist.* 39.

MARPLES, E. 1964. Quoted in London *Times*, 4 March.

MARSCHAK, J. 1954. Towards an economic theory of organization and information. In R. M. Thrall, C. H. Coombs & R. L. Davis (Eds.), *Decision processes.* New York: Wiley.

MARSCHAK, T. 1959. Centralization and decentralization in economic organizations. *Econometrica* 27, 399–429.

MARSHALL, S. L. A. 1947. *Men against fire.* New York: Morrow.

MARTINDALE, D. 1964. 'Introduction' to G. K. Zollschan & W. Kirsch (Eds.), *Explorations in social change.* Boston: Houghton Mifflin.

MASLOW, A. H. 1954. *Motivation and personality.* New York: Harper.

MAUTZ, R. K. & SHARAF, H. A. 1961. *The philosophy of auditing.* American Accounting Association Monograph. Menasha, Wis.: George Banta.

MEAD, M. 1957. Toward more vivid Utopias. *Science* 126, 957–61.

MEADE, J. E. 1954. *Trade and welfare.* London: Oxford Univ. Press.

MELLINGER, G. D. 1956. Interpersonal trust as a factor in communication. *J. abnorm. soc. Psychol.* 52, 304–9.

MELMAN, S. 1958. *Decision-making and productivity.* Oxford: Blackwell.

MENGES, G. 1958. Das Entscheidungsproblem in der Statistik (The decision problem in statistics). *Allgem. Statist. Arch.* 42, 101–7.

1959. *Stichproben aus endlichen Gesamtheiten* (Samples from finite populations). Frankfurt: V. Klostermann.

1963a. Gedanken zur Frage der Stabilität statistischer Entscheidungen (Thoughts on the problem of stability of statistical decisions). *Metrika 6*, 84–94.

1963b. The adaption of decision criteria and application patterns. *Proc. Third Int. Conf. Opns. Res. Oslo.* Paris: Dunod.

1963c. Kriterian optimaler Entschedungen unter Ungewisheit (Criterion for choosing optimal decisions under uncertainty). *Statist. Hefte* 4, 151–71.

MENGES, G. & BEHARA, M. 1962. Einige grundsätzliche Betrachtungen uber prozessuale Entscheidungen unter Ungewisheit (Some fundamental considerations about processual decisions under uncertainty). *Z. handels-wissent. Forsch.* 14, 483–94.

1963a. On decision criteria under various degrees of stability. *J. Indian statist. Ass.* 1, 185–95.

1963b. Das Bayesache Risiko bei sequentiellen Stichprobenentscheidungen (Bayes Risk of sequential sampling). *Statist. Hefte* 3, 39–61.

MERTON, R. K. 1949. *Social theory and social structure.* New York: Free Press.

MERTON, R. K. & LERNER, D. 1951. Social scientists and research policy. In D. Lerner & H. D. Lasswell (Eds.), *The policy sciences.* Stanford: Stanford Univ. Press.

METCALF, H. C. & URWICK, L. (Eds.) 1940. Dynamic administration. In *The collected papers of Mary Parker Follett.* New York: Harper.

MEYERSON, M. & BANFIELD, E. C. 1955. *Politics, planning and the public interest.* Glencoe: The Free Press.

MILES, M. B. (Ed.) 1964. *Innovation in education.* Bureau of Publications, Teachers College, Columbia Univ., New York.

MINAS, J. S. 1956. Formalism, realism, and management science. *Man. Sci.* **3**, 9–14.

MINISTRY OF TRANSPORT. 1963. Cost–benefit analysis and accessibility and environ ment. In *Traffic in Towns; Reports of the Steering Group and Working Group appointed by the Minister of Transport.* London: H.M.S.O.

MODIGLIANI, F. & MILLER, M. H. 1958. The cost of capital, corporation finance and theory of investment. *Amer. econ. Rev.* **48**, 261–97.

MOHRING, H. & HARWITZ, M. 1962. *Highway benefits.* Northwestern Univ. Press.

MOORE, W. E. 1960. A reconsideration of theories of social change. *Amer. sociol. Rev.* **25**, 810–18.

1964. *Social change.* Englewood Cliffs, N.J.: Prentice-Hall.

MORENO, J. L. 1953. *Who shall survive?* New York: Beacon House.

MORGENSTERN, O. 1963. *Spieltheorie und Wirtschaftswissenschaft.* (Game theory and economics.) Vienna-Munich: Oldenbourg.

MORGENTHAU, H. 1964. The sweet smell of success. *N.Y. Review of Books*, 2.6.

MUMFORD, L. 1956. *The transformation of man.* New York: Harper.

MYRDAL, G. 1954. *The political element in the development of economic theory.* Cambridge, Mass.: Harvard Univ. Press.

1958. *Value in social theory.* London: Kegan Paul; New York: Harper.

NAEGELE, K. D. 1961. In T. Parsons *et al.* (Eds.), *Theories of Society.* Vol. II. New York: Free Press.

NASH, J. 1950. Equilibrium point in *n*-person games. *Proc. Nat. Acad. Sci., U.S.A.* **36**, 48–9.

NELSON, H. W. & PETERSEN, J. W. 1962. *Integrated supply–support policies: The LP-III experience.* RAND Corp., RM-2839.

NERLOVE, M. & WAGE, S. 1964. On the optimality of adaptive forecasting. *Man. Sci.* **10**, 207–23.

NEWCOMB, T. M. 1947. Autistic hostility and social reality. *Hum. Relat.* **1**, 69–86.

1953. An approach to the study of communicative acts. *Psychol. Rev.* **60**, 393–404.

NORTH, R. C., KOCH, H. E. & ZINNES, D. A. 1960. The integrative functions of conflict. *J. Conflict Resol.* **6**, 355–74.

OESER, O. A. & HARARY, F. 1964. A mathematical model for structural role theory. *Hum. Relat.* **17**, 3–18.

PALGRAVE, SIR R. 1877. *The chairman's handbook.* London: Dent.

PARSONS, T. 1964. Evolutionary universals in society. *Amer. sociol. Rev.* **29**, 339–57.

PEACOCK, A. T. & ROBERTSON, D. J. 1963. *Public expenditure: Appraisal and control.* Edinburgh: Oliver & Boyd.

PEACOCK, A. T. & WISEMAN, J. 1961. *The growth of public expenditure in the United Kingdom.* Princeton, N.J.: Princeton University Press.

PHILIP, A. J. 1940. Strangers and friends as competitors and co-operators. *J. genet. Psychol.* **57**, 249–58.

PIERCE, J. R. 1961. *Symbols, signals, and noise.* New York: Harper.

PIGOU, A. C. 1920. *Economics of welfare.* London: Macmillan.

POOL, I. DE SOLA. (Ed.) 1959. Trends in content analysis. Urbana, Ill.: Univ. of Illinois Press.

POWERS, W. T. *et al.* 1963. General feedback theory of human behavior. I & II *Percept. Motor Skills Supplements.*

PRUZAN, P. M. & JACKSON, J. T. R. 1963. On the development of utility spaces for multi-goal systems. *Erhverskonomisk Tidsskr.* **4**, 257–74.

RADNOR, M. 1964. *The control of research and development by the top managers of large decentralized companies.* Ph.D. dissertation. Northwestern University, Evanston, Ill., August.

RADNOR, M. & RUBENSTEIN, A. H. 1964. *Top management control processes over research and development activities in large decentralized companies.* Working paper. Northwestern Univ.

RAO, C. R. 1952. *Advanced statistical methods in biometric research.* New York: Wiley.

RAPOPORT, A. 1956. The diffusion problem in mass behavior. *Gen. Systems* **1**, 48–55.

   1960. *Fights, games, and debates.* Ann Arbor: Univ. of Michigan Press.

   1961. Three modes of conflict. *Man. Sci.* **7**, 210–18.

   1964. A stochastic model for Prisoner's Dilemma. In J. Gurland (Ed.), *Stochastic models in medicine and biology.* Madison: Univ. of Wisconsin Press.

RAUNER, R. M. 1958. *Laboratory evaluation of supply and procurement policies.* RAND Corp., R-323.

RAUNER, R. M. & STEGER, W. A. 1961. *Simulation and long-range planning for resource allocation.* RAND Corp., P-2223-1.

RAVEN, B. H. & EUCHUS, H. T. 1963. Cooperation and competition in means-independent trials. *J. abnorm. Psychol.* **67**. 307–16.

REDFIELD, C. E. 1953. *Communication in management.* Chicago: Chicago Univ. Press.

RENSHAW, E. F. 1957. *Towards responsible government.*: Idyia Press.

REVANS, R. W. 1961. *The measurement of supervisory attitudes.* Paper presented at the Manchester Statistical Society, January meeting.

RICE, A. K. 1963. *The enterprise and its environment.* London: Tavistock Publications.

RICHARDSON, F. L. W. 1962. 'Foreword'. In R. J. Smith (Ed.), *Hum. Organiz.* **21**.

RICHARDSON, L. F. 1939. Generalized foreign policy. *Brit. J. Psychol. Monograph Supplement* **23**.

   1960. *Arms and insecurity.* London: Stevens.

ROBBINS, L. 1935. *An essay on the nature and significance of economic science.* London: Macmillan.

ROETHLISBERGER, F. J. & DICKSON, W. J. 1941. *Management and the worker.* Cambridge, Mass.: Harvard Univ. Press.

ROETHLISBERGER, F. & ROGERS, C. R. 1952. Barriers and gateways to communication. *Harvard bus. Rev.* **30**, 46–52.

ROGERS, E. M. 1962. *Diffusion of innovations.* New York: Free Press.

ROOSEVELT, J. (Ed.) 1962. *The Liberal papers.* New York: Anchor.

ROTHENBERG, J. 1961. *The measurement of social welfare.* Englewood Cliffs, N.J.: Prentice-Hall.

RUBIN, I. 1963. *A study of the goals and effort allocations of engineers.* Unpublished M.S. thesis, M.I.T.

RUBENSTEIN, A. H. 1959. *Rate of organization change, corporate decentralization and the constraints on research and development in the firm.* Presented at T.I.M.S., Chicago, June.

— 1960. *Organization and research and development decision-making within the decentralized firm.* (Mimeo). Presented to a Conference on the Economic and Social Factors determining the Rate and Direction of Inventive Activity. National Bureau of Economic Research, New York.

RUBENSTEIN, A. H. & RADNOR, M. 1963. Top management's role in research planning in large decentralized companies. *Proc. 3rd Int. Conf. Opns. Res., Oslo.* Paris: Dunod.

SALISBURY, H. E. 1960. *To Moscow and beyond.* New York: Harper.

SALTER, SIR A. 1921. *Allied shipping control.* Oxford: Clarendon Press.

SAMUELSON, P. A. 1950. Evaluation of real national income. *Oxford Econ. Papers* New Series, Vol. 2.

— 1954. Pure theory of public expenditure. *Rev. Econ. Statist.* **36.**

SAVAGE, L. J. *et al.* 1962. *The foundations of statistical inference.* London: Methuen.

SAYLES, L. 1962. The change process in organization. In R. J. Smith (Ed.), *Hum. Organiz.* **21.**

SCHALLER, H. G. (Ed.) 1963. *Public expenditure decisions in the urban community.* Baltimore: Johns Hopkins Press.

SCHEFF, T. J. 1963. Decision rules, types of errors, and their consequences in medical diagnosis. *Behav. Sci.* April, 97–107.

SCHEIN, E. H. & BENNIS, W. G. 1965. *Personal and organization change via group methods.* New York: Wiley.

SCHEIN, E. H., SCHNEIER, I. & BRAKER, C. H. 1961. *Coercive persuasion: A socio-psychological analysis of the 'brain-washing' of American civilian prisoners by the Chinese Communists.* New York: Norton.

SCHLAIFER, R. 1959. *Probability for business decisions.* New York: McGraw-Hill.

SCHUCHMAN, A. 1963. *Scientific decision making in business.* New York: Holt, Rinehart & Winston.

SCOTT, R. 1962. *Automation and the non-manual worker. Interim report.* O.E.C.D.

— 1965. *Automation and the non-manual worker. Final report.* O.E.C.D.

SCOTT, W. R. 1964. *Theory of organizations.* Unpublished MS.

SEASHORE, S. & VAN EGMOND, E. 1961. The consultant-trainer role. In Bennis, Benne & Chin. 1961. pp. 660–6. q.v.

SELZNICK, P. 1948. Foundation of the theory of organizations. *Amer. sociol. Rev.* **13,** 25–35.

— 1949. *TVA and the grass roots.* Berkeley: Univ. of California Press.

— 1957. *Leadership in administration.* Evanston, Ill.: Row Peterson.

— 1963. *Private government and the corporate conscience.* Presented at the Symposium on Business Policy, Harvard Business School, April 10th.

SEN, A. K. 1951. On optimising the rate of savings. *Econ. J.* **71.**

SHEPARD, H. A. 1960. Three management programs and the theories behind them. In *An action research program for organization improvement.* Foundation for Research on Human Behavior, Ann Arbor, Mich.

1964. Changing interpersonal and intergroup relationships in organizations. In J. March (Ed.), *Handbook of organization*. New York: Rand McNally.

SHEPARD, H. A. & BLAKE, R. R. 1962. Changing behavior through cognitive change. In R. J. Smith (Ed.), *Hum. organiz.* **21.**

SHERIF, M. & SHERIF, C. N. 1953. *Groups in harmony and tension.* New York: Harper.

SHEWART, W. A. 1931. *Economic control of quality of manufactured product.* New York: D. Van Nostrand.

SHUBIK, M. 1963. Behavioristic or normative decision criteria. *Proc. Third Int. Conf. Operations Research, Oslo.* Paris; Dunod.

1964. Incentives, decentralized control, the assignment of joint costs and internal pricing. In C. P. Bonini, R. K. Jaedicke & H. M. Wagner (Eds.), *Management controls: New directions in basic research.* New York: McGraw-Hill.

SIMON, H. A. 1947. *Administrative behavior.* New York: Macmillan.

1957. *Models of man.* New York: Wiley.

1964. On the concept of organizational goal. *Admin. Sci. Quart.* **9,** 1–22.

SLATER, P. E. & BENNIS, W. G. 1964. Democracy is inevitable. *Harv. bus. Rev.* **42,** 51–9.

SMITH, R. J. (Ed.) 1962. *Hum. organiz.* **21.**

SNOEK, J. D. 1962. Some effects of rejection upon attraction to a group. *J. abnorm. soc. Psychol.* **64,** 175–82.

SNOW, C. P. 1961. *Science and government.* Cambridge, Mass.: Harvard Univ. Press.

1962. The moral un-neutrality of science. In P. C. Obler and H. A. Estrin (Eds.), *The new scientist.* New York: Anchor.

SOFER, C. 1961. *The organization from within.* London: Tavistock Publications.

SOKAL, R. R. & SNEATH, P. H. A. 1963. *Principles of numerical taxonomy.* London: W. H. Freeman.

SOMMERHOFF, G. 1950. *Analytical biology.* London: Oxford University Press.

SPENCER, P. & SOFER, C. 1964. Organizational change and its management. *J. Man. Studies* **1,** 26–47.

SPICER, E. H. (Ed.) 1952. *Human problems in technological change.* New York: Russell Sage Foundation.

STANTON, A. H. & SCHWARTZ, M. S. 1954. *The mental hospital.* New York: Basic Books.

STEDRY, A. C. 1964. Budgeting and employee behavior: A reply. *J. Business* **37** (2), 195–202.

STEDRY, A. C. & CHARNES, A. 1962. *Some models or organization response to budgeted multiple goals.* M.I.T., School of Industrial Management, December.

STEDRY, A. C. & GRISWOLD, J. 1962. Development of supply control procedures for the Defense General Supply Center. *Proc. Army Opns. Res. Symp. Durham.* Army Research Office.

STEDRY, A. C. & KAY, E. 1964. *A study of goal difficulty in a manufacturing plant.* New York: Central Electric Co.

STEINER, P. O. 1959. Choosing among alternative public investments. *Amer. Econ. Rev.* **49** (5).

STENDLER, C., DAMRIN, D. & HAINES, A. 1951. Studies in cooperation and competition: I. Effects of working for group and individual rewards on the social climate of children's groups. *J. genet. Psychol.* **79,** 173–97.

STEVENS, S. S. 1951. Mathematics, measurement, and psychophysics. In S. S. Stevens (Ed.), *Handbook of experimental psychology.* New York: Wiley.

STOGDILL, R. M. & SHARTLE, C. L. 1955. *Methods in the study of administrative leadership*. Ohio State Univ., Bureau of Business Research, Research Monograph Number 80.

STRAUSS, G. 1962. Tactics of lateral relationships. *Admin. Sci. Quart.* **7**, 161–87.

1964. Work flow, interfunctional rivalry, and professionalism. *Hum. Organiz.* **23**, 137–49.

SYKES, G. M. 1958. *The society of captives*. Princeton, N.J.: Princeton Univ. Press.

Tanganyika Standard. 1964. We must all learn, 17 March.

TANNENBAUM, R., WECHSLER, I. R. & MASSARIK, F. 1961. *Leadership and organization*. New York: McGraw-Hill.

TAX, S. 1964. The uses of anthropology. In S. Tax (Ed.), *Horizons of anthropology*. Chicago: Aldine.

THOMPSON, C. 1958. A study of the emotional climates of psycho-analytic institutes. *Psychiatry* **21**, 42–52.

THOMPSON, J. S. & BATES, F. L. 1957. Technology, organization and administration. *Admin. Sci. Quart.* **2**, 325–43.

THORNDIKE, R. L. 1953. Who belongs in the family? *Psychometrika* **18**, 267–76.

THORSRUD, E. & EMERY, F. E. 1964. *Industrial democracy* (In Norwegian). Oslo: Univ. of Oslo Press.

TRIST, E. & EMERY, F. E. 1962–3. *Conceptualization and systems theory*. Unpublished manuscript. Tavistock Institute of Human Relations.

TRIST, E. L., HIGGIN, G. W., MURRAY, H. & POLLOCK, A. B. 1963. *Organizational choice*. London: Tavistock Publications.

TSCHUPROW, A. 1924. Zeile und Wege der stochastischen Grundlegung der statistischen Theorie (Aims and means of the stochastic foundation of statistical theory). *Nord. statist. Tidsskr.* **3**, 434–93.

TSIEN, M. S. 1954. *Engineering cybernetics*. New York: McGraw-Hill.

TUCHMAN, B. 1962. *The guns of August*. New York: Macmillan.

TURVEY, R. 1963. On divergences between social cost and private cost. *Economica* **119**.

UDY, S. H. 1959. *The organization of work*. New Haven, Conn.: H.R.A.T. Press.

1961. Technical and institutional factors in production organization. *Amer. J. Sociol.* **67**, 247–54.

URWICK, L. 1937. *Papers on the science of administration*. New York: Institute of Public Relations.

U.S. News and World Report 1964. 6 January.

VAN DE PANNE, C. & WHINSTON, A. 1964. The simplex and the dual method for quadratic programming. *Operat. Res. Quart.* **15**, 355–88.

VAIZEY, J. 1962. *The economics of education*. London: Faber & Faber.

VON BERTALANFFY, L. 1956. General system theory. *Gen. Systems* **1**, 1–10.

VON BERTALANFFY, L. & RAPOPORT, A. (Eds.) 1960. *Fifth General Systems Year Book*. An Arbor, Mich.: Society for General Systems Research.

VON NEUMANN, J. & MORGENSTERN, O. 1944. *Theory of games and economic behavior*. Princeton, N.J.: Princeton Univ. Press.

VROOM, V. H. 1960. *Some personality determinants of the effects of participation.* Englewood Cliffs, N.J.: Prentice-Hall.

VROOM, V. H. 1964. *Work and motivation.* New York: Wiley.

WALD, A. 1950. *Statistical decision functions.* New York: Wiley.

WALINSKY, L. J. 1960. *Economic development in Burma. 1951–1960.* New York: Twentieth Century Fund.

WALKER, C. 1962. *Technology and civilization.* New York: McGraw-Hill.

WALTON, R. E. & MCKERSIE, R. B. 1964. *Attitude changes in intergroup relations.* Institute for Research in the Behavioral, Economic and Management Sciences. Paper No. 86, October.

1965. *A behavioral theory of labor negotiations.* New York: McGraw-Hill.

WALTON, W. W. 1964. *Modern decision theory applied to medical diagnosis.* Doctoral dissertation, Johns Hopkins University.

WARD, J. H., Jr. 1963. Hierarchical grouping to optimise an objective function. *J. Amer. statist. Ass.* **58** (301), 236–44.

WEINGARTNER, H. M. 1963. *Mathematical programming and the analysis of capital budgeting problems.* London: Prentice-Hall.

WEINSHALL, T. 1960. *The effects of management changes on the organizational relationships and attitudes.* Unpublished Doctoral thesis, Harvard.

WEISBROD, B. 1961. *The economics of public health: Measuring the economic impact of diseases.* Philadelphia: Univ. of Pennsylvania Press.

WELFORD, A. T. 1962. In A. T. Welford, M. Argyle, D. V. Glass & J. N. Morris (Eds.), *Society: problems and methods of study.* London: Routledge & Kegan Paul.

WHINSTON, A. 1964. Price guides in decentralised organisations. In Cooper, Leavitt & Shelly (Eds.), *New perspectives in operations research.* New York: Wiley.

WHYTE, W. H. Jr. 1946. *The organization man.* New York: Simon & Schuster; London: Cape.

WIBBERLEY, C. P. 1959. *Agriculture and urban growth.* London: Michael Joseph.

WILES, P. J. D. 1962. *The political economy of Communism.* Cambridge, Mass.: Harvard Univ. Press.

WILSON, A. T. M. 1961. *The manager and his world.* Presented at the Centennial Symposium on Executive Development. Alfred P. Sloan School of Management, M.I.T., 27 April.

WOODWARD, J. 1959. *Nursing Mirror*, 11, 18, and 25 Dec.

1965. *Industrial organization: theory and practice.* London: Oxford Univ. Press.

YOVITS, M. C. & CAMERON, S. 1960. *Self-organizing systems.* New York: Pergamon.

ZAND, D. & BUCHANAN, P. (Eds.) 1965. *Organization development: Theory and practice.* [Not published at time of going to press.]

ZANDER, A. 1961. Resistance to change: Its analysis and prevention. In Bennis, Benne & Chin (1961), pp. 543–8. q.v.

ZETTERBERG, H. 1962. *Social theory and social practice.* New York: Bedminster.

Name Index

NOTE : *Page numbers in italics refer to reference lists at ends of chapters; n refers to footnote*